PEARSON

ALWAYS LEARNING

John W. Hill • Terry W. McCreary • Doris K. Kolb

Chemistry for Changing Times

Second Custom Edition for Northern Kentucky University

Taken from:
Chemistry for Changing Times, Thirteenth Edition
by John W. Hill, Terry W. McCreary, and Doris K. Kolb

D1418479

Cover Art: Courtesy of Photodisc/Getty Images.

Taken from:

Chemistry for Changing Times, Thirteenth Edition
by John W. Hill, Terry W. McCreary, and Doris K. Kolb
Copyright © 2013, 2010, 2007, 2004, 2001, 1998 by Pearson Education, Inc.
Published by Pearson
Upper Saddle River, New Jersey 07458

This special edition published in cooperation with Pearson Learning Solutions.

Pearson Learning Solutions, 501 Boylston Street, Suite 900, Boston, MA 02116
A Pearson Education Company
www.pearsoned.com

Printed in the United States of America

1 2 3 4 5 6 7 8 9 10 V092 16 15 14 13

000200010271793064

TM

ISBN 10: 1-269-40474-1
ISBN 13: 978-1-269-40474-7

TABLE OF ATOMIC MASSES BASED ON CARBON-12

Name	Symbol	Atomic Number	Atomic Mass	Name	Symbol	Atomic Number	Atomic Mass
Actinium	Ac	89	227.028	Meitnerium	Mt	109	(268)
Aluminum	Al	13	26.9815	Mendelevium	Md	101	(258)
Americium	Am	95	(243)	Mercury	Hg	80	200.59
Antimony	Sb	51	121.760	Molybdenum	Mo	42	95.94
Argon	Ar	18	39.948	Neodymium	Nd	60	144.24
Arsenic	As	33	74.9216	Neon	Ne	10	20.1797
Astatine	At	85	(210)	Neptunium	Np	93	237.048
Barium	Ba	56	137.327	Nickel	Ni	28	58.6934
Berkelium	Bk	97	(247)	Niobium	Nb	41	92.9064
Beryllium	Be	4	9.01218	Nitrogen	N	7	14.0067
Bismuth	Bi	83	208.980	Nobelium	No	102	(259)
Bohrium	Bh	107	(267)	Osmium	Os	76	190.23
Boron	B	5	10.811	Oxygen	O	8	15.9994
Bromine	Br	35	79.904	Palladium	Pd	46	106.42
Cadmium	Cd	48	112.411	Phosphorus	P	15	30.9738
Calcium	Ca	20	40.078	Platinum	Pt	78	195.078
Californium	Cf	98	(251)	Plutonium	Pu	94	(244)
Carbon	C	6	12.0107	Polonium	Po	84	(209)
Cerium	Ce	58	140.116	Potassium	K	19	39.0983
Cesium	Cs	55	132.905	Praseodymium	Pr	59	140.908
Chlorine	Cl	17	35.4527	Promethium	Pm	61	(145)
Chromium	Cr	24	51.9961	Protactinium	Pa	91	231.036
Cobalt	Co	27	58.9332	Radium	Ra	88	226.025
Copernicium	Cn	112	(285)	Radon	Rn	86	(222)
Copper	Cu	29	63.546	Rhenium	Re	75	186.207
Curium	Cm	96	(247)	Rhodium	Rh	45	102.906
Darmstadtium	Ds	110	(281)	Roentgenium	Rg	111	(272)
Dubnium	Db	105	(262)	Rubidium	Rb	37	85.4678
Dysprosium	Dy	66	162.50	Ruthenium	Ru	44	101.07
Einsteinium	Es	99	(252)	Rutherfordium	Rf	104	(261)
Erbium	Er	68	167.26	Samarium	Sm	62	150.36
Europium	Eu	63	151.964	Scandium	Sc	21	44.9559
Fermium	Fm	100	(257)	Seaborgium	Sg	106	(266)
Fluorine	F	9	18.9984	Selenium	Se	34	78.96
Francium	Fr	87	(223)	Silicon	Si	14	28.0855
Gadolinium	Gd	64	157.25	Silver	Ag	47	107.868
Gallium	Ga	31	69.723	Sodium	Na	11	22.9898
Germanium	Ge	32	72.61	Strontium	Sr	38	87.62
Gold	Au	79	196.967	Sulfur	S	16	32.066
Hafnium	Hf	72	178.49	Tantalum	Ta	73	180.948
Hassium	Hs	108	(269)	Technetium	Tc	43	(98)
Helium	He	2	4.00260	Tellurium	Te	52	127.60
Holmium	Ho	67	164.930	Terbium	Tb	65	158.925
Hydrogen	H	1	1.00794	Thallium	Tl	81	204.383
Indium	In	49	114.818	Thorium	Th	90	232.038
Iodine	I	53	126.904	Thulium	Tm	69	168.934
Iridium	Ir	77	192.217	Tin	Sn	50	118.710
Iron	Fe	26	55.845	Titanium	Ti	22	47.867
Krypton	Kr	36	83.80	Tungsten	W	74	183.84
Lanthanum	La	57	138.906	Uranium	U	92	238.029
Lawrencium	Lr	103	(262)	Vanadium	V	23	50.9415
Lead	Pb	82	207.2	Xenon	Xe	54	131.29
Lithium	Li	3	6.941	Ytterbium	Yb	70	173.04
Lutetium	Lu	71	174.967	Yttrium	Y	39	88.9059
Magnesium	Mg	12	24.3050	Zinc	Zn	30	65.39
Manganese	Mn	25	54.9380	Zirconium	Zr	40	91.224

Atomic masses in this table are relative to carbon-12 and limited to six significant figures, although some atomic masses are known more precisely. For certain radioactive elements the numbers listed (in parentheses) are the mass numbers of the most stable isotopes.

PERIODIC TABLE OF THE ELEMENTS

Main groups

1 / 1A[a][b]	2 / 2A	3 / 3B	4 / 4B	5 / 5B	6 / 6B	7 / 7B	8 / 8B	9 / 8B	10	11 / 1B	12 / 2B	13 / 3A	14 / 4A	15 / 5A	16 / 6A	17 / 7A	18 / 8A
1 **H** Hydrogen 1.00794																	2 **He** Helium 4.002602
3 **Li** Lithium 6.941	4 **Be** Beryllium 9.012182											5 **B** Boron 10.811	6 **C** Carbon 12.0107	7 **N** Nitrogen 14.00674	8 **O** Oxygen 15.9994	9 **F** Fluorine 18.998403	10 **Ne** Neon 20.1797
11 **Na** Sodium 22.989770	12 **Mg** Magnesium 24.3050											13 **Al** Aluminum 26.981538	14 **Si** Silicon 28.0855	15 **P** Phosphorus 30.973762	16 **S** Sulfur 32.066	17 **Cl** Chlorine 35.4527	18 **Ar** Argon 39.948
19 **K** Potassium 39.0983	20 **Ca** Calcium 40.078	21 **Sc** Scandium 44.95591	22 **Ti** Titanium 47.867	23 **V** Vanadium 50.9415	24 **Cr** Chromium 51.9961	25 **Mn** Manganese 54.938049	26 **Fe** Iron 55.845	27 **Co** Cobalt 58.933200	28 **Ni** Nickel 58.6934	29 **Cu** Copper 63.546	30 **Zn** Zinc 65.39	31 **Ga** Gallium 69.723	32 **Ge** Germanium 72.61	33 **As** Arsenic 74.92160	34 **Se** Selenium 78.96	35 **Br** Bromine 79.904	36 **Kr** Krypton 83.80
37 **Rb** Rubidium 85.4678	38 **Sr** Strontium 87.62	39 **Y** Yttrium 88.90585	40 **Zr** Zirconium 91.224	41 **Nb** Niobium 92.90638	42 **Mo** Molybdenum 95.94	43 **Tc** Technetium [98]	44 **Ru** Ruthenium 101.07	45 **Rh** Rhodium 102.90550	46 **Pd** Palladium 106.42	47 **Ag** Silver 107.8682	48 **Cd** Cadmium 112.411	49 **In** Indium 114.818	50 **Sn** Tin 118.710	51 **Sb** Antimony 121.760	52 **Te** Tellurium 127.60	53 **I** Iodine 126.90447	54 **Xe** Xenon 131.29
55 **Cs** Cesium 132.90545	56 **Ba** Barium 137.327	57 *****La** Lanthanum 138.9055	72 **Hf** Hafnium 178.49	73 **Ta** Tantalum 180.9479	74 **W** Tungsten 183.84	75 **Re** Rhenium 186.207	76 **Os** Osmium 190.23	77 **Ir** Iridium 192.217	78 **Pt** Platinum 195.078	79 **Au** Gold 196.96655	80 **Hg** Mercury 200.59	81 **Tl** Thallium 204.3833	82 **Pb** Lead 207.2	83 **Bi** Bismuth 208.98038	84 **Po** Polonium [209]	85 **At** Astatine [210]	86 **Rn** Radon [222]
87 **Fr** Francium [223]	88 **Ra** Radium 226.025	89 †**Ac** Actinium 227.028	104 **Rf** Rutherfordium [261]	105 **Db** Dubnium [262]	106 **Sg** Seaborgium [266]	107 **Bh** Bohrium [267]	108 **Hs** Hassium [269]	109 **Mt** Meitnerium [268]	110 **Ds** Darmstadtium [281]	111 **Rg** Roentgenium [272]	112 **Cn** Copernicium [285]	113[c] [284]	114 [285]	115 [288]	116 [289]	117[d] [294]	118 [294]

Metals Nonmetals Noble gases

Transition metals

*Lanthanide series

58 **Ce** Cerium 140.116	59 **Pr** Praseodymium 140.90765	60 **Nd** Neodymium 144.24	61 **Pm** Promethium [145]	62 **Sm** Samarium 150.36	63 **Eu** Europium 151.964	64 **Gd** Gadolinium 157.25	65 **Tb** Terbium 158.92534	66 **Dy** Dysprosium 162.50	67 **Ho** Holmium 164.93032	68 **Er** Erbium 167.26	69 **Tm** Thulium 168.93421	70 **Yb** Ytterbium 173.04	71 **Lu** Lutetium 174.967

†Actinide series

90 **Th** Thorium 232.0381	91 **Pa** Protactinium 231.03588	92 **U** Uranium 238.0289	93 **Np** Neptunium 237.048	94 **Pu** Plutonium [244]	95 **Am** Americium [243]	96 **Cm** Curium [247]	97 **Bk** Berkelium [247]	98 **Cf** Californium [251]	99 **Es** Einsteinium [252]	100 **Fm** Fermium [257]	101 **Md** Mendelevium [258]	102 **No** Nobelium [259]	103 **Lr** Lawrencium [262]

Atomic masses in brackets are the masses of the longest-lived or most important isotope of certain radioactive elements.

[a] The labels on top (1, 2, 3 ... 18) are the group numbers recommended by the International Union of Pure and Applied Chemistry (IUPAC).

[b] The labels on the bottom (1A, 2A, ... 8A) are the group numbers commonly used in the United States and the ones we use in this text.

[c] The names and symbols of elements 113 and above have not been assigned.

[d] Discovered in 2010, element 117 is under review by IUPAC.

Further information is available at the Web site of WebElements™.

Brief Contents

GREEN CHEMISTRY

The thirteenth edition of *Chemistry for Changing Times* is pleased to present the green chemistry essays listed below. The topics have been carefully chosen to introduce students to the concepts of green chemistry— a new approach to designing chemicals and chemical transformations that are beneficial for human health and the environment. The green chemistry essays in this edition highlight cutting-edge research by chemists, molecular scientists, and engineers to explore the fundamental science and practical applications of chemistry that is "benign by design." These examples emphasize the responsibility of chemists for the consequences of the new materials they create and the importance of building a sustainable chemical enterprise.

Contents

1 Chemistry   1

2 Atoms   41

3 Atomic Structure   61

4 Chemical Bonds 89

5 Chemical Accounting 125

6 Gases, Liquids, Solids . . . and Intermolecular Forces 152

7 Acids and Bases 175

8 Oxidation and Reduction   201

9 Organic Chemistry   229

10 Polymers   266

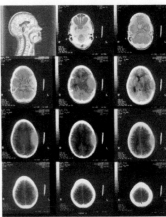

11 Nuclear Chemistry 295

15 Energy 411

Preface

Chemistry for Changing Times is now in its thirteenth edition. Times have changed immensely since the first edition appeared in 1972 and are changing more rapidly than ever—especially in the vital areas of biochemistry, the environment, energy, materials, drugs, and health and nutrition. This book has changed accordingly. We have thoroughly updated the text and integrated green chemistry throughout it, with a new or revised green chemistry essay in each chapter, as well as learning objectives and end-of-chapter problems correlated to each essay. In preparing this new edition, we have responded to suggestions from users and reviewers of the twelfth edition, and we have used our own writing, teaching, and life experiences. The text has been fully revised and updated to reflect the latest scientific developments in a fast-changing world.

New to This Edition

- We have incorporated a complete list of learning objectives at the beginning of each chapter and section-specific objectives at the beginning of each section. Another list placed just before the end-of-chapter problems correlates the learning objectives with particular problems. This will assist students in studying as well as aiding professors in assigning homework and assessing students' mastery of topics.
- We have reorganized sections within chapters to reflect the links between learning objectives and end-of-chapter questions both in the text and in MasteringChemistry®. In addition, Self-Assessment Questions at the end of each section will help facilitate student learning. These multiple-choice items provide immediate feedback to test students' understanding of the material.
- Green chemistry coverage has been increased and is now integrated into the text:
  - All essays have been carefully reviewed and have been rewritten extensively or replaced entirely.
  - Each essay identifies the principles of green chemistry that are applied in it.
  - Each end-of-chapter summary now includes a section on the green chemistry essay.
  - Learning objectives related to green chemistry have been added to each chapter and are linked to end-of-chapter problems in the textbook and to MasteringChemistry problems.
  - In each chapter, there are two to five end-of-chapter problems that relate to the green chemistry essay.
  - Chapter references have been added to the green chemistry essays when applicable.
- We have revised more than 25% of the end-of-chapter problems. Several of the worked-out examples and their accompanying exercises have also been modified or revised.
- The text has been enhanced with a new design. Each chapter starts with a compelling image and a set of questions called "Have You Ever Wondered?" These real-life questions will engage students in the chapter's content. Answers to the questions are found in the margins within the chapter, near the related text content. Those questions and answers are color-coded for connectivity.
- Critical Thinking Exercises have been revised or replaced in all chapters, with at least 25% being new or modified. These exercises require the student

to apply information and concepts learned from the chapter in both concrete and abstract fashion.

- Collaborative Group Projects, which follow the end-of-chapter problems, have been revised or replaced in all chapters. These projects make it easy for instructors who want to encourage collaborative work and to make group assignments for PowerPoint or poster presentations. These projects can extend the students' learning of chemistry far beyond the textbook.

To the Instructor

Our knowledge base has expanded enormously since this book's first edition, never more so than in the last few years. We have faced tough choices in deciding what to include and what to leave out. We now live in what has been called the Information Age. Unfortunately, information is not knowledge; the information may or may not be valid. Our focus, more than ever, is on helping students evaluate information. May we all someday gain the gift of wisdom.

A major premise is that a chemistry course for students who are not majoring in science should be quite different from the course offered to science majors. It must present basic chemical concepts with intellectual honesty, but it need not—probably should not—focus on esoteric theories or rigorous mathematics. It should include lots of modern everyday applications. The textbook should be appealing to look at, easy to understand, and interesting to read.

Three-fourths of the legislation considered by the U.S. Congress involves questions having to do with science or technology, yet only rarely does a scientist or engineer enter politics. Most of the people who make important decisions regarding our health and our environment are not trained in science, but it is critical that these decision makers be scientifically literate. In the judicial system, decisions often depend on scientific evidence, but judges and jurors frequently have little education in the sciences. A chemistry course for students who are not science majors should emphasize practical applications of chemistry to problems involving such things as environmental pollution, radioactivity, energy sources, and human health. The students who take liberal arts chemistry courses include future teachers, business leaders, lawyers, legislators, accountants, artists, journalists, jurors, and judges.

Objectives

Our main objectives for a chemistry course for students who are not majoring in science are as follows:

- To attract lots of students from a variety of disciplines. If students do not enroll in the course, we can't teach them.
- To help students learn so that they may become productive, creative, ethical, and engaged citizens.
- To use topics of current interest to illustrate chemical principles. We want students to appreciate the importance of chemistry in the real world.
- To relate chemical problems to the everyday lives of our students. Chemical problems become more significant to students when they can see a personal connection.
- To instill in students an appreciation for chemistry as an open-ended learning experience. We hope that our students will develop a curiosity about science and will want to continue learning throughout their lives.
- To acquaint students with scientific methods. We want students to be able to read about science and technology with some degree of critical judgment. This is especially important because many scientific problems are complex and controversial.
- To show students, by addressing the concepts of sustainability and green chemistry, that chemists seek better, safer, and more environmentally friendly processes and products.

■ To help students become literate in science. We want our students to develop a comfortable knowledge of science so that they find news articles relating to science interesting rather than intimidating.

Applications

Periodically through the text, the reader will find *boxed* features. These essays focus on interesting, relevant applications of the chemistry covered in a particular chapter or section and include the following:

■ What Science Is Not; Beyond the Alchemists' Wildest Dreams; Risks of Death; Nanoworld (Chapter 1)

■ Recycling (Chapter 2)

■ A Compound by Any Other Name . . . ; Useful Applications of Free Radicals (Chapter 4)

■ Why Doesn't Stomach Acid Dissolve the Stomach? (Chapter 7)

■ Photochromic Glass (Chapter 8)

■ Salicylates: Pain Relievers Based on Salicylic Acid (Chapter 9)

■ The Many Forms of Carbon; Conducting Polymers: Polyacetylene (Chapter 10)

■ Cell Phones and Microwaves and Power Lines, Oh My! (Chapter 11)

■ Energy Return on Energy Invested; Hydrogen in Your Future (Car) (Chapter 15)

■ Infectious Prions: Deadly Protein; Enzymes as Green Catalysts; DNA Profiling; Genetically Modified Organisms (Chapter 16)

■ It's a Drug! No, It's a Food! No, It's . . . a Dietary Supplement! Nanoscience in Foods (Chapter 17)

■ Chemistry, Allergies, and the Common Cold; Vaccine or No Vaccine? Diabetes; Love, Trust, Sexual Fidelity, and Chemistry (Chapter 18)

■ Improving Athletic Performance through Chemistry; Chemistry of Sports Materials (Chapter 19)

■ Fritz Haber; Development of Insect Resistance (Chapter 20)

■ Personal Cleanliness; Hazards of Mixing Cleaners; Antiaging Creams and Lotions; Nanoparticles in Cosmetics; Aromatherapy (Chapter 21)

■ Renaissance Poisoners; Getting Rid of "Toxins"; Chemistry and Counterterrorism (Chapter 22)

In addition, short *It DOES Matter!* items are presented in the margins. These features briefly discuss a specific application or phenomenon and show students that the material being studied does relate to the world in which we live.

Visualization

Visual material adds greatly to the general appeal of a textbook. For that reason, new photographs and diagrams have been added throughout this book. Color diagrams can be highly instructive, and colorful photographs relating to descriptive chemistry do much to enhance the learning process. We have added and revised illustrations that use both microscopic (molecular) and macroscopic (visual) views to help students visualize chemical phenomena. Some of the figure captions feature questions that focus students' attention on the concept illustrated in the figure.

Readability

Over the years, students have told us that they have found this textbook easy to read. The language is simple, and the style is conversational. Explanations are clear and easy to understand. The friendly tone of the book has been maintained in this edition. Since the format and the amount of open space on a page also contribute to readability, we have made conscious improvements in the design of this edition. For example, some of the margin notes that appeared in previous editions have been incorporated directly into the text to reduce crowding and improve the flow.

Units of Measurement

The United States continues to use the traditional English system for many kinds of measurements even though the metric system has long been used internationally. A modern version of the metric system, the Système International (SI), is now widely used, especially by scientists. So what units should be used in a text for liberal arts students? In presenting chemical principles, we use primarily metric units. In other parts of the book, we use those units that the students are most likely to encounter elsewhere in the same context.

Chemical Structures

The structures of many complicated molecules are presented in the text, especially in the later chapters. These structures are presented mainly to emphasize that they are actually known and to illustrate the fact that substances with similar properties often have similar structures. In many of the structures, functional groups or specific molecular features have been emphasized with color. For example, basic functional groups are usually shown in blue, acidic ones in red, and neutral in green. Students should not feel that they must learn all these structures, but they should take the time to look at them. We hope that they will come to recognize familiar features in these molecules.

Chapter Summaries and Glossary

Each chapter summary, with key terms highlighted in blue, provides a quick review. A list that follows the summary recaps the Learning Objectives and correlates them to the end-of-chapter problems. This correlation can help an instructor to make assignments. The Glossary gives definitions of terms that appear in boldface throughout the text and are highlighted in the chapter summaries, as well as some other terms frequently encountered.

Questions and Problems

Worked-out Examples and accompanying exercises are given within most chapters. Each Example carefully guides students through the process for solving a particular type of problem. It is then followed by one or more exercises that allow students to check their comprehension right away. Many Examples are followed by two exercises, labeled A and B. The goal in an A exercise is to apply to a similar situation the method outlined in the Example. In a B exercise, students must often combine that method with other ideas previously learned. Many of the B exercises provide a context closer to that in which chemical knowledge is applied, and they thus serve as a bridge between the worked Examples and the more challenging problems at the end of the chapter. The A and B exercises provide a simple way for the instructor to assign homework that is closely related to the Examples. Answers to all the in-chapter exercises are given in the Answers section at the back of the book.

Answers to all odd-numbered end-of-chapter problems, identified by blue numbers, are given in the Answers section at the back of the book. The end-of-chapter problems include the following:

- Review Questions for the most part simply ask for a recall of material in the chapter.
- A set of matched-pair problems is arranged according to subject matter in each chapter.

- Additional Problems are not grouped by type. Some of these are more challenging than the matched-pair problems and often require a synthesis of ideas from more than one chapter. Others pursue an idea further than is done in the text or introduce new ideas.
- Many colleges and universities now emphasize group learning as well as individual assignments. The Collaborative Group Projects permit an instructor to easily assign group work in an open-ended context; most of these projects can have multiple directions and multiple focus points.

Supplementary Materials

The most important learning aid is the teacher. In order to make the instructor's job easier and enrich the education of students, we have provided a variety of supplementary materials.

Instructor Resources

MasteringChemistry® with Pearson eText

www.masteringchemistry.com

MasteringChemistry® from Pearson has been designed and refined with a single purpose in mind: to help educators create that moment of understanding with their students. The Mastering platform delivers engaging, dynamic learning opportunities—focused on instructors' course objectives and responsive to each student's progress—that are proven to help students absorb course material and understand difficult concepts. By complementing their teaching with our engaging technology and content, instructors can be confident that their students will arrive at that moment—the moment of true understanding.

- The MasteringChemistry® tutorial system helps students figure out where they are going wrong when problem solving by providing answer-specific feedback and coaching. By offering feedback specific to wrong answers given, MasteringChemistry® tutorials coach 92% of students to the correct answer.
- The program enables professors to compare their class performance against the national average on specific questions or topics. At a glance, professors can see class distribution of grades, time spent, most difficult problems, most difficult steps, and even the most common answer.
- Pearson eText gives students access to the text whenever and wherever they can access the Internet. The eText pages look exactly like the printed text, and include powerful interactive and customization functions. This does not include the actual bound book.

Instructor Resource DVD

(0321767772) This DVD provides an integrated collection of resources to help instructors make efficient and effective use of their time. It features all artwork from the text, including figures and tables in PDF format for high-resolution printing, as well as four prebuilt PowerPoint™ presentations. The first presentation contains the images embedded within PowerPoint slides. The second includes a complete lecture outline that the instructor can modify. The final two presentations contain worked "in-chapter" sample exercises and questions to be used with classroom response systems. This DVD also contains movies, animations, and electronic files of the Instructor's Resource Manual, as well as the Test Item File.

Printed Test Bank

(0321767780) This test bank contains over 2500 multiple choice, true/false, and matching questions.

Instructor Manual (download only)

(0321767802) Organized by chapter, this useful guide includes objectives, lecture outlines, and references to figures and solved problems, as well as teaching tips.

Instructor Manual for Lab Manual (download only)

(0321767756) An online resource, the Instructor Manual for the Lab Manual provides instructors with useful tips, lab notes, and answers to lab report questions and pre- and post-lab questions.

Test Bank for WebCT (download only)

(0321767683) The WebCT Test Bank contains test bank questions for import into WebCT Learning System.

Test Bank for Blackboard (download only)

(0321767691) The Blackboard Test Bank contains test bank questions for import into Blackboard Learning System.

Student Resources

MasteringChemistry® with Pearson eText

www.masteringchemistry.com

MasteringChemistry® from Pearson has been designed and refined with a single purpose in mind: to help educators create that moment of understanding with their students. The Mastering platform delivers engaging, dynamic learning opportunities—focused on instructors' course objectives and responsive to each student's progress—that are proven to help students absorb course material and understand difficult concepts. By complementing their teaching with our engaging technology and content, instructors can be confident that their students will arrive at that moment—the moment of true understanding.

Study Guide and Selected Solutions Manual

(0321767810) The Study Guide and Selected Solutions Manual assists students with the text material. It contains learning objectives, chapter outlines, key terms, additional problems with self-tests and answers, and answers to the odd-numbered problems in the text.

Chemical Investigations for Changing Times

(0321767799) This resource contains 66 laboratory experiments and is specifically referenced to *Chemistry for Changing Times*.

Acknowledgments

Through the last four decades, we have greatly benefited from hundreds of helpful reviews. It would take far too many pages to list all of those reviewers here. Many of you have contributed to the flavor of the book and helped us minimize our errors. Please know that your contributions are deeply appreciated. For the thirteenth edition, we are grateful for challenging reviews from the following reviewers:

Reviewers of the Thirteenth Edition

Debe Bell, *Metro State College*

Mark Blazer, *Shasta College*

Kirsten Casey, *Anne Arundel Community College*

Alice Harper, *Berry College*

Alton Hassell, *Baylor University*

Donna K. Howell, *Park University*

David Lippman, *University of Texas, Austin*

James L. Marshall, *University of North Texas*

Douglas Mulford, *Emory University*

David S. Newman, *Bowling Green State University*

Charlotte A. Ovechka, *University of St. Thomas*

James K. Owen, *The Art Institute of Tennessee*

Christine Seppanen, *Riverland Community College*

Michael Dennis Seymour, *Hope College*

Shirish K. Shah, *Towson University*

Julianne Smist, *Springfield College*

Mona Uppal, *Tarrant County College, NE*

Paloma Valverde, *Wentworth Institute of Technology*

Matthew E. Wise, *University of Colorado, Boulder*

Accuracy Reviewers

Edie Banner, *Florida Southern College*

Rill Reuter, *Winona State University*

Bradley Sieve, *Northern Kentucky University*

Green Chemistry Contributors

We are enormously grateful to Jennifer Young, former manager of the American Chemical Society's Green Chemistry Institute®, who coordinated the development of the new and revised green chemistry essays and correlated the content of these essays. We thank her for her dedication to this project. We also thank the team of green chemists listed below who contributed the green essays and helped to integrate the each essay's content into the chapter with learning objectives, end-of-chapter problems, summaries, and section references.

David Brown, *Davidson College*

Amy Cannon, *Beyond Benign*

Scott Cummings, *Kenyon College*

Joseph Fortunak, *Howard University*

Tom Goodwin, *Hendrix College*

Michael Heben, *University of Toledo*

Randall Hicks, *Wheaton College*

Colin Horwitz, *GreenOx Catalysts*

Margaret Kerr, *Worcester State University*

Irv Levy, *Gordon College*

Doris Lewis, *Suffolk University*

Lallie C. McKenzie, *Chem11 LLC*

Martin Mulvihill, *University of California–Berkeley*

Bevin Parks-Lee

Bob Peoples, *ACS Green Chemistry Institute*

Douglas Raynie, *South Dakota State University*

Robert Tanguay, *Oregon State University*

David Vosburg, *Harvey Mudd College*

John Warner, *Warner Babcock Institute*

Denyce Wicht, *Suffolk University*

Jennifer Young, *ACS Green Chemistry Institute*

Reviewers of Previous Editions

Michelle Boucher, *Utica College*

Roxanne Finney, *Skagit Valley College*

Luther Giddings, *Salt Lake Community College*

Todd Hamilton, *Georgetown College*

Alton Hassell, *Baylor University*

Scott Hewitt, *California State University, Fullerton*

Sherell Hickman, *Brevard Community College, Cocoa*

Beth Hixon, *Tulsa Community College*

James L. Klino, *SUNY College of Agriculture and Technology, Cobleskill*

Meghan Knapp, *Georgetown College*

Kim Loomis, *Century College*

Jeremy Mason, *Texas Technical University*

Lois Schadenwald, *Normandale Community College*

Joseph Sinski, *Bellarmine University*

Kelli M. Slunt, *University of Mary Washington*

Jie Song, *University of Michigan, Flint*

Wayne M. Stalick, *University of Central Missouri*

Durwin Striplin, *Davidson College*

Shashi Unnithan, *Front Range Community College*

Edward Vitz, *Kutztown University*

Dan Wacks, *University of Redlands*

Elizabeth Wallace, *Western Oklahoma State College*

Matthew E. Wise, *University of Colorado, Boulder*

We also appreciate the many people who have called, written, or e-mailed with corrections and other helpful suggestions. Cynthia S. Hill prepared much of the original material on biochemistry, food, and health and fitness.

We owe a special debt of gratitude to Doris K. Kolb (1927–2005), who was an esteemed coauthor from the seventh through the eleventh editions. Doris and her husband Ken were friends and helpful supporters long before Doris joined the author team. She provided much of the spirit and flavor of the book. Doris's contributions to *Chemistry for Changing Times*—and indeed to all of chemistry and chemical education—will live on for many years to come, not only in her publications, but in the hearts and minds of her many students, colleagues, and friends.

Throughout her career as a teacher, scientist, community leader, poet, and much more, Doris was blessed with a wonderful spouse, colleague, and companion, Kenneth E. Kolb. Over the years, Ken did chapter reviews, made suggestions, and gave invaluable help for many editions. All who knew Doris miss her greatly. Those of us who had the privilege of working closely with her miss her wisdom and wit most profoundly. Let us all dedicate our lives, as Doris did hers, to making this world a better place.

We also want to thank our colleagues at the University of Wisconsin–River Falls, Murray State University, and Bradley University for all their help and support through the years.

We also owe a debt of gratitude to the many creative people at Pearson who have contributed their talents to this edition. Jennifer Hart, our chemistry project editor, has been a delight to work with, providing valuable guidance throughout the project. She showed extraordinary skill and diplomacy in coordinating all the many facets of this project. Development Editor Donald Gecewicz contributed greatly to this project, especially in challenging us to be better authors in every way. We treasure his many helpful suggestions of new material and better presentation of all the subject matter. We are grateful to Editor in Chief Adam Jaworski for his overall guidance and to production Project Manager Beth Sweeten for her diligence and patience in bringing all the parts together to yield a finished work. We are indebted to our copy editor, Jane Hoover, whose expertise helped improve the consistency of the text; and to proofreaders and accuracy checkers Rill Reuter, Brad Sieve, and Edie Banner, whose sharp eyes caught many of our errors and typos. We also salute our photo researcher, Eric Schrader, who vetted hundreds of images in the search for quality photographic illustrations.

John W. Hill owes a very special kind of thanks to his wonderful spouse, Ina, who over the years has done typing, library research, and so many other things that allow him time to concentrate on writing. Most of all, he is grateful for her boundless patience, unflagging support, understanding, and enduring love. He is also grateful to his beloved daughter Cindy for her help with the house and the yard and so many other things. Terry W. McCreary would like to thank his wife, Geniece, and children, Corinne and Yvette, for their unflagging support, understanding, and love.

Finally, we also thank all those many students whose enthusiasm has made teaching such a joy. It is gratifying to have students learn what you are trying to teach them, but it is a supreme pleasure to find that they want to learn even more. And, of course, we are grateful to all of you who have made so many helpful suggestions. We welcome and appreciate all your comments, corrections, and criticisms.

John W. Hill
jwhill602@comcast.net

Terry W. McCreary
terry.mccreary@murraystate.edu

Doris K. Kolb

To the Student

Tell me, what is it you plan to do
with your one wild and precious life?
  —American poet Mary Oliver (b. 1935)
  "The Summer Day," from *New and Selected Poems*
  (Boston, MA: Beacon Press, 1992)

Welcome to Our Chemical World!

Life is largely a do-it-yourself job, but others can help you make your life better. We hope to help by showing how chemistry can enhance your understanding of the world around you. You do not need to exclude chemistry from your learning experiences. Chemistry is fun. Through this book, we would like to share with you some of the excitement of chemistry and some of the joy of learning about it. Learning chemistry will enrich your life—now and long after this course is over—through a better understanding of the natural world, the technological questions now confronting us, and the choices you will face as a citizen in a scientific and technological society.

Learning chemistry involves thinking logically, critically, and creatively. Skills gained in this course can be exceptionally useful in many aspects of your life. You will learn how to use the language of chemistry: symbols, formulas, and equations. More important, you will learn how to obtain meaning from information. The most important thing you will learn is how to learn. Memorized material quickly fades into oblivion unless it is arranged on a framework of understanding.

Chemistry Directly Affects Our Lives

How does the human body work? How does aspirin cure headaches, reduce fevers, and lessen the chance of a heart attack or stroke? How does penicillin kill bacteria without harming our healthy body cells? Is ozone a good thing or a threat to our health? Are iron supplement pills poisonous? Do we really face climate change, and if so, how severe will it be? Do humans contribute to climate change, and if so, to what degree? Why do most weight-loss diets seem to work in the short run but fail in the long run? Why do our moods swing from happy to sad? Can a chemical test on urine predict possible suicide attempts? Chemists have found answers to questions such as these and continue to seek the knowledge that will unlock still other secrets of our universe. As these mysteries are resolved, the direction of our lives often changes—sometimes dramatically. We live in a chemical world—a world of drugs, biocides, food additives, fertilizers, fuels, detergents, cosmetics, and plastics. We live in a world with toxic wastes, polluted air and water, and dwindling petroleum reserves. Knowledge of chemistry will help you better understand the benefits and hazards of this world and will enable you to make intelligent decisions in the future.

We Are All Chemically Dependent

Even in the womb we are chemically dependent. We need a constant supply of oxygen, water, glucose, amino acids, triglycerides, and a multitude of other chemical substances.

Our bodies are intricate chemical factories. They are durable but delicate systems. Innumerable chemical reactions that allow our bodies to function properly occur constantly within us. Thinking, learning, exercising, feeling happy or sad, putting on too much weight or not gaining enough, and virtually all life processes are made possible by these chemical reactions. Everything that we ingest is part of a complex process that determines whether our bodies work effectively or not. The consumption of some substances can initiate chemical reactions that will stop body functions. Other substances, if consumed, can cause permanent handicaps, and still others can make living less comfortable. A proper balance of the right foods provides the chemicals that fuel the reactions we need in order to function at our best. The knowledge of chemistry that you will soon be gaining will help you better understand how your body works so that you will be able to take proper care of it.

Changing Times

We live in a world of increasingly rapid change. It has been said that the only constant is change itself. At present, we are facing some of the greatest problems that humans have ever encountered, and these dilemmas confronting us seem to have no perfect solutions. We are sometimes forced to make a best choice among only bad alternatives, and our decisions often provide only temporary solutions to our problems. Nevertheless, if we are to choose properly, we must understand what our choices are. Mistakes can be costly, and they cannot always be rectified. It is easy to pollute, but cleaning up pollution once it is there is enormously expensive. We can best avoid mistakes by collecting as much information as possible and evaluating it carefully before making critical decisions. Science is a means of gathering and evaluating information, and chemistry is central to all the sciences.

Chemistry and the Human Condition

Above all else, our hope is that you will learn that the study of chemistry need not be dull and difficult. Rather, it can enrich your life in so many ways—through a better understanding of your body, your mind, your environment, and the world in which you live. After all, the search to understand the universe is an essential part of what it means to be human. We offer you a challenge first issued by American educator Horace Mann (1796–1859) in his 1859 address at Antioch College: "Be ashamed to die until you have won some victory for humanity."

About the Authors

John W. Hill

Hill received his Ph.D. from the University of Arkansas. As an organic chemist, he has published more than 50 papers, most of which have an educational bent. He has authored or coauthored several introductory-level chemistry textbooks, all of which have been published in multiple editions. He has also presented over 60 papers at national conferences, many relating to science education. He has received several awards for outstanding teaching and has long been active in the American Chemical Society, both locally and nationally. Now professor emeritus at the University of Wisconsin–River Falls, Hill authored the first edition of *Chemistry for Changing Times* in 1972. Revising and updating this book has been a major focus of his life for four decades.

Terry W. McCreary

McCreary received his B.S. from St. Francis University, his M.S. from the University of Georgia, and his Ph.D. from Virginia Tech. He has taught chemistry at Murray State University since 1988, and was presented with the Regents Excellence in Teaching Award in 2008. He is a member of the American Chemical Society and the Kentucky Academy of Science and has served as technical editor for the *Journal of Pyrotechnics*. In his spare time, he designs, builds, and flies rockets with the Tripoli Rocketry Association; he was elected president of the association in 2010. McCreary is the author of several laboratory manuals; *General Chemistry* with John Hill, Ralph Petrucci, and Scott Perry; and *Experimental Composite Propellant*, a fundamental treatise on the preparation and properties of solid rocket propellant.

About Our Sustainability Initiatives

Pearson recognizes the environmental challenges facing this planet, as well as acknowledges our responsibility in making a difference.

This book is carefully crafted to minimize environmental impact. The materials used to manufacture this book originated from sources committed to responsible forestry practices. The paper is FSC® certified. The binding, cover, and paper come from facilities that minimize waste, energy consumption, and the use of harmful chemicals.

Pearson closes the loop by recycling every out-of-date text returned to our warehouse. Along with developing and exploring digital solutions to our market's needs, Pearson has a strong commitment to achieving carbon-neutrality. As of 2009, Pearson became the first carbon- and climate-neutral publishing company. Since then, Pearson remains strongly committed to measuring, reducing, and offsetting our carbon footprint.

The future holds great promise for reducing our impact on Earth's environment, and Pearson is proud to be leading the way. We strive to publish the best books with the most up-to-date and accurate content, and to do so in ways that minimize our impact on Earth. To learn more about our initiatives, please visit **www.pearson.com/responsibility**.

MasteringChemistry®

www.masteringchemistry.com

NEW for this edition! MasteringChemistry is designed with a single purpose: to help students reach the moment of understanding. The Mastering online homework and tutoring system delivers self-paced tutorials that provide students with individualized coaching set to instructors' course objectives. MasteringChemistry helps students arrive better prepared for lecture and lab.

Engaging Experiences

MasteringChemistry promotes interactivity and active learning in Liberal Arts Chemistry. Research shows that Mastering's immediate feedback and tutorial assistance help students understand and master concepts and skills in Chemistry—allowing them to retain more knowledge and perform better in this course and beyond.

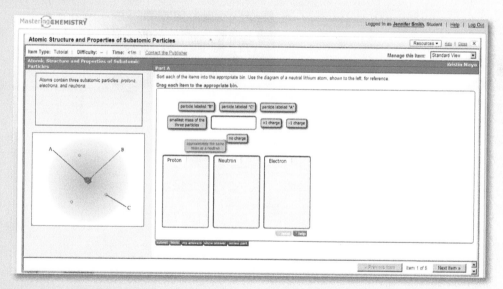

Student Tutorials

MasteringChemistry is the only system to provide instantaneous feedback to the most common wrong answers. Students can submit an answer and receive immediate, error-specific feedback, as well as request hints (simpler sub-problems).

Reading Quizzes

Reading Quizzes give instructors the opportunity to assign reading, and test students on their comprehension of chapter content.

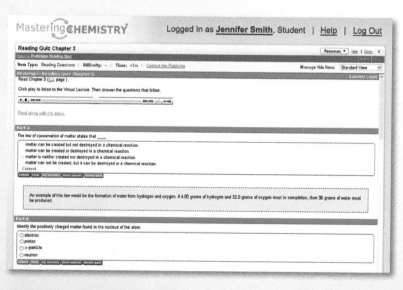

Annotation Function allows students to take notes.

Google®-based search function.

Highlight Function lets students highlight what they want to remember.

Zoom lets students zoom in and out for better viewing.

Hyperlinks link to quizzes, tests, activities, and animations.

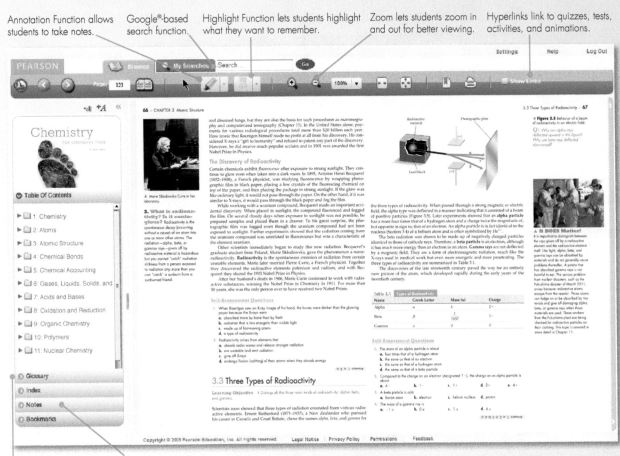

Interactive Glossary provides pop-up definitions and terms.

Instructor Notes allow instructors to share his or her notes and highlights with the class.

Pearson eText

Pearson eText gives students access to the text whenever and wherever they can access the Internet. The eText pages look exactly like the printed text, and include powerful interactive and customization functions. Users can create notes, highlight text in different colors, create bookmarks, zoom, click hyperlinked words and phrases to view definitions, and view as a single page or as two pages. Pearson eText also offers a full text search and the ability to save and export notes.

NEW! Learning Objectives

Learning Objectives appear in each section of **Chemistry for Changing Times** and at the beginning and end of the chapter. These objectives bring the main goals of each section to the foreground, and are linked to end-of-chapter problems in the text and in MasteringChemistry. These learning objectives give focus points to each section and will increase efficiencies in teaching and learning.

MasteringChemistry®

www.masteringchemistry.com

A Trusted Partner

The Mastering platform was developed by scientists for science students and instructors, and has a proven history with more than 10 years of student use. Mastering currently has more than 1.5 million active registrations with active users in 50 states and in 41 countries. The Mastering platform has 99.8% server reliability.

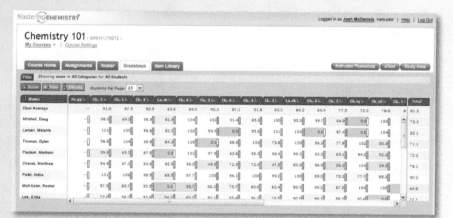

Gradebook

Every assignment is automatically graded. At a glance, shades of red highlight vulnerable students and challenging assignments.

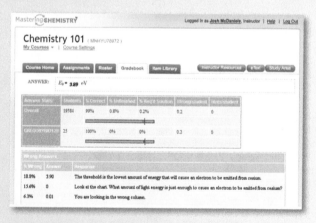

Student Performance Data

With a single click, Student Performance Data provides at-a-glance statistics on each class as well as national results. Wrong-answer summaries give insight into students' misconceptions and facilitate just-in-time teaching adjustments.

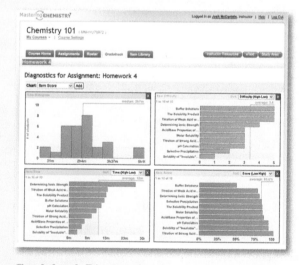

Gradebook Diagnostics

Gradebook Diagnostics provide unique insight into class and student performance. With a single click, charts summarize the most difficult problems, vulnerable students, grade distribution, and score improvement over the duration of the course.

Proven Results

The Mastering platform is the only online homework system with research showing that it improves student learning. A wide variety of published papers, based on NSF-sponsored research and tests, illustrate the benefits of the Mastering program. Results documented in scientifically valid efficacy papers are available at www.masteringchemistry.com/site/results

Green Chemistry Emphasis

The concept of green chemistry has been expanded in the **Thirteenth Edition,** and is integrated throughout with a framework incorporating the 12 Principles of Green Chemistry. Each chapter contains a green essay which identifies the principles that are applied in that essay. Chapters are further enhanced by the inclusion of green chemistry content within the learning objectives as well as the end-of-chapter summaries and questions.

GREEN CHEMISTRY

Principles 1, 4, 7, 9, 10

Irvin Levy, *Gordon College*

Sustainability: It's Basic (and Acidic)

Green chemistry is a part of sustainable chemistry. Sustainability, often defined as "meeting the needs of the present generation without compromising the ability of future generations to meet their needs," is much in the news these days. Green chemistry is one of the critical means of attaining sustainability. Understanding of acids and bases has led to greener, more sustainable methods for producing consumer products. Two important examples are soap and renewable biofuels.

Soap traditionally has been made from fats left from cooking meats and from vegetable oils. Fats and oils contain substances composed of three long chains of carbon atoms connected to a central set of three carbon atoms, an arrangement called a *triglyceride* (Chapter 16). To make soap, the fats are heated and mixed with lye solution (aqueous sodium hydroxide—a base). Each mole of triglyceride reacts with three moles of base to produce three moles of soap and one mole of the byproduct glycerol (also called glycerin). Soaps are salts (Section 7.2) of carboxylic acids that usually have a long chain of carbon atoms. An example of a typical soap is sodium palmitate. Its chemical formula is shown here.

$$CH_3(CH_2)_{14}COO^-Na^+$$

The byproduct glycerol has a number of uses, including as a moisturizing ingredient in soap. Chemists at Gordon College (Wenham, MA) found that adding glycerol to the fats and oils traditionally used in soap-making decreased the quantity of starting materials required for soap production. Much more glycerol byproduct is produced industrially than can be used by the soap industry, however, so the search continues for other green uses for glycerol.

The chemistry of biodiesel fuel production (also see Chapter 15) is much like that of soap-making. In both processes, bases are used and glycerol is formed. With the use of methanol (CH_3OH) in place of water and a catalytic amount of base, though, the triglycerides are converted to compounds called *esters* (Section 9.7). An example of a typical biodiesel molecule is shown here.

$$CH_3(CH_2)_{14}COOCH_3$$

Although the long chains of carbon atoms in biodiesel often are the same as in soap molecules, biodiesel molecules have a different group on one end of the chain. Compare these compounds to a typical diesel molecule from petroleum that does not contain any atoms other than carbon and hydrogen.

$$CH_3(CH_2)_{14}CH_3$$

What do soap, biodiesel, and glycerol have to do with sustainability and green chemistry? The first principle of green chemistry encourages the prevention of waste. Sometimes wastes also are harmful to the environment. Wouldn't it be better to redirect apparently useless materials into something useful?

Consider this: Each year billions of gallons of fats and oils are used to fry foods. Fryer oils degrade fairly quickly in commercial kitchens. For many years the used oils were carted off by disposal companies as waste. Today, much of that used oil is converted into biodiesel fuel, providing an alternative fuel that doesn't deplete fossil petroleum reserves. This approach satisfies the green chemistry principle of using renewable resources while providing new use for what was once considered waste. And it gets better! Petroleum diesel fuel is hazardous to humans and toxic to the environment. Biodiesel is much safer.

Acids also are involved in green processes such as cleaning. For example, polylactic acid (PLA) is a type of biodegradable and renewable plastic made from chemicals derived from corn (see Green Chemistry essay, Chapter 10). PLA plastic, made by companies such as NatureWorks, is found in many consumer materials, such as plastic cups. Research at Simmons College in Boston has led to a new way to convert used PLA cups into an antimicrobial cleaning solution containing lactic acid ($CH_3CHOHCOOH$). The shredded plastic is mixed with alcohol and base to break down the polymer to sodium lactate ($CH_3CHOHCOONa$). The basic sodium lactate solution is neutralized with acid to form the lactic acid cleaner, which is useful for wiping away soap scum.

In the quest for sustainability, acids and bases are an essential part of the toolbox that will continue to be used as chemists search for better ways to prevent waste and use renewable starting materials. You might argue that sustainability is basic—not to mention acidic.

182

Green Chemistry Essays

Green Chemistry essays, written by experts in the field, include topics that have been carefully chosen to introduce students to one or more of the 12 Principles of Green Chemistry. The Principles that are applied in the essays are clearly identified, and references to the chapter are included when applicable.

SUMMARY

Section 7.1—Acids taste sour, turn litmus red, and react with active metals to form hydrogen. Bases taste bitter, turn litmus blue, and feel slippery to the skin. Acids and bases react to form salts and water. An acid–base indicator such as litmus has different colors in acid and in base and is used to determine whether solutions are acidic or basic.

Section 7.2—According to Arrhenius's definition, an *acid* produces hydrogen ions (H^+, also called protons) in aqueous solution, and a *base* produces hydroxide ions (OH^-). Neutralization is the combination of H^+ and OH^- to form water. The anion and cation that were associated with H^+ and OH^- ions combine to form an ionic salt. In the more general Brønsted–Lowry acid–base theory, an acid is a proton donor and a base is a proton acceptor. When a Brønsted–Lowry acid dissolves in water, the H_2O molecules pick up H^+ to form hydronium ions (H_3O^+). A Brønsted–Lowry base in water accepts a proton from a water molecule, forming OH^-.

Section 7.3—Some nonmetal oxides (such as CO_2 and SO_3) are acidic anhydrides in that they react with water to form acids. Some metal oxides (such as Li_2O and CaO) are basic anhydrides; they react with water to form bases.

Section 7.4—A strong acid is one that ionizes completely in water to form H^+ ions and anions. A weak acid ionizes only slightly in water; most of the acid exists as intact molecules. Common strong acids are sulfuric, hydrochloric, and nitric acids. Likewise, a strong base is completely ionized in water, and a weak base is only slightly ionized. Sodium hydroxide and potassium hydroxide are common strong bases.

Section 7.5—The reaction between an acid and a base is called *neutralization*. In aqueous solution, it is the combination of H^+ and OH^- that forms water. The other anions and cations form an ionic salt.

Section 7.6—The pH scale indicates the degree of acidity or basicity; pH is defined as $pH = -\log[H^+]$, where $[H^+]$ is the molar concentration of hydrogen ion. A pH of 7 ($[H^+] = 1 \times 10^{-7}$ M) is neutral; pH values lower than 7 represent increasing acidity, and pH values greater than 7 represent increasing basicity. A change in pH of one unit represents a tenfold change in $[H^+]$.

Section 7.7—A pair of compounds or ions that differ by one proton (H^+) is called a conjugate acid–base pair. A buffer solution is a mixture of a weak acid and its conjugate base or a weak base and its conjugate acid. A buffer maintains a nearly constant pH when a small amount of a strong acid or a strong base is added.

Section 7.8—An antacid is a base such as sodium bicarbonate, magnesium hydroxide, aluminum hydroxide, or calcium carbonate that is taken to relieve hyperacidity. Overuse of some antacids can make the blood too alkaline (basic), a condition called alkalosis. Acid rain is rain with a pH less than 5.6. The acidity is due to sulfur oxides and nitrogen oxides from natural sources as well as industrial air pollution and automobile exhaust fumes. Acid rain can have serious effects on plant and animal life. Sulfuric acid is the number one chemical produced in the United States and is used for making fertilizers and other industrial chemicals. Hydrochloric acid is used for rust removal and etching mortar and concrete. Lime (calcium oxide) is made from limestone and is the cheapest and most widely used base. It is an ingredient in plaster and cement and is used in agriculture. Sodium hydroxide is used to make many industrial products, as well as soap. Amm onia is a weak base produced mostly for use as fertilizer. Concentrated strong acids and bases are corrosive poisons that can cause serious burns. Living cells have an optimal pH that is necessary for the proper functioning of proteins.

Green chemistry Base is used to convert renewable fats and oils into products such as soaps and biofuels. Treatment with acid can decompose special plastics (such as polylactic acid, PLA) into a useful antimicrobial cleaner. Application of the "12 Principles of Green Chemistry" can guide us to find practical uses for materials that were once considered waste.

End-of-Chapter Summaries

Each end-of-chapter summary now includes a section summarizing the green chemistry within each chapter essay.

Learning Objectives

› Distinguish between acids and bases using their chemical and physical properties. (7.1)	Problems 1, 26, 27
› Explain how an acid–base indicator works. (7.1)	Problem 2
› Identify Arrhenius and Brønsted–Lowry acids and bases. (7.2)	Problems 4, 12–22, 59
› Write a balanced equation for a neutralization or an ionization. (7.2)	Problems 8, 39–46, 60, 67
› Identify acidic and basic anhydrides, and write equations showing their reactions with water. (7.3)	Problems 7, 29, 30
› Define and identify strong and weak acids and bases. (7.4)	Problems 5, 9, 10, 31–38, 61
› Identify the reactants and predict the products in a neutralization reaction. (7.5)	
› Describe the relationship between the pH of a solution and its acidity or basicity. (7.6)	Problems 47–54
› Find the molar concentration of hydrogen ion, $[H^+]$, from a pH value or the pH value from $[H^+]$. (7.6)	
› Write the formula for the conjugate base of an acid or for the conjugate acid of a base. (7.7)	Problems 55, 56
› Describe the action of a buffer. (7.7)	Problem 65
› Describe everyday uses of acids and bases and how they affect daily life. (7.8)	Problems 11, 57, 58
› Write equations for the production of soap and of biofuel.	Problem 73
› Describe ways by which acids and bases can contribute to greener production of consumer products.	Problems 71, 72, 74

51. What is the hydrogen ion concentration of a solution that has a pH of 3?
52. What is the hydrogen ion concentration of a solution that has a pH of 11?
53. Milk of magnesia has a hydrogen ion concentration between 1.0×10^{-10} M and 1.0×10^{-11} M. What two whole-number values is the pH of milk of magnesia between?
54. Oven cleaner has a pH between 13 and 14. What two whole-number values of x should be used in 1.0×10^{-x} M to express the range of hydrogen ion concentration?

Conjugate Acid–Base Pairs

55. In the following reaction in aqueous solution, identify **(a)** which of the reactants is the acid and which is the base, **(b)** the conjugate base of the acid, and **(c)** the conjugate acid of the base.

$$HNO_3(aq) + NH_3(aq) \longrightarrow NO_3^-(aq) + NH_4^+(aq)$$

56. In the following reaction in aqueous solution, identify **(a)** which of the reactants is the acid and which is the base, **(b)** the conjugate base of the acid, and **(c)** the conjugate acid of the base.

$$CH_3CH_2COOH + H_2O \longrightarrow CH_3CH_2COO^- + H_3O^+$$

Antacids

57. Mylanta liquid has 200 mg of $Al(OH)_3$ and 200 mg of $Mg(OH)_2$ per teaspoonful. Write the equation for the neutralization of stomach acid [represented as HCl(aq)] by each of these substances.
58. What is the Brønsted–Lowry base in each of the following compounds, which are ingredients in antacids?
    a. $NaHCO_3$
    b. $Mg(OH)_2$
    c. $MgCO_3$
    d. $CaCO_3$

Learning Objectives

Learning Objectives for each section in the text and related to green chemistry have been added to every chapter. They are linked to end-of-chapter problems in the textbook and to MasteringChemistry problems.

End-of-Chapter Questions

In each chapter, two to five end-of-chapter problems relate to the green chemistry in that chapter.

Focus on Relevance

Abundant applications and examples fill each chapter of this edition, and material is updated throughout to mirror the latest scientific developments in a fast-changing world. Compelling visuals and features such as "It DOES Matter!" highlight current events and enable students to relate to the text more readily.

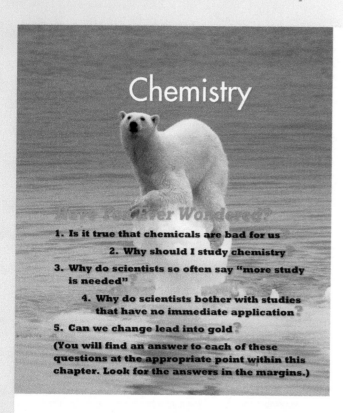

Chemistry

Have You Ever Wondered?

1. **Is it true that chemicals are bad for us**

2. **Why should I study chemistry**

3. **Why do scientists so often say "more study is needed"**

4. **Why do scientists bother with studies that have no immediate application**

5. **Can we change lead into gold**

(You will find an answer to each of these questions at the appropriate point within this chapter. Look for the answers in the margins.)

A Science for All Seasons Chemistry pervades every aspect of our lives. Look around you. Everything you see is made of chemicals: the food we eat, the air we breathe, the clothes we wear, the medicines we take, the vehicles we ride in, and the buildings we live and work in.

Everything we *do* also involves chemistry. Whenever we eat a sandwich, bathe, drive a car, listen to music, or ride a bicycle, we use chemistry. Even when we are asleep, chemical reactions go on constantly throughout our bodies.

Chemistry also affects society as a whole. Developments in health and medicine involve a lot of chemistry.
The astounding advances in

Chemistry is everywhere, not just in laboratories. Chemistry occurs in soil and rocks, in waters, in clouds, and in us. Knowledge of chemistry enhances our understanding of climate change, helps to provide food for Earth's increasing population, and is crucial to the development and production of sustainable fuels.

Learning Objectives

> Distinguish science from technology. (1.1)
> Define *alchemy* and *natural philosophy*. (1.1)
> Briefly describe the contributions of Bacon, Galileo, and Carson to the changing perceptions of science. (1.2)
> Define *green chemistry* and *sustainable chemistry*. (1.2)
> Define *hypothesis, scientific law, scientific theory,* and *scientific model,* and explain their relationships in science. (1.3)
> Explain what a variable is, and describe how variables introduce uncertainty. (1.3)
> Define *risk* and *benefit*, and give an example of each. (1.4)
> Estimate a desirability quotient, given information about benefits and risks. (1.4)
> Give an example of a use of chemistry in your daily life and in society at large. (1.5)
> Distinguish basic research from applied research. (1.6)
> Distinguish mass from weight, physical change from chemical change, and physical properties from chemical properties. (1.7)
> Classify matter according to state and as mixture, substance, compound, and/or element. (1.8)
> Assign proper units of measurement to observations, and manipulate units in conversions. (1.9)
> Calculate the density, mass, or volume of an object given the other two quantities. (1.10)
> Distinguish between heat and temperature. (1.11)
> Explain how the different temperature scales are related. (1.11)
> Use critical thinking to evaluate claims and statements. (1.12)
> Define green chemistry.
> Describe how *green chemistry* reduces risk and prevents environmental problems.

1

Have You Ever Wondered? Questions

"Have You Ever Wondered?" chapter-opening questions reflect real-life queries that may arise in students' minds and are related to the chapter content. Answers are included at appropriate locations within the chapter.

▲ It DOES Matter!

Polyethylene with a molecular mass from two to six million, called *ultra-high-molecular-weight polyethylene (UHMWPE)*, is used to make fibers 10 times stronger than steel and around 40% stronger than Kevlar (see Problem 30 on page 292) for use in body armor. Most modern skis are coated with UHMWPE on the bottom surface.

It DOES Matter! Boxes

A stronger emphasis on relevance is found in the "It DOES Matter!" boxes. There are approximately 10% more "It DOES Matter!" boxes in the Thirteenth Edition.

Cell Phones and Microwaves and Power Lines, Oh My!

There are many types of radiation. *Ionizing* radiation that comes from decaying atomic nuclei is highly energetic and can damage tissue, as discussed above. *Electromagnetic* radiation has many forms—visible light, radio waves, television broadcast waves, microwaves, ultraviolet light, military ULF (ultra-low-frequency), and others. A few types of electromagnetic radiation—X-rays and gamma rays—have enough energy to ionize tissue, and ultraviolet light has been strongly implicated in *melanoma* (skin cancer). But what about microwaves and radio waves, which don't have nearly as much energy? Although very large amounts of microwaves can cause burns (by heating), there is no conclusive evidence that low levels of microwaves pose significant threat to human health. A 2006 study involving almost half a million Danish citizens failed to show a relationship between cell phone use and cancer, though some scientists consider this study inconclusive. However, higher levels of radio frequencies over long periods of time *may* be a

different matter. In May 2011, the World Health Organization (WHO) classified heavy cell phone use—30 minutes of talking daily for ten years—as possible posing an increased risk of *glioma*, a type of brain cancer. The WHO's press release was very cautious, stating that "there could be some risk ... therefore we need to keep a close watch for a link between cell phones and cancer risk." For low levels of exposure to non-ionizing electromagnetic radiation, the hazard appears to be difficult to measure, let alone assess.

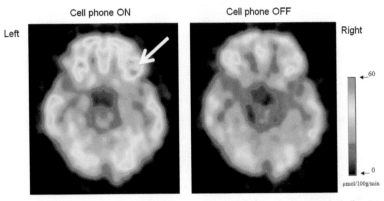

▲ A brain scan shows slight differences when a cell phone held to the ear is on (left) and off (right).

Current Environmental and Relevant Applications

These applications include many interesting and relevant topics to help students connect chemistry to the world around them.

Self-Assessment Questions

1. Consider how the qualities *discrete* and *continuous* apply to materials at the macroscopic (visible to the unaided eye) level. Which of the following is continuous?
   a. apple juice
   b. a ream of paper
   c. a bowl of cherries
   d. chocolate chips

2. The view that matter is continuous rather than atomic prevailed for centuries because it was
   a. actually correct
   b. not considered important
   c. not tested by experiment
   d. tested and found to be true

Answers: 1, a; 2, c

Self-Assessment Questions

Self-Assessment Questions appear in each section as a concept check for students as they progress through the chapter.

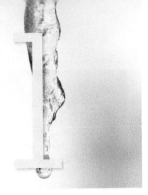

Chemistry

Have You Ever Wondered?

1. **Is it true that chemicals are bad for us**

2. **Why should I study chemistry**

3. **Why do scientists so often say "more study is needed"**

4. **Why do scientists bother with studies that have no immediate application**

5. **Can we change lead into gold**

(You will find an answer to each of these questions at the appropriate point within this chapter. Look for the answers in the margins.)

A Science for All Seasons

Chemistry pervades every aspect of our lives. Look around you. Everything you see is made of chemicals: the food we eat, the air we breathe, the clothes we wear, the medicines we take, the vehicles we ride in, and the buildings we live and work in.

Everything we *do* also involves chemistry. Whenever we eat a sandwich, bathe, drive a car, listen to music, or ride a bicycle, we use chemistry. Even when we are asleep, chemical reactions go on constantly throughout our bodies.

Chemistry also affects society as a whole. Developments in health and

Chemistry is everywhere, not just in laboratories. Chemistry occurs in soil and rocks, in waters, in clouds, and in us. Knowledge of chemistry enhances our understanding of climate change, helps to provide food for Earth's increasing population, and is crucial to the development and production of sustainable fuels.

medicine involve a lot of chemistry. The astounding advances in biotechnology—decoding the human genome, developing new drugs, improving nutrition, and much more—have a huge chemical component. Understanding and solving environmental problems require knowledge and application of chemistry. The worldwide issues of climate change and ozone depletion involve chemistry.

So what is chemistry anyway? We explore that question in some detail in Section 1.7. And just what is a chemical? The word *chemical* may sound ominous, but it is simply a name for any material. Gold, water, salt, sugar, air, coffee, ice cream, a computer, a pencil—all are chemicals or are made entirely of chemicals.

Material things undergo changes. Sometimes these changes occur naturally—maple leaves turn yellow and red in autumn. Often, we change material things intentionally, to make them more useful, as when we light a candle or cook an egg. Most of these changes are accompanied by changes in energy. For example, when we burn gasoline, the process releases energy that we can use to propel an automobile.

Your own body is a marvelous chemical factory. It takes the food you eat and turns it into skin, bones, blood, and muscle, while also generating energy for all your activities. This amazing chemical factory operates continuously 24 hours a day for as long as you live. Chemistry affects your own life every moment, and it also transforms society as a whole. Chemistry shapes our civilization.

▲ Organic foods are not chemical-free. In fact, they are made entirely of chemicals!

▲ A century ago, contaminated drinking water was often the cause of outbreaks of cholera. Modern water treatment uses chemicals to remove solid matter and kill disease-causing bacteria, making water safe to drink.

1. Is it true that chemicals are bad for us? Everything you can see, smell, taste, or touch is either a chemical or is made of chemicals. Chemicals are neither good nor bad in themselves. They can be put to good use, bad use, or anything in between.

2. Why should I study chemistry? Chemistry is a part of many areas of study and affects everything you do. Knowledge of chemistry helps you to understand many facets of modern life.

1.1 Science and Technology: The Roots of Knowledge

Chemistry is a *science*, but what is science? **Science** is an accumulation of knowledge about nature and our physical world and of theories that we use to explain that knowledge. Let's examine the roots of science. Our study of the material universe has two interrelated facets: the *technological* (or *factual*) and the *philosophical* (or *theoretical*).

Technology is the application of knowledge for practical purposes. It arose long before science, originating in prehistoric times. Early people used fire to bring about chemical changes. They cooked food, baked pottery, and smelted ores to produce metals such as copper. They made beer and wine by fermentation and obtained dyes and drugs from plants. These tasks—and many others—were accomplished without an understanding of the scientific principles involved.

About 2500 years ago, Greek philosophers were among the first to formulate *theories* of chemistry—rational explanations of the behavior of matter. Those philosophers generally did not test their theories by experimentation. Nevertheless, their view of nature—attributed mainly to Aristotle—dominated Western thinking about the workings of the material world for the next 20 centuries.

The experimental roots of chemistry are in **alchemy**, a mixture of chemistry and magic that flourished in Europe during the Middle Ages, from about C.E. 500 to 1500. Alchemists searched for a "philosophers' stone" that would turn cheaper metals into gold and for an elixir that would bring eternal life. Although alchemists never achieved these goals, they discovered many new chemical substances and perfected techniques such as distillation and extraction that are still used today. Modern chemists inherited from the alchemists an abiding interest in human health and the quality of life.

Technology also developed rapidly during the late Middle Ages in Europe, though its progress was hampered by the Aristotelian philosophy that still prevailed. The beginnings of modern science are more recent, however, and coincide with the emergence of the experimental method. What we now call science grew out of **natural philosophy**—philosophical speculation about nature. Science had its true beginnings in the seventeenth century, when astronomers, physicists, and physiologists began to rely on experimentation.

▲ Aristotle (384–322 B.C.E.), Greek philosopher and tutor of Alexander the Great, believed that we could understand nature through logic. The idea of experimental science did not triumph over Aristotelian logic until about C.E. 1500.

Beyond the Alchemists' Wildest Dreams

Modern chemists can transform matter in ways that would astound the alchemists. They can change ordinary salt into lye and laundry bleach. They can convert sand into transistors and computer chips. And they can turn crude oil into plastics, fibers, pesticides, drugs, detergents, and a host of other products. Many products of modern chemistry are much more valuable than the glittering metal that the alchemists vainly sought. For example, a form of carbon called *nanotubes* (see the box on page 25) has thousands of potential uses but is extremely expensive to make. A kilogram of purified nanotubes costs more than $2,500,000, while a kilogram of gold will set you back only about $50,000.

Self-Assessment Questions

Match each term in the left column with the best definition or explanation of it in the right column.

1. alchemy
2. natural philosophy
3. science
4. technology

a. application of knowledge for practical purposes
b. grew out of Greek philosophy, alchemy, and natural philosophy
c. a mixture of chemistry and magic
d. philosophical speculation about nature

Answers: 1, c; 2, d; 3, b; 4, a

1.2 Changing Perceptions and Changing Practices

Learning Objectives ❯ Briefly describe the contributions of Bacon, Galileo, and Carson to the perceptions of science.

Science is ever-changing. Francis Bacon, a philosopher who practiced law and served as a judge, was among the first to argue that science should be experimental. His dream was that science could solve the world's problems and enrich human life with new inventions, thereby increasing happiness and prosperity. Bacon was not a scientist, and it was left to others to bring about the birth of modern science. Notable

▲ Alchemists made many positive contributions to chemistry. This illustration from the 1512 edition of Hieronymus Brunschwig's *Liber de arte distillandi* (On the art of distilling) shows a distillation apparatus. *(Source: Donald and Mildred Othmer Collection)*

▲ Francis Bacon (1561–1626), English philosopher and Lord Chancellor to King James I.

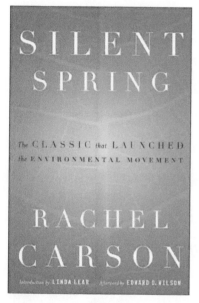

▲ Rachel Carson's *Silent Spring* was one of the first publications to point out a number of serious environmental issues.

among these was the Italian Galileo Galilei (1564–1642). Galileo developed a vastly improved telescope and advanced the science of astronomy through observations such as sunspots, the moons of Jupiter, and the phases of Venus. He also did experiments and made many other observations that led many to call him the father of modern science.

The science of chemistry also has changed over the years. Early people used plant, animal, and mineral materials much as they occurred in nature. They later learned to modify materials to better meet their needs—for example, baking clay to make ceramic materials, cooking food to make it more digestible, and obtaining metals from ores. For most of human history, people exploited resources such as metals and petroleum and gave little thought to ever running out of such resources. An environmental movement arose in the 1970s as people became increasingly aware that reckless use of resources not only caused appalling pollution but would lead in the end to severe shortages. Rachel Carson, a biologist, was an early proponent of environmental awareness. The main theme of her book *Silent Spring* (1962) was that our use of chemicals to control insects was threatening to destroy all life, including ourselves. People in the pesticide industry and their allies roundly denounced Carson as a "propagandist," while some scientists rallied to support her. By the late 1960s, however, the threatened extinction of several species of birds and the disappearance of fish from many rivers, lakes, and areas of the ocean caused many scientists to move into Carson's camp. Popular support for Carson's views became overwhelming.

In response to growing public concern, chemists developed the concept of **green chemistry**, which uses materials and processes that are intended to prevent or reduce pollution at its source. This approach was further extended in the first decade of the twenty-first century to include the idea of sustainability. **Sustainable chemistry** is designed to meet the needs of the present generation without compromising the needs of future generations. Sustainability preserves resources and aspires to produce environmentally friendly products from renewable resources.

Some chemicals can indeed cause problems, especially when misused, but many others have extremely helpful uses. Chemicals are used to kill bacteria that cause dreadful diseases, to relieve pain and suffering, to increase food production, to provide fuel for heating, cooling, lighting, and transportation, and to provide materials for building our machines, making our clothing, and constructing our houses. Chemistry has provided ordinary people with luxuries that were not available even to the mightiest rulers in ages past. Chemicals are essential to our lives—life itself would be impossible without chemicals.

Self-Assessment Questions

Select the best answer or response.

1. Francis Bacon thought that science would
   a. destroy life on Earth
   b. increase human happiness and prosperity
   c. find a way to turn lead to gold
   d. produce toxic chemicals

2. The main theme of Rachel Carson's *Silent Spring* was that life on Earth would be destroyed by
   a. botulism
   b. nuclear war
   c. overpopulation
   d. pesticides

3. Galileo has been called the father of modern science because he
   a. anticipated environmental problems
   b. made observations and did experiments
   c. thought that science would destroy life on Earth
   d. tried to use science to get rich

4. A goal of green chemistry is to
   a. produce cheap green dyes
   b. provide great wealth for corporations
   c. reduce pollution
   d. turn deserts into forests and grasslands

5. Which best exemplifies sustainable chemistry?
   a. Toluene, extracted from coal, is used to make TNT, an explosive.
   b. Paper is made from hardwood trees.
   c. Minerals mined in South America are used in China to make LCD screens.
   d. Plastic bottles are made from both petroleum and recycled plastic.

Answers: 1, b; 2, d; 3, b; 4, c; 5, b

1.3 Science: Reproducible, Testable, Tentative, Predictive, and Explanatory

Learning Objectives ❯ Define *hypothesis, scientific law, scientific theory,* and *scientific model,* and explain their relationships in science.

We have defined science, but science has *characteristics* that distinguish it from other studies.

Scientists often disagree about what is and what will be, but does that make science merely a guessing game in which one guess is as good as another? Not at all. Science is based on observations and experimental tests of our assumptions. However, it is not a collection of unalterable facts; we cannot force nature to fit our preconceived ideas. Science is good at correcting errors, but it is not especially good at establishing truths. Science is an unfinished work. The things we have learned from science fill millions of books and scholarly journals, but what we know pales in comparison to what we do not yet know.

Scientific Data Must Be Reproducible

Scientists collect data by making careful observations. Data reported by a scientist must also be observable by other scientists. The data must be *reproducible.* Careful measurements are required, conditions are thoroughly controlled and described, and scientific work is not fully accepted until it has been verified by other scientists.

Observations, though, are just the beginning of the intellectual processes of science. There are many different paths to scientific discovery, and there is no general set of rules. Science is not a straightforward process for cranking out discoveries.

Scientific Hypotheses Are Testable

Scientists do not merely state what they feel may be true. They develop *testable* **hypotheses** (educated guesses) as tentative explanations of observed data. They test these hypotheses by designing and performing experiments. Experimentation distinguishes science from the arts and humanities. In the humanities, people still argue about some of the same questions that were being debated thousands of years ago: What is truth? What is beauty? These arguments persist because the proposed answers cannot be tested and confirmed objectively.

Like artists and poets, scientists are often imaginative and creative. The tenets of science, however, are *testable.* Experiments can be devised to answer most scientific questions. Ideas can be tested and thereby either verified or rejected. For example, it was long thought that exercise caused muscles to tire and become sore from a buildup of lactic acid. Recent findings suggest instead that lactic acid *delays* muscle tiredness and that the cause of tired, sore muscles may be related to other factors, including leakage of calcium ions inside muscle cells, which weakens contractions. Through many experiments, scientists have established a firm foundation of knowledge, allowing each new generation to build on the past.

Scientific Laws Summarize Observations

Large amounts of scientific data can sometimes be summarized in brief statements called **scientific laws.** For example, Robert Boyle (1627–1691), an Irishman, conducted

3. Why do scientists so often say "more study is needed"? More data help scientists refine a hypothesis so that it is better defined, clearer, or more applicable.

many experiments on gases. In each experiment, he found that the volume of the gas decreased when the pressure applied to the gas was increased.

Many scientific laws can be stated mathematically. For example, Boyle's law can be written as $PV = k$, where P is the pressure on a gas, V is its volume, and k is a constant number. If P is doubled, V will be cut in half. Scientific laws are *universal*. Under the specified conditions, they hold everywhere in the observable universe.

Scientific Theories Are Tentative and Predictive

Scientists organize the knowledge they accumulate on a framework of detailed explanations called theories. A **theory** represents the best current explanation for a phenomenon, but it is always *tentative*. In the future, a theory may have to be modified or even discarded as a result of new observations, for the body of knowledge that is science is rapidly growing and always changing.

Theories provide organization for scientific knowledge, but they are also useful for their *predictive* value. Predictions based on theories are tested by further experiments. Theories that make successful predictions are usually widely accepted by the scientific community. A theory developed in one area is often found to apply in others.

Scientific Models Are Explanatory

Scientists often use models to help *explain* complicated phenomena. A *scientific model* uses tangible items or pictures to represent invisible processes. For example, the invisible particles of a gas can be visualized as billiard balls, as marbles, or as dots or circles on paper. We know that when a glass of water is left standing for a period of time, the water disappears through the process of evaporation (Figure 1.1). Scientists explain evaporation with a theory, the kinetic–molecular theory, which proposes that a liquid is composed of tiny particles called *molecules* that are in constant motion. (This theory is discussed further in Chapter 6; here it is used simply as an example.) In the bulk of the liquid, these molecules are held together by forces of attraction. The molecules collide with one another like billiard balls on a playing table. Sometimes, a "hard break" of billiard balls causes one ball to fly off the table. Likewise, some of the molecules of a liquid gain enough energy through collisions to break the attraction to their neighbors, escape from the liquid, and disperse among the widely spaced molecules in air. The water in the glass gradually disappears. This model gives us more than a name for evaporation; it gives us an understanding of the phenomenon.

▲ A molecular model of diamond shows the tightly linked, rigid structure that explains why diamonds are so hard.

▶ **Figure 1.1** The evaporation of water. (a) When a container of water is left standing open to the air, the water slowly disappears. (b) Scientists explain evaporation in terms of the motion of molecules.

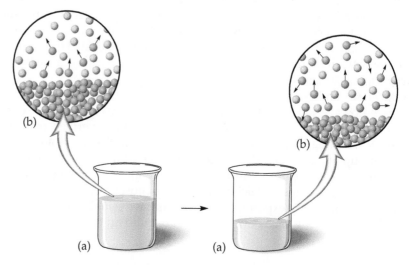

● = Water molecule

◐ = Air (nitrogen or oxygen) molecule

What Science Is Not

Responsible news media generally try to be fair, presenting both sides of an issue regardless of where the prevailing evidence lies. In science, the evidence often indicates that one side is simply wrong. Scientists strive for accuracy, not balance. The idea of a flat Earth is not given equal credence to a (roughly) spherical Earth. Only ideas that have survived experimental testing or that can be tested by experiment are considered valid. Ideas that are beautiful, elegant, or even sacrosanct can be invalidated by experimental data.

Science is not a democratic process. Majority rule does not determine what constitutes sound science. Science does not accept notions that are proven false or remain untested by experiment.

When doing experiments, developing theories, and constructing models, it is important to note that a *correlation* between two items is not necessarily evidence that one *causes* the other. For example, many people suffer from allergies in the fall when goldenrod is in bloom. However, research has shown that the main cause of these allergies is ragweed pollen. There is a correlation between the blooming of goldenrod and autumnal allergies, but goldenrod pollen is not the cause. Ragweed happens to bloom at the same time.

The Limitations of Science

Some people say that we could solve many of our problems if we would only attack them using the methods of science. Why can't the procedures of the scientist be applied to social, political, ethical, and economic problems? And why do scientists disagree over environmental, social, and political issues?

Disagreement often results from the inability to control *variables*. A **variable** is something that can change over the course of an experiment. If, for example, we wanted to study in the laboratory how the volume of a gas varies with changes in pressure, we could hold constant such factors as temperature and the amount and kind of gas. If, on the other hand, we wanted to determine the effect of low levels of a particular pollutant on the health of a human population, we would find it almost impossible to control such variables as individuals' diets, habits, and exposure to other substances, all of which affect health. Although we could make observations, formulate hypotheses, and conduct experiments on the health effect of the pollutant, interpretation of the results would be difficult and subject to disagreement.

Self-Assessment Questions

Select the best answer or response.

1. To gather information to support or discredit a hypothesis, a scientist
   a. conducts experiments
   b. consults an authority
   c. establishes a scientific law
   d. formulates a scientific theory

2. The statement that mass is always conserved when chemical changes occur is an example of a scientific
   a. experiment
   b. hypothesis
   c. law
   d. theory

3. A successful theory
   a. can be used to make predictions
   b. eventually becomes a scientific law
   c. is not subject to further testing
   d. is permanently accepted as true

4. Which of the following is *not* a hypothesis?
   a. All solutions of seaborgium (element 106) are blue.
   b. Copernicum (element 112) will have properties similar to those of mercury.
   c. Extrasensory perception works only when no negative forces are present.
   d. Water reacts with seaborgium to form hydrogen gas.

5. A possible explanation for a collection of observations is called a(n)
   a. experiment
   b. law
   c. myth
   d. theory

6. Social problems are difficult to solve because it is difficult to
   a. control variables
   b. discount paranormal events
   c. form hypotheses
   d. formulate theories

1.4 Science and Technology: Risks and Benefits

Learning Objectives ❯ Define *risk* and *benefit*, and give an example of each.
❯ Estimate a desirability quotient from benefit and risk data.

Most people recognize that society has benefited from science and technology, but many seem not to realize that there are risks associated with every technological advance. How can we determine when the benefits outweigh the risks? One approach, called **risk–benefit analysis**, involves the estimation of a desirability quotient (DQ).

$$DQ = \frac{\text{Benefits}}{\text{Risks}}$$

A *benefit* is anything that promotes well-being or has a positive effect. Benefits may be economic, social, or psychological. A *risk* is any hazard that leads to loss or injury. Some of the risks associated with modern technology have led to disease, death, economic loss, and environmental deterioration. Risks and benefits may involve one individual, a group, or society as a whole.

Every technological advance has both benefits and risks. Most people recognize the benefits of the automobile. But driving a car involves risk—individual risks of injury or death in a traffic accident and societal risks such as pollution and climate change. Most people consider the benefits of driving a car to outweigh the risks.

Weighing the benefits and risks connected with a product is more difficult when considering a group of people. For example, pasteurized low-fat milk is a safe, nutritious beverage for many people of northern European descent. However, a few people in this group can't tolerate lactose, the sugar in milk. And some are allergic to milk proteins. For these individuals, drinking milk can be harmful. But milk allergies and lactose intolerance are relatively uncommon among people of northern European descent, so the benefits of milk are large and the risks are small, resulting in a large DQ. However, adults of other ethnic backgrounds often are lactose-intolerant, and for them, milk has a small DQ. Thus, milk is not always suitable for use in programs to relieve malnutrition.

The artificial sweetener aspartame is the most highly studied of all food additives. There is little evidence that use of an artificial sweetener helps with efforts to lose weight. (Aspartame may provide some benefit to diabetics, however, because sugar consumption presents a large risk to them.) There are anecdotal reports of problems due to use of the sweetener, but these have not been confirmed in controlled studies. To most people, the risk involved in using aspartame is small. This leads to an uncertain DQ—and, it seems, to endless debate over the product's safety.

Other technologies provide large benefits and present large risks. For these technologies, too, the DQ is uncertain. An example is the conversion of coal to liquid fuels. Most people find liquid fuels to be very beneficial in transportation, home heating, and industry. There are great risks associated with coal conversion, however, including risks to coal mine workers, air and water pollution, and the exposure of conversion plant workers to toxic chemicals. The result, again, is an uncertain DQ and political controversy.

There are yet other problems in risk–benefit analysis. Some technologies benefit one group of people while presenting a risk to another. For example, gold plating and gold wires in computers and other consumer electronics benefit the consumer, providing greater reliability and longer life. But when the devices are scrapped,

▲ It DOES Matter!
For most people of northern European ancestry, milk is a wholesome food; its benefits far outweigh its risks. Other ethnic groups have high rates of lactose intolerance among adults, and the desirability quotient for milk is much smaller.

small-scale attempts to recover the gold often produce serious pollution in the area of recovery. Difficult political decisions are needed in such cases.

Other technologies provide current benefits but present future risks. For example, although nuclear power now provides useful electricity, improperly stored wastes from nuclear power plants might present hazards for centuries. Thus, the use of nuclear power is controversial.

Science and technology obviously involve *both* risks and benefits. The determination of benefits is almost entirely a social judgment. Although risk assessment also involves social and personal decisions, it can often be greatly aided by scientific investigation.

CONCEPTUAL Example 1.1   Risk–Benefit Analysis

Heroin is thought by some to be more effective than other drugs for the relief of severe pain. For example, heroin is a legal prescription drug in the United Kingdom. People can become addicted to heroin with continued use in as little as three days, and recreational use often renders addicts unable to function in society. Do a risk–benefit analysis of the use of heroin in treating the pain of **(a)** a young athlete with a broken leg and **(b)** a terminally ill cancer patient.

Solution

a. The heroin would provide the benefit of pain relief, but its use for such purposes has been judged to be too risky by the U.S. Food and Drug Administration. The DQ is low.

b. The heroin would provide the benefit of pain relief. The risk of addiction in a dying person is irrelevant. Heroin is banned for any purpose in the United States. The DQ is uncertain. (Both answers involve judgments that are not clearly scientific; people can differ in their assessments of each.)

■ EXERCISE 1.1A

Chloramphenicol is a powerful antibacterial drug that often destroys bacteria unaffected by other drugs. It is highly dangerous to some individuals, however, causing fatal aplastic anemia in about 1 in 30,000 people. Do a risk–benefit analysis of administering chloramphenicol to **(a)** sick farm animals, whose milk or meat might contain residues of the drug, and **(b)** a person with Rocky Mountain spotted fever facing a high probability of death or permanent disability.

■ EXERCISE 1.1B

The drug thalidomide was introduced in the 1950s as a sleeping aid. It was found to be a *teratogen*, a substance that causes birth defects, and was removed from the market after children in Europe whose mothers took it during pregnancy were born with deformed limbs. Recently, thalidomide has been investigated as an effective treatment for the lesions caused by leprosy and for Kaposi's sarcoma (a form of cancer often suffered by AIDS patients). Do a risk-benefit analysis of prescribing thalidomide to **(a)** all women and **(b)** women with AIDS.

Self-Assessment Questions

Select the best answer or response.

1. Our perception of risk is
   a. always based on sound science
   b. always higher than actual risk
   c. always lower than actual risk
   d. often different from actual risk

2. Among the following, the highest risk of death (see Table 1.1) is associated with
   a. airplane accident
   b. car accident
   c. cigarettes
   d. radon

Answers: 1, d; 2, c

Risks of Death

Our perception of risk often differs from the actual risk we face. Some people fear flying but readily assume the risk of an automobile trip. The odds of dying from various causes are listed in Table 1.1.

Table 1.1	Approximate Lifetime Risks of Death in the United States		
Action	**Lifetime Risk[a]**	**Approximate Lifetime Odds**	**Details/Assumptions**
All causes	1	1 in 1	We all die of something.
Cigarettes	0.25	1 in 4	Cigarette smoking, 1 pack/day
Heart disease	0.20	1 in 5	Heart attacks, congestive heart failure
All cancers	0.14	1 in 7	All cancers
Motor vehicles	0.011	1 in 88	Death in motor vehicle accident
Home accidents	0.010	1 in 100	Home accident death
Radon	0.0030	1 in 300	Radon in homes, cancer deaths
Background radiation	0.0010	1 in 1000	Sea level background radiation, cancers
Peanut butter (aflatoxin)	0.00060	1 in 1700	4 tablespoons peanut butter per day
Airplane accidents	0.0002	1 in 5000	Death in aircraft crashes
Terrorist attack[b]	0.00077	1 in 1300	One 9/11-level attack per year
Terrorist attack[c]	0.000077	1 in 13,000	One 9/11-level attack every 10 years

[a]The odds of dying of a particular cause in a given year are calculated by dividing the population by the number of deaths by that cause in that year. Lifetime odds of dying of a specific cause are calculated by dividing the one-year odds by the life expectancy of a person born in that year.

[b]Unlikely scenario

[c]More reasonable scenario

1.5 Chemistry: Its Central Role

Learning Objective ❯ Give an example of a use of chemistry in your daily life and in society at large.

Science is a unified whole. Common scientific laws apply everywhere and on all levels of organization. The various areas of science interact and support one another. Accordingly, chemistry is not only useful in itself but also fundamental to other scientific disciplines. The application of chemical principles has revolutionized biology and medicine, has provided materials for powerful computers used in mathematics, and has profoundly influenced other fields such as psychology. The social goals of better health, nutrition, and housing are dependent to a large extent on the knowledge and techniques of chemists. Many modern materials have been developed by chemists, and even more amazing materials are in the works. Recycling of basic materials—paper, glass, and metals—involves chemical processes. Chemistry is indeed a central science (Figure 1.2). There is no area of our daily lives that is not affected by chemistry.

Chemistry is also important to the *economy* of industrial nations. In the United States, the chemical industry makes thousands of consumer products, including personal-care products, agricultural products, plastics, coatings, soaps, and detergents. It produces 80% of the materials used to make medicines. The U.S. chemical industry is one of the country's largest industries, with sales of more than $675 billion per year, and it accounts for 10% of all U.S. exports. It employs 800,000 workers, including scientists, engineers, and technicians, and it generates nearly 11% of all U.S. patents. And despite widespread fear of chemicals, workers in the chemical industry are five times safer than the average worker in the U.S. manufacturing sector.

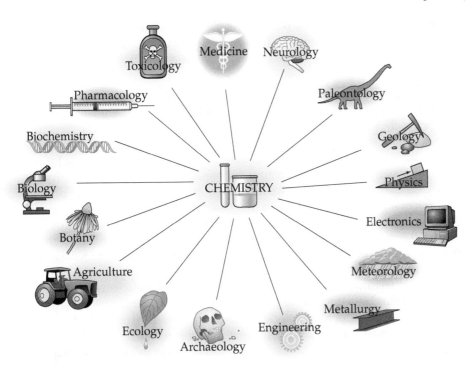

◀ **Figure 1.2** Chemistry has a central role among the sciences.

Select the best answer or response.

1. Chemistry is called the central science because
   a. the chemical industry is based mainly in the U.S. Midwest
   b. it is the core course in all college curricula
   c. it is fundamental to other scientific disciplines
   d. the source of many environmental problems

2. The U.S. chemical industry is
   a. patently unsafe
   b. the source of nearly all pollution
   c. the source of many consumer products
   d. unimportant to the U.S. economy

Answers: 1, c; 2, c

1.6 Solving Society's Problems: Scientific Research

Learning Objective ❯ Distinguish basic research from applied research.

Chemistry is a powerful force in shaping society today. Chemical research not only plays a pivotal role in other sciences but it also has a profound influence on society as a whole. Chemists, like other scientists, do one of two categories of research: *applied research* or *basic research*. The two often overlap, and it isn't always possible to label a particular project as one or the other.

Applied Research

Some chemists test polluted soil, air, and water. Others analyze foods, fuels, cosmetics, detergents, and drugs. Still others synthesize new substances for use as drugs or pesticides or formulate plastics for new applications. These activities are examples of **applied research**—work oriented toward the solution of a particular problem in an industry or the environment.

Among the most monumental accomplishments in applied research were those of George Washington Carver. Born in slavery, Carver attended Simpson College and later graduated from Iowa State University. A botanist and agricultural chemist, Carver taught and did research at Tuskegee Institute. He developed over 300 products from peanuts, from peanut butter to hand cleaner to insulating board. He created other new

▲ George Washington Carver (1864–1943), research scientist, in his laboratory at Tuskegee Institute.

products from sweet potatoes, pecans, and clay. Carver also taught southern farmers to rotate crops and to use legumes to replenish the nitrogen removed from the soil by cotton crops. Carver's work helped to revitalize the economy of the South.

Basic Research: The Search for Knowledge

Many chemists are involved in **basic research**, the search for knowledge for its own sake. Some chemists work out the fine points of atomic and molecular structure. Others measure the intricate energy changes that accompany complex chemical reactions. Some synthesize new compounds and determine their properties. Done for the sheer joy of unraveling the secrets of nature and discovering order in our universe, basic research is characterized by the absence of any predictable, marketable product.

Lack of a product doesn't mean that basic research is useless. Far from it! Findings from basic research often *are* applied at a later time. This may be the hope, but it is not the main goal of the researcher. In fact, most of our modern technology is based on results obtained in basic research. Without this base of factual information, technological innovation would be haphazard and slow.

Applied research is carried out mainly by industries seeking to gain a competitive edge by developing a novel, better, or more salable product. The ultimate aim of such research is usually profit for the stockholders. Basic research is conducted mainly at universities and research institutes. Most support for this research comes from federal and state governments and foundations, although some larger industries also support it.

An example of basic research that was later applied to improving human welfare is the work of Gertrude Elion (1918–1999) and George Hitchings (1905–1998), who studied compounds called *purines* in an attempt to understand their role in the chemistry of the cell. Their basic research at Burroughs Wellcome Research Laboratories in North Carolina led to the discovery of a number of valuable new drugs that facilitate organ transplants and treat various diseases such as gout, malaria, herpes, and cancer. Elion and Hitchings shared the 1988 Nobel Prize in Physiology or Medicine, and in 1991 Elion became the first woman to be inducted into the National Inventors Hall of Fame.

Another example involves the work of two physicists. In 1930, Otto Stern (1888–1969) and Walther Gerlach (1889–1979) determined that certain atomic nuclei (Chapter 3) have a property called *spin*, which causes these nuclei to act as tiny magnets. Isidor Isaac Rabi (1898–1988) later developed a method for recording the magnetic properties of atomic nuclei. For their basic research in studying and measuring these minuscule magnetic fields, Stern and Rabi won the Nobel Prize in Physics in 1943 and 1944, respectively. In the 1940s, teams led by Edward M. Purcell and Felix Bloch used nuclear spins to work out the structure of complicated molecules. Their technique, called *nuclear magnetic resonance* (NMR), has become a major tool of chemists for determining molecular structure. Purcell and Bloch shared the Nobel Prize in Physics in 1952 for their research. Still later, in the 1960s, Paul Lauterbur, Peter Mansfield, and other scientists applied the principles of NMR to performing scans of the human body. This noninvasive diagnostic technique, called *magnetic resonance imaging* (MRI), has replaced many exploratory surgical operations and made other surgical procedures much more precise. Lauterbur and Mansfield won the 2003 Nobel Prize in Physiology or Medicine for their work.

4. Why do scientists bother with studies that have no immediate application? The results of basic research may not have an immediate practical use; however, basic research extends our understanding of the world and can be considered an investment in the future.

▲ **It DOES Matter!**
Gertrude Elion won a Nobel Prize for her basic research on purines. Her work has led to many applications in pharmaceuticals and medicine. Many important modern applications started out with basic research.

Importance of Basic Research

"There are two compelling reasons why society must support basic science. One is substantial: The theoretical physics of yesterday is the nuclear defense of today; the obscure synthetic chemistry of yesterday is curing disease today. The other reason is cultural. The essence of our civilization is to explore and analyze the nature of man and his surroundings. As proclaimed in the Bible in the Book of Proverbs: 'Where there is no vision, the people perish.'"

Arthur Kornberg (1918–2007), American biochemist and recipient of Nobel Prize in Physiology or Medicine, 1959

Classify each of the following as (a) basic research or (b) applied research.

1. A chemist tries to develop a new antibiotic similar to ampicillin.
2. A team of scientists tries to genetically engineer a variety of rice that contains vitamin A.
3. A scientist seeks to extract biologically active compounds from sea sponges.
4. Scientists identify adrenal hormones and determine their structure and biological effects.

Answers: 1, b; 2, b; 3, a; 4, a

1.7 Chemistry: A Study of Matter and Its Changes

Learning Objective ❯ Differentiate: mass and weight; physical and chemical change; and physical and chemical properties.

Chemistry is often defined as the study of matter and the changes it undergoes. Because the entire physical universe is made up of matter and energy, the field of chemistry extends from atoms to stars, from rocks to living organisms. Now let's look at matter a little more closely.

Matter is the stuff that makes up all material things. It is anything that occupies space and has mass. Matter has *mass*; you can weigh it. Wood, sand, water, air, and people have mass and are therefore matter. **Mass** is a measure of the quantity of matter that an object contains. The greater the mass of an object, the more difficult it is to change its velocity. You can easily deflect a tennis ball coming toward you at 30 meters per second (m/s), but you would have difficulty stopping a cannonball of the same size moving at the same speed. A cannonball has more mass than a tennis ball of equal size.

The mass of an object does not vary with location. An astronaut has the same mass on the moon as on Earth. In contrast, **weight** measures a force. On Earth, it measures the force of attraction between our planet and the mass in question. On the moon, where gravity is one-sixth that on Earth, an astronaut weighs only one-sixth as much as on Earth (Figure 1.3). Weight varies with gravity; mass does not.

▲ **Figure 1.3** Astronaut John W. Young leaps from the lunar surface, where gravity pulls at him with only one-sixth as much force as on Earth.

Q: *If an astronaut has a mass of 72 kg, what would be his mass on the moon? If an astronaut weighs 180 lb on Earth, what would he weigh on the moon?*

CONCEPTUAL Example 1.2   Mass and Weight

Gravity on the planet Mercury is 0.376 times that on Earth. **(a)** What would be the mass on Mercury of a person who has a mass of 62.5 kilograms (kg) on Earth? **(b)** What would be the weight on Mercury of a person who weighs 124 pounds (lb) on Earth?

Solution

a. The person's mass would be the same as on Earth (62.5 kg). The quantity of matter has not changed.
b. The person would weigh only 0.376 × 124 lb = 46.6 lb; the force of attraction between Mercury and the person would be only 0.376 times that between Earth and the person.

■ EXERCISE 1.2

At the surface of Venus, the force of gravity is 0.903 times that at Earth's surface. **(a)** What would be the mass of a 1.00-kg object on Venus? **(b)** How much would a man who weighs 198 lb on Earth weigh on the surface of Venus?

▶ **Figure 1.4** A comparison of the physical properties of two elements. Copper (left), obtained as pellets, can be hammered into thin foil or drawn into wire. Iodine (right) consists of brittle gray crystals that crumble into a powder when struck.

Q: *What additional physical properties of copper and iodine are apparent from the photographs?*

Physical and Chemical Properties

We can use our knowledge of chemistry to change matter to make it more useful. Chemists can change crude oil into gasoline, plastics, pesticides, drugs, detergents, and thousands of other products. Changes in matter are accompanied by changes in energy. Often, we change matter to extract part of its energy. For example, we burn gasoline to get energy to propel our automobiles.

To distinguish between samples of matter, we can compare their properties (Figure 1.4). A **physical property** of a substance is a characteristic or behavior that can be observed or measured without generating new types of matter. Color, odor, and hardness are physical properties (Table 1.2). A **chemical property** describes how a substance reacts with other types of matter—how its basic building blocks can change (Table 1.3).

A **physical change** involves an alteration in the physical appearance of matter without changing its chemical identity or composition. An ice cube can melt to form a liquid, but it is still water. Melting is a physical change, and the temperature at which it occurs—the melting point—is a physical property.

A **chemical change** involves a change in the chemical identity of matter into other substances that are chemically different. In exhibiting a chemical property, matter undergoes a chemical change. At least one substance in the original matter is replaced by one or more new substances. Iron metal reacts with oxygen from the air to form rust (iron oxide). When sulfur burns in air, sulfur, which is made up of

Table 1.2	Some Examples of Physical Properties
Property	**Examples**
Temperature	0 °C for ice water, 100 °C for boiling water.
Mass	A nickel weighs 5 g. A penny weighs 2.5 g.
Color	Sulfur is yellow. Bromine is reddish-brown.
Taste	Acids are sour. Bases are bitter.
Odor	Benzyl acetate smells like jasmine. Hydrogen sulfide smells like rotten eggs.
Boiling point	Water boils at 100 °C. Ethyl alcohol boils at 78.5 °C.
Hardness	Diamond is exceptionally hard. Sodium metal is soft.
Density	1.00 g/mL for water, 19.3 g/cm^3 for gold.

Table 1.3	Some Examples of Chemical Properties
Substance	**Typical Chemical Property**
Iron	rusts (combines with oxygen to form iron oxide).
Carbon	burns (combines with oxygen to form carbon dioxide).
Silver	tarnishes (combines with sulfur to form silver sulfide).
Nitroglycerin	explodes (decomposes to produce a mixture of gases).
Carbon monoxide	is toxic (combines with hemoglobin, causing anoxia).
Neon	is inert (does not react with anything).

one type of atom, and oxygen (from air), which is made up of another type of atom, combine to form sulfur dioxide, which is made up of molecules that have sulfur and oxygen atoms in the ratio 1:2. (A *molecule* is a group of atoms bound together as a single unit. You'll learn more about atoms and molecules later.)

It is difficult at times to determine whether a change is physical or chemical, but we can decide on the basis of what happens to the composition or structure of the matter involved. *Composition* refers to the types of atoms that are present and their relative proportions, and *structure* to the arrangement of those atoms with respect to one another or in space. A chemical change results in a change in composition or structure, whereas a physical change does not.

CONCEPTUAL Example 1.3   Chemical Change and Physical Change

Which of the following events involve chemical changes and which involve physical changes?

a. You trim your fingernails.
b. Lemon juice converts milk to curds and whey.
c. Molten aluminum is poured into a mold, where it solidifies.
d. Sodium chloride (table salt) is broken down into sodium metal and chlorine gas.

Solution

We examine each change and determine whether there has been a change in composition or structure. In other words, we ask, "Have any substances that are chemically different been created?" If so, the change is chemical; if not, it is physical.

a. Physical change: The composition of a fingernail is not changed by cutting.
b. Chemical change: The compositions of curds and whey are different from the composition of milk.
c. Physical change: Whether it is solid or liquid, aluminum is the same substance with the same composition.
d. Chemical change: New substances, sodium and chlorine, are formed.

▪ EXERCISE 1.3A

Which of the following events involve chemical changes and which involve physical changes?

a. Gasoline vaporizes from an open container.
b. Magnesium metal burns in air to form a white powder called *magnesium oxide*.
c. A dull knife is sharpened with a whetstone.

▪ EXERCISE 1.3B

Which of the following events involve chemical changes and which involve physical changes?

a. A steel wrench left out in the rain becomes rusty.
b. A stick of butter melts.
c. Charcoal briquettes are burned.
d. Peppercorns are ground into flakes.

Self-Assessment Questions

Select the best answer or response.

1. Which of the following is *not* an example of matter?
   a. gasoline fumes **b.** ether fumes **c.** gold **d.** a sentiment

2. Which of the following is an example of matter?
   a. air **b.** a prayer **c.** a thought **d.** yellow light

3. Two identical items are taken from Earth to Mars, where they have
   a. both the same mass and the same weight as on Earth
   b. neither the same mass nor the same weight as on Earth
   c. the same mass but not the same weight as on Earth
   d. the same weight but not the same mass as on Earth

4. What kind of change does not alter the identity of a material?
   a. chemical **b.** physical **c.** physical state **d.** temperature

5. Bending glass tubing in a hot flame involves
   a. applied research **b.** a chemical change
   c. an experiment **d.** a physical change

6. Transforming liquid water into steam involves
   a. removing energy from the water **b.** a change in chemical makeup
   c. a chemical change **d.** a physical change

7. Which of the following is a chemical property?
   a. iodine vapor is purple **b.** copper tarnishes
   c. salt dissolves in water **d.** balsa wood is easily carved

8. Which of the following is an example of a physical change?
   a. A cake is baked from flour, baking powder, sugar, eggs, shortening, and milk.
   b. Milk left outside a refrigerator overnight turns sour.
   c. Sheep are sheared, and the wool is spun into yarn.
   d. Spiders eat flies and make silk.

9. Which of the following is an example of a chemical change?
   a. An egg is broken and poured into an eggnog mix.
   b. A tree is pruned, shortening some branches.
   c. A tree is watered and fertilized, and it grows larger.
   d. Frost forms on a cold windowpane.

Answers: 1. d; 2, a; 3, c; 4, b; 5, d; 6, d; 7, b; 8, c; 9, c

1.8 Classification of Matter

Learning Objective ❯ Classify matter according to state and as mixture, substance, compound, and/or element.

In this section, we examine three of the many ways of classifying matter. First, we look at the physical forms or *states of matter*.

The States of Matter

There are three familiar states of matter: solid, liquid, and gas (Figure 1.5). They can be classified by bulk properties (a *macro* view) or by arrangement of the particles that comprise them (a *molecular*, or *micro*, view). A **solid** object maintains its shape and volume regardless of its location. A **liquid** occupies a definite volume but assumes the shape of the portion of a container that it occupies. If you have 355 milliliters (mL) of a soft drink, you have 355 mL whether the soft drink is in a can, in a bottle, or, through a mishap, on the floor—which demonstrates another property of liquids. Unlike solids, liquids flow readily. A **gas** maintains neither shape nor volume. It expands to fill completely whatever container it occupies. Gases flow and are easily compressed. For example, enough air for many minutes of breathing can be compressed into a steel tank for SCUBA diving.

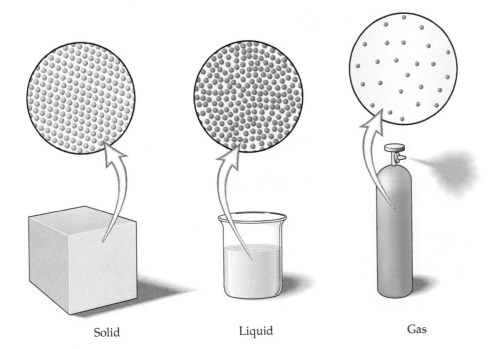

Solid   Liquid   Gas

◀ **Figure 1.5** The kinetic–molecular theory can be used to interpret (or explain) the bulk properties of *solids, liquids,* and *gases*. In solids, the particles are close together and in fixed positions. In liquids, the particles are close together, but they are free to move about. In gases, the particles are far apart and are in rapid random motion.

Q: *Based on this figure, why does a quart of water vapor weigh so much less than a quart of liquid water?*

Bulk properties of *solids, liquids,* and *gases* are explained using the kinetic–molecular theory. In solids, the particles are close together and in fixed positions. In liquids, the particles are close together, but they are free to move about. In gases, the particles are far apart and are in rapid random motion. We discuss the states of matter in more detail in Chapter 5.

Substances and Mixtures

Matter can be either pure or mixed (Figure 1.6). Pure matter is considered to be a **substance**, defined as having a definite, or fixed, composition that does not vary from one sample to another. Pure gold (24-karat gold) consists entirely of gold atoms; it is a substance. All samples of pure water are comprised of molecules consisting of two hydrogen atoms and one oxygen atom; water is a substance.

The composition of a **mixture** of two or more substances is variable. The substances retain their identities. They do not change chemically; they simply mix. Mixtures can be separated by physical means. Mixtures can be either *homogeneous* or *heterogeneous*. All parts of a homogeneous mixture have the same composition (Section 6.4) and the same appearance. A saline solution—a solution of salt in water—is a homogeneous mixture. The proportions of salt and water can vary from one solution to another, but the water is still water and the salt remains salt. The two substances can be separated by physical means. For example, the water can be boiled away, leaving the salt behind.

Sand and water form a heterogeneous mixture. The appearance is not the same throughout. The grains of sand are different from the liquid water. Most things we deal with each day are heterogeneous mixtures. All you have to do is look at a computer, a book, a pen, or a person to see that different parts of those mixtures have different compositions (your hair is quite different from your skin, for example).

Elements and Compounds

A *substance* is either an element or a compound. An **element** is one of the fundamental substances from which all material things are constructed. Elements cannot be broken down into simpler substances by any chemical process. There are more than 100 known elements, of which this book deals with only about a third, which are listed on the inside front cover. Oxygen, carbon, sulfur, aluminum, and iron are familiar elements.

A **compound** is a substance made up of two or more elements chemically combined in a fixed ratio. For example, water is a compound because it has fixed

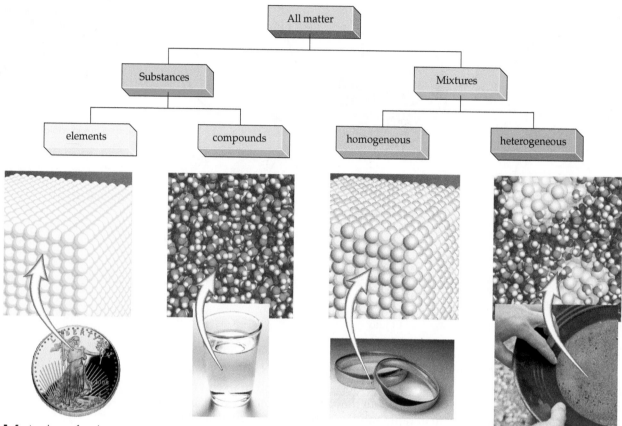

▲ **Figure 1.6** A scheme for classifying matter. The "molecular-level" views are of gold, an *element*; water, a *compound*; 12-karat gold, a *homogeneous mixture* of silver and gold; and the contents of a prospector's pan, a *heterogeneous mixture* of gold flakes in water.

5. Can we change lead into gold? One element cannot be changed into another element by chemical reactions. An element cannot be created or destroyed, although an element can be extracted from a mixture or compound containing the element.

A chemical symbol in a formula stands for one atom of the element. If more than one atom is included in a formula, a subscript number is used after the symbol. For example, the formula H_2 represents two atoms of hydrogen, and the formula CH_4 stands for one atom of carbon and four atoms of hydrogen. Mixtures do not have such formulas because a mixture does not have a fixed composition.

proportions of hydrogen (H) and oxygen (O). Aluminum oxide (the "sand" on sandpaper), carbon dioxide, and iron disulfide (FeS_2, "fool's gold") are other compounds.

Because elements are so fundamental to our study of chemistry, we find it useful to refer to them in a shorthand form. Each element can be represented by a **chemical symbol** made up of one or two letters derived from the name of the element. Symbols for the elements are listed in the Table of Atomic Masses (inside front cover). The first letter of a symbol is always capitalized. The second (if there are two) is always lowercase. (It makes a difference. For example, Co is the symbol for cobalt, a metallic element, but CO is the formula for carbon monoxide, a poisonous compound.)

The elements' symbols are the alphabet of chemistry. Most are based on the English names of the elements, but a few are based on Latin names (Table 1.4).

CONCEPTUAL Example 1.4 Elements and Compounds

Which of the following represent elements and which represent compounds?

C   Cu   HI   BN   In   HBr

Solution

The periodic table shows that C, Cu, and In represent elements (each is a single symbol). HI, BN, and HBr are each composed of two symbols and represent compounds.

■ EXERCISE 1.4A

Which of the following represent elements and which represent compounds?

He   CuO   No   NO   KF   Os

■ EXERCISE 1.4B

How many *different* elements are represented in the list in Exercise 1.4A?

Table 1.4	Some Elements with Symbols Derived from Latin Names			
Usual English Name	**Latin Name**	**Symbol**	**Spanish Name**[b]	**French Name**[b]
Copper	cuprum	Cu	cobre	cuivre
Gold	aurum	Au	oro	or
Iron	ferrum	Fe	hierro	fer
Lead	plumbum	Pb	plomo	plomb
Mercury	hydrargyrum	Hg	mercurio	mercure
Potassium	kalium[a]	K	potasio	potassium
Silver	argentum	Ag	plata	argent
Sodium	natrium[a]	Na	sodio	sodium
Tin	stannum	Sn	estaño	étain

[a]The elements potassium and sodium were unknown in ancient times. The names *kalium* and *natrium* are the names that were used then for the compounds potassium carbonate and sodium carbonate.

[b]Note that element names in Spanish and French are often close to the Latin names.

Atoms and Molecules

An **atom** is the smallest characteristic part of an element. Each element is composed of atoms of a particular kind. For example, the element copper is made up of copper atoms, and gold is made up of gold atoms. All copper atoms are alike in a fundamental way and are different from gold atoms.

The smallest characteristic part of most compounds is a molecule. A **molecule** is a group of atoms bound together as a unit. All the molecules of a given compound have the same atoms in the same proportions. For example, all water molecules have two hydrogen (H) atoms and one oxygen (O) atom, as indicated by the formula (H_2O). We will discuss atoms in some detail in Chapter 2, and much of the focus of many later chapters is on molecules.

Self-Assessment Questions

1. Which state of matter has neither a definite volume nor a definite shape?
   a. gas
   b. homogeneous
   c. liquid
   d. solid

2. Which of the following is a mixture?
   a. carbon
   b. copper
   c. silver
   d. soda water

3. Which of the following is *not* an element?
   a. aluminum
   b. brass
   c. lead
   d. sulfur

4. A compound can be separated into its elements
   a. by chemical means
   b. by mechanical means
   c. by physical means
   d. using a magnet

5. The smallest part of an element is a(n)
   a. atom
   b. corpuscle
   c. mass
   d. molecule

6. The symbol for potassium is
   a. K
   b. P
   c. Pm
   d. Po

7. Br is the symbol for
   a. beryllium
   b. boron
   c. brass
   d. bromine

Answers: 1, a; 2, d; 3, b; 4, a; 5, a; 6, a; 7, d

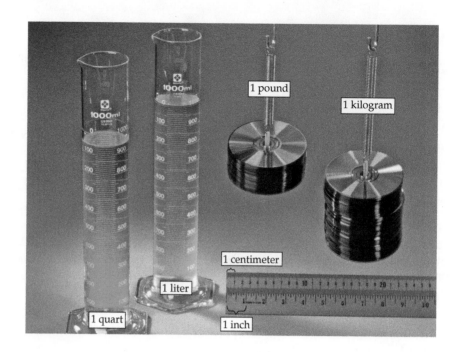

1.9 The Measurement of Matter

Learning Objective ❯ Assign proper units of measurement to observations, and manipulate units in conversions.

Accurate measurements of such properties as mass, volume, time, and temperature are essential to the compilation of dependable scientific data. Such data are of critical importance in all science-related fields. Measurements of temperature and blood pressure are routinely made in medicine, and modern medical diagnosis depends on a whole battery of other measurements, including careful chemical analyses of blood and urine.

The measurement system agreed on by scientists since 1960 is the *International System of Units*, or **SI units** (from the French *Système Internationale*), a modernized version of the metric system established in France in 1791. Most countries use metric measures in everyday life. In the United States these units are used mainly in science laboratories, although they are increasingly being used in commerce, especially in businesses with an international component. The contents of most bottled beverages are given in metric units, and metric measurements are also common in sporting events. Figure 1.7 compares some metric and customary units.

Because SI units are based on the decimal system, it is easy to convert from one unit to another. All measured quantities can be expressed in terms of the seven base units listed in Table 1.5. We use the first six in this text.

Table 1.5   The Seven SI Base Units

Physical Quantity	Name of Unit	Symbol of Unit
Length	meter[a]	m
Mass	kilogram	kg
Time	second	s
Temperature	kelvin	K
Amount of substance	mole	mol
Electric current	ampere	A
Luminous intensity	candela	cd

[a]Spelled *metre* in most countries.

Exponential Numbers: Powers of Ten

Scientists deal with objects smaller than atoms and as large as the universe. We usually use exponential notation to describe the sizes of such objects. A number is in *exponential notation* when it is written as the product of a coefficient and a power of 10, such as 1.6×10^{-19} or 35×10^{6}. A number is said to be expressed in *scientific notation* when the coefficient has a value between 1 and 10. Appendix A.2 provides a more detailed discussion of scientific notation.

An electron has a diameter of about 10^{-15} meter (m) and a mass of about 10^{-30} kilogram (kg). At the other extreme, a galaxy typically measures about 10^{23} m across and has a mass of about 10^{41} kg. It is difficult even to imagine numbers so small and so large. The accompanying figure offers some perspectives on size.

Because measurements using the basic SI units can be of awkward magnitude, we often use exponential numbers. However, it is sometimes more convenient to use prefixes (Table 1.6) to indicate units larger and smaller than the base unit. The following examples show how prefixes and powers of ten are interconverted.

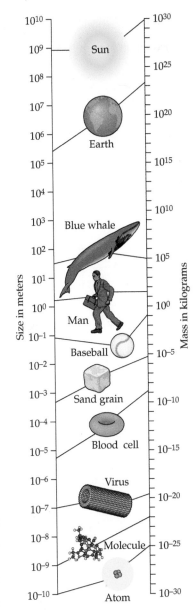

▲ Comparison of very large and very small objects is much easier with exponential notation.

Example 1.5 Prefixes and Powers of Ten

Convert each of the following measurements to a unit that replaces the power of ten by a prefix.
   a. 2.89×10^{-6} g   **b.** 4.30×10^{3} m

Solution
Our goal is to replace each power of ten with the appropriate prefix from Table 1.6. For example, $10^{-3} = 0.0001$ corresponds to milli(unit). (It doesn't matter what the unit is; here we are dealing only with the prefixes.)

   a. 10^{-6} corresponds to the prefix *micro-*, that is, $10^{-6} \times$ (unit) = micro (unit); so we have 2.89 μg

   b. 10^{3} corresponds to the prefix *kilo-*, that is, $10^{3} \times$ (unit) = kilo (unit); so we have 4.30 km

▪ **EXERCISE 1.5**
Convert each of the following measurements to a unit that replaces the power of ten by a prefix.
   a. 7.24×10^{3} g   **b.** 4.29×10^{-6} m   **c.** 7.91×10^{-3} s
   d. 2.29×10^{-2} g   **e.** 7.90×10^{6} m

Example 1.6 Prefixes and Powers of Ten

Use scientific notation to express each of the following measurements in terms of an SI base unit.
   a. 4.12 cm   **b.** 947 ms   **c.** 3.17 nm

Solution
   a. Our goal is to find the power of ten that relates the given unit to the SI base unit. That is, centi (base unit) = $10^{-2} \times$ (base unit)

$$4.12 \text{ cm} = 4.12 \text{ centimeter} = 4.12 \times 10^{-2} \text{ m}$$

   b. To change millisecond (ms) to the base unit second, we replace the prefix *milli-* by 10^{-3}. To obtain an answer in conventional scientific notation, we also need to replace the coefficient 947 by 9.47×10^{2}. The result of these two changes is

$$9.47 \text{ ms} = 9.47 \times 10^{-3}\text{s} = 9.47 \times 10^{2} \times 10^{-3}\text{s} = 9.47 \times 10^{-1}\text{s}$$

   c. To change nanometer (nm) to the base unit meter, we replace the prefix *nano-* by 10^{-9}. The answer in exponential form is 3.17×10^{-9} m.

Table 1.6 **Approved Numerical Prefixes**[a]

Exponential Expression	Decimal Equivalent	Prefix	Pronounced	Symbol
10^{12}	1,000,000,000,000	tera-	TER-uh	T
10^{9}	1,000,000,000	giga-	GIG-uh	G
10^{6}	1,000,000	mega-	MEG-uh	M
10^{3}	1,000	kilo-	KIL-oh	k
10^{2}	100	hecto-	HEK-toe	h
10^{1}	10	deka-	DEK-uh	da
10^{-1}	0.1	deci-	DES-ee	d
10^{-2}	0.01	centi-	SEN-tee	c
10^{-3}	0.001	milli-	MIL-ee	m
10^{-6}	0.000 001	micro-	MY-kro	μ
10^{-9}	0.000 000 001	nano-	NAN-oh	n
10^{-12}	0.000 000 000 001	pico-	PEE-koh	p
10^{-15}	0.000 000 000 000 001	femto-	FEM-toe	f

[a]The most commonly used prefixes are shown in color.

■ EXERCISE 1.6

Use scientific notation to express each of the following measurements in terms of an SI base unit.

   a. 7.45 nm   **b.** 5.25 μs   **c.** 1.415 km

   d. 2.06 mm   **e.** 6.19×10^{6} mm

Mass

The SI base unit for mass is the **kilogram (kg)**, about 2.2 pounds (lb). This base unit is unusual in that it already has a prefix. A more convenient mass unit for most laboratory work is the gram (g).

$$1 \text{ kg} = 10^{3} \text{ g} = 1000 \text{ g} \quad \text{or} \quad 1 \text{ g} = 0.001 \text{ kg} = 10^{-3} \text{ kg}$$

The milligram (mg) is a suitable unit for small quantities of materials, such as some drug dosages.

$$1 \text{ mg} = 10^{-3} \text{ g} = 0.001 \text{ g}$$

Chemists can now detect masses in the microgram (μg), nanogram (ng), picogram (pg), and even smaller ranges.

Length, Area, and Volume

The SI base unit of length is the **meter (m)**, a unit about 10% longer than 1 yard (yd). The kilometer (km) is used to measure distances along highways.

$$1 \text{ km} = 1000 \text{ m}$$

In the laboratory, we usually find lengths smaller than the meter to be more convenient. For example, we use the centimeter (cm), which is about the width of a typical calculator button, or the millimeter (mm), which is about the thickness of the cardboard backing in a notepad.

$$1 \text{ cm} = 0.01 \text{ m} \quad 1 \text{ mm} = 0.001 \text{ m}$$

For measurements at the atomic and molecular level, we use the micrometer (μm), the nanometer (nm), and the picometer (pm). For example, a hemoglobin molecule, which is nearly spherical, has a diameter of 5.5 nm or 5500 pm, and the diameter of a sodium atom is 372 pm.

The units for area and volume are derived from the base unit of length. The SI unit of area is the square meter (m^2), but we often find square centimeters (cm^2) or square millimeters (mm^2) to be more convenient for laboratory work.

$$1\ cm^2 = (10^{-2}\ m)^2 = 10^{-4}\ m^2 \qquad 1\ mm^2 = (10^{-3}\ m)^2 = 10^{-6}\ m^2$$

Similarly, the SI unit of volume is the cubic meter (m^3), but two units more likely to be used in the laboratory are the cubic centimeter (cm^3 or cc) and the cubic decimeter (dm^3). A cubic centimeter is about the volume of a sugar cube, and a cubic decimeter is slightly larger than 1 quart (qt).

$$1\ cm^3 = (10^{-2}\ m)^3 = 10^{-6}\ m^3 \qquad 1\ dm^3 = (10^{-1}\ m)^3 = 10^{-3}\ m^3$$

The cubic decimeter is commonly called a liter. A **liter (L)** is 1 cubic decimeter or 1000 cubic centimeters.

$$1\ L = 1\ dm^3 = 1000\ cm^3$$

The milliliter (mL) or cubic centimeter is frequently used in laboratories. A milliliter is about one "squirt" from a medicine dropper.

$$1\ mL = 1\ cm^3$$

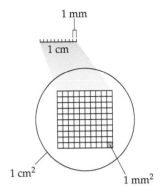

▲ Units of area such as mm^2 and cm^2 are derived from units of length.

Q: *How many mm are in 1 cm? How many mm^2 are in 1 cm^2?*

Time

The SI base unit for measuring intervals of time is the second (s). Extremely short time periods are expressed using SI prefixes: millisecond (ms), microsecond (μs), nanosecond (ns), and picosecond (ps).

$$1\ ms = 10^{-3}\ s \qquad 1\ \mu s = 10^{-6}\ s \qquad 1\ ns = 10^{-9}\ s \qquad 1\ ps = 10^{-12}\ s$$

Long time intervals, in contrast, are usually expressed in traditional, non-SI units: minute (min), hour (h), day (d), and year (y).

$$1\ min = 60\ s \qquad 1\ h = 60\ min \qquad 1\ d = 24\ h \qquad 1\ y = 365\ d$$

Problem Solving: Estimation

Many chemistry problems require calculations that yield numerical answers. When you use a calculator, it will always give you an answer—but the answer may not be correct. You may have punched a wrong number or used the wrong function. You can learn to estimate answers so you can tell whether your calculated answers are reasonable. At times an estimated answer is good enough, as the following Example and Exercises illustrate. This ability to estimate answers can be important in everyday life as well as in a chemistry course. Note that estimation does *not* require a detailed calculation. Only a rough calculation—or none at all—is required.

Example 1.7 Mass, Length, Area, Volume

Without doing detailed calculations, determine which of the following is a reasonable **(a)** mass (weight) and **(b)** height for a typical two-year-old child.

Mass:	10 mg	10 g	10 kg	100 g
Height:	85 mm	85 cm	850 cm	8.5 m

Solution

a. In customary units, a two-year-old child should weigh about 20–25 lb. Since 1 kg is a little more than 2 lb, the only reasonable answer is 10 kg.

b. In customary units, a two-year-old child should be about 30–36 in. tall. Since 1 cm is a little less than 0.5 in., the answer must be a little more than twice that range, or a bit over 60–72 cm. Thus the only reasonable answer is 85 cm.

■ **EXERCISE 1.7A**

Without doing a detailed calculation, determine which of the following is a reasonable area for the front cover of your textbook.

$$500 \text{ mm}^2 \qquad 50 \text{ cm}^2 \qquad 500 \text{ cm}^2 \qquad 50 \text{ m}^2$$

■ **EXERCISE 1.7B**

Without doing a detailed calculation, determine which of the following is a reasonable volume for your textbook.

$$1600 \text{ mm}^3 \qquad 16 \text{ cm}^3 \qquad 1600 \text{ cm}^3 \qquad 1.6 \text{ m}^3$$

Problem Solving: Unit Conversions

It is easy to convert from one metric unit to another using the *unit conversion* method of problem solving. If you are not familiar with this method, you should study it now in Appendix A.3, which also discusses the conversion of common units to metric units. You can find a discussion of *significant figures*, a way of indicating the precision of measurements, in Appendix A.4. In the following problems and throughout the text, we will simply carry three digits in most calculations.

Example 1.8 Unit Conversions

Convert **(a)** 1.83 kg to grams and **(b)** 729 μL to milliliters.

Solution

a. We start with the given quantity, 1.83 kg, and use the equivalence 1 kg = 1000 g to form a conversion factor (see Appendix A.3) that allows us to cancel the unit kg and end with the unit g.

$$1.83 \text{ kg} \times \frac{1000 \text{ g}}{1 \text{ kg}} = 1830 \text{ g}$$

b. Here we start with the given quantity, 729 μL, and use the equivalences 10^6 μL = 1 L and 10^3 mL = 1 L to form conversion factors that allow us to cancel the unit μL and end with the unit mL.

$$729 \text{ μL} \times \frac{1 \text{ L}}{10^6 \text{ μL}} \times \frac{1000 \text{ mL}}{1 \text{ L}} = 0.729 \text{ mL}$$

■ **EXERCISE 1.8**

Convert **(a)** 0.755 m to millimeters, **(b)** 205.6 mL to liters, **(c)** 0.206 g to micrograms, and **(d)** 7.38 cm to millimeters.

Self-Assessment Questions

1. The SI unit of length is the
   a. foot   b. kilometer   c. pascal   d. meter

2. The SI unit of mass is the
   a. dram   b. gram   c. grain   d. kilogram

3. The prefix that means 10^{-6} is
   a. centi-   b. deci-   c. micro-   d. milli-

4. A meter is about 10% longer than a(n)
   a. foot   b. inch   c. mile   d. yard

5. One cubic centimeter is equal to one
   a. deciliter   b. dram   c. liter   d. milliliter

6. One quart is slightly less than one
   a. deciliter   b. kiloliter   c. liter   d. milliliter

Nanoworld

For over two centuries, chemists have been able to re-arrange atoms to make molecules, which have dimensions in the *picometer* (10^{-12} m) range. This ability has led to revolutions in the design of drugs, plastics, and many other materials. Over the last several decades, scientists have made vast strides in handling materials with dimensions in the *micrometer* (10^{-6} m) range. The revolution in electronic devices—computers, cell phones, and so on—was spurred by the ability of scientists to produce computer chips by photolithography on a micrometer scale.

Now many scientists focus on *nanotechnology*. The prefix *nano-* means one-billionth (10^{-9}). Nanotechnology bridges the gap between picometer-sized molecules and micrometer-sized electronics. A nanometer-sized object contains just a few hundred to a few thousand atoms or molecules, and such objects often have different properties than large objects of the same substance. For example, bulk gold is yellow, but a ring made up of nanometer-sized gold particles appears red. Carbon in the form of graphite (pencil lead) is quite weak and soft, but carbon nanotubes can be 100 times stronger than steel. Nanotubes, so called because of their size (only one 10,000th the thickness of a human hair) and their shape (hollow tube), have thousands of potential uses but are extremely expensive to make. Scientists can now manipulate matter on every scale, from nanometers to meters, greatly increasing the scope of materials design. We will examine some of the many practical applications of nanotechnology in subsequent chapters.

7. A rope is 5.775 cm long. What is its length in millimeters?
   a. 0.05775 mm
   b. 0.5775 mm
   c. 5.775 mm
   d. 57.75 mm

8. Which of the following has a mass of roughly 1 g?
   a. an ant
   b. an orange
   c. a peanut
   d. a watermelon

9. Which of the following has a thickness of roughly 1 cm?
   a. a brick
   b. a cell phone
   c. a knife blade
   d. this textbook

10. Which of the following has a volume of roughly 250 mL (0.250 L)?
   a. 1 cup
   b. 1 gallon
   c. 1 pint
   d. 1 tablespoon

Answers: 1, d; 2, d; 3, c; 4, d; 5, d; 6, c; 7, d; 8, c; 9, b; 10, a

▲ Molecular view of a carbon nanotube—stronger than steel and more expensive than gold.

1.10 **Density**

Learning Objective ❯ Calculate the density, mass, or volume of an object given the other two quantities.

In everyday life, we might speak of lead as "heavy" or aluminum as "light," but such descriptions are imprecise at best. Scientists use the term *density* to describe this important property. The **density**, *d*, of a substance is the quantity of mass, *m*, per unit of volume, *V*.

$$d = \frac{m}{V}$$

For substances that don't mix, such as oil and water, the concept of density allows us to predict which will float on the other. It isn't just the mass of each material, but the *mass per unit volume*—the density—that determines the result. Density is the property that explains why oil (lower density) floats on water (higher density) in a bottle of Italian salad dressing. Figure 1.8 shows other examples.

We can rearrange the equation for density to give

$$m = d \times V \quad \text{and} \quad V = \frac{m}{d}$$

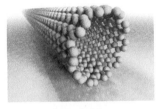

▲ One cubic centimeter of copper weighs 8.94 g, so the density of copper is 8.94 g/cm³.

Q: *What is the mass of 2 cm³ of copper? What is the density of 2 cm³ of copper?*

▲**Figure 1.8** At room temperature, the density of water is 1.00 g/mL. A coin sinks in water, but a cork floats on water.

Q: *Is the density of these coins less than, equal to, or greater than 1.00 g/mL? Is the density of the corks less than, equal to, or greater than 1.00 g/mL?*

You can do your own demonstration of a density difference. Make a classic French vinaigrette salad dressing by adding 10 mL of red wine vinegar to 30–40 mL of extra virgin olive oil. Add seasonings such as salt, pepper, oregano, thyme, Dijon mustard, and garlic. Which material, oil or vinegar, forms the top layer? Enjoy!

Table 1.7	Densities of Some Common Substances at Specified Temperatures	
Substance*	**Density**	**Temperature**
Solids		
Copper (Cu)	8.94 g/cm^3	25 °C
Gold (Au)	19.3 g/cm^3	25 °C
Magnesium (Mg)	1.738 g/cm^3	20 °C
Water (ice) (H_2O)	0.917 g/cm^3	0 °C
Liquids		
Ethanol (CH_3CH_2OH)	0.789 g/mL	20 °C
Hexane ($CH_3CH_2CH_2CH_2CH_2CH_3$)	0.660 g/mL	20 °C
Mercury (Hg)	13.534 g/mL	25 °C
Urine (a mixture)	1.003–1.030 g/mL	25 °C
Water (H_2O)	0.998 g/mL	0 °C
	1.000 g/mL	4 °C
	0.998 g/mL	20 °C

*Formulas are provided for possible future reference.

These equations are useful for calculations. Densities of some common substances are listed in Table 1.7. They are customarily reported in grams per milliliter (g/mL) for liquids and grams per cubic centimeter (g/cm^3) for solids. Values listed in the table are used in some of the following Examples and Exercises and in some of the end-of-chapter problems.

As with problems involving mass, length, area, and volume (page 23), it is often sufficient to estimate answers to problems involving densities, for example, in determining relative volumes of materials or whether or not a material will float or sink in water. Such estimation is illustrated in the following Example and Exercises. Note again that estimation does *not* require a detailed calculation.

Example 1.9   Mass, Volume, and Density

Answer the following without doing detailed calculations. **(a)** Which has the greater volume, a 50.0-g block of copper or a 50.0-g block of gold? **(b)** Which has the greater mass, 225 mL of ethanol or 225 mL of hexane?

Solution

a. From Table 1.7, we see that the density of gold (19.3 g/cm^3) is greater than that of copper (8.94 g/cm^3). A block of copper thus has to be larger in volume than a block of gold of the same mass. A 50.0-g block of copper has a greater volume than a 50.0-g block of gold.

b. From Table 1.7, we see that the density of ethanol (0.789 g/mL) is greater than that of hexane (0.660 g/mL). Because ethanol is more dense (that is, it has more mass in each unit of volume), 225 mL of it has a greater mass than does 225 mL of hexane.

■ **EXERCISE 1.9A**

Without doing a detailed calculation, determine which has the greater volume, a 500.0-g block of ice or a 500.0-g block of magnesium.

■ **EXERCISE 1.9B**

Wood does not dissolve in water and will float on water if its density is less than that of water. Padauk (*d* = 0.86 g/cm^3) and ebony (*d* = 1.2 g/cm^3) are tropical woods. Which will float on water and which will sink in water? What will padauk and ebony do in ethyl alcohol?

When we need a numerical answer, we can use the relationship of mass and volume to density to form conversion factors. Then we use the unit conversion method of problem solving.

Example 1.10 Density from Mass and Volume

What is the density of iron if 156 g of iron occupies a volume of 20.0 cm³?

Solution
The given quantities are

$$m = 156 \text{ g} \quad \text{and} \quad V = 20.0 \text{ cm}^3$$

We use the equation that defines density.

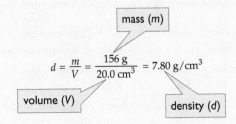

$$d = \frac{m}{V} = \frac{156 \text{ g}}{20.0 \text{ cm}^3} = 7.80 \text{ g/cm}^3$$

■ EXERCISE 1.10A
What is the density, in grams per milliliter, of a salt solution if 210 mL has a mass of 234 g?

■ EXERCISE 1.10B
What is the density, in grams per cubic centimeter, of a metal alloy if a cube of it that measures 2.00 cm on an edge has a mass of 94.3 g?

Example 1.11 Mass from Density and Volume

What is the mass in grams of 1.00 L of gasoline if its density is 0.703 g/mL?

Solution
We can express the given density as a ratio, 0.703 g/1.00 mL, and use it as a conversion factor. We also need the factor 1000 mL/1 L to convert liters to milliliters.

$$m = d \times V = \frac{0.703 \text{ g}}{1 \text{ mL}} \times 1 \text{ L} \times \frac{1000 \text{ mL}}{1 \text{ L}} = 703 \text{ g}$$

■ EXERCISE 1.11A
What is the mass in grams of 250.0 mL of glycerol, which has a density of 1.264 g/mL at 20 °C?

■ EXERCISE 1.11B
What is the mass in kilograms of the ethanol that fills a 16-gallon "gas tank"? (1 gallon = 3.78 L; also see Table 1.7)

Example 1.12 Volume from Mass and Density

What volume in milliliters is occupied by 461 g of mercury? (See Table 1.7.)

Solution
Here we can express the inverse of the density as a ratio, 1 mL/13.534 g, and use it as a conversion factor.

$$V = 461 \text{ g} \times \frac{1 \text{ mL}}{13.534 \text{ g}} = 34.1 \text{ mL}$$

▪ EXERCISE 1.12A
What volume in cubic centimeters is occupied by a 25.8-g piece of magnesium? (See Table 1.7.)

▪ EXERCISE 1.12B
You need 875 g of hexane. Will it fit in a 1.00-L container? (See Table 1.7.)

Self-Assessment Questions

1. The density of a wood plank floating on a lake is
   a. less than that of air
   b. less than that of water
   c. more than that of water
   d. the same as that of water

2. A pebble and a lead sinker both sink when dropped into a pond. This shows that the two objects
   a. are both less dense than water
   b. are both more dense than water
   c. have different densities
   d. have the same density

3. Ice floats on liquid water. A reasonable value for the density of ice is
   a. 0.92 g/cm^3 b. 1.08 g/cm^3 c. 1.98 g/cm^3 d. 4.90 g/cm^3

4. A prospector panning for gold swirls a mixture of mud, gravel, and water in a pan. He looks for gold at the bottom because gold
   a. dissolves in water and sinks
   b. has a high density and sinks
   c. is less dense than rocks
   d. is repelled by the other minerals

5. Which of the following metals will sink in a pool of mercury ($d = 13.534 \text{ g/cm}^3$)?
   a. aluminum ($d = 2.6 \text{ g/cm}^3$)
   b. iron ($d = 7.9 \text{ g/cm}^3$)
   c. lead ($d = 11.34 \text{ g/cm}^3$)
   d. uranium ($d = 19.5 \text{ g/cm}^3$)

6. If the volume of a rock is 80.0 cm^3 and its mass is 160.0 g, its density is
   a. 0.03 g/cm^3 b. 0.50 g/cm^3 c. 2.0 g/cm^3 d. 128 g/cm^3

Answers: 1, b; 2, b; 3, a; 4, b; 5, d; 6, c

1.11 Energy: Heat and Temperature

Learning Objectives ❯ Distinguish between heat and temperature. ❯ Explain how the temperature scales are related.

The physical and chemical changes that matter undergoes are almost always accompanied by changes in energy. **Energy** is required to make something happen that wouldn't happen by itself. Energy is the ability to change matter, either physically or chemically.

Two important concepts in science that are related, and sometimes confused, are *temperature* and *heat*. When two objects at different temperatures are brought together, heat flows from the warmer to the cooler object until both are at the same temperature. **Heat** is energy on the move, the energy that flows from a warmer object to a cooler one. **Temperature** is a measure of how hot or cold an object is. Temperature tells us the direction in which heat will flow. Heat flows from more energetic (higher-temperature) to less energetic (lower-temperature) atoms or molecules. For example, if you touch a hot test tube, heat will flow from the tube to your hand. If the tube is hot enough, your hand will be burned.

The SI base unit of temperature is the **kelvin (K)**. For laboratory work, we often use the more familiar **Celsius scale**. On this temperature scale, the freezing point of water is 0 degrees Celsius (°C) and the boiling point is 100 °C. The interval between these two reference points is divided into 100 equal parts, each a *degree Celsius*. The Kelvin scale is called an *absolute scale* because its zero point is the coldest temperature possible, or absolute zero. (This fact was determined by theoretical considerations and has been confirmed by experiment, as we will see in Chapter 6.) The zero point on the Kelvin scale, 0 K, is equal to −273.15 °C, which we often round to −273 °C. A kelvin is the same size as a degree Celsius, so the freezing point of water on the Kelvin scale is 273 K. The Kelvin scale has no negative temperatures, and we don't use a degree sign with the K. To convert from degrees Celsius to kelvins, simply add 273.15 to the Celsius temperature.

$$K = °C + 273.15$$

Example 1.13 Temperature Conversions

Diethyl ether boils at 36 °C. What is the boiling point of this liquid on the Kelvin scale?

Solution

$$K = °C + 273.15$$
$$K = 36 + 273.15 = 309 \text{ K}$$

■ EXERCISE 1.13A
What is the boiling point of ethanol (78 °C) expressed in kelvins?

■ EXERCISE 1.13B
At atmospheric pressure, liquid nitrogen boils at –196 °C. Express that temperature in kelvins.

The Fahrenheit temperature scale is widely used in the United States. Figure 1.9 compares the three temperature scales. Note that on the Fahrenheit scale, there are 180 Fahrenheit degrees between the freezing point and the boiling point of water. On the Celsius scale there are 100 Celsius degrees between these two points. Thus, one Celsius degree equals 1.8 Fahrenheit degrees. Conversions between Fahrenheit and Celsius temperatures use this relationship, which is discussed in Appendix A.5.

The SI-derived unit of energy is the **joule (J)**, but the **calorie (cal)** is the more familiar unit in everyday life.

$$1 \text{ cal} = 4.184 \text{ J}$$

A calorie is the amount of heat required to raise the temperature of 1 g of water by 1 °C.

The "calorie" used for expressing the energy content of foods is actually a **kilocalorie (kcal)**.

$$1000 \text{ cal} = 1 \text{ kcal} = 4184 \text{ J}$$

A dieter might be aware that a banana split contains 1500 "calories." If the dieter realized that this was really 1500 *kilo*calories, or 1,500,000 calories, giving up the banana split might be easier! The concept of heat is discussed further in Appendix A.5.

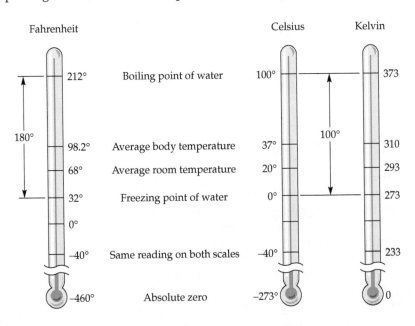

◀ **Figure 1.9** A comparison of the Fahrenheit, Celsius, and Kelvin temperature scales.

▶ **Figure 1.10** Temperature and heat are different phenomena. Both the tub and the pool are at roughly the same temperature—about 40 °C—but it took much more heat to warm the pool to that temperature than it did the tub of water.

Example 1.14 Energy Conversions

When 1.00 g of gasoline burns, it yields about 10.3 kcal of energy. What is this quantity of energy in kilojoules (kJ)?

Solution

$$10.3 \text{ kcal} \times \frac{1000 \text{ cal}}{1 \text{ kcal}} \times \frac{4.184 \text{ J}}{1 \text{ cal}} \times \frac{1 \text{ kJ}}{1000 \text{ J}} = 43.1 \text{ kJ}$$

■ **EXERCISE 1.14A**

Each day the average European woman consumes food with an energy content of 7525 kJ. What is this daily intake in kilocalories (food calories)?

■ **EXERCISE 1.14B**

It takes about 12 kJ of energy to melt a single ice cube. How much energy in kilocalories does it take to melt a tray of 12 ice cubes?

Self-Assessment Questions

1. Heat is
   a. an element
   b. the energy flow from a hot object to a cold one
   c. a measure of energy intensity
   d. a temperature above room temperature

2. The SI scale for temperature is known as the
   a. Celsius scale
   b. Fahrenheit scale
   c. Kelvin scale
   d. Richter scale

3. Water freezes at
   a. 0 °C
   b. 0 °F
   c. 273 °C
   d. 373 K

4. To convert a temperature on the Kelvin scale to degrees Celsius, we
   a. add 100
   b. add 273
   c. subtract 100
   d. subtract 273

5. The SI unit of energy is the
   a. ampere
   b. joule
   c. newton
   d. watt

Answers: 1, b; 2, c; 3, a; 4, d; 5, b

Normal Body Temperature

Carl Wunderlich (1815–1877), a German physician, first recognized that fever is a symptom of disease. He recorded thousands of temperature measurements from healthy people and reported the average value as 37 °C. When this value was converted to the Fahrenheit scale, it somehow (improperly) acquired an extra significant figure, and 98.6 °F became widely (and incorrectly) known as the *normal body temperature*. In recent years, millions of measurements have revealed that *average* normal body temperature is actually 98.2 °F and that body temperatures in healthy people range from 97.7 °F to 99.5 °F.

GREEN CHEMISTRY

Jennifer L. Young and Robert Peoples, *ACS Green Chemistry Institute*®

Green chemistry is the design of chemical products and processes that reduce or eliminate the generation and use of hazardous substances. To put this definition into practice, chemists follow the twelve principles of green chemistry, which are listed in the inside front cover. Overall, green chemistry is about preventing waste, using nonhazardous chemicals, conserving energy, using renewable resources, and making products that degrade after use. The goal of green chemistry is to minimize the harmful impacts of substances on human health and the environment by using safer alternatives. As you will learn in each chapter, green chemistry applies to all chemistry areas and concepts, and pervades all types of chemistry.

Green chemistry was developed about 20 years ago as a new, holistic way of thinking about chemicals and chemistry—considering the sources of chemicals, where they will end up, and what impact they will have on human beings and the planet. The proven twelve principles are in commercial practice around the world, and a growing number of products on store shelves have been made by green chemistry.

Green chemistry is as rigorous as traditional chemistry. The scientific method involving hypotheses, laws, theories, and models (Section 1.3) still applies in green chemistry. Because some concepts of green chemistry are still relatively new, especially compared to other chemistry ideas that have been around for centuries, many students and even professional chemists are learning about green chemistry for the first time. Green chemistry is a hard science and a new science that will be critical for developing future technologies that are safe for people and the planet.

This chapter discusses the risk associated with science (Section 1.5). Risk includes both hazard and exposure; reducing either one reduces risk. Protective equipment and other safety measures can prevent exposure of workers, the public, and the environment to hazardous chemicals. However, there is always a possibility that the protection will fail (because of human error or acts of nature), causing exposure to the materials. Green chemistry, on the other hand, aims to dramatically reduce risk by using chemicals that are inherently safer and less hazardous. When selecting chemicals to use in a product or process, chemists consider the physical and chemical properties (Section 1.7). Green chemists also evaluate other properties, including toxicity toward human beings and degradability in the environment.

The world faces a growing number of environmental problems, some of which have been caused by chemicals. However, green chemistry can provide solutions and minimize future problems by avoiding hazardous materials and preventing pollution. You will read about many green chemistry technologies and solutions throughout this book. Each chapter contains a green chemistry essay that presents some of the latest technologies in areas such as biofuels, plastics, medicine, and food.

Many companies are using green chemistry to design new products and processes. Companies that make or use chemicals are choosing to use less energy, create less waste, and select chemicals and solvents that are less hazardous. They are making these decisions based on green chemistry, not only because it's the right thing to do but also because these actions save money and make good business sense. Between 1996 and 2011, 82 professors, small businesses, and large companies were presented with the Presidential Green Chemistry Challenge Award (PGCCA). These awards have recognized advances in pest control, plastics, medicines, fuel, paints, electronics, textiles, cosmetics, cleaning products, and a wide range of other areas that depend on chemistry. Several of the award-winning technologies are featured throughout this book.

The future of this planet and its growing number of inhabitants will all depend on clean energy, water, air, food, medicine, and technology. You can contribute to sustainability through the products you purchase, recycling, conserving energy, and even through your career choices. Green chemistry is essential to a sustainable future!

▲ Natular™ is a greener mosquito larvicide, developed by Clarke, for which the company won a 2010 PGCCA. Mosquitoes are much more than a summer annoyance; they spread malaria, yellow fever, and other diseases, and their control is a huge issue worldwide. Natular™ is a new, environmentally more responsible weapon in this control.

1.12 Critical Thinking

Learning Objective ❯ Use critical thinking to evaluate claims and statements.

One of the hallmarks of science is the ability to think critically—to evaluate statements and claims in a rational, objective fashion. For example, a diet-plan advertisement shows people who have lost a lot of weight. Somewhere in the ad, in tiny print, you may find a statement such as "results may vary" or "results not typical." Such ads also often advise combining the plan with diet and exercise. Does an ad like this prove that a diet plan works? You can use critical thinking to evaluate the ad's claim. Critical thinking involves gathering facts, assessing them, using logic to reach a conclusion, and then evaluating the conclusion. The ability to think critically can be learned, and it will serve you well in everyday life as well as in science courses. Critical thinking is important for workers in all types of professions and employees in all kinds of industries. We will use an approach adapted from one developed by James Lett.[1] This approach is outlined below and followed by several examples.

You can use the acronym **FLaReS** (ignore the vowels) to remember four principles used to test a claim: *f*alsifiability, *l*ogic, *r*eplicability, and *s*ufficiency.

- **Falsifiability:** Can any conceivable evidence show the claim to be false? It must be possible to think of evidence that would prove the claim false. A hypothesis that cannot be falsified is of no value. Science cannot prove anything true in an absolute sense, although it can provide overwhelming evidence. Science *can* prove something false.

- **Logic:** Any argument offered as evidence in support of a claim must be sound. An argument is sound if its conclusion follows inevitably from its premises and if its premises are true. It is unsound if a premise is false, and it is unsound if there is a single exception in which the conclusion does not necessarily follow from the premises.

- **Replicability:** If the evidence for a claim is based on an experimental result, it is necessary that the evidence be replicable in subsequent experiments or trials. Scientific research is almost always reviewed by other qualified scientists. The peer-reviewed research is then published in a form that enables others to repeat the experiment. Sometimes bad science slips through the peer-review process, but such results eventually fail the test of replicability. For example, in May 2005 the journal *Science* published research by Korean biomedical scientist Hwang Woo-suk in which he claimed to have tailored embryonic stem cells so that every patient could receive custom treatment. Others were unable to reproduce Hwang's findings, and evidence emerged that he had intentionally fabricated results. *Science* retracted the article in January 2006. Research results published in media that are not peer reviewed have little or no standing in the scientific community—nor should you rely on them.

- **Sufficiency:** The evidence offered in support of a claim must be adequate to establish the truth of that claim, with these stipulations: (1) The burden of evidence for any claim rests on the claimant, (2) extraordinary claims demand extraordinary evidence, and (3) evidence based on an authority figure or on testimony is never adequate.

If a claim passes all four FLaReS tests, then it *might* be true. On the other hand, it could still be proven false. However, if a claim fails even one of the FLaReS tests, it is likely to be false. The FLaReS method is a good starting point for evaluating the myriad claims that you will find on the Internet and elsewhere.We apply one or more of the FLaReS principles to evaluate a claim in each of the following examples.

---

[1]Lett used the acronym FiLCHeRS (ignore the vowels) as a mnemonic for six rules: *f*alsifiability, *l*ogic, *c*omprehensiveness, *h*onesty, *r*eplicability, and *s*ufficiency. See Lett, James, "A Field Guide to Critical Thinking," *The Skeptical Inquirer*, Winter 1990, pp. 153–160.

CRITICAL THINKING EXAMPLES

1.1 A practitioner claims outstanding success in curing cancer with a vaccine made from a patient's own urine. However, the vaccine works only if the patient's immune system is still sufficiently strong. Is the claim falsifiable?

Solution

No. The practitioner can always say that the patient's immune system was no longer sufficiently strong.

1.2 A website claims, "The medical-industrial complex suppresses natural treatments because they cure the patient. A cured patient no longer needs a doctor, and the doctor loses income." Is the claim logical?

Solution

No. Doctors do not cure all patients. Many remain ill and some die.

1.3 Many "psychics" claim to be able to predict the future. These predictions are often made near the end of one year and concern the next year. Apply all the FLaReS tests to evaluate this claim.

Solution

1. Is the claim falsifiable? Yes. You could write down a prediction and then check it yourself at the end of the year.

2. Is the claim logical? No. If psychics could really predict the future, they could readily win lotteries, ward off all kinds of calamities by providing advance warning, and so on.

3. Is the claim reproducible? No. Psychics often make broad, general predictions, such as "tornadoes will hit Oklahoma in April and May." (It would be a rare year when there were no tornadoes in Oklahoma in those months.) The psychics later make claim-specific references to "hits" while ignoring "misses." Here are some past predictions of Sylvia Browne, a self-proclaimed world-famous psychic: Bill Bradley would be elected U.S. president in 2000; Michael Jackson would be found guilty in his 2005 child molestation trial (he was acquitted); a cure for breast cancer would be found by the end of 1999. None of the well-known psychics, including Browne, James Van Praagh, John Edward, and the Jamison sisters (Terry and Linda), predicted the terrorist attacks on the United States on September 11, 2001.

4. Is the claim sufficient? No. Any such claim is extraordinary; it would require extraordinary evidence. The burden of proof for the claim rests on the claimant.

CRITICAL THINKING EXERCISES

Apply knowledge that you have gained in this chapter and one or more of the FLaReS principles to evaluate the following statements or claims.

1.1 An alternative health practitioner claims that a nuclear power plant releases radiation at a level so low that it cannot be measured, but that this radiation is harmful to the thyroid gland. He sells a thyroid extract that he claims can prevent the problem.

1.2 A doctor claims that she can cure a patient of arthritis by simply massaging the affected joints. If she has the patient's complete trust, she can cure the arthritis within a year. Several of her patients have testified that the doctor has cured their arthritis.

1.3 German physicist Jan Hendrik Schön of Bell Labs claimed in 2001 that he had produced a molecular scale transistor. Others scientists noted that his data contained irregularities. Attempts to perform experiments similar to Schön's did not give similar results.

1.4 A mercury-containing preservative called thiomersal was used to prevent bacterial and fungal contamination in vaccines from the 1930s until its use was phased out starting in 1999. In the United States, a widespread concern arose that these vaccines caused autism. There was no such concern in the United Kingdom, although the vaccine with the same preservative was used there. Is the concern valid?

1.5 A woman claims that she has memorized the New Testament. She offers to quote any chapter of any book entirely from memory.

1.6 The label on a bag of Morton solar salt crystals has the statement "No chemicals or additives."

SUMMARY

Section 1.1—**Technology** is the practical application of knowledge, while **science** is an accumulation of knowledge about nature and our physical world along with our explanations of that knowledge. The roots of chemistry lie in **natural philosophy**, philosophical speculation about nature, and in **alchemy**, a mixture of chemistry and magic practiced in Europe in the Middle Ages.

Section 1.2—**Green chemistry** uses materials and processes that are intended to prevent or reduce pollution at its source. **Sustainable chemistry** is designed to meet the needs of the present generation without compromising the needs of future generations.

Section 1.3—Science is *reproducible, testable, predictive, explanatory,* and *tentative.* In one common scientific method, a set of confirmed observations about nature may lead to a **hypothesis**— a tentative explanation of the observations. A **scientific law** is a brief statement that summarizes large amounts of data. If a hypothesis stands up to testing and further experimentation, it may become a **theory**—the best current explanation for a phenomenon. A theory is always tentative and can be rejected if it does not continue to stand up to further testing. A valid theory can be used to predict new scientific facts. Scientists disagree over social and political issues partly because of the inability to control **variables**, factors that can change during an experiment.

Section 1.4—Science and technology have provided many benefits for our world, but they have also introduced new risks. A **risk–benefit analysis** can help us decide which outweighs the other.

Section 1.5—Chemistry is fundamental to other scientific disciplines and plays a central role in society and daily life.

Section 1.6—Most chemists are involved in some kind of research. The purpose of **applied research** is to make useful products or to solve a particular problem, while **basic research** is carried out simply to obtain new knowledge or to answer a fundamental question. Basic research often also leads to a useful product or process.

Section 1.7—Chemistry is the study of matter and the changes it undergoes. **Matter** is anything that has mass and takes up space. **Mass** is a measure of the amount of matter in an object, while **weight** represents the gravitational force of attraction for an object. **Physical properties** of matter can be observed without making new substances. When **chemical properties** are observed, new substances are formed. A **physical change** does not entail a change in chemical composition. A **chemical change** does involve such a change.

Section 1.8—Matter can be classified according to physical state. A **solid** has definite shape and volume. A **liquid** has

definite volume but takes the shape of its container. A **gas** takes both the shape and the volume of its container. Matter also can be classified according to composition. A **substance** always has the same composition, no matter how it is made or where it is found. A **mixture** can have different compositions depending on how it is prepared. Substances are either elements or compounds. An **element** is composed of atoms of one type, an **atom** being the smallest characteristic particle of an element. There are over a hundred elements, each of which is represented by a **chemical symbol** consisting of one or two letters derived from the element's name. A **compound** is made up of two or more elements, chemically combined in a fixed ratio. Most compounds exist as **molecules**, groups of atoms bound together as a unit.

Section 1.9—Scientific measurements are expressed with **SI units**, which comprise an agreed-on standard version of the metric system. Base units include the **kilogram (kg)** for mass and the **meter (m)** for length. Although it is not the SI standard unit of volume, the **liter (L)** is widely used. Prefixes make basic units larger or smaller by factors of ten.

Section 1.10—**Density** can be thought of as "how heavy something is for its size." It is the amount of mass per unit volume.

$$d = \frac{m}{V}$$

Density can be used as a conversion factor. The density of water is almost exactly 1 g/mL.

Section 1.11—When matter undergoes a physical or chemical change, a change in **energy** is involved. Energy is the *ability* to cause these changes. **Heat** is energy flow from a warmer object to a cooler one. **Temperature** is a measure of how hot or cold an object is. The **kelvin (K)** is the SI base unit of temperature, but the **Celsius scale (°C)** is more commonly used. On the Celsius scale, water boils at 100 °C and freezes at 0 °C. The SI unit of heat is the **joule (J)**. A more familiar unit, the **calorie (cal)**, is the amount of heat needed to raise the temperature of 1 g of water by 1 °C. The food "calorie" is actually a **kilocalorie (kcal)**, or 1000 calories.

Section 1.12—Claims may be tested by applying critical thinking. The acronym **FLaReS** represents four principles used to test a claim: *falsifiability, logic, replicability,* and *sufficiency.*

Green chemistry Green chemistry means preventing waste, using nonhazardous chemicals and renewable resources, conserving energy, and making products that degrade after use. Developed about 20 years ago, green chemistry takes into account the sources and ultimate destinations of chemicals, and the impact they will have on humans and the planet.

Learning Objectives

❭ Distinguish science from technology. (1.1)	Problem 1
❭ Define *alchemy* and *natural philosophy.* (1.1)	Problems 43, 44
❭ Briefly describe the contributions of Bacon, Galileo, and Carson to the perceptions of science. (1.2)	Problem 2
❭ Define *hypothesis, scientific law, theory,* and *scientific model,* and explain their relationships in science. (1.3)	Problems 3, 71, 72, 74, 75

❭ Define *risk* and *benefit*, and give an example of each. (1.4) Problem 5

❭ Estimate a desirability quotient from benefit and risk data. (1.4) Problems 7, 13–18

❭ Give an example of a use of chemistry in your daily life and in society at large. (1.5) Problems 15, 72

❭ Distinguish basic research from applied research. (1.6) Problems 8, 9

❭ Differentiate: mass and weight; physical and chemical change; and physical and chemical properties. (1.7) Problems 29–32

❭ Classify matter in three ways. (1.8) Problems 33–44

❭ Assign proper units of measurement to observations, and manipulate units in conversions. (1.9) Problems 10–12, 19–28, 45–52, 69, 70, 73, 78–80

❭ Calculate the density, mass, or volume of an object given the other two quantities. (1.10) Problems 53–64, 76, 77, 81–83, 85–88

❭ Distinguish between heat and temperature. (1.11) Problems 67, 68

❭ Explain how the temperature scales are related. (1.11) Problems 65, 66

❭ Use critical thinking to evaluate claims and statements. (1.12) Problem 6, Critical Thinking 1.1–1.6

❭ Define green chemistry. Problem 89

❭ Describe how green chemistry reduces risk and prevents environmental problems. Problems 90–92

REVIEW QUESTIONS

1. State five distinguishing characteristics of science. Which characteristic best serves to distinguish science from other disciplines?

2. Why is Galileo regarded by some as the father of modern science?

3. Why can't scientific methods always be used to solve social, political, ethical, and economic problems?

4. How does technology differ from science?

5. What is risk–benefit analysis?

6. What sorts of judgments go into (a) the evaluation of benefits and (b) the evaluation of risks?

7. What is a DQ? What does a large DQ mean? Why is it often difficult to estimate a DQ?

8. What derived units of (a) mass and (b) length are commonly used in the laboratory?

9. What is the SI-derived unit for volume? What volume units are more often used in the laboratory?

10. Following is an incomplete table of SI prefixes, their symbols, and their meanings. Fill in the blank cells. The first row is completed as an example.

11. Identify the following research projects as either applied or basic.
    a. A Virginia Tech chemist tests a method for analyzing coal powder in less than a minute, before the powder goes into a coal-fired energy plant.
    b. A Purdue engineer develops a method for causing aluminum to react with water to generate hydrogen for automobiles.
    c. A worker at University of Illinois Urbana-Champaign examines the behavior of atoms at high temperatures and low pressures.

12. Identify the following work as either applied research or basic research.
    a. An engineer determines the strength of a titanium alloy that will be used to construct notebook-computer cases.
    b. A biochemist runs experiments to determine how oxygen binds to the blood cells of lobsters.
    c. A biologist determines the number of eagles that nest annually in Kentucky's Land Between the Lakes area over a six-year period.

Prefix	Symbol	Definition
tera-	T	10^{12}
_____	M	_____
centi-	_____	_____
_____	μ	_____
milli-	_____	_____
_____	_____	10^{-1}
_____	K	_____
nano-	_____	_____

PROBLEMS

A Word of Advice You cannot learn to work problems by reading them or by watching your instructor work them, just as you cannot become a piano player solely by reading about piano-playing skills or by attending performances. Working problems will help you improve your understanding of the ideas presented in the chapter and your ability to synthesize concepts as well as allow you to practice your estimation skills. Plan to work through the great majority of these problems.

Risk–Benefit Analysis

13. Penicillin kills bacteria, thus saving the lives of thousands of people who otherwise might die of infectious diseases. Penicillin causes allergic reactions in some people, which can lead to death if the resulting condition is not treated. Do a risk–benefit analysis of the use of penicillin by society as a whole.

14. Do a risk–benefit analysis of the use of penicillin by a person who is allergic to it. (See Problem 13.)

15. Paints used on today's automobiles are often composed of two components and harden several hours after mixing. One component is an *isocyanate* that can sensitize a person, causing an allergic reaction, if it is breathed (even in small amounts) over a long time period. Do a risk-benefit analysis of the use of these paints by **(a)** an automotive factory worker and **(b)** a hobbyist who is restoring a 1965 Mustang. How might the DQ for both of these people be increased?

16. X-rays are widely used in medicine and dentistry. Do a risk-benefit analysis for **(a)** a dental patient who has one set of x-rays done per year and **(b)** a dentist who stays in the room with a patient while x-rays are taken, three times each day.

17. Synthetic food colorings make food more attractive and increase sales. A few such dyes are suspected *carcinogens* (cancer inducers). Who derives most of the benefits from the use of food colorings? Who assumes most of the risk associated with use of these dyes?

18. The virus called HIV causes AIDS, a devastating and often deadly disease. Several drugs are available to treat HIV infection, but all are expensive. Used separately and in combination, these drugs have resulted in a huge drop in AIDS deaths. An expensive new drug shows promise for treating HIV/AIDS patients, especially in preventing passage of the HIV virus from a pregnant woman to her fetus. What is the DQ for administering this drug to **(a)** a man who thinks he may be infected with HIV, **(b)** a pregnant woman who is HIV positive, and **(c)** an unborn child whose mother has AIDS?

Mass and Weight

19. Which are realistic masses for a cellular telephone and a laptop computer, respectively?

    100 mg, 100 g   100 g, 100 mg   100 g, 2 kg   1 kg, 2 kg

20. In Europe, A2 sized paper measures 594 mm × 420 mm. Is this larger or smaller than the standard 8½ in. × 11 in. paper used in the United States?

21. Two samples are weighed under identical conditions in a laboratory. Sample A weighs 1.00 lb and Sample B weighs 2.00 lb. Does Sample B have twice the mass of Sample A?

22. Sample X on the moon has exactly the same mass as Sample Y on Earth. Do the two samples weigh the same? Explain.

Length, Area, and Volume

23. Which of the following is a reasonable volume for a teacup?

    25 mL   250 mL   2.5 L   25 L

24. Which of the following is a reasonable approximation for the area of a credit card?

    4 cm^2 40 cm^2 400 cm^2 4 m^2

25. Earth's oceans contain 3.50×10^8 mi^3 of water and cover an area of 1.40×10^8 mi^2. What is the volume of ocean water in cubic kilometers?

26. What is the area of Earth's oceans in square kilometers? See Problem 25.

27. Consider the two tubes shown below. The aluminum tube has an outside diameter of 0.998 in. and an inside diameter of 0.782 in. Without doing a detailed calculation, determine whether the aluminum tube will fit inside another aluminum tube with an inside diameter of 26.3 mm.

28. Which one(s) of the following could be the inside diameter of the paper tube shown above (with Problem 27): 19.9 mm; 24.9 mm, 18.7 mm?

Physical and Chemical Properties and Changes

29. Identify the following as physical or chemical properties.
    a. Zinc metal can be shaped into many different forms by hammering.
    b. Silver metal tarnishes, forming black silver sulfide.
    c. Sodium metal is soft enough to cut with a butter knife.
    d. Gold melts at 1064 °C.

30. Identify the following as physical or chemical properties.
    a. Milk chocolate melts in the mouth.
    b. A laser printer prints faster than an inkjet printer.
    c. Titanium chips burn with a brilliant white light.
    d. Yogurt is made by allowing a bacterial culture to ferment in warm milk.

31. Identify the following changes as physical or chemical.
  a. Bits of yellow plastic are melted and forced into a mold to make a yellow toy.
  b. Waste oil from restaurants is converted to biodiesel fuel that burns differently from cooking oil.
  c. Orange juice is prepared by adding three cans of water to one can of orange-juice concentrate.

32. Identify the following changes as physical or chemical.
  a. Bacteria are killed by chlorine added to a swimming pool.
  b. Brown print is created in an inkjet printer by mixing cyan, magenta, and yellow inks.
  c. Sugar is dissolved in water to make syrup.

Substances and Mixtures

33. Identify each of the following as a substance or a mixture.
  a. helium gas used to fill a balloon
  b. the juice squeezed from an orange
  c. distilled water
  d. carbon dioxide gas

34. Identify each of the following as a substance or a mixture.
  a. hydrogen peroxide, H_2O_2
  b. oxygen
  c. smog
  d. a carrot
  e. blueberry pancakes
  f. cellophane tape

35. Which of the following mixtures are homogeneous and which are heterogeneous?
  a. copper water pipe   **b.** distilled water
  c. liquid oxygen   **d.** chicken noodle soup

36. Which of the following mixtures are homogeneous and which are heterogeneous?
  a. gasoline
  b. Italian salad dressing
  c. rice pudding
  d. an intravenous glucose solution

37. Every sample of the sugar glucose (no matter where on Earth it comes from) consists of 8 parts (by mass) oxygen, 6 parts carbon, and 1 part hydrogen. Is glucose a substance or a mixture? Explain.

38. An advertisement for shampoo says, "Pure shampoo, with nothing artificial added." Is this shampoo a substance or a mixture? Explain.

Elements and Compounds

39. Which of the following represent elements and which represent compounds?
  a. H   **b.** He   **c.** HF   **d.** Hf

40. Which of the following represent elements and which represent compounds?
  a. Li   **b.** CO   **c.** Cf   **d.** CF_4

41. Without consulting tables, name each of the following.
  a. Al   **b.** Ca   **c.** Cl   **d.** Ag

42. Without consulting tables, write a symbol for each of the following.
  a. oxygen   **b.** phosphorus
  c. sodium   **d.** helium

43. In his 1789 textbook, *Traité élémentaire de Chimie*, Antoine Lavoisier (Chapter 2) listed 33 known elements, one of which was baryte. Which of the following observations best shows that baryte cannot be an element?
  a. Baryte is insoluble in water.
  b. Baryte melts at 1580 °C.
  c. Baryte has a density of 4.48 g/cm^3.
  d. Baryte is formed in hydrothermal veins and around hot springs.
  e. Baryte is formed as a solid when sulfuric acid and barium hydroxide are mixed.
  f. Baryte is formed as a sole product when a particular metal is burned in oxygen.

44. In 1774 Joseph Priestley isolated a gas that he called "dephlogisticated air." Which of the following observations best shows that dephlogisticated air is an element?
  a. Dephlogisticated air combines with charcoal to form "fixed air."
  b. Dephlogisticated air combines with "inflammable air" to form water.
  c. Dephlogisticated air combines with a metal to form a solid called a "calx."
  d. Dephlogisticated air has never been separated into simpler substances.
  e. Dephlogisticated air and "mephitic air" are the main components of the atmosphere.

The Metric System: Measurement and Unit Conversion

45. Change the unit for each of the following measurements by replacing the power of ten with an appropriate SI prefix.
  a. 8.01×10^{-6} g   **b.** 7.9×10^{-3} L
  c. 1.05×10^3 m

46. Use exponential notation to express each of the following measurements in terms of an SI base unit.
  a. 45 mg   **b.** 125 ns   **c.** 10.7 μL

47. Carry out the following conversions.
  a. 37.4 mL to L   **b.** 1.55×10^2 km to m
  c. 0.198 g to mg   **d.** 1.19 m^2 to cm^2
  e. 78 μs to ms

48. Carry out the following conversions.
  a. 546 mm to m
  b. 65 ns to μs
  c. 87.6 mg to kg
  d. 46.3 dm^3 to L
  e. 181 pm to μm

49. Indicate which is the larger unit in each pair.
  a. mm or cm   **b.** kg or g   **c.** dL or μL

50. Indicate which is the larger unit in each pair.
  a. L or cm^3 **b.** dm^3 or mL   **c.** μs or ps

51. How many millimeters are there in 1.00 cm? In 1.83 m?

52. How many milliliters are there in 1.00 cm^3? In 15.3 cm^3?

Density

(You may need data from Table 1.7 for some of these problems.)

53. What is the density, in grams per milliliter, of **(a)** a salt solution if 37.5 mL has a mass of 43.75 g and **(b)** 2.75 L of the liquid glycerol, which has a mass of 3465 g?

54. What is the density, in grams per milliliter, of **(a)** a sulfuric acid solution if 10.00 mL has a mass of 15.04 g and **(b)** a 10.0-cm^3 block of plastic with a mass of 9.23 g?

55. What is the mass, in grams, of **(a)** 125 mL of castor oil, a laxative, which has a density of 0.962 g/mL and **(b)** 477 mL of blood plasma, with $d = 1.027$ g/mL?

56. What is the mass, in grams, of **(a)** 30.0 mL of the liquid propylene glycol, a moisturizing agent for foods, which has a density of 1.036 g/mL at 25 °C and **(b)** 1.000 L of mercury at 25 °C?

57. What is the volume of **(a)** 227 g of hexane (in milliliters) and **(b)** a 454-g block of ice (in cubic centimeters)?

58. What is the volume of **(a)** a 475-g piece of copper (in cubic centimeters) and **(b)** a 253-g sample of mercury (in milliliters)?

59. Suppose you put 40 mL of mercury, 40 mL of hexane, and 80 mL of water in the 250-mL beaker shown here. The three liquids do not mix with one another. Provide a sketch that shows the relative locations and depths of the three liquids in the container.

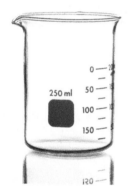

60. A piece of red maple wood ($d = 0.49$ g/cm^3), a piece of balsa wood ($d = 0.11$ g/cm^3), a copper coin, a gold coin, and a piece of ice are dropped into the mixture of Problem 59. Where will each solid end up in the beaker?

61. A metal stand specifies a maximum load of 450 lb. Will it support an aquarium that weighs 59.5 lb and is filled with 37.9 L of seawater ($d = 1.03$ g/mL)?

62. E85 fuel is a mixture of 85% ethanol and 15% gasoline by volume. What mass in kilograms of E85 ($d = 0.758$ g/mL) can be contained in a 14.0-gal tank?

63. An artist wants to produce a pot with a mass of 2.45 kg. She starts with wet clay that loses 10.9% of its mass after firing. The wet clay has a density of 1.60 g/cm^3. What should be the diameter of a sphere of wet clay that she starts with? (*Hint*: The volume of a sphere is $4\pi r^3/3$ where r is the radius.)

64. Air has an average density of about 1.29 g/L. What is the mass in grams of the air inside a car that has a volume of about 2550 L?

Energy: Heat and Temperature

65. Convert 195 K to degrees Celsius.

66. Normal body temperature is about 37 °C. What is this temperature in kelvins?

67. The label on a 100-mL container of orange juice packaged in New Zealand reads in part, "energy . . . 161 kJ." What is that value in kilocalories (food "calories")?

68. To vaporize 1.00 g of sweat (water) from your skin, the water must absorb 584 calories. What is that value in kilojoules?

ADDITIONAL PROBLEMS

69. A certain chemistry class is 1.00 microcentury (µcen) long. What is its length in minutes?

70. A unit of beauty, a *helen*, thought to have been invented by British mathematician W.A.H. Rushton, is based on Helen of Troy (from Christopher Marlowe's translation of Homer's *Iliad*), who is widely known as having "the face that launched a thousand ships." How many ships could be launched by a face with 1.00 millihelen of beauty?

71. English chemist William Henry studied the amounts of gases absorbed by water at different temperatures and under different pressures. In 1803, he stated a formula, $p = k_H c$, which related the concentration of the dissolved gas at a constant temperature to the partial pressure of that gas in equilibrium with that liquid. This relationship describes a scientific

   a. hypothesis
   b. law
   c. observation
   d. theory

72. Which of the following activities involve chemistry?

   a. cooking breakfast
   b. eating breakfast
   c. riding a bicycle to classes
   d. working on a laptop computer
   e. sleeping

73. American writer Cullen Murphy coined a unit of fame, the warhol, based on artist Andy Warhol's claim that "everyone will be famous for fifteen minutes."

    1 warhol = 15 min of fame

    Entertainer Herbert Khaury (stage name Tiny Tim) was famous, starting in 1962, for about 200 kilowarhols. How long was that in years?

For Problems 74 and 75, classify each of the numbered statements as (a) an experiment, (b) a hypothesis, (c) a scientific law, (d) an observation, or (e) a theory. (It is not necessary to understand the science involved to do these problems.)

74. Many scientific advances of the nineteenth century came from the study of gases. (1) For example, Joseph Gay-Lussac reacted hydrogen and oxygen to produce water vapor and he reacted nitrogen and oxygen to form either dinitrogen oxide (N_2O) or nitrogen monoxide (NO). Gay-Lussac found that hydrogen and oxygen react in a 2:1 volume ratio and that nitrogen and oxygen can react in 2:1 or 1:1 volume ratios, depending on the product. (2) In 1808 Gay-Lussac published a paper in which he stated that the relative volumes of gases in a chemical reaction are present in the ratio of small integers provided that all gases are measured at the same temperature and pressure. (3) In 1811 Amedeo Avogadro proposed that equal volumes of all gases measured at the same temperature and pressure contain the same number of molecules. (4) By the middle of the century, Rudolf Clausius, James Clerk Maxwell, and others had developed a detailed rationalization of the behavior of gases in terms of molecular motions.

75. Potassium bromate acts as a conditioner in flour dough. Flour contains a protein called *gluten.* Proteins consist of amino-acid units linked in long chains. (1) Dough to which potassium bromate has been added rises better, producing a lighter, larger volume loaf. (2) Potassium bromate acts by oxidizing the gluten and cross-linking tyrosine (an amino acid) units of the protein molecules, enabling the dough to retain gas better. (3) A scientist wonders if sodium bromate might cross-link separate tyrosine molecules, forming a dimer (a molecule consisting of two subunits). (4) She adds sodium bromate to a solution of tyrosine. (5) She notes that a precipitate (solid falling out of solution) is formed.

76. A glass container weighs 48.462 g. A sample of 8.00 mL of antifreeze solution is added, and the container and the antifreeze together weigh 60.562 g. Calculate the density of the antifreeze solution.

77. A rectangular block of balsa wood ($d = 0.11 \text{ g/cm}^3$) measures 7.6 cm × 7.6 cm × 94 cm. What is the mass of the block in grams?

78. Arrange the following in order of increasing length (shortest first): (1) a 1.21-m chain, (2) a 75-in. board, (3) a 3-ft 5-in. rattlesnake, (4) a yardstick.

79. Arrange the following in order of increasing mass (lightest first): (1) a 5-lb bag of potatoes, (2) a 1.65-kg cabbage, (3) 2500 g of sugar.

80. One of the people in the photo has a mass of 47.2 kg and a height of 1.53 m. Which one is it likely to be?

81. Some metal chips having a volume of 3.29 cm³ are placed on a piece of paper and weighed. The combined mass is found to be 18.43 g. The paper itself weighs 1.21 g. Calculate the density of the metal.

82. A 10.5-inch (26.7-cm) iron skillet has a mass of 7.00 lb (3180 g). How many cubic centimeters of iron does it contain? (See Table 1.7.)

83. A 5.79-mg piece of gold is hammered into gold leaf of uniform thickness with an area of 44.6 cm². What is the thickness of the gold leaf? (See Table 1.7.)

84. Suppose that you were assigned to determine the effect of saturated fat intake in mice. List three specific variables that would exist in such an experiment, and suggest a way to minimize each variable.

85. What is the mass, in metric tons, of a cube of gold that is 36.1 cm on each side? (1 metric ton = 1000 kg) (See Table 1.7.)

86. A collection of gold-colored metal beads has a mass of 425 g. The volume of the beads is found to be 48.0 cm³. Using the given densities and those in Table 1.7, identify the metal: bronze ($d = 9.87 \text{ g/cm}^3$), copper, gold, or nickel silver ($d = 8.86 \text{ g/cm}^3$).

87. The density of a planet can be approximated from its radius and estimated mass. Calculate the approximate average density, in grams per cubic centimeter, of **(a)** Jupiter, which has a radius of about 7.0×10^4 km and a mass of 1.9×10^{27} kg; **(b)** Earth, radius of 6.4×10^3 km and mass of 5.98×10^{24} kg; and **(c)** Saturn, radius 5.82×10^4 km and mass of 5.68×10^{26} kg. The volume of a sphere is $4\pi r^3/3$ where r = radius. How does the density of each planet compare to that of water?

88. The extrasolar planet HAT-P-1 orbits a star 450 light-years from Earth. The planet has about half the mass of Jupiter, and its radius is about 1.38 times that of Jupiter (see Problem 87). Calculate the approximate average density, in grams per cubic centimeter, of HAT-P-1. How does this density compare to that of water?

89. Define green chemistry.
90. List six of the Twelve Principles of Green Chemistry.
91. How does green chemistry reduce risk? (choose one)
    a. by reducing hazard and exposure
    b. by avoiding the use of chemicals
    c. by increasing exposures to higher levels
    d. by reducing human errors

92. For companies implementing green chemistry, how does green chemistry save money?
    a. by lowering costs
    b. by using less energy
    c. by creating less waste
    d. all of the above

COLLABORATIVE GROUP PROJECTS

Prepare a PowerPoint, poster, or other presentation (as directed by your instructor) to share with the class.

1. The Global University Leadership Forum has developed a Sustainable Campus Charter by which a school's core mission is aligned with sustainable development, facilities, research, and education. Is your school committed to sustainability? If so, in what way is it working toward sustainability? If not, consult with administrative, faculty, and student groups on how to get such a program started.

2. Prepare a brief biographical report on one of the following.
   a. Francis Bacon
   b. Rachel Carson
   c. Galileo
   d. George Washington Carver

(The following problem is best done in a group of four students.)

3. Make copies of the following form. Student 1 should write a word from the list in the first column of the form and its definition in the second column. Then, she or he should fold the first column under to hide the word and pass the sheet to Student 2, who uses the definition to determine what word was defined and place that word in the third column. Student 2 then folds the second column under to hide it and passes the sheet to Student 3, who writes a definition for the word in the third column and then folds the third column under and passes the form to Student 4. Finally, Student 4 writes the word corresponding to the definition given by Student 3.

Compare the word in the last column with that in the first column. Discuss any differences in the two definitions. If the word in the last column differs from that in the first column, determine what went wrong in the process.
   a. hypothesis   b. theory
   c. mixture   d. substance

Text Entry	Student 1	Student 2	Student 3	Student 4
Word	Definition	Word	Definition	Word

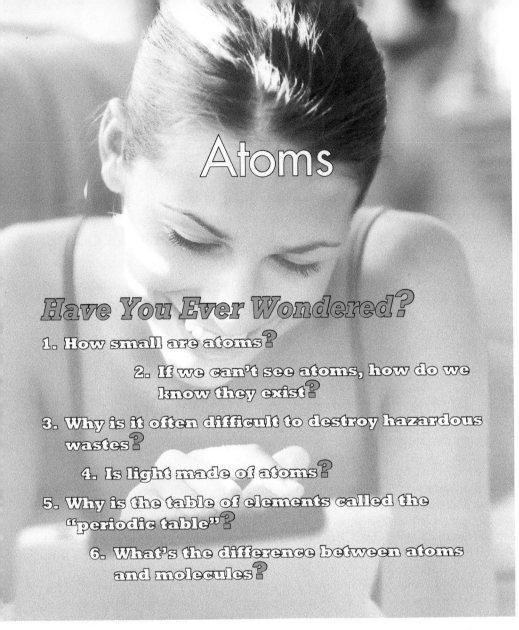

Atoms

Have You Ever Wondered?

1. How small are atoms?

2. If we can't see atoms, how do we know they exist?

3. Why is it often difficult to destroy hazardous wastes?

4. Is light made of atoms?

5. Why is the table of elements called the "periodic table"?

6. What's the difference between atoms and molecules?

Are They for Real?

We hear something about atoms almost every day. The twentieth century saw the start of the so-called Atomic Age. The terms *atomic power*, *atomic energy*, and *atomic bomb* are a part of our ordinary vocabulary. But just what are atoms?

Every material thing in the world is made up of atoms, tiny particles that are much, much too small to see even with the finest optical microscope. The smallest speck of matter that can be detected by the human eye is made up of many billions of atoms. There are more than 10^{22} (10,000,000,000,000,000,000,000) atoms in a penny. Imagine that the

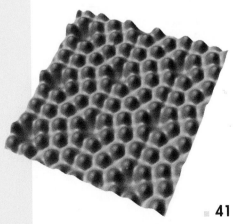

At the heart of every tablet computer (above), printer, telephone, television, MP3 player, and virtually every other electronic device lies a wafer of silicon (above right) in one or more integrated circuits (ICs or "chips"). The silicon used for electronics must be so pure that these devices were not possible until zone-refining purification was developed, about sixty years ago. Silicon is an *element*, made of a single type of atom. For making ICs, only about one atom of impurity can be present for every billion atoms of silicon. But how do we even know that atoms exist? The false-color image at the right shows individual silicon atoms in a hexagonal arrangement, using a recently developed technique called *scanning tunneling microscopy*. However, the behavior of matter led scientists to the atomic nature of matter over two hundred years ago. In this chapter, we will see some of that history, and we will explore the properties of atoms.

1. How small are atoms? Atoms are so small that the smallest particle of matter visible to your eye contains more atoms than you could count in a lifetime!

atoms in a penny were enlarged until they were barely visible, like tiny grains of sand. The atoms in a single penny would then make enough "sand" to cover the entire state of Texas several feet deep. Comparing an atom to a penny is like comparing a grain of sand to a Texas-size sandbox.

Why should we care about something as tiny as an atom? Because our world is made up of atoms, and atoms are a part of all we do. *Everything* is made of atoms, including you and me. And because chemistry is the study of the behavior of matter, it observes the behavior of atoms. The behavior and interactions of atoms determine the behavior and interactions of matter.

Atoms are not all alike. Each element has its own kind of atom. On Earth, about 90 elements occur in nature. About two dozen more have been synthesized by scientists. As far as we know, the entire universe is made up of these same few elements. An **atom** is the smallest particle that is characteristic of a given element.

▲ A marble statue of Democritus, who first formulated the atomic nature of matter.

2.1 Atoms: Ideas from the Ancient Greeks

Learning Objective ❯ Explain the ancient Greeks' ideas about the characteristics of matter.

A pool of water can be separated into drops, and then each drop can be split into smaller and smaller drops. Suppose that you could keep splitting the drops into still smaller ones even after they became much too small to see. Would you ever reach a point at which a tiny drop could no longer be separated into smaller droplets of water? Is water infinitely divisible, or would you eventually come to a particle that, if divided, would no longer be water?

The Greek philosopher Leucippus, who lived in the fifth century B.C.E., and his pupil Democritus (ca. 460–ca. 370 B.C.E.) might well have discussed this question as they strolled along the beach by the Aegean Sea. Leucippus reasoned that there must ultimately be tiny particles of water that could not be divided further. After all, from a distance the sand on the beach looked continuous, but closer inspection showed it to be made up of tiny grains (Figure 2.1).

Democritus expanded on Leucippus's idea. He called the particles *atomos* (meaning "cannot be cut"), from which we derive the modern name *atom* for the tiny, discrete particle of an element. Democritus thought that each kind of atom was distinct in shape and size (Figure 2.2). He thought that real substances were

▶ **Figure 2.1** A sandy beach.

Q: *Sand looks continuous—infinitely divisible—when you look at a beach from a distance. Is it really continuous? Water looks continuous, even when viewed up close. Is it really continuous? Is a cloud continuous? Is air?*

mixtures of various kinds of atoms. The Greeks at that time believed that there were four basic elements: earth, air, fire, and water. These "elements" were related by four "principles"—hot, moist, dry, and cold—as shown in Figure 2.3. These ideas seem strange to us today, but they persisted for two millennia.

Four centuries after Democritus, the Roman poet Lucretius (ca. 95–ca. 55 B.C.E.) wrote a long didactic poem (a poem meant to teach), *On the Nature of Things*, in which he presented strong arguments for the atomic nature of matter. Unfortunately, a few centuries earlier, the famous Greek philosopher Aristotle (ca. 384–ca. 322 B.C.E.) had declared that matter was continuous (infinitely divisible) rather than discrete (consisting of tiny indivisible particles). The people of that time had no way to determine which view was correct. To most of them, Aristotle's continuous view of matter seemed more logical and reasonable, and so it prevailed for 2000 years, even though it was wrong.

Self-Assessment Questions

1. Consider how the qualities *discrete* and *continuous* apply to materials at the macroscopic (visible to the unaided eye) level. Which of the following is continuous?
   a. apple juice
   b. a ream of paper
   c. a bowl of cherries
   d. chocolate chips

2. The view that matter is continuous rather than atomic prevailed for centuries because it was
   a. actually correct
   b. not considered important
   c. not tested by experiment
   d. tested and found to be true

Answers: 1, a; 2, c

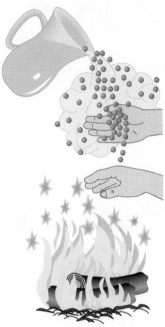

▲ **Figure 2.2** Democritus imagined that "atoms" of water might be smooth, round balls and that atoms of fire might have sharp edges.

2.2 Scientific Laws: Conservation of Mass and Definite Proportions

Learning Objectives ❯ Describe the significance of the laws of conservation of mass and definite proportions. ❯ Calculate the amounts of elements from the composition of a compound.

The eighteenth century saw the triumph of careful observation and measurement in chemistry. Antoine Lavoisier (1743–1794) perhaps did more than anyone to establish chemistry as a quantitative science. He found that when a chemical reaction was carried out in a closed container, the total mass of the system was not changed. Perhaps the most important chemical reaction that Lavoisier performed was decomposition of a red compound containing mercury to form metallic mercury and a gas he named *oxygen*. Both Carl Wilhelm Scheele (1742–1786), a Swedish apothecary, and Joseph Priestley (1733–1804), a Unitarian minister who later fled England and settled in America in 1794, had carried out the same reaction earlier, but Lavoisier was the first to weigh all the substances present before and after the reaction. He was also the first to interpret the reaction correctly.

The Law of Conservation of Mass

Lavoisier carried out many quantitative experiments. He found that when coal was burned, it united with oxygen to form carbon dioxide. He experimented with animals, observing that when a guinea pig breathed, oxygen was consumed and carbon dioxide was formed. Lavoisier therefore concluded that respiration was related

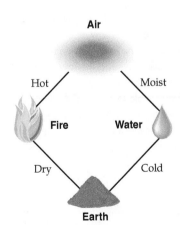

▲ **Figure 2.3** The Greek view of matter was that there were only four elements (in bold) connected by four "principles."

▲ The work of Antoine Lavoisier marked the beginning of chemistry as a quantitative science. Here, Lavoisier is shown with his wife, Marie, in a painting by Jacques Louis David in 1788.

100.00 grams of mercuric oxide

92.61 grams of mercury

7.39 grams of oxygen

| 100.00 | = | 92.61 | + | 7.39 |

▲ **Figure 2.4** Although mercuric oxide (a red solid) has none of the properties of mercury (a silver liquid) or oxygen (a colorless gas), when 100.00 g of mercuric oxide is decomposed by heating, the products are 92.61 g of mercury and 7.39 g of oxygen. Properties are completely changed in this reaction, but there is no change in mass.

Q: *When 10.00 g of mercuric oxide decomposes, 0.739 g of oxygen forms. What mass of mercury forms?*

to combustion. In each of these reactions, he found that matter was *conserved*—the amount remained constant.

Lavoisier summarized his findings as the **law of conservation of mass**, which states that matter is neither created nor destroyed during a chemical change (Figure 2.4). The total mass of the reaction products is always equal to the total mass of the reactants (starting materials). We will discuss chemical reactions in more detail beginning with Chapter 4. For now, some simple examples and discussion will illustrate the conservation of mass.

Scientists by this time had abandoned the Greek idea of the four elements and were almost universally using Robert Boyle's working definition of an element presented in his book *The Sceptical Chymist* (published in 1661). Boyle said that a supposed *element* must be tested. If a substance could be broken down into simpler substances, it was not an element. The simpler substances might be elements and should be regarded as such until the time (if it ever came) when they in turn could be broken down into still simpler substances. On the other hand, two or more elements might combine to form a more complex substance called a *compound*.

Using Boyle's definition, Lavoisier included a table of elements in his book *Elementary Treatise on Chemistry*. (The table included some substances that we now know to be compounds, as well as light and heat, which are actually forms of energy.) Lavoisier was the first to use systematic names for chemical elements. He is often called the "father of modern chemistry," and his book is usually regarded as the first chemistry textbook.

The law of conservation of mass is the basis for many chemical calculations. This law states that we cannot create materials from nothing. We can make new materials only by changing the way atoms are combined. For example, we can obtain iron metal from iron ore only because the ore contains iron atoms. Furthermore, we cannot get rid of wastes by the destruction of matter. We must put wastes somewhere. However, through chemical reactions, we can change some kinds of potentially hazardous wastes to less harmful forms. Such transformations of matter from one form to another are what chemistry is all about.

2. If we can't see atoms, how do we know they exist?
If matter had no "smallest particles," the law of conservation of mass, the law of definite proportions, and the law of multiple proportions would be almost impossible to explain. Atomic theory provides a simple explanation for these laws and for many others.

The Law of Definite Proportions

By the end of the eighteenth century, Lavoisier and other scientists noted that many substances were compounds, composed of two or more elements. Each compound had the same elements in the same proportions, regardless of where

(a) (b) (c)

▲ **Figure 2.5** The compound known as *basic copper carbonate* has the formula $Cu_2(OH)_2CO_3$ and occurs in nature as the mineral *malachite* **(a)**. It is formed as a patina on copper roofs **(b)**. It can also be synthesized in the laboratory **(c)**. Regardless of its source, basic copper carbonate always has the same composition. Analysis of this compound led Proust to formulate the law of definite proportions.

it came from or who prepared it. The painstaking work of Joseph Louis Proust (1754–1826) convinced most chemists of the general validity of these observations. In one set of experiments, for example, Proust found that basic copper carbonate, whether prepared in the laboratory or obtained from natural sources, was always composed of 57.48% by mass copper, 5.43% carbon, 0.91% hydrogen, and 36.18% oxygen (Figure 2.5).

To summarize these and many other experiments, Proust formulated a new scientific law in 1799. The **law of definite proportions** states that a compound always contains the same elements in certain definite proportions and in no others. (This generalization is also sometimes called the *law of constant composition*.)

An early illustration of the law of definite proportions is found in the work of the noted Swedish chemist J. J. Berzelius, illustrated in Figure 2.6. Berzelius heated a quantity (say, 10.00 g) of lead with various amounts of sulfur to form lead sulfide. Lead is a soft, grayish metal, and sulfur is a yellow solid. Lead sulfide is a shiny, black solid. Therefore, it was easy to tell when all the lead had reacted. Excess sulfur was washed away with carbon disulfide, a solvent that dissolves sulfur but not lead sulfide. As long as he used at least 1.55 g of sulfur with 10.00 g of lead, Berzelius got exactly 11.55 g of lead sulfide. Any sulfur in excess of 1.55 g was left over; it did not react. If Berzelius used more than 10.00 g of lead with 1.55 g of sulfur, he got 11.55 g of lead sulfide, with some lead left over.

▲ Jöns Jacob Berzelius (1779–1848) was the first person to prepare an extensive list of atomic weights. Published in 1828, it agrees remarkably well with most of today's accepted values.

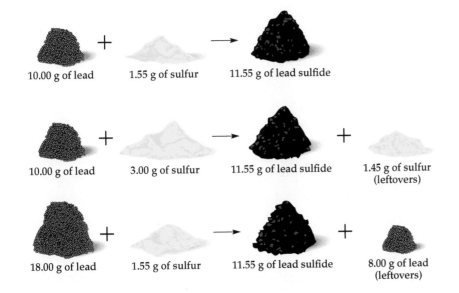

10.00 g of lead + 1.55 g of sulfur → 11.55 g of lead sulfide

10.00 g of lead + 3.00 g of sulfur → 11.55 g of lead sulfide + 1.45 g of sulfur (leftovers)

18.00 g of lead + 1.55 g of sulfur → 11.55 g of lead sulfide + 8.00 g of lead (leftovers)

◀ **Figure 2.6** An example showing how Berzelius's experiments illustrate the law of definite proportions.

Q: *What mass of sulfur can react completely with 20.00 g of lead? What mass of lead sulfide forms?*

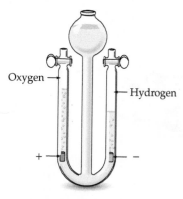

Oxygen —

— Hydrogen

+ —

▲ **Figure 2.7** Electrolysis of water. Hydrogen and oxygen are always produced in a volume ratio of 2:1.

Q: *If 24 cubic feet of hydrogen gas is produced by electrolysis, how much oxygen gas will be produced?*

The law of definite proportions is further illustrated by the electrolysis of water. In 1783, Henry Cavendish (1731–1810), a wealthy, eccentric English nobleman, found that water forms when hydrogen burns in oxygen. (It was Lavoisier, however, who correctly interpreted the experiment and who first used the names *hydrogen* and *oxygen*.) Later, in 1800, the English chemists William Nicholson and Anthony Carlisle decomposed water into hydrogen and oxygen gases by passing an electric current through the water (Figure 2.7). (The Italian scientist Alessandro Volta had invented the chemical battery only six weeks earlier.) The two gases are always produced in a 2:1 volume ratio. Although this is a volume ratio and Berzelius's experiment gave a mass ratio, both substantiate the law of definite proportions. This scientific law led to rapid developments in chemistry and dealt a death blow to the ancient Greek idea of water as an element.

The law of definite proportions is the basis for chemical formulas (Chapter 4), such as H_2O for water. Constant composition also means that substances have constant properties. Pure water always dissolves salt or sugar, and at normal pressure it always freezes at 0 °C and boils at 100 °C.

Self-Assessment Questions

1. In any chemical change, compared to the mass of the reactants, the mass of the products is
   a. always equal
   b. always greater
   c. always less
   d. often different

2. In an experiment in which 36.04 g of liquid water is decomposed into hydrogen gas and oxygen gas, the total mass of the products is
   a. 0 g
   b. 18.02 g
   c. 36.04 g
   d. uncertain

3. The ancient Greeks thought that water was an element. In 1800, Nicholson and Carlisle decomposed water into hydrogen and oxygen. Their experiment proved that
   a. electricity causes decomposition
   b. the Greeks were correct
   c. hydrogen and oxygen are elements
   d. water is not an element

4. The fact that salt (sodium chloride) from any place on Earth is always 39.34% sodium and 60.66% chlorine by mass illustrates
   a. Dalton's atomic theory
   b. Democritus's atomic theory
   c. the law of definite proportions
   d. the law of conservation of mass

5. Ammonia produced in an industrial plant contains 3.0 kg of hydrogen for every 14.0 kg of nitrogen. The ammonia dissolved in a window-cleaning preparation contains 30.0 g of hydrogen for every 140.0 g of nitrogen. What law does this illustrate?
   a. Dalton's atomic theory
   b. Democritus's atomic theory
   c. the law of definite proportions
   d. the law of conservation of mass

6. When 60.0 g of carbon is burned in 160.0 g of oxygen, 220.0 g of carbon dioxide is formed. What mass of carbon dioxide is formed when 60.0 g of carbon is burned in 750.0 g of oxygen?
   a. 60.0 g
   b. 160.0 g
   c. 220.0 g
   d. 810.0 g

2.3 John Dalton and the Atomic Theory of Matter

Learning Objectives ❯ Explain why the idea that matter is made of atoms is a theory.
❯ Understand how atomic theory explains the law of conservation of mass.

Lavoisier's law of conservation of mass and Proust's law of definite proportions were repeatedly verified by experiment. This work led to attempts to develop theories to explain these laws.

In 1803, John Dalton, an English schoolteacher, proposed a model to explain the accumulating experimental data. By this time, the composition of a number of substances was known with a fair degree of accuracy. (To avoid confusion, we will use modern values, terms, and examples rather than those actually used by Dalton.) For example, all samples of water have an oxygen-to-hydrogen mass ratio of 7.94:1.00. Similarly, all samples of ammonia have a nitrogen-to-hydrogen mass ratio of 4.63:1.00 (14:3). Dalton explained these unvarying ratios by assuming that matter is made of atoms.

As Dalton continued his work, he discovered another law that his theory would have to explain. Proust had stated that a compound contains elements in certain proportions and only those proportions. Dalton's new law, called the **law of multiple proportions**, stated that elements might combine in *more* than one set of proportions, with each set corresponding to a different compound. For example, carbon combines with oxygen in a mass ratio of 1.00:2.66 (or 3.00:8.00) to form carbon dioxide, a gas that is a product of respiration and of the burning of coal or wood. But Dalton found that carbon also combines with oxygen in a mass ratio of 1.00:1.33 (or 3.00:4.00) to form carbon monoxide, a poisonous gas produced when a fuel is burned in the presence of a limited air supply.

Dalton then used his **atomic theory** to explain the various laws. Following are the important points of Dalton's atomic theory, with some modern modifications that we will consider later.

▲ John Dalton (1766–1844), who, in addition to developing the atomic theory, carried out important investigations of the behavior of gases. All of his contributions to science were made in spite of the fact that he was color-blind.

Dalton's Atomic Theory	Modern Modifications
1. All matter is composed of extremely small particles called atoms.	1. Dalton assumed atoms to be indivisible. This isn't quite true, as we will see in Chapter 3.
2. All atoms of a given element are alike, but atoms of a given element differ from the atoms of any other element.	2. Dalton assumed that all the atoms of a given element were identical in all respects, including mass. We now know this to be incorrect, as we will see on page 48.
3. Compounds are formed when atoms of different elements combine in fixed proportions.	3. Unmodified. The numbers of each kind of atom in simple compounds usually form a simple ratio. For example, the ratio of carbon atoms to oxygen atoms is 1:1 in carbon monoxide and 1:2 in carbon dioxide.
4. A chemical reaction involves a *rearrangement* of atoms. No atoms are created, destroyed, or broken apart in a chemical reaction.	4. Unmodified for *chemical* reactions. Atoms are broken apart in *nuclear* reactions. We will discuss chemical reactions in Chapter 5 and nuclear reactions in Chapter 11.

3. Why is it often difficult to destroy hazardous wastes?
Hazardous wastes that are compounds or mixtures can be converted to other compounds or mixtures—but the elements from those compounds or mixtures are still present and may be hazardous as well. For example, insecticide containing arsenic oxide can be broken down into the elements arsenic and oxygen—but the element arsenic is poisonous and can't be broken down into something else.

Explanations Using Atomic Theory

Dalton's theory clearly explains the difference between elements and compounds. *Elements* are composed of only one kind of atom. For example, a sample of the element phosphorus contains only phosphorus atoms. *Compounds* are made up of two

▶ **Figure 2.8** The law of definite proportions and the law of conservation of mass interpreted in terms of Dalton's atomic theory.

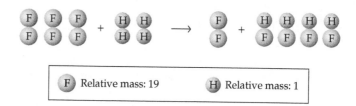

(F) Relative mass: 19	(H) Relative mass: 1

Q: *If 20 molecules of fluorine and 28 molecules of hydrogen react, how many molecules of HF can form? Which element is left over? How many molecules of the leftover element are there?*

or more kinds of atoms chemically combined in definite proportions. (We will see exactly what *kind* means in Section 3.5.)

Dalton set up a table of relative atomic masses based on hydrogen having a mass of 1. Many of Dalton's atomic masses were inaccurate, as we might expect because of the equipment available at that time. The masses we use today are relative atomic masses, usually called simply *atomic masses*. Historically, these relative masses were determined by comparison with a standard mass, a technique called *weighing*. For this historical reason, these relative masses are often called *atomic weights*. You will find a table of atomic masses on the inside front cover of this book. We will use these modern values in some examples showing how Dalton's atomic theory explains the various laws.

To explain the law of definite proportions, Dalton's reasoning went something like this: Why should 1.0 g of hydrogen always combine with 19 g of fluorine? Why shouldn't 1.0 g of hydrogen also combine with 18 g, or 20 g, or any other mass of fluorine? If an atom of fluorine has a mass 19 times that of a hydrogen atom, the compound formed by the union of one atom of each element would have to consist of 1 part by mass of hydrogen and 19 parts by mass of fluorine. Matter must be atomic for the law of definite proportions to be valid (Figure 2.8).

Atomic theory also explains the law of conservation of mass. When fluorine atoms combine with hydrogen atoms to form hydrogen fluoride, the atoms are merely rearranged. Matter is neither lost nor gained; the mass does not change.

Finally, atomic theory explains the law of multiple proportions. For example, 1.00 g of carbon combines with 1.33 g of oxygen to form carbon monoxide or with 2.66 g of oxygen to form carbon dioxide. Carbon dioxide has twice the mass of oxygen per gram of carbon as carbon monoxide does. This is because one atom of carbon combines with *one* atom of oxygen to form carbon monoxide, whereas one atom of carbon combines with *two* atoms of oxygen to form carbon dioxide.

Using modern values, we assign an oxygen atom a relative mass of 16.0 and a carbon atom a relative mass of 12.0. One atom of carbon combined with one atom of oxygen (in carbon monoxide) means a mass ratio of 12.0 parts carbon to 16.0 parts oxygen, or 3.00 : 4.00. One atom of carbon combined with two atoms of oxygen (in carbon dioxide) gives a mass ratio of 12.0 parts carbon to 2 × 16.0 = 32.0 parts oxygen, or 3.00 : 8.00. Because all oxygen atoms have the same average mass, and all carbon atoms have the same average mass, the ratio of oxygen in carbon dioxide to oxygen in carbon monoxide is 8.00 to 4.00 or 2:1. The same law holds true for other compounds formed from the same two elements. Table 2.1 shows another example of the law of multiple proportions, involving nitrogen and oxygen.

Dalton also invented a set of symbols (Figure 2.9) to represent the different kinds of atoms. These symbols have since been replaced by modern symbols of one or two letters (inside front cover).

▲ **It DOES Matter!**

A molecule with one carbon (C) atom and two oxygen (O) atoms is carbon dioxide (CO_2), a gas that you exhale and that provides the "fizz" in soft drinks. Cooled to about −80 °C, it becomes dry ice (shown above), used to keep items frozen during shipping. But a molecule with one less O atom is deadly carbon monoxide, CO. Just 0.2% CO in the air is enough to kill. Unfortunately, most fuels produce a little CO when they burn, which is why a car engine should never be left running in a closed garage.

Isotopes: Atoms of an Element with Different Masses

As we have noted, Dalton's second assumption, that all atoms of an element are alike, has been modified. Atoms of an element can have different masses, and such atoms are called *isotopes*. For example, most carbon atoms have a relative atomic

Table 2.1 The Law of Multiple Proportions

Compound	Representation[a]	Mass of N per 1.000 g of O	Ratio of the Masses of N[b]
Nitrous oxide	●●◯	1.750 g	$(1.750 \div 0.4375) = 4.000$
Nitric oxide	●◯	0.8750 g	$(0.8750 \div 0.4375) = 2.000$
Nitrogen dioxide	●◯◯	0.4375 g	$(0.4375 \div 0.4375) = 1.000$

[a] ● = nitrogen atom and ◯ = oxygen atom

[b] We obtain the ratio of the masses of N that combine with a given mass of O by dividing each quantity in the third column by the smallest (0.4375 g).

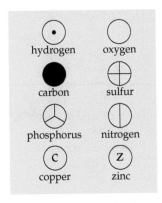

▲ **Figure 2.9** Some of Dalton's symbols for the elements.

Q: *Using Dalton's symbols, draw diagrams for sulfur dioxide and sulfur trioxide. (Place the sulfur atom in the center and arrange the oxygen atoms around it.) What law do these two compounds illustrate?*

mass of 12 (carbon-12), but 1.1% of carbon atoms have a relative atomic mass of 13 (carbon-13). We discuss isotopes in more detail in Chapter 3.

Problem Solving: Mass and Atom Ratios

We can use proportions, such as those determined by Dalton, to calculate the amount of a substance needed to combine with (or form) a given quantity of another substance. To learn how to do this, let's look at some examples.

CONCEPTUAL Example 2.1 | Mass Ratios

Hydrogen gas for fuel cells can be made by decomposing *methane* (CH_4), the main component of natural gas. The decomposition gives carbon (C) and hydrogen (H) in a ratio of 3.00 parts by mass of carbon to 1.00 part by mass of hydrogen. How much hydrogen can be made from 90.0 g of methane?

Solution

We can express the ratio of parts by mass in any units we choose—pounds, grams, kilograms—as long as it is the same for both elements. Using grams as the units, we see that 3.00 g of C and 1.00 g of H would be produced if 4.00 g of CH_4 were decomposed. To convert g CH_4 to g H, we need a conversion factor that includes 1.00 g H and 4.00 g CH_4.

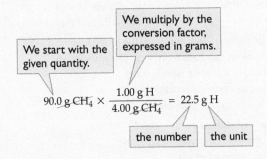

We start with the given quantity.

We multiply by the conversion factor, expressed in grams.

$$90.0 \text{ g } CH_4 \times \frac{1.00 \text{ g H}}{4.00 \text{ g } CH_4} = 22.5 \text{ g H}$$

the number   the unit

■ EXERCISE 2.1A

The gas ammonia can be decomposed to give 3.00 parts by mass of hydrogen and 14.0 parts by mass of nitrogen. What mass of nitrogen is obtained if 10.2 g of ammonia is decomposed?

■ EXERCISE 2.1B

Nitrous oxide, sometimes called "laughing gas," can be decomposed to give 7.00 parts by mass of nitrogen and 4.00 parts by mass of oxygen. What mass of nitrogen is obtained if enough nitrous oxide is decomposed to yield 36.0 g of oxygen?

4. Is light made of atoms? Light is not matter and is not made of atoms. Light is a form of *energy.* Energy—including chemical energy, electrical energy, and nuclear energy—is defined as the ability to do work. We will learn more about energy in Chapter 15.

CONCEPTUAL Example 2.2 Atom Ratios

Hydrogen sulfide gas can be decomposed to give sulfur and hydrogen in a mass ratio of 16.0:1.00. If the relative mass of sulfur is 32.0 when the mass of hydrogen is taken to be 1.00, how many hydrogen atoms are combined with each sulfur atom in the gas?

Solution

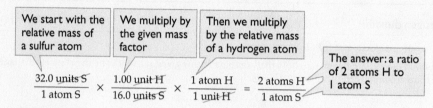

We start with the relative mass of a sulfur atom   We multiply by the given mass factor   Then we multiply by the relative mass of a hydrogen atom   The answer: a ratio of 2 atoms H to 1 atom S

$$\frac{32.0 \text{ units S}}{1 \text{ atom S}} \times \frac{1.00 \text{ unit H}}{16.0 \text{ units S}} \times \frac{1 \text{ atom H}}{1 \text{ unit H}} = \frac{2 \text{ atoms H}}{1 \text{ atom S}}$$

■ **EXERCISE 2.2**

Phosphine gas can be decomposed to give phosphorus and hydrogen in a mass ratio of 10.3:1.00. If the relative mass of phosphorus is 31.0 when the mass of hydrogen is taken to be 1.00, how many hydrogen atoms are combined with each phosphorus atom in the gas?

Despite some inaccuracies, Dalton's atomic theory was a great success. Why? Because it served—and still serves—to explain a large amount of experimental data. It also successfully predicted how matter would behave under a wide variety of circumstances. Dalton arrived at his atomic theory by basing his reasoning on experimental findings, and with modest modification, the theory has stood the test of time and of modern, highly sophisticated instrumentation. Formulation of so successful a theory was quite a triumph for a Quaker schoolteacher in 1803.

Self-Assessment Questions

1. Two compounds, ethylene and acetylene, both contain only carbon and hydrogen. A sample of acetylene contains 92.26 g of C and 7.74 g H. An ethylene sample contains 46.13 g of C and 7.74 g H. If the formula for acetylene is C_2H_2, the formula for ethylene is
   a. CH   **b.** C_2H
   c. CH_3 **d.** C_2H_4

2. According to Dalton, elements are distinguished from each other by
   a. density in the solid state   **b.** nuclear charge
   c. shapes of their atoms   **d.** weights of their atoms

3. Dalton postulated that atoms were indestructible to explain why
   a. the same two elements can form more than one compound
   b. no two elements have the same atomic mass
   c. mass is conserved in chemical reactions
   d. nuclear fission (splitting) is impossible

4. Dalton viewed chemical change as
   a. a change of atoms from one type into another
   b. creation and destruction of atoms
   c. a rearrangement of atoms
   d. a transfer of electrons

5. How many types of atoms are present in a given compound?
   a. at least two   **b.** hundreds
   c. three or more   **d.** depends on the mass of the compound

6. Hydrogen and carbon combine in a 4.0:12.0 mass ratio to form methane. If every molecule of methane contains 4 H atoms and 1 C atom, an atom of carbon must have a mass that is
   a. $\frac{4}{12}$ times the mass of a hydrogen atom   **b.** 4 times the mass of a hydrogen atom
   c. $\frac{12}{3}$ times the mass of a hydrogen atom   **d.** 12 times the mass of a hydrogen atom

Questions 7–9 refer to the following figures:

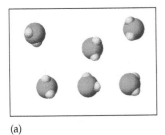
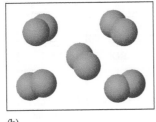
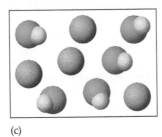

(a)   (b)   (c)

7. Which figure represents an element?
8. Which figure represents a compound?
9. Which figure represents a mixture?

Answers: 1, d; 2, d; 3, c; 4, c; 5, a; 6, d; 7, b; 8, a; 9, c

2.4 Mendeleev and the Periodic Table

Learning Objective ❯ Describe how the elements are arranged in the periodic table and why the arrangement is important.

During the eighteenth and nineteenth centuries, new elements were discovered with surprising frequency. By 1830 there were 55 known elements, all with different properties that demonstrated no apparent order. Dalton had set up a table of relative atomic masses in his 1808 book *A New System of Chemical Philosophy*. Dalton's rough values were improved in subsequent years, notably by Berzelius, who, in 1828, published a table of atomic weights containing 54 elements. Most of Berzelius's values agree well with modern values.

Relative Atomic Masses

Although it was impossible to determine actual masses of atoms in the nineteenth century, chemists were able to determine relative atomic masses by measuring the amounts of various elements that combined with a given mass of another element. Dalton's atomic masses were based on an atomic mass of 1 for hydrogen. As more accurate atomic masses were determined, this standard was replaced by one in which the atomic mass of naturally occurring oxygen was assigned a value of 16.0000. Because the isotopic composition of oxygen varies a bit depending on its source, the oxygen standard was replaced in 1961 by a more logical one based on a single isotope of carbon, carbon-12. Adoption of this new standard caused little change in atomic masses. These relative atomic masses are usually expressed in **atomic mass units (amu)**, commonly referred to today simply as *units* (*u*).

In December 2010, the atomic masses for eleven elements were adjusted slightly. Although their atomic masses had not actually changed, the isotopic composition of these elements varies slightly from location to location. For example, boron's atomic mass is now listed in some sources as 10.806–10.821 u. Most periodic tables still list a single value, however, which is accurate enough for most purposes.

Mendeleev's Periodic Table

Various attempts were made to arrange the elements in some sort of systematic fashion. The most successful arrangement—one that soon became widely accepted by chemists—was published in 1869 by Dmitri Ivanovich Mendeleev (1834–1907), a Russian chemist. Mendeleev's **periodic table** arranged the 63 elements known at the time primarily in order of increasing atomic mass. However, his first consideration in this table was an element's *properties*. He placed silver, gold, and several other

▲ Dmitri Mendeleev, the Russian chemist who arranged the 63 known elements into a periodic table similar to the one we use today, was considered one of the great teachers of his time. Unable to find a suitable chemistry textbook, he wrote his own, *The Principles of Chemistry*. Mendeleev also studied the nature and origin of petroleum and made many other contributions to science. Element 101 is named mendelevium (Md) in his honor.

Tabelle II.

Reihen	Gruppe I. — R^2O	Gruppe II. — RO	Gruppe III. — R^2O^3	Gruppe IV. RH^4 RO^2	Gruppe V. RH^3 R^2O^5	Gruppe VI. RH^2 RO^3	Gruppe VII. RH R^2O^7	Gruppe VIII. — RO^4
1	H = 1							
2	Li = 7	Be = 9,4	B = 11	C = 12	N = 14	O = 16	F = 19	
3	Na = 23	Mg = 24	Al = 27,3	Si = 28	P = 31	S = 32	Cl = 35,5	
4	K = 39	Ca = 40	— = 44	Ti = 48	V = 51	Cr = 52	Mn = 55	Fe = 56, Co = 59, Ni = 59, Cu = 63.
5	(Cu = 63)	Zn = 65	— = 68	— = 72	As = 75	Se = 78	Br = 80	
6	Rb = 85	Sr = 87	?Yt = 88	Zr = 90	Nb = 94	Mo = 96	— = 100	Ru = 104, Rh = 104, Pd = 106, Ag = 108.
7	(Ag = 108)	Cd = 112	In = 113	Sn = 118	Sb = 122	Te = 125	J = 127	
8	Cs = 133	Ba = 137	?Di = 138	?Ce = 140				— — —
9	(—)							
10	—	—	?Er = 178	?La = 180	Ta = 182	W = 184	—	Os = 195, Ir = 197, Pt = 198, Au = 199.
11	(Au = 199)	Hg = 200	Ti = 204	Pb = 207	Bi = 208		—	
12	—	—	—	Th = 231	—	U = 240	—	— — —

der chemischen Elemente.

▲ **Figure 2.10** Mendeleev's periodic table. In this 1898 version, he wrongly "corrected" the atomic weight of tellurium to be less than that of iodine.

metals slightly out of order. This allowed sulfur, selenium, and tellurium, which have similar chemical properties, to appear in the same column. This rearrangement also put iodine in the same column as chlorine and bromine, which it resembles chemically.

To place elements in groups with similar properties, Mendeleev also had to leave gaps in his table. Instead of considering these blank spaces as defects, he boldly predicted the existence of elements yet undiscovered. Further, he even predicted the properties of some of the missing elements. For example, three of the missing elements were soon discovered and named scandium, gallium, and germanium. As can be seen in Table 2.2, Mendeleev's predictions for germanium were amazingly successful. This remarkable predictive value led to wide acceptance of Mendeleev's table.

The modern periodic table (inside front cover) contains 118 elements, some of which have reportedly been observed or synthesized but have not yet been verified or named. Each element is represented by a box in the periodic table, as shown in Figure 2.11. We will discuss the periodic table and its theoretical basis in Chapter 3.

5. Why is the table of elements called the "periodic table"?

Periodic indicates that something occurs regularly. The physical and chemical properties of the elements are periodic. That is, many of those properties are similar for elements in a given column of the table.

26 ◄— atomic number, Z
Fe ◄— chemical symbol
55.847 ◄— atomic mass (weighted average)

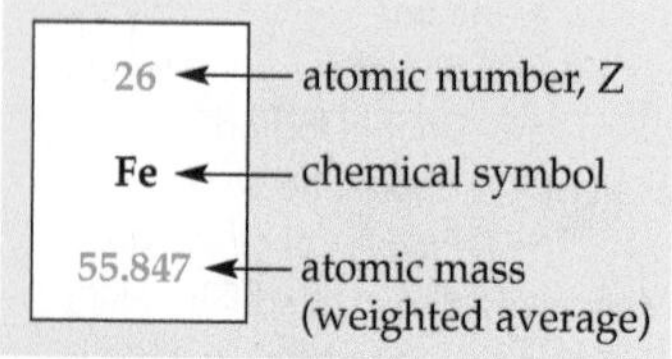

▲ **Figure 2.11** Representation of an element on the modern periodic table.

Table 2.2	Properties of Germanium: Predicted and Observed	
Property	**Predicted by Mendeleev for Eka-Silikon (1871)**	**Observed by Winkler for Germanium (1886)**
Atomic mass	72	72.6
Density (g/cm³)	5.5	5.47
Color	Dirty gray	Grayish white
Density of oxide (g/cm³)	EsO_2: 4.7	GeO_2: 4.703
Boiling point of chloride	$EsCl_4$: below 100 °C	$GeCl_4$: 86 °C

In 1829, Johann Dobereiner, a German chemist, published his observations that there were several groups of three elements that were quite similar. In each case, the middle element seemed to be halfway between the other two in atomic mass, reactivity, and other properties. One such group, which he called *alkali formers*, was lithium, sodium, and potassium. Show that the relative atomic mass of the middle element in this triad is close to the average of the relative atomic masses of the other two elements.

Solution

The atomic mass of lithium (Li) is 6.941 u and that of potassium (K) is 39.098 u. The average of the two is (6.941 u + 39.098 u) ÷ 2 = 22.795 u, quite close to the modern value for sodium (Na) of 22.989 u.

■ **EXERCISE 2.3**

Another of Dobereiner's triads was the *salt formers* chlorine, bromine, and iodine. Show that the relative atomic mass of the middle element in this triad is close to the average of the relative atomic masses of the other two elements.

Self-Assessment Questions

1. Which of the following is *not* true of Mendeleev's periodic table?
   a. It includes new elements that he had just discovered.
   b. The elements are arranged generally in order of increasing atomic mass.
   c. He left gaps for predicted new elements.
   d. He placed some heavier elements before lighter ones.

2. Relative masses in the modern periodic table are based on the value for
   a. the carbon-12 isotope   **b.** the hydrogen atom
   c. naturally occurring oxygen   **d.** the oxygen-16 isotope

3. The number of elements known today is approximately
   a. 12   **b.** 100
   c. 1000   **d.** 30 million

Answers: 1, a; 2, a; 3, b

▲ An image of atoms of manganese obtained using STM.

2.5 Atoms and Molecules: Real and Relevant

Learning Objective ❯ Distinguish atoms from molecules.

Are atoms real? Certainly they are real as a concept, a highly useful concept. And scientists today can observe computer-enhanced images of individual atoms. These portraits provide powerful (though still indirect) evidence that atoms exist.

Are atoms relevant? Much of modern science and technology—including the production of new materials and the technology of pollution control—is based on the concept of atoms. We have seen that atoms are conserved in chemical reactions. Thus, material things—things made of atoms—can be recycled, for the atoms are not destroyed no matter how we use them. The one way we might "lose" a material from a practical standpoint is to spread its atoms so thinly that it would take too much time and energy to put them back together again. The essay on recycling (page 54) describes a real-world example of such loss.

Now back to Leucippus and Democritus and their musings on that Greek beach. We now know that if we keep dividing drops of water, we will ultimately obtain a small particle—called a *molecule*—that is still water. A **molecule** is a group of atoms chemically bonded, or connected, to one another. Molecules are represented by chemical formulas. The symbol H represents an *atom* of hydrogen. The formula

6. What's the difference between atoms and molecules? A molecule is made of atoms that are combined in fixed proportions. A carbon atom is the smallest particle of the element carbon, and a carbon dioxide molecule is the smallest particle of the compound carbon dioxide. As you have probably figured out, molecules can be broken down into their atoms.

Recycling

Because it is an element, iron cannot be created or destroyed, but that does not mean it always exists in its elemental state. Let's consider two different pathways for the recycling of iron.

1. Hematite, an iron ore, is obtained from a mine and converted into pig iron, which is used to make steel cans. Once discarded, the cans rust. Iron ions (ions are explained in Chapter 4) slowly leach from the rust into groundwater and eventually wind up in the ocean. These dissolved ions can be absorbed by and incorporated into marine plants. Marine creatures that eat the plants will in turn absorb and incorporate iron ions. The original iron atoms are now widely separated in space. Some of them might even become part of the hemoglobin in your blood. The iron has been recycled, but it will never again resemble the original pig iron.

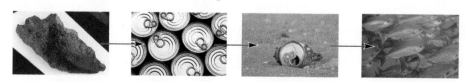

2. Iron ore is taken from a mine and converted to pig iron and then into steel. The steel is used in making an automobile, which is driven for a decade and then sent to the junkyard. There it is compacted and sent to a recycling plant, where the steel is recovered and ultimately used again in a new automobile. Once the iron was removed from its ore, it was conserved in its elemental metallic form. In this form of recycling, the iron continues to be useful for a long time.

H_2 represents a *molecule* of hydrogen, which is composed of two hydrogen atoms. The formula H_2O represents a molecule of water, which is composed of two hydrogen atoms and one oxygen atom. If we divide a water molecule, we will obtain *two atoms* of hydrogen and *one atom* of oxygen.

And if we divide those atoms . . . but that is a story for another time.

Dalton regarded the atom as indivisible, as did his successors up until the discovery of radioactivity in 1895. We examine the evolving concept of the atom in Chapter 3.

Self-Assessment Questions

1. We can recycle materials because atoms
   a. always combine in the same way
   b. are conserved
   c. are indivisible
   d. combine in multiple portions

2. A molecule is
   a. a collection of like atoms
   b. conserved in chemical reactions
   c. a group of atoms chemically bonded to one another
   d. indivisible

Answers: 1, b; 2, c

Lallie C. McKenzie, *Chem11 LLC*

It's Elemental

In this chapter, you learned that everything is made up of atoms and that atoms are the smallest particles of an element. Although the universe is composed of an uncountable number of compounds and mixtures, the basic building blocks of these are elements. The periodic table (inside front cover) organizes the elements by relative mass and, more importantly, by their predictable chemical properties.

What do elements have to do with green chemistry? When chemists design products and processes, they take advantage of the entire periodic table, including elements used rarely or not at all in nature or in our bodies. It is important to think about possible impacts of the chosen elements on human health and on the environment. Two important factors to evaluate are inherent hazard and natural abundance. Hazard can be different for the element itself or when it is in a compound, so the element's form can determine whether it causes harm. For example, sodium is very reactive with water, but sodium chloride is a compound that we eat. Also, as you learned from the law of conservation of mass (Section 2.2), elements cannot be created or destroyed. Therefore, the amounts of these materials on the planet are limited and may be scarce.

Green Chemistry Principles 3, 7, and 10 apply to products and processes that involve hazardous and rare elements. Understanding the impacts of toxic elements and compounds on human health and the environment lets us reduce or eliminate their use by developing safer alternatives. Also, designing new technologies that rely on abundant elements can prevent depletion of resources. Finally, reclaiming materials after use is critical if they can cause harm or are scarce.

The use of lead and mercury, two particularly hazardous elements, has been reduced through green chemistry. These elements are known to harm many of the systems of the human body and can impact children's development. Although lead and mercury are important in many products, the urgent need to limit exposure to them has led to their replacement with safer alternatives. For example, lead in paints has been replaced with titanium dioxide, compounds with lower toxicity now substitute for lead stabilizers in plastics, and new lead-free chemicals are being used instead of traditional solder in electronics. In addition, recent developments have reduced the liquid mercury required in fluorescent lighting, and mercury-based thermometers and switches have been replaced with electronic or non-hazardous versions. Because coal-fired power plants emit mercury, advances in alternative energy sources also reduce our exposure to this element.

Many current technologies may be limited by their need for scarce elements. For example, the permanent magnets in computer hard drives, wind turbines, and hybrid cars are mainly made of neodymium and dysprosium. Green chemistry can promote new opportunities. Although almost all of the elements are found in the Earth's crust, eight account for more than 98% of the total. In fact, almost three-fourths of the crust is comprised of two elements, silicon and oxygen. Besides being scarce, some elements, such as rare earth metals like cerium, yttrium, neodymium, and lanthanum, are drawn from a single source and can be difficult to separate from other materials. Current supplies are much lower than needed to support projected growth.

Approaches based on earth-abundant elements (such as silicon, iron, and aluminum) would support technology and protect resources. As discussed in the essay on page 54, atoms of a material can be reclaimed directly through recycling processes or spread through the environment. If released, hazardous materials can impact health and the environment, so recycling of these elements should be a priority. Reclaimed raw materials reduce the demand for natural resources—notably, scarce elements. Green chemistry supports the design of materials where the individual elemental components can be recycled easily.

Green chemistry approaches are especially important when products and processes present health or environmental risks. Identifying and replacing hazardous and rare elements can lead to greener technologies and a sustainable future for everyone.

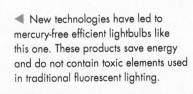

◀ New technologies have led to mercury-free efficient lightbulbs like this one. These products save energy and do not contain toxic elements used in traditional fluorescent lighting.

CRITICAL THINKING EXERCISES

Apply knowledge that you have gained in this chapter and one or more of the FLaReS principles (Chapter 1) to evaluate the following statements or claims.

2.1 In a science fiction movie, a woman proceeds through nine months of pregnancy in minutes. She takes in no nutrients during this time. She dies during labor and an emergency C-section is performed to save the child. The child lives for only a matter of hours, rapidly aging, and dies a withered old man. A classmate claims that the movie is based on a documented, secret alien encounter.

2.2 A health-food store has a large display of bracelets made of copper metal. Some people claim that wearing such a bracelet will protect the wearer from arthritis or rheumatoid diseases.

2.3 An old cookbook claims that cooking acidic food, such as spaghetti sauce, in an iron pot provides more nutrients than cooking the same food in an aluminum pot.

2.4 A company markets a device it calls a "water energizer." It claims the device can supply so much energy to drinking water that the mass of oxygen in the water is increased, thereby providing more oxygen to the body.

SUMMARY

Section 2.1—The concept of atoms was first suggested in ancient Greece by Leucippus and Democritus. However, this idea was rejected for almost 2000 years in favor of Aristotle's view that matter was continuous in nature.

Section 2.2—The law of conservation of mass resulted from careful experiments by Lavoisier and others, who weighed all the reactants and products for a number of chemical reactions and found that no change in mass occurred. Boyle said that a proposed element must be tested. If it could be broken down into simpler substances, it was not an element. The law of definite proportions (law of constant composition) was formulated by Proust, based on his experiments and on those of Berzelius. It states that a given compound always contains the same elements in exactly the same proportions by mass.

Section 2.3—In 1803, Dalton explained the laws of definite proportions and conservation of mass with his atomic theory, which had four main points: (1) Matter is made up of tiny particles called atoms; (2) atoms of the same element are alike; (3) compounds are formed when atoms of different elements combine in certain proportions; and (4) during chemical reactions, atoms are rearranged, not destroyed. Dalton also discovered the law of multiple proportions, which states that different elements might combine in two or more different sets of proportions, each set corresponding to a different compound. His atomic theory also explained this new law. These laws can be used to perform calculations to find the amounts of elements that combine or are present in a compound or reaction. In more than two centuries atomic theory has undergone only minor modification.

Section 2.4—Berzelius published a table of atomic weights in 1828, and his values agree well with modern ones. In 1869, Mendeleev published his version of the periodic table, a systematic arrangement of the elements that allowed him to predict the existence and properties of undiscovered elements. In the modern periodic table, each element is listed, along with its symbol and the average mass of an atom of that element in atomic mass units, which are very tiny units of mass.

Section 2.5—Because atoms are conserved in chemical reactions, matter (which is made of atoms) can always be recycled. Atoms can be lost, in effect, if they are scattered in the environment. A molecule is a group of atoms chemically bonded together. Just as an atom is the smallest particle of an element, a modecule is the smallest particle of most compounds.

Green chemistry When chemists design products and processes, potential impacts on human health and the environment of the incorporated elements should be considered. Identifying and replacing toxic and rare elements can lead to greener technologies and enhance sustainability.

Learning Objectives

› Explain the ancient Greeks' ideas about the characteristics of matter. (2.1)	Problems 1–3
› Describe the significance of the laws of conservation of mass and definite proportions. (2.2)	Problems 6, 10, 15–28, 45, 48
› Calculate the amounts of elements from the composition of a compound. (2.2)	Problems 41–43, 46, 49–51
› Explain why the idea that matter is made of atoms is a theory. (2.3)	Problem 8
› Understand how atomic theory explains the law of conservation of mass. (2.3)	Problem 11, 35–40, 44, 47

❯ Describe how the elements are arranged in the periodic table and why the arrangement is important. (2.4)	Problem 50
❯ Distinguish atoms from molecules. (2.5)	Problem 12
❯ Identify elements that can be classified as hazardous or rare.	Problem 52
❯ Explain how green chemistry can change technologies that rely on hazardous or rare elements.	Problems 53, 54

REVIEW QUESTIONS

1. Distinguish between **(a)** the atomic view and the continuous view of matter and **(b)** the ancient Greek definition of an element and the modern one.

2. What was Democritus's contribution to atomic theory? Why did the idea that matter was continuous (rather than atomic) prevail for so long? What discoveries finally refuted the idea?

3. Consider the following *macroscopic* (visible to the unaided eye) objects. Which are best classified as *discrete* (like Democritus's description of matter) and which are *continuous* (like Aristotle's description)?
   a. people
   b. cloth
   c. calculators
   d. milk chocolate
   e. M&M's candies

4. Describe Lavoisier's contribution to the development of modern chemistry.

5. How did Boyle define an element?

6. State the law of definite proportions, and illustrate it using the compound zinc sulfide, ZnS.

7. State the law of multiple proportions. For a fixed mass of the first element in each of the following compounds, what is the relationship between (ratio of) the
   a. masses of oxygen in ClO_2 and in ClO?
   b. masses of fluorine in ClF_3 and ClF?
   c. masses of oxygen in P_4O_6 and P_4O_{10}?

8. Outline the main points of Dalton's atomic theory.

9. In the figure, the blue spheres represent phosphorus atoms, and the red ones represent oxygen atoms. The box labeled "Initial" represents a mixture. Which one of the other three boxes (A, B, or C) could *not* represent that mixture after a chemical reaction occurred? Explain briefly.

10. Fructose (fruit sugar) is always composed of 40.0% carbon, 53.3% oxygen, and 6.7% hydrogen regardless of the fruit that it comes from. What law does this illustrate?

11. Use Dalton's atomic theory to explain each of the following laws and give an example that illustrates each law.
    a. conservation of mass
    b. definite proportions
    c. multiple proportions

12. Lavoisier considered *alumina* an element. In 1825, the Danish chemist Hans Christian Oersted isolated aluminum metal by reacting aluminum chloride with potassium. Later experiments showed that alumina is formed by reacting aluminum metal with oxygen. What did these experiments prove?

13. What law does the following list of compounds illustrate? N_2O, NO, NO_2, N_2O_4

14. What did each of the following contribute to the development of modern chemistry?
    a. J. J. Berzelius
    b. Henry Cavendish
    c. Joseph Proust
    d. Dmitri Mendeleev

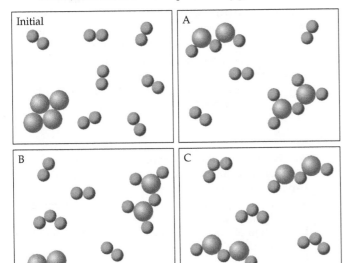

 PROBLEMS

Conservation of Mass

15. If 45.0 g of vinegar is added to 5.0 g of baking soda in an open beaker, the total mass after reaction is less than 50.0 g. The vinegar bubbles and fizzes during the reaction. Has the law of conservation of mass been violated? Explain.

16. An iron nail dissolves in a solution of hydrochloric acid. The nail disappears. Have the iron atoms been destroyed? If so, how? If not, where are they?

17. Water is about 11.2% hydrogen and 88.8% oxygen by weight. If you fill a container with 11.2 g of hydrogen and 88.8 g of oxygen, does that vessel contain water? Explain.

18. Many reactions seem to violate the law of conservation of mass. For example, (a) when an iron object rusts, the rusty object has a greater mass than before, and (b) when a piece of charcoal burns, the remaining material (ash) has less mass than the charcoal. Explain these observations, and suggest an experiment that would demonstrate that mass is conserved in each case.

19. Acetylene, used for welding, contains 24.02 g of carbon for every 2.02 g of hydrogen. If you have 78.5 g of carbon that can be converted to acetylene, what mass of hydrogen will be needed for the conversion?

20. Nitrous oxide (N_2O, "laughing gas") contains 28.01 g of nitrogen in every 44.01 g of nitrous oxide. What mass of nitrous oxide can be formed from 48.7 g of nitrogen?

21. A student in a chemistry class calculates the mass of titanium(IV) oxide (which contains only titanium and oxygen) that can be formed from 37.7 g of titanium and 20.1 g of oxygen. Her calculated answer is 59.8 g of titanium(IV) oxide. Explain to the student why her answer is impossible.

22. A student heats 2.796 g of zinc powder with 2.414 g of sulfur. He reports that he obtains 4.169 g of zinc sulfide and recovers 1.041 g of unreacted sulfur. Show by calculation whether or not his results obey the law of conservation of mass.

23. When 1.00 g zinc and 0.80 g sulfur are allowed to react, all the zinc is used up, 1.50 g of zinc sulfide is formed, and some unreacted sulfur remains. What is the mass of *unreacted* sulfur (choose one)?
    a. 0.20 g
    b. 0.30 g
    c. 0.50 g
    d. impossible to determine from this information alone

24. A city has to come up with a plan to dispose of its solid wastes. The solid wastes consist of many different kinds of materials, and the materials are comprised of many different kinds of atoms. The options for disposal include burying the wastes in a landfill, incinerating them, and dumping them at sea. Which method, if any, will get rid of the atoms that make up the wastes? Which method, if any, will immediately change the chemical form of the wastes?

Definite Proportions

25. When 18.02 g of water is decomposed by electrolysis, 16.00 g of oxygen and 2.02 g of hydrogen are formed. According to the law of definite proportions, what masses, in grams, of (a) hydrogen and (b) oxygen will be formed by the electrolysis of 775 g of water?

26. Hydrogen from the decomposition of water has been promoted as the fuel of the future (Chapter 15). What mass of water, in kilograms, would have to be electrolyzed to produce 125 kg of hydrogen? (See Problem 25.)

27. Given a plentiful supply of air, 3.0 parts carbon will react with 8.0 parts oxygen by mass to produce carbon dioxide. Use this mass ratio to calculate the mass of carbon required to produce 14 kg of carbon dioxide.

28. When 31 g of phosphorus reacts with oxygen, 71 g of an oxide of phosphorus is the product. What mass of phosphorus is needed to produce 39 g of this product?

Multiple Proportions

29. Carbon combines with oxygen in a mass ratio of $1.000 : 2.664$ to form carbon dioxide (CO_2) and in a mass ratio of $1.000 : 1.332$ to form carbon monoxide (CO). A third carbon-oxygen compound, called carbon suboxide, is 52.96% C by mass and 47.04% O by mass. Show that these compounds follow the law of multiple proportions.

30. A compound containing only oxygen and rubidium has 0.187 g of O per 1.00 g of Rb. The relative atomic masses are 16.0 for O and 85.5 for Rb. What is a possible O-to-Rb mass ratio for a different oxide of rubidium (choose one)?
    a. $8.0 : 85.5$ b. $16.0 : 85.5$
    c. $32.0 : 85.5$ d. $16.0 : 171$

31. A sample of an oxide of tin with the formula SnO consists of 0.742 g of tin and 0.100 g of oxygen. A sample of another oxide of tin consists of 0.555 g of tin and 0.150 g of oxygen. What is the formula of the second oxide?

32. Consider three oxides of nitrogen, X, Y, and Z. Oxide X has an oxygen-to-nitrogen mass ratio of 2.28:1.00, oxide Y has an oxygen-to-nitrogen mass ratio of 1.14:1.00, and oxide Z has an oxygen-to-nitrogen mass ratio of 0.57:1.00. What is the whole-number ratio of masses of oxygen in these compounds given a fixed mass of nitrogen?

33. Sulfur forms two compounds with fluorine, T and U. Compound T has 0.447 g of sulfur combined with 1.06 g of fluorine; compound U has 0.438 g of sulfur combined with 1.56 g of fluorine. Show that these data support the law of multiple proportions.

34. Two compounds, V and W, are composed only of hydrogen and carbon. Compound V is 80.0% carbon by mass and 20.0% hydrogen by mass. Compound W is 83.3% carbon by mass and 16.7% hydrogen by mass. What is the ratio of masses of hydrogen in these compounds given a fixed mass of carbon?

Dalton's Atomic Theory

35. Are the following findings, expressed to the nearest atomic mass unit, in agreement with Dalton's atomic theory? Explain your answers.
    a. An atom of calcium has a mass of 40 u; an atom of vanadium, 50 u.
    b. An atom of calcium has a mass of 40 u; an atom of potassium, 40 u.

36. To the nearest atomic mass unit, one calcium atom has a mass of 40 u and another calcium atom has a mass of

44 u. Do these findings support or contradict Dalton's atomic theory? Explain.

37. An atom of uranium splits into two smaller atoms when struck by a particle called a *neutron*. Do these findings support or contradict Dalton's atomic theory? Explain.

38. According to Dalton's atomic theory, when elements react, their atoms combine in (choose one)
    a. a simple whole-number ratio that is unique for each set of elements
    b. exactly a 1:1 ratio
    c. one or more simple whole-number ratios
    d. pairs
    e. random proportions

39. Hydrogen and oxygen combine in a mass ratio of about 1:8 to form water. If every water molecule consists of two atoms of hydrogen and one atom of oxygen, what fraction or multiple of the mass of a hydrogen atom is the mass of an oxygen atom?
    a. $\frac{1}{16}$ b. $\frac{1}{8}$ c. 8 times   d. 16 times

40. The elements fluorine and nitrogen combine in a mass ratio of 57:14 to form a compound. If every molecule of the compound consists of three atoms of fluorine and one atom of nitrogen, what fraction or multiple of the mass of a fluorine atom is the mass of a nitrogen atom?
    a. $\frac{19}{14}$ b. 3 times   c. $\frac{14}{19}$ d. 14 times

Chemical Compounds

41. A blue solid called *azulene* is thought to be a pure compound. Analyses of three samples of the material yield the following results.

	Mass of Sample	Mass of Carbon	Mass of Hydrogen
Sample 1	1.000 g	0.937 g	0.0629 g
Sample 2	0.244 g	0.229 g	0.0153 g
Sample 3	0.100 g	0.094 g	0.0063 g

Could the material be a pure compound?

42. A colorless liquid is thought to be a pure compound. Analyses of three samples of the material yield the following results.

	Mass of Sample	Mass of Carbon	Mass of Hydrogen
Sample 1	1.000 g	0.862 g	0.138 g
Sample 2	1.549 g	1.295 g	0.254 g
Sample 3	0.988 g	0.826 g	0.162 g

Could the material be a pure compound? Explain.

ADDITIONAL PROBLEMS

43. When 0.2250 g of magnesium is heated with 0.5331 g of nitrogen in a closed container, the magnesium is completely converted to 0.3114 g of magnesium nitride. What mass of unreacted nitrogen must remain?

44. Gasoline can be approximated by the formula C_8H_8. An environmental advocate points out that burning one gallon (about 7 lb) of gasoline produces about 19 lb of carbon dioxide, a greenhouse gas that raises the temperature of the atmosphere. Explain this seeming contradiction of the law of conservation of mass.

45. A compound of uranium and fluorine is used to generate uranium for nuclear power plants. The gas can be decomposed to yield 2.09 parts by mass of uranium for every 1 part by mass of fluorine. If the relative mass of a uranium atom is 238 and the relative mass of a fluorine atom is 19, calculate the number of fluorine atoms that are combined with one uranium atom.

46. Two experiments were performed in which sulfur was burned completely in pure oxygen gas, producing sulfur dioxide and leaving some unreacted oxygen. In the first experiment, burning 0.312 g of sulfur produced 0.623 g of sulfur dioxide. In the second experiment, 1.305 g of sulfur was burned. What mass of sulfur dioxide was produced?

47. In an experiment illustrated at right, about 15 mL of hydrochloric acid solution was placed in a flask and approximately 3 g of sodium carbonate was put into a balloon. The opening of the balloon was then carefully stretched over the top of the flask, taking care not

to allow the sodium carbonate to fall into the acid in the flask. The flask was placed on an electronic balance, and the mass of the flask and its contents was found to be 38.61 g. The sodium carbonate was then slowly shaken into the acid. The balloon began to fill with gas. When the reaction was complete, the mass of the flask and its contents, including the gas in the balloon, was found to be 38.61 g. What law does this experiment illustrate? Explain.

48. In one experiment, 3.06 g hydrogen was allowed to react with an excess of oxygen to form 27.35 g water. In a second experiment, electric current broke down a sample of water into 1.45 g hydrogen and 11.51 g oxygen. Are these results consistent with the law of definite proportions? Show why or why not.

49. Use Figure 2.4 to calculate the mass of mercuric oxide that would be needed to produce 100.0 g of mercury metal.

50. Gold chloride, $AuCl_3$, is formed when gold metal is dissolved in *aqua regia*, a highly corrosive mixture of acids. Determine the mass ratio of gold to chlorine in gold chloride:
   a. based on Mendeleev's values from his periodic table (Figure 2.10)
   b. based on values in the modern periodic table in the inside front cover of this book

51. See Table 2.1. Another compound of nitrogen and oxygen contains 0.5836 g of nitrogen per 1.000 g of oxygen. Calculate the ratio of mass of N in this compound to mass of N in nitrogen dioxide. What *whole-number* ratio does this value represent?

52. Identify whether the following elements are hazardous, rare, or neither.
   a. silicon
   b. neodymium
   c. mercury
   d. oxygen
   e. lead

53. Give two examples of how green chemistry has helped to reduce the use of lead in consumer products.

54. Why is it important to recycle mercury-based fluorescent lightbulbs instead of putting them in landfills?

COLLABORATIVE GROUP PROJECTS

Prepare a PowerPoint, poster, or other presentation (as directed by your instructor) to share with the class.

1. Prepare a brief biographical report on one of the following.
   a. Henry Cavendish   **b.** Joseph Proust
   c. John Newlands   **d.** Lothar Meyer
   e. Dmitri Mendeleev   **f.** John Dalton
   g. Antoine Lavoisier   **h.** Marie-Anne Pierrette Paulze

2. Prepare a brief report on early Greek contributions to and ideas in the field of science, focusing on the work of one of the following: Aristotle, Leucippus, Democritus, Thales, Anaximander, Anaximenes of Miletus, Heraclitus, Empedocles, or another Greek philosopher of the time before 300 B.C.E.

3. Prepare a brief report on the *phlogiston theory*. Describe what the theory was, how it explained changes in mass when something is burned, and why it was finally abandoned.

4. Write a brief essay on recycling of one of the following: metals, paper, plastics, glass, food wastes, or grass clippings. Contrast a recycling method that maintains the properties of an element with one that changes them.

Atomic Structure

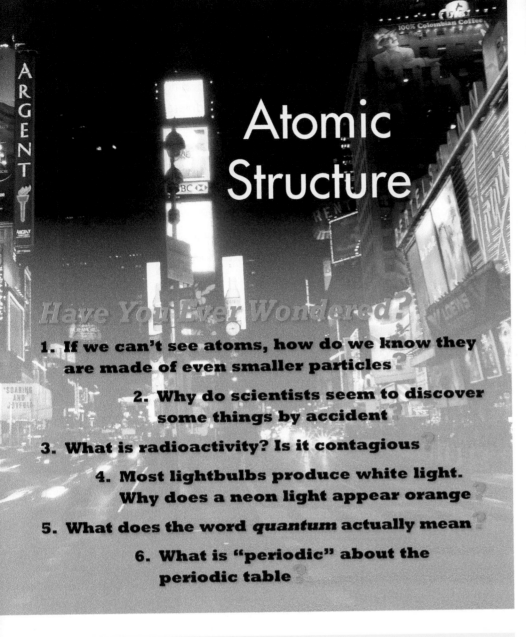

Have You Ever Wondered?

1. **If we can't see atoms, how do we know they are made of even smaller particles**

2. **Why do scientists seem to discover some things by accident**

3. **What is radioactivity? Is it contagious**

4. **Most lightbulbs produce white light. Why does a neon light appear orange**

5. **What does the word *quantum* actually mean**

6. **What is "periodic" about the periodic table**

Images of the Invisible

Atoms are exceedingly tiny particles, much too small to see even with an optical microscope. It is true that scientists can obtain images of individual atoms, but they use special instruments such as the scanning tunneling microscope (STM, page 53). Even so, we can see only outlines of atoms and their arrangements in a substance. If atoms are so small, how can we possibly know anything about their inner structures?

Although scientists have never examined the interior of an atom directly, they have been able to obtain a great deal of *indirect* information. By designing clever experiments and exercising their powers of deduction, scientists have constructed an amazingly detailed model of what an atom's interior must be like.

Neon lights—the signature of entertainment, restaurants, bars, and the big city. Interestingly enough, most of the flickering illumination seen at the Radio City Music Hall, on Times Square, and in Las Vegas is not from the element neon. The liquid fire of real neon lights is a characteristic orange-red color, and neon cannot be made to glow in any other color. Other colors are created by coating the inside of the tubing with a *phosphor* that glows in a specific color when current is applied to the tube. But why will neon only give off orange-red light? The answer lies in the structure of its atoms—the subject of this chapter.

Why do we care about the structure of particles as tiny as atoms? The reason is that the arrangement of various parts of atoms determines the properties of different kinds of matter. Only by understanding atomic structure can we learn how atoms combine to make millions of different substances. With such knowledge, we can modify and synthesize materials to meet our needs more precisely. Knowledge of atomic structure is even essential to good health care. Many medical diagnoses are based on chemical analyses that have been developed from our understanding of atomic structure.

Perhaps of greater interest to you is the fact that your understanding of chemistry (as well as much of biology and other sciences) depends, at least in part, on your knowledge of atomic structure. Let's begin by going back to the time of John Dalton.

3.1 Electricity and the Atom

Learning Objectives ❯ Explain the electrical properties of an atom. ❯ Describe how the properties of electricity explain the structure of atoms.

Dalton, who set forth his atomic theory in 1803, regarded the atom as hard and indivisible. However, it wasn't long before evidence accumulated to show that matter has electrical properties. Indeed, the electrolytic decomposition of water by Nicholson and Carlisle in 1800 (Section 2.2) had already indicated this. Electricity played an important role in unraveling the structure of the atom.

Static electricity has been known since ancient times, but continuous electric current was born with the nineteenth century. In 1800, Alessandro Volta invented an electrochemical cell much like a modern battery. If the poles of such a cell are connected by a wire, current flows through the wire. The current is sustained by chemical reactions inside the cell. Volta's invention soon was applied in many areas of science and everyday life.

Electrolysis

Soon after Volta's invention, Humphry Davy (1778–1829), a British chemist, built a powerful battery that he used to pass electricity through molten (melted) salts. Davy quickly discovered several new elements. In 1807, he liberated highly reactive potassium metal from molten potassium hydroxide. Shortly thereafter, he produced sodium metal by passing electricity through molten sodium hydroxide. Within a year, Davy had also produced magnesium, strontium, barium, and calcium metals for the first time. The science of electrochemistry was born. (We will study electrochemistry in more detail in Chapter 8.)

Davy's protégé, Michael Faraday (1791–1867), greatly extended this new science. Lacking in formal education, Faraday consulted others to define many of the terms we still use today. His physician, Whitlock Nicholl (1786–1838), helped coin the term **electrolysis** for chemical reactions caused by electricity (Figure 3.1) and the name **electrolyte** for a compound that conducts electricity when melted or dissolved in water. English classical scholar William Whewell (1794–1866) suggested the names for the parts of the electrolytic apparatus. The carbon rods or metal strips inserted into a molten compound or a solution to carry the electric current are called **electrodes**. The electrode that bears a positive charge is the **anode**, and the negatively charged electrode is the **cathode**. The entities that carry the electric current through a melted compound or a solution are called *ions*. An **ion** is an atom or a group of atoms bonded together that has an electric charge. An ion with a negative charge is an **anion**; it travels toward the anode. A positively charged ion is a **cation**; it moves toward the cathode.

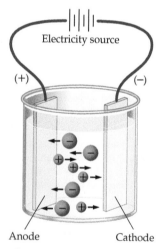

▲ In addition to Michael Faraday's work in electrochemistry, he also devised methods for liquefying gases such as chlorine and invented the electrical transformer.

Electricity source

(+)   (−)

Anode   Cathode

▲ **Figure 3.1** An electrolysis apparatus. The electricity source (for example, a battery) directs electrons through wires from the anode to the cathode. Cations (+) are attracted to the cathode (−), and anions (−) are attracted to the anode (+). This migration of ions is the flow of electricity through the solution.

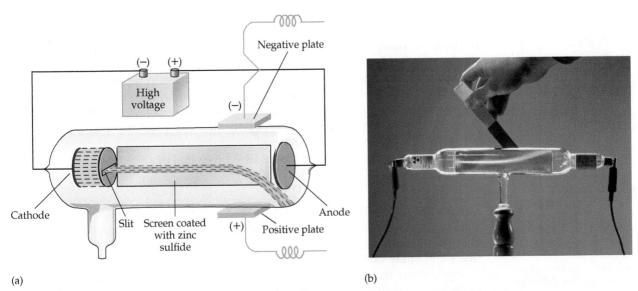

(a)

(b)

▲ **Figure 3.2** Thomson's apparatus, showing deflection of the cathode rays (a beam of electrons). Cathode rays are invisible but can be observed because they produce a green fluorescence when they strike a zinc sulfide–coated screen. The diagram (a) shows deflection of the beam in an electric field. The photograph (b) shows the deflection in a magnetic field. Cathode rays travel in straight lines unless some kind of external field is applied.

Faraday's work established that atoms have electrical properties, but further details of atomic structure had to wait several decades for more powerful sources of electricity and better vacuum pumps.

Cathode-Ray Tubes

In 1875, William Crookes (1832–1919), an English chemist, was able to construct a low-pressure gas-discharge tube that would allow electricity to pass through it. His experiment is shown in Figure 3.2. Crookes's tube is the antecedent of neon tubes used for signs and of cathode-ray tubes used in old television sets and computer monitors. Metal electrodes are sealed in the tube, which is connected to a vacuum pump so that most of the air can be removed from it. A beam of current produces a green fluorescence when it strikes a screen coated with zinc sulfide. This beam, which seems to leave the cathode and travel to the anode, was called a **cathode ray**.

Thomson's Experiment: Mass-to-Charge Ratio

Considerable speculation arose about the nature of cathode rays, and many experiments were undertaken. Were these rays beams of particles, or did they consist of a wavelike form of energy much like visible light? The answer came (as scientific answers should) from an experiment performed by the English physicist Joseph John Thomson in 1897. Thomson showed that cathode rays were deflected in an electric field (look again at Figure 3.2a). The beam was attracted to the positive plate and repelled by the negative plate. Thomson concluded that cathode rays consisted of negatively charged particles. His experiments also showed that the particles were the same regardless of the materials from which the electrodes were made or the type of gas in the tube. He concluded that these negative particles are part of all kinds of atoms. Thomson named these negatively charged units **electrons**. Cathode rays, then, are beams of electrons emanating from the cathode of a gas-discharge tube.

Cathode rays are deflected in magnetic fields as well as in electric fields. The greater the charge on a particle, the more it is deflected in an electric (or magnetic) field. The heavier the particle, the less it is deflected by a force. By measuring the amount of deflection in fields of known strength, Thomson was able to calculate the *ratio* of the mass of the electron to its charge. (He could not measure either the mass or the charge separately.) Thomson was awarded the Nobel Prize in Physics in 1906.

1. If we can't see atoms, how do we know they are made of even smaller particles? The existence of electrons and other subatomic particles was deduced from the behavior of electricity. The existence and behavior of the subatomic particles make atoms behave the way they do.

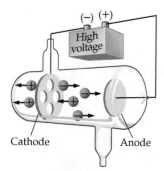

▲ **Figure 3.3** Goldstein's apparatus for the study of positive particles. This apparatus, with holes in the cathode, is a modification of the cathode-ray tube in Figure 3.2. Some positive ions, attracted toward the cathode, pass through the holes in the cathode. The deflection of these particles (not shown) in a magnetic field can be studied in the region to the left of the cathode.

You can find out more about numbers like 9.1×10^{-28} and 1×10^{27} in the Appendix. However, in practice, we seldom use the actual mass and charge of the electron. For many purposes, the electron is considered the unit of electrical charge. The charge is shown as a superscript minus sign (meaning $^{1-}$). In indicating charges on ions, we use $^-$ to indicate a net charge due to one "extra" electron, $^{2-}$ to indicate a charge due to two "extra" electrons, and so on.

Goldstein's Experiment: Positive Particles

In 1886, German scientist Eugen Goldstein performed experiments with gas-discharge tubes that had perforated cathodes (Figure 3.3). He found that although electrons were formed and sped off toward the anode as usual, positive particles were also formed and shot in the opposite direction, toward the cathode. Some of these positive particles went through the holes in the cathode. In 1907, a study of the deflection of these particles in a magnetic field indicated that they were of varying mass. The lightest particles, formed when there was a little hydrogen gas in the tube, were later shown to have a mass 1837 times that of an electron.

Millikan's Oil-Drop Experiment: Electron Charge

The charge on the electron was determined in 1909 by Robert A. Millikan (1868–1953), a physicist at the University of Chicago. Millikan observed electrically charged oil drops in an electric field. A diagram of his apparatus is shown in Figure 3.4. A spray bottle is used to form tiny droplets of oil. Some acquire negative charges, either from irradiation with X-rays or from the friction generated as the particles rub against the opening of the spray nozzle and against each other. (The charge is static electricity, just like the charge you get from walking across a nylon carpet.) Either way, the droplets acquire one or more extra electrons.

Some of the oil droplets pass into a chamber where they can be viewed through a microscope. The negative plate at the bottom of the chamber repels the negatively charged droplets, and the positive plate attracts them. By manipulating the charge on each plate and observing the behavior of the droplets, the charge on each droplet can be determined. Millikan took the smallest possible difference in charge between two droplets to be the charge of an individual electron. For his research, he received the Nobel Prize in Physics in 1923.

From Millikan's value for the charge and Thomson's value for the mass-to-charge ratio, the mass of the electron was readily calculated. That mass was found to be only 9.1×10^{-28} g. To have a mass of 1 g would require more than 1×10^{27} electrons—that's a 1 followed by 27 zeros, or a billion billion billion electrons. More important, the electron's mass is much *smaller* than that of the lightest atom. This means that electrons are much smaller than atoms.

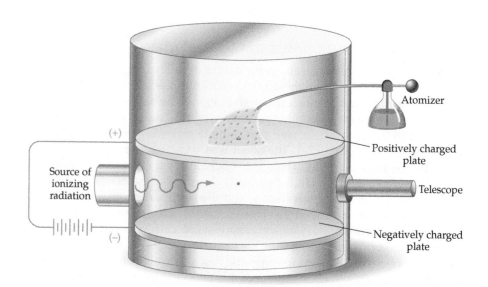

▲ **Figure 3.4** The Millikan oil-drop experiment. Oil drops irradiated with X-rays pick up electrons and become negatively charged. Their fall due to gravity can be balanced by adjusting the voltage of the electric field. The charge on the oil drop can be determined from the applied voltage and the mass of the oil drop. The charge on each drop is that of some whole number of electrons.

Self-Assessment Questions

1. The use of electricity to cause a chemical reaction is called
   a. anodizing   **b.** corrosion   **c.** electrolysis   **d.** hydrolysis

2. During electrolysis of molten sodium hydroxide, chloride anions move to the
   a. anode, which is negatively charged
   b. anode, which is positively charged
   c. cathode, which is negatively charged
   d. cathode, which is positively charged

3. Cathode rays are *not*
   a. composed of negatively charged particles
   b. composed of particles with a mass of 1 u
   c. deflected by electric fields
   d. the same from element to element

4. Thomson used a cathode-ray tube to discover that cathode rays
   a. are deflected by an electric field
   b. are radiation similar to X-rays
   c. could ionize air inside the tube
   d. could ionize the air outside the far end of the tube

5. When J. J. Thomson discovered the electron, he measured its
   a. atomic number   **b.** charge   **c.** mass   **d.** mass-to-charge ratio

6. In his oil-drop experiment, Millikan determined the charge of an electron by
   a. measuring the diameters of the tiniest drops
   b. noting that the drops had either a certain minimum charge or multiples of that charge
   c. using an atomizer that could spray out individual electrons
   d. viewing the smallest charged drops microscopically and noting that they had one extra electron

Answers: 1, c; 2, b; 3, b; 4, a; 5, d; 6, b

3.2 Serendipity in Science: X-Rays and Radioactivity

Learning Objective ❯ Describe the experiments that led to the discovery of X-rays and an explanation of radioactivity.

Let's take a look at two serendipitous discoveries of the last years of the nineteenth century that profoundly changed the world and are related to atomic structure.

Roentgen: The Discovery of X-Rays

In 1895, German scientist Wilhelm Conrad Roentgen (1845–1923) was working in a dark room, studying the glow produced in certain substances by cathode rays. To his surprise, he noted this glow on a chemically treated piece of paper some distance from the cathode-ray tube. The paper even glowed when a wall separated the tube from the paper; this type of ray could travel through walls. When he waved his hand between the radiation source and the glowing paper, he was able to see an image of the bones of his hand in darker shades on the paper. He called these mysterious rays **X-rays**. He found in general that X-rays were absorbed more by bone or other hard and fairly dense materials than by soft, less dense tissues.

X-rays are a form of electromagnetic radiation—energy with electric and magnetic components. Among other types, electromagnetic radiation also includes visible light, radio waves, microwaves, infrared radiation, ultraviolet light, and gamma rays (Section 3.3). These forms differ in energy, with radio waves lowest in energy, followed by microwaves, infrared radiation, visible light, ultraviolet light, X-rays, and gamma rays.

Today, X-rays are one of the most widely used tools in the world for medical diagnosis. Not only are they employed for examining decayed teeth, broken bones,

2. Why do scientists seem to discover some things by accident? *Serendipity*—a "happy accident" like drilling for water and striking oil—happens to everyone at times. Scientists, however, are trained observers. When something unexpected happens, they often wonder why and investigate. The same accident might happen to an untrained person and go unnoticed (though often even scientists miss important finds at first). Or, if noticed, its significance might not be grasped.

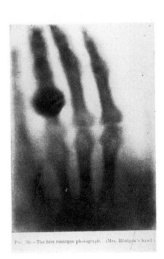

Fig. 20.—The first roentgen photograph. (Mrs. Röntgen's hand.)

▲ X-rays were used in medicine shortly after they were discovered by Wilhelm Roentgen in 1895. In fact, the first known X-ray photograph is the one seen here—of Mrs. Roentgen's hand!

▲ Marie Sklodowska Curie in her laboratory.

3. What is radioactivity? Is it contagious? Radioactivity is the spontaneous decay (occurring without a cause) of an atom into one or more other atoms. The radiation—alpha, beta, or gamma rays—given off by radioactive material is hazardous but you cannot "catch" radiation sickness from a person exposed to radiation any more than you can "catch" a sunburn from a sunburned friend.

and diseased lungs, but they are also the basis for such procedures as mammography and computerized tomography (Chapter 11). In the United States alone, payments for various radiological procedures total more than $20 billion each year. How ironic that Roentgen himself made no profit at all from his discovery. He considered X-rays a "gift to humanity" and refused to patent any part of the discovery. However, he did receive much popular acclaim and in 1901 was awarded the first Nobel Prize in Physics.

The Discovery of Radioactivity

Certain chemicals exhibit *fluorescence* after exposure to strong sunlight. They continue to glow even when taken into a dark room. In 1895, Antoine Henri Becquerel (1852–1908), a French physicist, was studying fluorescence by wrapping photographic film in black paper, placing a few crystals of the fluorescing chemical on top of the paper, and then placing the package in strong sunlight. If the glow was like ordinary light, it would not pass through the paper. On the other hand, if it was similar to X-rays, it would pass through the black paper and fog the film.

While working with a uranium compound, Becquerel made an important accidental discovery. When placed in sunlight, the compound fluoresced and fogged the film. On several cloudy days when exposure to sunlight was not possible, he prepared samples and placed them in a drawer. To his great surprise, the photographic film was fogged even though the uranium compound had not been exposed to sunlight. Further experiments showed that the radiation coming from the uranium compound was unrelated to fluorescence but was a characteristic of the element uranium.

Other scientists immediately began to study this new radiation. Becquerel's graduate student from Poland, Marie Sklodowska, gave the phenomenon a name: radioactivity. **Radioactivity** is the spontaneous emission of radiation from certain unstable elements. Marie later married Pierre Curie, a French physicist. Together they discovered the radioactive elements polonium and radium, and with Becquerel they shared the 1903 Nobel Prize in Physics.

After her husband's death in 1906, Marie Curie continued to work with radioactive substances, winning the Nobel Prize in Chemistry in 1911. For more than 50 years, she was the only person ever to have received two Nobel Prizes.

Self-Assessment Questions

1. When Roentgen saw an X-ray image of his hand, the bones were darker than the glowing paper because the X-rays were
   a. absorbed more by bone than by flesh
   b. radiation that is less energetic than visible light
   c. made up of fast-moving atoms
   d. a type of radioactivity

2. Radioactivity arises from elements that
   a. absorb radio waves and release stronger radiation
   b. are unstable and emit radiation
   c. give off X-rays
   d. undergo fission (splitting) of their atoms when they absorb energy

Answers: 1, a; 2, b

3.3 Three Types of Radioactivity

Learning Objective ❯ Distinguish the three main kinds of radioactivity: alpha, beta, and gamma.

Scientists soon showed that three types of radiation emanated from various radioactive elements. Ernest Rutherford (1871–1937), a New Zealander who pursued his career in Canada and Great Britain, chose the names *alpha*, *beta*, and *gamma* for

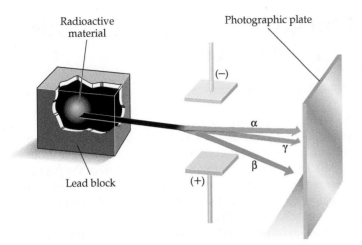

Radioactive material

Photographic plate

Lead block

(−)

(+)

α

γ

β

◀ **Figure 3.5** Behavior of a beam of radioactivity in an electric field.

Q: *Why are alpha rays deflected upward in this figure? Why are beta rays deflected downward?*

▲ **It DOES Matter!**

It is important to distinguish between the *rays* given off by a radioactive element and the radioactive element itself. Like light, alpha, beta, and gamma rays can be absorbed by materials and do not generally cause problems thereafter. A potato that has absorbed gamma rays is not harmful to eat. The serious problem from nuclear disasters, such as the Fukushima disaster of March 2011, arises because radioactive atoms escape from the reactor. Those atoms can lodge on or be absorbed by materials and give off damaging alpha, beta, or gamma rays when those materials are used. These workers from the Fukushima plant are being checked for radioactive particles on their clothing. This topic is covered in more detail in Chapter 11.

the three types of radioactivity. When passed through a strong magnetic or electric field, the alpha type was deflected in a manner indicating that it consisted of a beam of positive particles (Figure 3.5). Later experiments showed that an **alpha particle** has a mass four times that of a hydrogen atom and a charge twice the magnitude of, but opposite in sign to, that of an electron. An alpha particle is in fact identical to the nucleus (Section 3.4) of a helium atom and is often symbolized by He^{2+}.

The beta radiation was shown to be made up of negatively charged particles identical to those of cathode rays. Therefore, a **beta particle** is an electron, although it has much more energy than an electron in an atom. **Gamma rays** are not deflected by a magnetic field. They are a form of electromagnetic radiation, much like the X-rays used in medical work but even more energetic and more penetrating. The three types of radioactivity are summarized in Table 3.1.

The discoveries of the late nineteenth century paved the way for an entirely new picture of the atom, which developed rapidly during the early years of the twentieth century.

Table 3.1   Types of Radioactivity

Name	Greek Letter	Mass (u)	Charge
Alpha	α	4	2+
Beta	β	$\frac{1}{1837}$	1−
Gamma	γ	0	0

Self-Assessment Questions

1. The mass of an alpha particle is about
   a. four times that of a hydrogen atom
   b. the same as that of an electron
   c. the same as that of a hydrogen atom
   d. the same as that of a beta particle

2. Compared to the charge on an electron (designated 1−), the charge on an alpha particle is about
   a. 4−   b. 1−   c. 1+   d. 2+   e. 4+

3. A beta particle is a(n)
   a. boron atom   b. electron   c. helium nucleus   d. proton

4. The mass of a gamma ray is
   a. −1 u   b. 0 u   c. 1 u   d. 4 u

Answers: 1, a; 2, d; 3, b; 4, b

3.4 Rutherford's Experiment: The Nuclear Model of the Atom

Learning Objectives ❯ Sketch the nuclear model of the atom, and identify its parts.

At Rutherford's suggestion, two of his coworkers—Hans Geiger (1882–1945), a German physicist, and Ernest Marsden (1889–1970), an English undergraduate student—bombarded very thin metal foils with alpha particles from a radioactive source (Figure 3.6). In an experiment with gold foil, most of the particles behaved as Rutherford expected, going right through the foil with little or no scattering. However, a few particles were deflected sharply. Occasionally, one was sent right back in the direction from which it had come!

Rutherford had assumed that positive charge was spread evenly over all the space occupied by the atom, but obviously it was not. To explain the results, Rutherford concluded that all the positive charge and nearly all the mass of an atom are concentrated at the center of the atom in a tiny core called the **nucleus**.

When an alpha particle, which is positively charged, directly approached the positively charged nucleus, it was strongly repelled and therefore sharply deflected (Figure 3.7). Because only a few alpha particles were deflected, Rutherford concluded that the nucleus must occupy only a tiny fraction of the volume of an atom. Most of the alpha particles passed right through because most of an atom is empty space. The space outside the nucleus isn't completely empty, however. It contains

▶ **Figure 3.6** Rutherford's gold-foil experiment. Most alpha particles passed right through the gold foil, but now and then a particle was deflected.

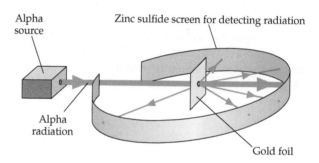

▶ **Figure 3.7** Model explaining the results of Rutherford's gold-foil experiment. Most of the alpha particles pass right through the foil because the gold atoms are mainly empty space. But some alpha particles are deflected as they pass close to a dense, positively charged atomic nucleus. Once in a while, an alpha particle encounters an atomic nucleus head-on and is knocked back in the direction from which it came.

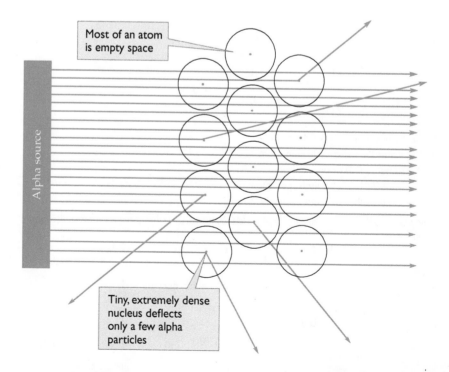

the negatively charged electrons. Rutherford concluded that the electrons had so little mass that they were no match for the alpha particle "bullets." It would be analogous to a mouse trying to stop a charging hippopotamus.

Rutherford's nuclear theory of the atom, set forth in 1911, was revolutionary. He postulated that all the positive charge and nearly all the mass of an atom are concentrated in a tiny, tiny nucleus. The negatively charged electrons have almost no mass, yet they occupy nearly all the volume of an atom. To picture Rutherford's model, visualize a sphere as big as the largest covered football stadium. The nucleus at the middle of the sphere is as small as a pea but weighs several million tons. A few flies flitting here and there throughout the sphere represent the electrons.

Self-Assessment Questions

1. The most persuasive evidence from Rutherford's gold-foil experiment was that
   a. all the alpha particles were deflected a bit
   b. most of the alpha particles went right through the foil, but a tiny fraction were reflected right back toward the source
   c. some gold atoms were converted to lead atoms
   d. some gold atoms were split

2. Rutherford's gold-foil experiment showed that
   a. gold atoms consisted of protons in a "pudding" of electrons
   b. the nucleus was huge and positively charged
   c. the nucleus was tiny and positively charged
   d. some gold atoms were shattered by alpha particles

3. From his gold-foil experiment, Rutherford concluded that atoms consist mainly of
   a. electrons
   b. empty space
   c. neutrons
   d. protons

4. The positively charged part of the atom is its
   a. cation
   b. nucleus
   c. outer electrons
   d. widespread cloud of electrons

Answers: 1, b; 2, c; 3, b; 4, b

3.5 The Atomic Nucleus

Learning Objectives ❯ List the particles that make up the nucleus of an atom, and give their relative masses and electric charges. ❯ Identify elements and isotopes from their nuclear particles.

In 1914, Rutherford suggested that the smallest positive particle (the one formed when there is hydrogen gas in Goldstein's apparatus—see Section 3.1) is the unit of positive charge in the nucleus. This particle, called a **proton**, has a charge equal in magnitude to that of the electron and has nearly the same mass as a hydrogen atom. Rutherford's suggestion was that protons constitute the positively charged matter in all atoms. The nucleus of a hydrogen atom consists of one proton, and the nuclei of larger atoms contain greater numbers of protons.

But most atomic nuclei are heavier than is indicated by the number of positive charges (number of protons). For example, the helium nucleus has a charge of 2+ (and therefore two protons, according to Rutherford's theory), but its mass is *four* times that of hydrogen. This excess mass puzzled scientists at first. Then, in 1932, English physicist James Chadwick (1891–1974) discovered a particle with about the same mass as a proton but with no electrical charge. It was called a **neutron**, and its existence explains the unexpectedly high mass of the helium nucleus. Whereas the

Table 3.2 Subatomic Particles

Particle	Symbol	Mass (u)	Charge	Location in Atom
Proton	p^+	1	1+	Nucleus
Neutron	n	1	0	Nucleus
Electron	e^-	$\dfrac{1}{1837}$	1−	Outside nucleus

hydrogen nucleus contains only one proton of mass 1 u, the helium nucleus contains not only two protons (2 u) but also two neutrons (2 u), giving it a total mass of 4 u.

With the discovery of the neutron, the list of "building blocks" we will need for "constructing" atoms is complete. The properties of these particles are summarized in Table 3.2. (There are dozens of other subatomic particles, but most exist only momentarily and are not important to our discussion.)

Atomic Number

The number of protons in the nucleus of an atom of any element is the **atomic number (Z)** of that element. This number determines the kind of atom—that is, the identity of the element—and it is found on any periodic table or list of the elements. Dalton thought that the mass of an atom determines the element. We now know it is not the mass but the number of protons that determines the identity of an element. For example, every atom with 26 protons is an atom of iron (Fe), whose atomic number $Z = 26$. Any atom with 50 protons is an atom of tin (Sn), which has $Z = 50$. In a neutral atom (one with no electrical charge), the positive charge of the protons is exactly neutralized by the negative charge of the electrons. The attractive forces between the unlike charges help hold the atom together.

A proton and a neutron have almost the same mass, 1.0073 u and 1.0087 u, respectively. This difference is so small that it usually can be ignored. Thus, for many purposes, we can assume that the masses of the proton and the neutron are the same, 1 u. The proton has a charge equal in magnitude but opposite in sign to that of an electron. This charge on a proton is written as 1+. The electron has a charge of 1− and a mass of 0.00055 u. The electrons in an atom contribute so little to its total mass that their mass is usually disregarded (treated as if it were 0).

Isotopes

We can now more precisely define *isotopes*, a term we mentioned in Section 2.3. Atoms of a given element can have different numbers of neutrons in their nuclei. For example, most hydrogen atoms have a nucleus consisting of a single proton and no neutrons. However, about 1 hydrogen atom in 6700 has a neutron as well as a proton in its nucleus. This heavier hydrogen atom is called *deuterium*. A third, rare isotope of hydrogen is *tritium*, which has two neutrons and one proton in the nucleus. Whether it has one neutron, two neutrons, or none, any atom with $Z = 1$—that is, with one proton—is a hydrogen atom. Atoms that have this sort of relationship—having the same number of protons but different numbers of neutrons—are called **isotopes** (Figure 3.8).

▶ **Figure 3.8** The three isotopes of hydrogen. Each has one proton and one electron, but they differ in the number of neutrons in the nucleus.

Q: *What is the atomic number and mass number of each of the isotopes? What is the mass of each, in atomic mass units, to the nearest whole number?*

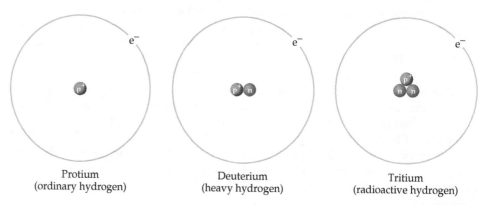

Protium
(ordinary hydrogen)

Deuterium
(heavy hydrogen)

Tritium
(radioactive hydrogen)

Most, but not all, elements exist in nature in isotopic forms. For example, tin is present in nature in 10 different isotopic forms. It also has 15 radioactive isotopes that do not occur in nature. Aluminum, on the other hand, has only one naturally occurring isotope.

Isotopes usually have little or no effect on ordinary chemical reactions. For example, all three hydrogen isotopes react with oxygen to form water. Because these isotopes differ in mass, compounds formed with them have different physical properties, but such differences are usually slight. For example, water in which both hydrogen atoms are deuterium is called *heavy water*, often represented as D_2O. Heavy water boils at 101.4 °C (instead of 100 °C) and freezes at 3.8 °C (instead of 0 °C). In nuclear reactions, however, isotopes are of the utmost importance, as we shall see in Chapter 11.

Symbols for Isotopes

Collectively, the two main nuclear particles, protons and neutrons, are called **nucleons**. Isotopes are represented by symbols with subscripts and superscripts.

$$^A_Z X$$

In this general symbol, Z is the nuclear charge (atomic number, or number of protons), and A is the **mass number**, or the **nucleon number** because it is the number of nucleons. (*Nucleon number* is the term recommended by the International Union of Pure and Applied Chemistry.) As an example, the isotope with the symbol

$$^{35}_{17}Cl$$

has 17 protons and 35 nucleons. The number of neutrons is therefore $35 - 17 = 18$.

Isotopes often are named by adding the mass number as a suffix to the name of the element. The three hydrogen isotopes are represented as

$$^1_1H \quad ^2_1H \quad ^3_1H$$

and named hydrogen-1, hydrogen-2, and hydrogen-3.

Example 3.1 Number of Neutrons

How many neutrons are there in the $^{235}_{92}U$ nucleus?

Solution

We simply subtract the atomic number Z (number of protons) from the mass number A (number of protons plus number of neutrons).

$$A - Z = \text{number of neutrons}$$
$$235 - 92 = 143$$

There are 143 neutrons in the $^{235}_{92}U$ nucleus.

■ EXERCISE 3.1A
How many neutrons are there in the $^{60}_{27}Co$ nucleus?

■ EXERCISE 3.1B
An iodine isotope has 78 neutrons in its nucleus. What is the mass number and the name of the isotope?

CONCEPTUAL Example 3.2 Isotopes

Refer to the following isotope symbols, in which the letter X replaces each element symbol. **(a)** Which represent isotopes of the same element? **(b)** Which have the same mass number? **(c)** Which have the same number of neutrons?

$$^{16}_8X \quad ^{16}_7X \quad ^{14}_7X \quad ^{14}_6X \quad ^{12}_6X$$

Solution

a. Isotopes of the same element have the same atomic number (subscript). Therefore, $^{16}_{7}X$ and $^{14}_{7}X$ are isotopes of nitrogen (N), and $^{14}_{6}X$ and $^{12}_{6}X$ are isotopes of carbon (C).

b. The mass number is the superscript, so $^{16}_{8}X$ and $^{16}_{7}X$ have the same mass number. The first is an isotope of oxygen, and the second an isotope of nitrogen. $^{14}_{7}X$ and $^{14}_{6}X$ also have the same mass number. The first is an isotope of nitrogen, and the second an isotope of carbon.

c. To determine the number of neutrons, we subtract the atomic number from the mass number. We find that $^{16}_{8}X$ and $^{14}_{6}X$ each have eight neutrons ($16 - 8 = 8$ and $14 - 6 = 8$, respectively).

■ **EXERCISE 3.2A**

Which of the following represent isotopes of the same element?

$$^{90}_{37}X \quad ^{90}_{35}X \quad ^{88}_{37}X \quad ^{88}_{38}X \quad ^{93}_{38}X$$

■ **EXERCISE 3.2B**

How many different elements are represented in Exercise 3.2A?

Self-Assessment Questions

1. The three basic components of an atom are
   a. protium, deuterium, and tritium
   b. protons, neutrinos, and ions
   c. protons, neutrons, and electrons
   d. protons, neutrons, and ions

2. The identity of an element is determined by its
   a. atomic mass
   b. number of atoms
   c. number of electrons
   d. number of protons

3. How many electrons are required to equal the mass of one proton?
   a. 1   b. 18   c. about 1800   d. 1×10^{27}

4. Which particles have approximately the same mass?
   a. electrons and neutrons
   b. electrons and protons
   c. electrons, neutrons, and protons
   d. neutrons and protons

5. A change in the number of protons of an atom produces a(n)
   a. compound
   b. atom of a different element
   c. ion
   d. different isotope of the same element

6. The number of protons plus neutrons in an atom is its
   a. atomic mass   b. atomic number   c. isotope number   d. nucleon number

7. How many protons (p) and how many neutrons (n) are there in a $^{15}_{7}N$ nucleus?
   a. 7 p, 7 n   b. 7 p, 8 n   c. 7 p, 15 n   d. 8 p, 8 n

8. A neutral atom has 5 electrons and 6 neutrons. Its atomic number is
   a. 1   b. 5   c. 6   d. 11

9. The symbol for the isotope potassium-40 is
   a. $^{21}_{19}K$ b. $^{39}_{19}K$ c. $^{40}_{19}K$ d. $^{19}_{40}K$

3.6 Electron Arrangement: The Bohr Model

Learning Objectives ❯ Define *quantum.* ❯ Arrange the electrons in a given atom in energy levels (shells).

Let's turn our attention once more to electrons. Rutherford demonstrated that atoms have a tiny, positively charged nucleus with electrons outside it. Evidence soon accumulated that the electrons were not randomly distributed but were arranged in an ordered fashion. We will examine that evidence soon. But first, let's take a side trip into some colorful chemistry and physics to provide a background for our study of the arrangement of electrons in atoms.

▲ The brilliant colors of a fireworks display come from compounds added to the fireworks. Strontium compounds produce red, copper compounds produce blue or violet, and barium compounds produce green.

Fireworks and Flame Tests

Chemists of the eighteenth and nineteenth centuries developed flame tests that used the colors of flames to identify several elements (Figure 3.9). Sodium salts produce a persistent yellow flame, potassium salts a fleeting lavender flame, and lithium salts a brilliant red flame. It was not until the structure of atoms was better understood, however, that scientists could explain why each element emits a distinctive color of light.

Fireworks originated earlier than flame tests, in ancient China. The brilliant colors of aerial displays still mark our celebrations of patriotic holidays. The colors of fireworks are attributable to specific elements. Brilliant reds are produced by strontium compounds, whereas barium compounds are used to produce green, sodium compounds yield yellow, and copper salts produce blue or violet. However, the colors of fireworks and flame tests are not as simple as they seem to the unaided eye.

Continuous and Line Spectra

When white light from an incandescent lamp is passed through a prism, it produces a continuous spectrum, or rainbow of colors (Figure 3.10). A similar phenomenon occurs when sunlight passes through raindrops. The different colors of light correspond to different wavelengths. Blue light has shorter wavelengths than red light, but there is no sharp transition in moving from one color to the next. All wavelengths are present in a continuous spectrum (Figure 3.11, top). White light is simply a combination of all the various colors.

If the light from a colored flame test or a gas-discharge tube containing a particular element is passed through a prism, only narrow colored lines are observed (Figure 3.11). Each line corresponds to light of a particular wavelength. The pattern of lines emitted by an element is called its *line spectrum.* The line spectrum of an element is characteristic of that element and can be used to identify it. Not all the lines in the spectrum of an atom are visible; some are infrared or ultraviolet radiation.

4. Most lightbulbs produce white light. Why does a neon light appear orange? When a solid is heated, it goes through a stage of red heat, then yellow, and finally white light is emitted, which consists of all wavelengths. When a gas such as neon is heated, we get a line spectrum (Figure 3.11), which gives a specific color to the light.

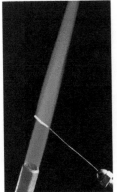
Lithium, Li

Sodium, Na

Potassium, K

Calcium, Ca

Strontium, Sr

▲ **Figure 3.9** Certain chemical elements can be identified by the characteristic colors their compounds impart to flames. Five examples are shown here.

▲ **Figure 3.10** A glass prism separates white light into a continuous spectrum, or rainbow, of colors just as sunlight passing through raindrops causes a rainbow in the sky.

▲ Danish physicist Niels Bohr received the 1922 Nobel Prize in Physics for his planetary model of the atom with its quantized electron energy levels. Element 107 is named bohrium (Bh) in his honor.

5. What does the word *quantum* actually mean? Just as an atom is the smallest unit of an element, a quantum is the smallest unit of energy. There are different sizes of quanta, but energy is produced or consumed in discrete rather than continuous units. "Quantum leap" comes from the idea suggested by Figure 3.12, where an electron can "leap" from one energy level to another.

▶ **Figure 3.12** Possible electron shifts between energy levels in atoms to produce the lines found in spectra. Not all of the lines are in the visible portion of the spectrum. The four colored arrows correspond to the four colored lines in the hydrogen spectrum seen in Figure 3.11.

Q: *Which transition involves the greater change in energy, a drop from energy level 6 to energy level 2, or a drop from energy level 7 to energy level 6? What color of light is absorbed when an electron in a hydrogen atom is boosted from energy level 2 to energy level 3?*

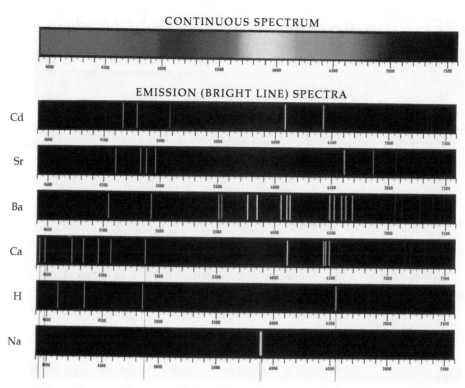

▲ **Figure 3.11** Line spectra of selected elements. Some of the components of the light emitted by excited atoms appear as colored lines. A continuous spectrum is shown at the top for comparison. The numbers are wavelengths of light given in Angstrom units (1 Å = 10^{-10} m). Each element has its own characteristic line spectrum that differs from all others and can be used to identify the element.

The visible line spectrum of hydrogen is fairly simple, consisting of four lines in that portion of the electromagnetic spectrum. To explain the hydrogen spectrum, Danish physicist Niels Bohr (1885–1962) worked out a model for the electron arrangement of the hydrogen atom.

Bohr's Explanation of Line Spectra

Niels Bohr presented his explanation of line spectra in 1913. He suggested that electrons cannot have just any amount of energy but can have only certain specified amounts; that is, the energy of an electron is *quantized*. A **quantum** (plural: *quanta*) is a tiny unit of energy, whose value depends on the frequency of the radiation. A specified energy value for an electron is called its **energy level**.

By absorbing a quantum of energy (for example, when atoms of the element are heated), an electron is elevated to a higher energy level (Figure 3.12). By giving up

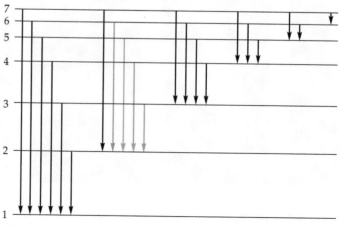

Energy level

a quantum of energy, the electron can return to a lower energy level. The energy released shows up as a line spectrum. Each line has a specific wavelength corresponding to a quantum of energy. An electron moves practically instantaneously from one energy level to another, and there are no intermediate stages.

Consider the analogy of a person on a ladder. A person can stand on the first rung, the second rung, the third rung, and so on, but is unable to stand between rungs. As the person goes from one rung to another, the potential energy (energy due to position) changes by definite amounts. As an electron moves from one energy level to another, its total energy (both potential and kinetic) also changes by definite amounts, or quanta.

Bohr based his model of the atom on the laws of planetary motion that had been set down by the German astronomer Johannes Kepler (1571–1630) three centuries before. Bohr imagined the electrons to be orbiting about the nucleus much as planets orbit the sun (Figure 3.13). Different energy levels were pictured as different orbits. The modern picture of the atom is different, as we will see in the next section.

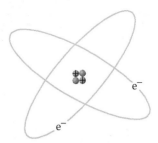

▲ **Figure 3.13** The nuclear atom, as envisioned by Bohr. Most of its mass is in an extremely small nucleus. Bohr thought that electrons orbited about the nucleus in the same way that planets orbit the sun.

Ground States and Excited States

The electron in a hydrogen atom is usually in the first, or lowest, energy level. Electrons tend to stay in their lowest possible energy levels (those nearest the nucleus). Atoms with their electrons thus situated are said to be in their **ground state**. When a flame or other source supplies energy to an atom (of hydrogen, for example) and an electron jumps from the lowest possible level to a higher level, the atom is said to be in an **excited state**. An atom in an excited state eventually emits a quantum of energy—often a *photon*, or "particle," of light—as the electron jumps back down to one of the lower levels and ultimately reaches the ground state.

Bohr's theory was spectacularly successful in explaining the line spectrum of hydrogen. It established the important idea of energy levels in atoms. Bohr was awarded the Nobel Prize in Physics in 1922 for this work.

Atoms larger than hydrogen have more than one electron, and Bohr was also able to deduce that a given energy level of an atom could contain at most only a certain number of electrons. The maximum number of electrons that can be in a given level is indicated by the formula

$$\text{Maximum number of electrons} = 2n^2$$

where n is the energy level being considered. For the first energy level ($n = 1$), the maximum number of electrons is $2 \times 1^2 = 2 \times 1 = 2$. For the second energy level ($n = 2$), the maximum number is $2 \times 2^2 = 2 \times 4 = 8$. For the third level, the maximum number is $2 \times 3^2 = 2 \times 9 = 18$.

The various energy levels are often called **shells**. The first energy level ($n = 1$) is the first shell, the second energy level ($n = 2$) is the second shell, and so on.

Example 3.3 Electron-Shell Capacity

What is the maximum number of electrons in the fifth shell (fifth energy level)?

Solution
The maximum number of electrons in a given shell is given by $2n^2$. For the fifth level, $n = 5$, and so we have

$$2 \times 5^2 = 2 \times 25 = 50 \text{ electrons}$$

▪ EXERCISE 3.3A
What is the maximum number of electrons in the fourth shell (fourth energy level)?

▪ EXERCISE 3.3B
What is the lowest energy level that can hold 18 electrons?

Building Atoms: Main Shells

Imagine building up atoms by adding one electron to the proper shell as *each* proton is added to the nucleus, keeping in mind that electrons will go to the lowest energy level (shell) available. For hydrogen, with a nucleus containing only one proton ($Z = 1$), the single electron goes into the first shell. For helium, with a nucleus having two protons ($Z = 2$), both electrons go into the first shell. According to Bohr, two electrons is the maximum population of the first shell, and that level is filled in the helium atom. (We can ignore the neutrons in the nucleus; they are not involved in this process.)

With lithium ($Z = 3$), two electrons go into the first shell, and the third must go into the second shell. This process of adding electrons is continued until the second shell is filled with eight electrons, as in a neon atom ($Z = 10$), which has two of its 10 electrons in the first shell and the remaining eight in the second shell.

A sodium atom ($Z = 11$) has 11 electrons. Two are in the first shell, the second shell is filled with eight electrons, and the remaining electron is in the third shell. We can represent the **electron configuration** (or arrangement) of the first 11 elements as follows:

Element	1st shell	2nd shell	3rd shell
H	1		
He	2		
Li	2	1	
⋮	⋮	⋮	
Ne	2	8	
Na	2	8	1

Sometimes the main-shell electron configuration is abbreviated by writing the symbol for the element followed by the numbers of electrons in each shell, separated by commas, starting with the lowest energy level. Following the color scheme from the preceding table, the main-shell configuration for sodium is simply

$$\text{Na } 2, 8, 1$$

We can continue to add electrons to the third shell until we get to argon. The main-shell configuration for argon is

$$\text{Ar } 2, 8, 8$$

After argon, the notation for electron configurations is enhanced with more detail. This notation is discussed in greater detail in Section 3.8. Meanwhile, Example 3.4 shows how to determine a few main-shell configurations.

Example 3.4 | Main-Shell Electron Configurations

What is the main-shell electron configuration for fluorine?

Solution

Fluorine has the symbol F ($Z = 9$). It has nine electrons. Two of these electrons go into the first shell, and the remaining seven go into the second shell.

$$\text{F } 2, 7$$

■ EXERCISE 3.4

Write the main-shell electron configurations for (a) beryllium and (b) magnesium. These elements are in the same column of the periodic table. What do you notice about the number of electrons in their outermost shells?

Self-Assessment Questions

1. When electrified in a gas-discharge tube, different elements emit light that forms narrow lines that are
   a. characteristic of each particular element
   b. the same as those of the hydrogen spectrum
   c. the same for all elements but with differing colors
   d. the same for all elements but with differing intensities

2. When an electron in an atom goes from a higher energy level to a lower one, the electron
   a. absorbs energy
   b. changes its volume
   c. changes its charge
   d. releases energy

3. An atom in an excited state is one with an electron that has
   a. moved to a higher energy level
   b. been removed
   c. bonded to another atom to make a molecule
   d. combined with a proton to make a neutron

4. The maximum number of electrons in the first shell of an atom is
   a. 2   b. 6   c. 8   d. unlimited

5. The maximum number of electrons in the third shell of an atom is
   a. 6   b. 8   c. 18   d. 32

6. The main-shell electron configuration of aluminum is
   a. 2, 8, 1   b. 2, 8, 3   c. 2, 8, 13   d. 2, 8, 8, 8, 1

7. The main-shell electron configuration of sulfur is
   a. 2, 8, 4   b. 2, 8, 6   c. 2, 8, 8, 8, 6   d. 2, 8, 18, 4

Answers: 1, a; 2, d; 3, a; 4, a; 5, c; 6, b; 7, b

3.7 Electron Arrangement: The Quantum Model

Learning Objectives ❯ Relate the idea of a quantum of energy to an orbital. ❯ Write an electron configuration (in subshell notation) for a given atom.

Bohr's simple planetary model of the atom has been replaced for many purposes by more sophisticated models in which electrons are treated as *both* particles and waves. The electrons have characteristic wavelengths and their locations are indicated as probabilities. The theory that the electron should have wavelike properties was first suggested in 1924 by Louis de Broglie (1892–1987), a young French physicist. Although it was hard to accept because of Thomson's evidence that electrons are particles, de Broglie's theory was experimentally verified within a few years.

Erwin Schrödinger (1887–1961), an Austrian physicist, used highly mathematical *quantum mechanics* in the 1920s to develop equations that describe the properties of electrons in atoms. Fortunately, we can make use of some of Schrödinger's results without understanding his elaborate equations. The solutions to these equations express the probability of finding an electron in a given volume of space. These variously shaped volumes of space, called **orbitals**, replace the planetary orbits of the Bohr model.

Suppose you had a camera that could photograph electrons and you left the shutter open while an electron zipped about the nucleus. The developed picture would give a record of where the electron had been. (Doing the same thing with an electric fan would give a blurred image of the rapidly moving blades, an image resembling a disk.) The electrons in the first shell would appear as a fuzzy ball (often referred to as a *charge cloud* or an *electron cloud* [Figure 3.14]).

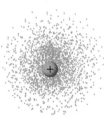

An *s* orbital

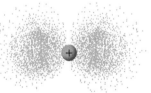

A *p* orbital

▲ **Figure 3.14** The modern charge-cloud representation of an atomic orbital is more accurate than the Bohr model (Figure 3.13). An electron cloud is the "fuzzy" region around an atomic nucleus where an electron is likely to be. The type of orbital determines the general shape of the cloud, as seen here.

▶ **Figure 3.15** Electron orbitals of the second main shell. In these drawings, the nucleus of the atom is located at the intersection of the axes. The eight electrons that would be placed in the second shell of Bohr's model are distributed among these four orbitals in the current model of the atom, with two electrons per orbital.

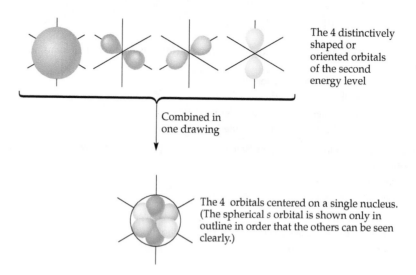

The 4 distinctively shaped or oriented orbitals of the second energy level

Combined in one drawing

The 4 orbitals centered on a single nucleus. (The spherical s orbital is shown only in outline in order that the others can be seen clearly.)

Building Atoms by Orbital Filling

Schrödinger concluded that each electron orbital could contain a maximum of two electrons and that some shells could contain more than one orbital. The first shell contains a single spherical orbital called 1s. The second shell contains four orbitals: 2s is spherical, and the other three orbitals, called 2p, are dumbbell-shaped (Figure 3.15). Orbitals in the same shell that have the same letter designation make up a **subshell (sublevel)**. The second shell has two subshells, the 2s subshell with only one orbital and the 2p subshell with three orbitals. The third shell contains nine orbitals distributed among three subshells: a spherical 3s orbital in the 3s subshell, three dumbbell-shaped 3p orbitals in the 3p subshell, and five 3d orbitals with more complicated shapes in the 3d subshell.

In building up the electron configurations of atoms of the various elements, the lower sublevels (subshells) are filled first.

Hydrogen ($Z = 1$) has only one electron in the s orbital of the first shell. The electron configuration is

$$\text{H} \quad 1s^1$$

Helium ($Z = 2$) has two electrons and its electron configuration is

$$\text{He} \quad 1s^2$$

Lithium ($Z = 3$) has three electrons—two in the first shell and one in the s orbital of the second shell:

$$\text{Li} \quad 1s^2 2s^1$$

Skipping to nitrogen ($Z = 7$), the seven electrons are arranged as follows:

$$\text{N} \quad 1s^2 2s^2 2p^3$$

Let's review what this notation means:

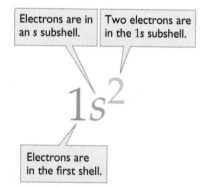

Electrons are in an s subshell.

Two electrons are in the 1s subshell.

Electrons are in the first shell.

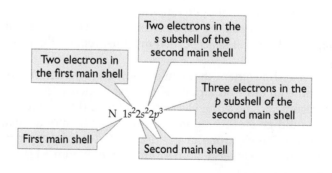

Two electrons in the first main shell

Two electrons in the s subshell of the second main shell

Three electrons in the p subshell of the second main shell

First main shell

Second main shell

For argon ($Z = 18$), with its 18 electrons, the configuration is

$$\text{Ar} \quad 1s^2 2s^2 2p^6 3s^2 3p^6$$

Note that the highest occupied subshell, $3p$, is filled. However, the order of subshell filling for elements with Z greater than 18 is not intuitively obvious. In potassium ($Z = 19$), for example, the $4s$ subshell fills before the $3d$ subshell. The order in which the various subshells are filled is shown in Figure 3.16, and Table 3.3 gives the electron configurations for the first 20 elements. The electrons in the outermost main shell, called *valence electrons* (Section 3.8), are shown in color.

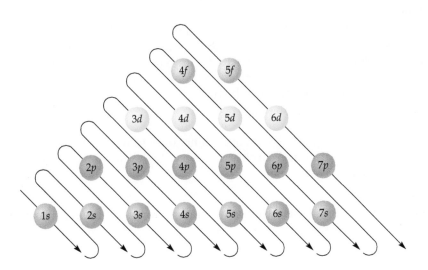

◀ **Figure 3.16** An order-of-filling chart for determining the electron configurations of atoms.

Table 3.3	Electron Configurations for Atoms of the First 20 Elements	
Name	**Atomic Number**	**Electron Configuration**
Hydrogen	1	$1s^1$
Helium	2	$1s^2$
Lithium	3	$1s^2 2s^1$
Beryllium	4	$1s^2 2s^2$
Boron	5	$1s^2 2s^2 2p^1$
Carbon	6	$1s^2 2s^2 2p^2$
Nitrogen	7	$1s^2 2s^2 2p^3$
Oxygen	8	$1s^2 2s^2 2p^4$
Fluorine	9	$1s^2 2s^2 2p^5$
Neon	10	$1s^2 2s^2 2p^6$
Sodium	11	$1s^2 2s^2 2p^6 3s^1$
Magnesium	12	$1s^2 2s^2 2p^6 3s^2$
Aluminum	13	$1s^2 2s^2 2p^6 3s^2 3p^1$
Silicon	14	$1s^2 2s^2 2p^6 3s^2 3p^2$
Phosphorus	15	$1s^2 2s^2 2p^6 3s^2 3p^3$
Sulfur	16	$1s^2 2s^2 2p^6 3s^2 3p^4$
Chlorine	17	$1s^2 2s^2 2p^6 3s^2 3p^5$
Argon	18	$1s^2 2s^2 2p^6 3s^2 3p^6$
Potassium	19	$1s^2 2s^2 2p^6 3s^2 3p^6 4s^1$
Calcium	20	$1s^2 2s^2 2p^6 3s^2 3p^6 4s^2$

Example 3.5 Subshell Notation

Without referring to Table 3.3, use subshell notation to write the electron configurations for (a) oxygen and (b) sulfur. What do the electron configurations of these two elements have in common?

Solution

a. Oxygen ($Z = 8$) has eight electrons. We place them in subshells, starting with the lowest energy level. Two go into the $1s$ orbital and two into the $2s$ orbital. That leaves four electrons to be placed in the $2p$ subshell. The electron configuration is $1s^2 2s^2 2p^4$.

b. Sulfur ($Z = 16$) atoms have 16 electrons each. The electron configuration is $1s^2 2s^2 2p^6 3s^2 3p^4$. Note that the total of the superscripts is 16 and that we have not exceeded the maximum capacity for any sublevel.

   Both O and S have electron configurations with four electrons in the highest energy sublevel (outermost subshell).

■ EXERCISE 3.5A

Without referring to Table 3.3, use subshell notation to write out the electron configurations for (a) fluorine and (b) chlorine. What do the electron configurations for these two elements have in common?

■ EXERCISE 3.5B

Use Figure 3.16 to write the electron configurations for (a) titanium (Ti) and (b) gallium (Ga).

Self-Assessment Questions

1. The shape of a $1s$ orbital is
   a. circular
   b. a dumbbell
   c. spherical
   d. variable

2. The maximum number of electrons in an atomic orbital
   a. depends on the main shell
   b. depends on the subshell
   c. is always 2
   d. is always 8

3. Which of the following subshells has the highest energy?
   a. $2p$ b. $2s$ c. $3p$ d. $3s$

4. What is the lowest-numbered main shell to have d orbitals?
   a. 1   b. 2   c. 3   d. 4

5. Which of the following atoms has a half-filled subshell in the ground state?
   a. beryllium
   b. neon
   c. nitrogen
   d. oxygen

6. Which subshell has a total of three orbitals?
   a. d b. f c. p d. s

7. In what main shell is a $3d$ subshell located?
   a. 1   b. 3   c. 5   d. none

8. The electron capacity of the $4p$ subshell is
   a. 3   b. 4   c. 6   d. 10

3.8 Electron Configurations and the Periodic Table

Learning Objective ❯ Describe how an element's electron configuration relates to its location in the periodic table.

In general, the properties of elements can be correlated with their electron configurations. (We will explore bond formation using electron configurations in Chapter 4.) Because the number of electrons equals the number of protons, the periodic table tells us about electron configuration as well as atomic number.

The modern periodic table (inside front cover) has horizontal rows and vertical columns.

- Each vertical column is a **group**, or *family*. Elements in a group have similar chemical properties.
- A horizontal row of the periodic table is called a **period**. The properties of elements change in a recurring manner across a period.

In the United States, the groups are often indicated by a numeral followed by the letter A or B.

- An element in an A group is a **main group element**.
- An element in a B group is a **transition element**.

The International Union of Pure and Applied Chemistry (IUPAC) recommends numbering the groups from 1 to 18. Both systems are indicated on the periodic table on the inside front cover, but this book uses the traditional U.S. system.

Family Features: Outer Electron Configurations

The period in which an element appears in the periodic table tells us how many main shells an atom of that element has. Phosphorus, for example, is in the third period, and so the phosphorus atom has three main shells. The U.S. group number (for main group elements) tells us how many electrons are in the outermost shell. An electron in the outermost shell of an atom is called a **valence electron**. From the fact that phosphorus is in group 5A, we can deduce that it has five valence electrons. Two of these are in an s orbital, and the other three are in p orbitals. We can indicate the outer electron configuration of the phosphorus atom as

$$P \quad 3s^2 3p^3$$

The valence electrons determine most of the chemistry of an atom. Since all the elements in the same group of the periodic table have the same number of valence electrons, they should have similar chemistry, and they do. Figure 3.17 relates the subshell configurations to the groups in the periodic table.

Family Groups

Elements within a group have similar properties. All the elements in group 1A have one valence electron, and all except hydrogen are very reactive metals (hydrogen is a nonmetal). All group 1A elements have the outer electron configuration ns^1, where n denotes the number of the outermost main shell.

The metals in group 1A are called **alkali metals**. They react vigorously with water, producing hydrogen gas. There are noticeable trends in properties within this family. For example, lithium is the hardest metal in the group. Sodium is softer than lithium; potassium is softer still; and so on down the group. Lithium is also the least reactive toward water. Sodium, potassium, rubidium, and cesium are progressively more reactive. Francium is highly radioactive and extremely rare. Few of its properties have been measured.

6. What is periodic about the periodic table? Figure 3.17 shows why there are periodic, or recurring, trends in the periodic table. Elements in the same column have similar electron configurations and often have similar chemical and physical characteristics as well.

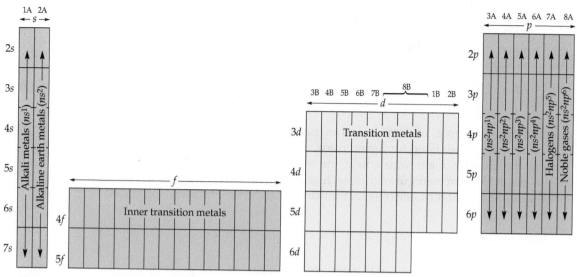

▲ **Figure 3.17** Valence-shell electron configurations and the periodic table.

▲ (Above) Lithium, an alkali metal, reacts with water to form hydrogen gas. (Below) Potassium, another alkali metal, undergoes the same reaction but much more vigorously.

Hydrogen is the odd one in group 1A. It is not an alkali metal but rather a typical nonmetal. Based on its properties, hydrogen probably should be put in a group of its own.

Group 2A elements are known as **alkaline earth metals**. The metals in this group have the outer electron configuration ns^2. Most are fairly soft and moderately reactive with water. Beryllium is the odd member of the group in that it is rather hard and does not react with water. As in other families, there are trends in properties within the group. For example, magnesium, calcium, strontium, barium, and radium are progressively more reactive toward water.

Group 7A elements, often called **halogens**, also consist of reactive elements. All have seven valence electrons with the configuration ns^2np^5. Halogens react vigorously with alkali metals to form crystalline solids (this is discussed further in Chapter 4). There are trends in the halogen family as you move down the group. Fluorine is most reactive toward alkali metals, chlorine is the next most reactive, and so on. Fluorine and chlorine are gases at room temperature, bromine is a liquid, and iodine is a solid. (Astatine, like francium, is highly radioactive and extremely rare; few of its properties have been determined.)

Members of group 8A, to the far right on the periodic table, have a complete set of valence electrons and therefore undergo few, if any, chemical reactions. They are called **noble gases**, for their lack of chemical reactivity.

Example 3.6   Valence-Shell Electron Configurations

Use subshell notation to write the electron configurations for the outermost main shell of **(a)** strontium (Sr) and **(b)** arsenic (As).

Solution

a. Strontium is in group 2A and thus has two valence electrons in an s subshell. Because strontium is in the fifth period of the periodic table, its outer main shell is $n = 5$. Its outer electron configuration is therefore $5s^2$.

b. Arsenic is in group 5A and the fourth period. Its five outer (valence) electrons are in the $n = 4$ shell, and the configuration is $4s^2 4p^3$.

■ EXERCISE 3.6A

Use subshell notation to write the configurations for the outermost main shell of **(a)** rubidium (Rb), **(b)** selenium (Se), and **(c)** germanium (Ge).

■ **EXERCISE 3.6B**

The valence electrons in aluminum have the configuration $3s^2 3p^1$. In the periodic table, gallium is directly below aluminum, and indium is directly below gallium. Use only this information to write the configurations for the valence electrons in (a) gallium and (b) indium.

Metals and Nonmetals

Elements in the periodic table are divided into two classes by a heavy, stepped line (see inside front cover). Those to the left of the line are *metals*. A **metal** has a characteristic luster (shininess) and generally is a good conductor of heat and electricity. Except for mercury, which is a liquid, all metals are solids at room temperature. Metals generally are *malleable*; that is, they can be hammered into thin sheets. Most also are *ductile*, which means that they can be drawn into wires.

Elements to the right of the stepped line are *nonmetals*. A **nonmetal** lacks metallic properties. Several nonmetals are gases (oxygen, nitrogen, fluorine, and chlorine). Others are solids (e.g., carbon, sulfur, phosphorus, and iodine). Bromine is the only nonmetal that is a liquid at room temperature.

Some of the elements bordering the stepped line are called *semimetals*, or *metalloids*, and these have intermediate properties that may resemble those of both metals and nonmetals. There is a lack of agreement on just which elements fit in this category.

Which Model to Use

For some purposes in this text, we use only main-shell configurations of atoms to picture the distribution of electrons in atoms. At other times, the electron clouds of the quantum mechanical model are more useful. Even Dalton's model sometimes proves to be the best way to describe certain phenomena (the behavior of gases, for example). The choice of model is always based on which one is most helpful in understanding a particular concept. This, after all, is the purpose of scientific models.

▲ (Top) Metals such as gold are easily shaped, and they conduct heat and electricity well. (Bottom) Nonmetals such as sulfur are usually brittle, melt at low temperatures, and often are good insulators.

Self-Assessment Questions

1. Which pair of elements has the most similar chemical properties?
   a. Ca and Cd   **b.** Cl and Br   **c.** P and S   **d.** Sb and Sc

2. Elements within a period of the periodic table have the same number of
   a. electrons in the outermost shell
   b. neutrons in the nucleus
   c. occupied main shells
   d. protons in the nucleus

3. The valence-shell electron configuration of the halogens is
   a. ns^1 **b.** $ns^2 np^3$ **c.** $ns^2 np^5$ **d.** $ns^2 np^6$

4. The alkali metals are members of group
   a. 1A   **b.** 2A   **c.** 7A   **d.** 8A

5. What is the total number of valence electrons in an atom of bromine?
   a. 5   **b.** 7   **c.** 17   **d.** 35

6. Which of the following sets of elements exhibits the most similar chemical properties?
   a. Al, Sc, Si   **b.** Hg, Br, Se   **c.** Li, Na, K   **d.** N, O, F

7. In the ground state, atoms of a fourth period element must have
   a. a 3f sublevel
   b. electrons in the fourth shell
   c. four valence electrons
   d. properties similar to those of other elements in the fourth period

Scott Cummings, *Kenyon College*

Clean Energy from Solar Fuels

Imagine a world powered by a clean fuel which is manufactured using sunlight and water, and produces no carbon dioxide emissions when used. This has been the dream of chemists around the world, who have been working for many years to develop a "solar fuel" that might someday replace some of the fossil fuels that are so important to us—oil, coal, and natural gas.

Sunlight is a free and abundant power source. More solar energy reaches Earth's surface in one hour than all of the fossil fuel energy that human beings use in one year. The goal for chemists is to develop efficient methods to capture just a tiny part of this sunlight and convert it into a useful form such as electricity. For now, this is accomplished using solar panels constructed from photovoltaic cells, devices usually made of silicon. But sunshine is intermittent; we need to convert radiant solar energy into chemical energy—a storable fuel. One idea for a solar fuel is hydrogen. Learning how to utilize sunlight to make hydrogen is one of the grand challenges of chemistry.

A full hydrogen energy cycle uses solar energy to split water (H_2O) into hydrogen (H_2) and oxygen (O_2) and then uses the hydrogen as a clean fuel to produce either heat (when burned) or electricity (using a fuel cell). Splitting water requires energy input to break the bonds that hold together the O and H atoms in water molecules. One of the simplest ways to do this is by electrolysis (Section 3.1), which requires electrical energy. If the electricity is produced using a solar panel, then the hydrogen formed is a solar fuel. This approach is currently quite expensive, and much research in chemistry is aimed at discovering new and inexpensive photovoltaic materials—including plastics—from which to construct solar panels. Chemists also seek electrodes and other components that can be made from abundant elements instead of the precious metal platinum (Pt) that is typically used.

For a different approach to hydrogen production, chemists are turning to green plants for inspiration. Plants use photosynthesis to take energy from the sun and store it in the chemical bonds of compounds known as *carbohydrates* (Section 8.10). This chemical

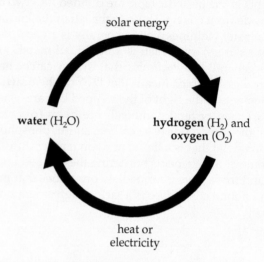

Clean energy cycle. Solar energy is used to produce hydrogen and oxygen from water (top). Hydrogen fuel reacts with oxygen to produce water and releases energy as either heat or electricity.

process is essential to sustain life on the planet and depends on the ability to split water molecules with sunlight. Chemists are hoping to unlock the secrets of the leaf to develop "artificial photosynthesis" and use solar energy to produce hydrogen fuel from water.

In natural photosynthesis, plants employ many different molecules to capture and convert solar energy. Chlorophyll molecules absorb part of the solar spectrum, giving a leaf its green color. To mimic this process, chemists are designing colorful synthetic dyes to capture photons from the sun. When a dye absorbs light, one of its electrons is excited, which generates an excited-state molecule. But rather than emitting the energy back as a photon (Section 3.6), the energy can be harnessed to split water. Plants also employ a cluster of manganese, calcium, and oxygen atoms to crack apart water molecules and produce oxygen. Chemists have been active in trying to mimic this reaction as well, using compounds made in the laboratory.

Solar fuels such as hydrogen embody several green chemistry principles. Hydrogen fuel is only as green as the method used to make it. If produced using sunlight as the energy source and water as the chemical feedstock, though, the fuel can be clean and renewable (Principle 7). Unlike fossil fuels, hydrogen is a carbon-free fuel that, when produced from sunlight, prevents carbon dioxide emissions (Principle 1). A solar-hydrogen system relies on compounds that increase efficiency and facilitate both the water-splitting chemistry and the use of hydrogen (Principle 9). If these materials are earth-abundant and do not cause harm to the environment, this process closes the clean-fuel cycle.

PHOTOSYNTHESIS

carbon dioxide + water ⟶ carbohydrate + oxygen

ARTIFICIAL PHOTOSYNTHESIS

water ⟶ hydrogen + oxygen

Two ways to make solar fuels. Green plants use photosynthesis to produce carbohydrate fuels. Chemists are trying to produce hydrogen fuel. Both reactions use water and solar energy.

CRITICAL THINKING EXERCISES

Apply knowledge that you have gained in this chapter and one or more of the FLaReS principles (Chapter 1) to evaluate the following statements or claims.

3.1 Suppose you read in the newspaper that a chemist in South America claims to have discovered a new element with an atomic mass of 34. Extremely rare, it was found in a sample taken from the Andes Mountains. Unfortunately, the chemist has used all of the sample in his analyses.

3.2 Some aboriginal tribes have rain-making ceremonies in which they toss pebbles of gypsum up into

the air. (Gypsum is the material used to make plaster of Paris by heating the rock to remove some of its water.) Sometimes it does rain several days after these rain-making ceremonies.

3.3 Some scientists have recently suggested that bacteria from California's Mono Lake may be able to use arsenic (As) in place of phosphorus (P) in their proteins and DNA.

■ SUMMARY

Section 3.1—Davy, Faraday, and others showed that matter is electrical in nature. They were able to decompose compounds into elements by electrolysis or passing electricity through molten salts. Electrodes are carbon rods or metal strips that carry electricity into the electrolyte, the solution or compound that conducts electricity. The electrolyte contains ions—charged atoms or groups of atoms. The anode is the positive electrode, and anions (negatively charged ions) move toward it. The cathode is the negative electrode, and cations (positively charged ions) move toward it. Experiments with cathode rays in gas-discharge tubes showed that matter contained negatively charged particles, which were called electrons. Thomson determined the mass-to-charge ratio for the electron. Goldstein's experiment showed that matter also contained positively charged particles. Millikan's oil-drop experiment measured the charge on the electron, so its mass could then be calculated.

Section 3.2—In his studies of cathode rays, Roentgen accidentally discovered X-rays, a highly penetrating form of radiation now used in medical diagnosis. Becquerel accidentally discovered another type of radiation that comes from certain unstable elements. Marie Curie named this new discovery radioactivity and studied it extensively.

Section 3.3—Radioactivity was soon classified as three different types of radiation: Alpha particles have four times the mass of a hydrogen atom and a positive charge twice that of an electron. Beta particles are energetic electrons. Gamma rays are a form of energy like X-rays but more penetrating.

Section 3.4—Rutherford's experiments with alpha particles and gold foil showed that most of the alpha particles emitted toward the foil passed through it. A few were deflected or, occasionally, bounced back almost directly toward the source. This indicated that all the positive charge and most of the mass of an atom must be in a tiny core, which Rutherford called the nucleus.

Section 3.5—Rutherford called the smallest unit of positive charge the proton; it has about the mass of a hydrogen atom and a charge equal in size but opposite in sign to the electron. In 1932, Chadwick discovered the neutron, a nuclear particle as massive as a proton but with no charge. The number of

protons in an atom is the atomic number (Z). Atoms of the same element have the same number of protons but may have different numbers of neutrons; such atoms are called isotopes. Different isotopes of an element are nearly identical chemically. Protons and neutrons collectively are called nucleons, and the number of nucleons is called the mass number or nucleon number. The difference between the mass number and the atomic number is the number of neutrons. The general symbol for an isotope of element X is written $^A_Z X$, where A is the mass number and Z is the atomic number.

Section 3.6—Light from the sun or from an incandescent lamp produces a continuous spectrum, containing all colors. Light from a gas-discharge tube produces a line spectrum, containing only certain colors. Bohr explained line spectra by proposing that an electron in an atom resides only at certain discrete energy levels, which differ from one another by a quantum, or discrete unit of energy. An atom drops to the lowest energy state, or ground state, after being in a higher energy state, or excited state. The energy emitted when electrons move to lower energy levels manifests as a line spectrum characteristic of the particular element, with the lines corresponding to specific wavelengths (colors) of light. Bohr also deduced that the energy levels of an atom could hold at most $2n^2$ electrons, where n is the number of the energy level, or shell. A description of the shells occupied by the electrons of an atom is one way of giving the atom's electron configuration, or arrangement of electrons.

Section 3.7—de Broglie theorized that electrons have wave properties. Schrödinger developed equations that described each electron's location in terms of an orbital, a volume of space that the electron usually occupies. Each orbital holds at most two electrons. Orbitals in the same shell and with the same energy make up a subshell, or sublevel, each of which is designated by a letter. An s orbital is spherical and a p orbital is dumbbell-shaped. The d and f orbitals have more complex shapes. The first main shell can hold only one s orbital; the second can hold one s and three p orbitals; and the third can hold one s, three p, and five d orbitals. In writing an electron configuration using subshell notation, we give the shell number and subshell letter, followed by a superscript indicating the number of electrons in that sub-shell. The order of the shells and subshells can be remembered with a chart or by looking at the periodic table.

Section 3.8—Elements in the periodic table are arranged vertically in **groups** and horizontally in **periods**. Electrons in the outermost shell of an atom, called **valence electrons**, determine the reactivity of that atom. Elements in a group usually have the same number of valence electrons and similarities in properties. We designate groups by a number and the letter A or B. The A-group elements are **main group elements**. The B-group elements are **transition elements**. Group 1A elements are the **alkali metals**. Except for hydrogen, they are all soft, low-melting, highly reactive metals. Group 2A consists of the **alkaline earth metals**, fairly soft and reactive metals. Group 7A elements, the **halogens**, are reactive

nonmetals. Group 8A elements, the **noble gases**, react very little or not at all. A stepped line divides the periodic table into **metals**, which conduct electricity and heat and are shiny, malleable, and ductile, and **nonmetals**, which tend to lack the properties of metals. Some elements bordering the stepped line, called *metalloids*, have properties intermediate between those of metals and nonmetals.

Green chemistry Hydrogen is a promising clean fuel because it can be manufactured using sunlight and water and using it does not produce carbon dioxide as waste. Using a solar cell, energy from sunlight can be converted into electricity, which can then be used to split water into hydrogen and oxygen; this splitting of water can also be accomplished by a process that mimics photosynthesis. The hydrogen can be burned to produce heat or used in a fuel cell to produce electricity.

Learning Objectives

❯ Explain the electrical properties of an atom. (3.1)	Problems 16, 23, 24
❯ Describe how the properties of electricity explain the structure of atoms. (3.1)	Problems 13, 14, 19, 20
❯ Describe the experiments that led to the discovery of X-rays and an explanation of radioactivity. (3.2)	Problem 2
❯ Distinguish the three main kinds of radioactivity: alpha, beta, and gamma. (3.3)	Problem 3
❯ Sketch the nuclear model of the atom, and identify its parts. (3.4)	Problem 6
❯ List the particles that make up the nucleus of an atom, and give their relative masses and electric charges. (3.5)	Problems 7–9
❯ Identify elements and isotopes from their nuclear particles. (3.5)	Problems 8, 9, 15–18
❯ Define *quantum*. (3.6)	Problem 10
❯ Arrange the electrons in a given atom in energy levels (shells). (3.6)	Problems 33, 38–40
❯ Relate the idea of a quantum of energy to an orbital. (3.7)	Problem 11
❯ Write an electron configuration (in subshell notation) for a given atom. (3.7)	Problems 19–32, 37
❯ Describe how an element's electron configuration relates to its location in the periodic table. (3.8)	Problems 34 and 35
❯ Distinguish the conversion of solar energy into electrical energy in a solar cell from the conversion of solar energy into the chemical-bond energy of a solar fuel.	Problems 42–44
❯ Explain why splitting water into the elements hydrogen and oxygen requires an energy input and producing water by the reaction of hydrogen and oxygen releases energy.	Problem 43

■ REVIEW QUESTIONS

1. What did each of the following scientists contribute to our knowledge of the atom?
   a. William Crookes   b. Eugen Goldstein
   c. Michael Faraday   d. J. J. Thomson

2. What is radioactivity? How did the discovery of radioactivity contradict Dalton's atomic theory?

3. How are X-rays and gamma rays similar? How are they different?

4. Define or identify each of the following.
   a. deuterium   b. tritium
   c. photon

5. The following table describes four atoms.

	Atom A	Atom B	Atom C	Atom D
Number of protons	17	18	18	17
Number of neutrons	18	17	18	17
Number of electrons	17	18	18	17

Are atoms A and B isotopes? A and C? A and D? B and C?

6. Compare Dalton's model of the atom with the nuclear model of the atom.

7. Which two atoms in Question 5 have about the same mass?

8. What are the symbol, name, and atomic number of the element with Z = 76 ? You may use the periodic table and a table of atomic masses.

9. What are the symbol, name, and atomic number of the element that has 21 protons in the nuclei of its atoms?

10. Explain what is meant by the term *quantum*.

11. Which atom absorbs more energy, one in which an electron moves from the second shell to the third shell or an otherwise identical atom in which an electron moves from the first to the third shell?

12. How did Bohr refine the model of the atom?

13. Use the periodic table to determine the number of protons in an atom of each of the following elements.
    a. lithium   b. magnesium
    c. chlorine   d. fluorine
    e. aluminum   f. phosphorus

14. How many electrons are there in each neutral atom of the elements listed in Question 13?

PROBLEMS

Nuclear Symbols and Isotopes

15. Give the symbol and name for **(a)** an isotope with a mass number of 42 and an atomic number of 20 and **(b)** an isotope with 28 neutrons and 23 protons.

16. Fill in the table:

Element	Mass Number	Number of Protons	Number of Neutrons
Nickel	60		
	108	46	
		7	7
Iodine			74

17. How many different elements are listed here?
    $_{11}^{23}X$ $_{10}^{22}X$ $_{5}^{11}X$ $_{11}^{24}X$ $_{12}^{25}X$

18. How many different isotopes of silver are listed here? (The X does not necessarily represent any specific element.)
    $_{47}^{108}X$ $_{48}^{108}X$ $_{47}^{110}X$ $_{46}^{109}X$ $_{47}^{107}X$

Subshell Notation for Electron Configurations

19. Without referring to the periodic table, give the atomic numbers of the elements with the following electron configurations.
    a. $1s^2\,2s^2\,2p^3$
    b. $1s^2\,2s^2\,2p^6\,3s^2\,3p^1$
    c. $1s^2\,2s^2\,2p^6\,3s^2\,3p^6\,4s^1$

20. Without referring to the periodic table, give the atomic numbers of the elements with the following electron configurations.
    a. $1s^2\,2s^2\,2p^6\,3s^2\,3p^3$
    b. $1s^2\,2s^2\,2p^4$
    c. $1s^2\,2s^2\,2p^6\,3s^1$

21. Indicate whether each electron configuration represents an atom in the ground state or in a possible excited state or is incorrect. In each case, explain why.
    a. $1s^1 2s^1$ b. $1s^2 2s^2 2p^7$
    c. $1s^2 2p^2$ d. $1s^2 2s^2 2p^2$

22. Indicate whether each electron configuration represents an atom in the ground state or in a possible excited state or is incorrect. In each case, explain why.
    a. $1s^2 2s^2 3s^2$
    b. $1s^2 2s^2 2p^2 3s^1$
    c. $1s^2 2s^2 2p^6 2d^5$
    d. $1s^2 2s^4 2p^2$

23. Suppose that one electron is added to the outermost shell of a fluorine atom. What element's electron configuration would the atom then have?

24. Suppose that each of the following changes is made. Give the symbol for the element whose electron configuration matches the result.
    a. Two electrons are added to an oxygen atom.
    b. Two electrons are removed from a calcium atom.
    c. Three electrons are removed from an aluminum atom.

25. Referring only to the periodic table, tell how the electron configurations of silicon (Si) and germanium (Ge) are similar. How are they different?

26. Referring only to the periodic table, tell how the electron configurations of fluorine (F) and chlorine (Cl) are similar. How are they different? How do you expect the electron configurations of bromine (Br) and iodine (I) to be similar to those of fluorine and chlorine?

27. Refer to the periodic table to identify each element as a metal or a nonmetal.
    a. manganese
    b. strontium
    c. cesium
    d. argon

Use the following list of elements to answer Problems 28–32:
Mg, Cs, Ne, P, Kr, K, Ra, N, Fe, Ca, Mo

28. Which element(s) is (are) alkali metals?

29. Which element(s) is (are) noble gases?

30. Which element(s) is (are) transition metals?

31. How many of the elements are nonmetals?

32. All elements with more than 83 protons are *radioactive*, as we shall see in Chapter 11. Are any of the elements in the list above necessarily radioactive? If so, which one(s)?

ADDITIONAL PROBLEMS

33. An atom of an element has two electrons in the first shell, eight electrons in the second shell, and five electrons in the third shell. From this information, give the element's **(a)** atomic number, **(b)** name, **(c)** total number of electrons in each of its atoms, **(d)** total number of s electrons, and **(e)** total number of d electrons.

34. Refer to Problem 24. Explain how you can answer the three parts of that problem just by looking at a periodic table, and without writing electron structures.

35. Without referring to any tables in the text, mark an appropriate location for each of the following in the blank periodic table provided: **(a)** the fourth period noble gas, **(b)** the third period alkali metal, **(c)** the fourth period halogen, and **(d)** a metal in the fourth period and in group 3B.

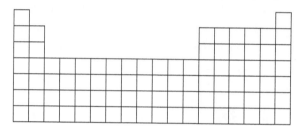

36. Look again at Figure 3.11. A patient is found to be suffering from heavy-metal poisoning. An emission spectrum is obtained from a sample of the patient's blood, by spraying a solution of the blood into a flame. The brightest emission lines are found at 5520, 5580, 5890, and 5900 Å. What two elements are likely to be present? Which one is more likely to be the culprit?

37. Refer to Figure 3.16 and write the electron configurations of **(a)** iron (Fe), **(b)** tin (Sn), and **(c)** lead (Pb).

38. Atoms of two adjacent elements in the third period are in the ground state. An atom of element A has only s electrons in its valence shell. An atom of element B has at least one p electron in its valence shell. Identify elements A and B.

39. Atoms of two adjacent elements in the fifth period are in the ground state. An atom of element L has only s electrons in its valence shell. An atom of element M has at least one d electron in an unfilled shell. Identify elements L and M.

40. Atoms of two elements, one above the other in the same group, are in the ground state. An atom of element Q has two s electrons in its outer shell and no d electrons. An atom of element R has d electrons in its configuration. Identify elements Q and R.

41. Which of the following is true of the water-splitting reaction on page 84?
   a. It produces energy, for example, electricity or heat.
   b. It requires an energy input, for example, electricity or sunlight.
   c. It produces twice as much oxygen as hydrogen.
   d. It occurs inside a fuel cell.

42. What is produced when solar energy is converted into chemical-bond energy in the water-splitting reaction?
   a. hydrogen and nitrogen
   b. oxygen and carbon
   c. hydrogen and oxygen
   d. oxygen and calcium

43. Which of the following is *not* a benefit of using a solar fuel such as hydrogen?
   a. A solar fuel can store the energy of sunlight, which is intermittent.
   b. A solar fuel can replace some fossil fuels.
   c. Using a solar fuel such as hydrogen produces no carbon dioxide emissions.
   d. Electrodes used in electrolysis rely on platinum metal.

44. Isotopes played an important role in one of the most important experiments investigating photosynthesis, the chemical reaction that converts water (H_2O) and carbon dioxide (CO_2) into glucose ($C_6H_{12}O_6$) and oxygen (O_2). For most of the early twentieth century, scientists thought that the oxygen produced by photosynthetic plants and algae came from carbon dioxide they absorbed. To investigate this question, in the early 1940s, chemists at Stanford University used an isotope of oxygen to study the mechanism of the photosynthetic reaction. The researchers fed photosynthesizing algae with water enriched with oxygen-18 and discovered that the oxygen produced was enriched with oxygen-18. Did this result support or refute the hypothesis that the O_2 produced by photosynthesis comes from CO_2?

COLLABORATIVE GROUP PROJECTS

Prepare a PowerPoint, poster, or other presentation (as directed by your instructor) to share with the class.

1. Prepare a brief biographical report on one of the following.
   a. Humphry Davy   **b.** William Crookes
   c. Wilhelm Roentgen   **d.** Marie Curie
   e. Robert Millikan   **f.** Niels Bohr
   g. Alessandro Volta   **h.** Ernest Rutherford
   i. Michael Faraday   **j.** J. J. Thomson

2. Draw a grid containing 16 squares, in two rows of 8, representing the 16 elements in the periodic table from lithium to argon. For each of the elements, give **(a)** the main-shell electron configuration and **(b)** the subshell notation for the electron configuration.

3. Prepare a brief report on one of the **(a)** alkali metals, **(b)** alkaline earth metals, **(c)** halogens, or **(d)** noble gases. List sources and commercial uses.

4. Many different forms of the periodic table have been generated. Prepare a brief report showing at least three different versions of the periodic table, and comment on their utility.

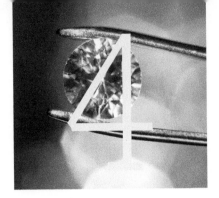

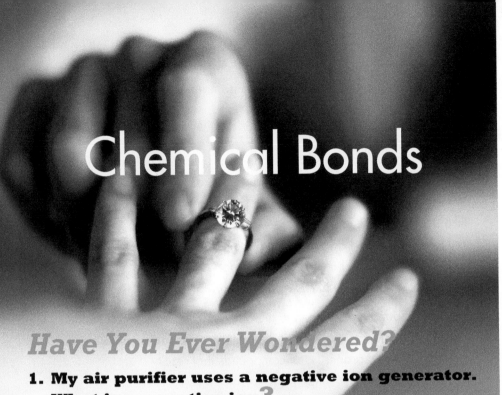

Chemical Bonds

Have You Ever Wondered?

1. My air purifier uses a negative ion generator. What is a negative ion?

2. Why does chlorine in a swimming pool have an odor, but chlorine in salt doesn't

3. My father is on a low-sodium diet. What exactly does that mean?

4. If there is iron in blood, why aren't we magnetic

Learning Objectives

> Determine the number of electrons in an ion. (4.1)

> Write the Lewis symbol for an atom or ion. (4.2)

> Distinguish between an ion and an atom. (4.3)

> Describe the nature of the attraction that leads to formation of an ionic bond. (4.3)

> Write symbols for common ions, and determine their charges. (4.4)

> Describe the relationship between the octet rule and the charge on an ion. (4.4)

> Name and write formulas for binary ionic compounds. (4.5)

> Explain the difference between a covalent bond and an ionic bond. (4.6)

> Name and write formulas for covalent compounds. (4.6)

> Classify a covalent bond as polar or nonpolar. (4.7)

> Use electronegativities of elements to determine bond polarity. (4.7)

> Predict the number of bonds formed by common nonmetals (the HONC rules). (4.8)

> Recognize common polyatomic ions and be able to use them in naming and writing formulas for compounds. (4.9)

> Write Lewis formulas for simple molecules and polyatomic ions. (4.10)

> Identify free radicals. (4.10)

> Predict the shapes of simple molecules from their Lewis formulas. (4.11)

> Classify a simple molecule as polar or nonpolar from its shape and the polarity of its bonds. (4.12)

> Explain how shape and composition change the properties of molecules.

> Describe the concept of molecular recognition.

> Explain the green chemistry advantages of using production methods based on molecular recognition.

The Ties that Bind

The element carbon is commonly found as soft, black soot formed by incomplete combustion. By heating that soot under tremendous pressure, we can make the hardest material known—diamond. We have not changed the carbon in soot to a different element in this process ... so why is diamond so different from soot? The answer lies in the bonds that hold the carbon atoms together. We have learned a bit about the structure of the atom. Now we are ready to consider chemical bonds, the ties that bind atoms together.

Chemical bonds are the forces that hold atoms together in molecules and hold ions together in ionic crystals. The vast number and incredible

Atoms combine by forming chemical bonds. These bonds determine, to a great extent, the properties of the substance. Here we see carbon in the form of diamonds, which can form from carbon in the form of graphite (pencil lead) or soot. The only difference between the forms of carbon are the bonds between the carbon atoms. The arrangement and number of these bonds in diamond make it by far the hardest natural material in the world. In this chapter, we will look at the different kinds of bonding that can occur.

89

variety of chemical compounds—tens of millions are known—result from the fact that atoms can form bonds with many other types of atoms. In addition, chemical bonds determine the three-dimensional shapes of molecules. Some important consequences of chemical structure and bonding include

- Whether a substance is a solid, liquid, or gas at room temperature
- The strengths of materials (as well as adhesives that hold materials together) used for building bridges, houses, and many other structures
- Whether a liquid is light and volatile (like gasoline) or heavy and viscous (like corn syrup)
- The taste, odor, and drug activity of chemical compounds
- The structural integrity of skin, muscles, bones, and teeth
- The toxicity of certain molecules to living organisms

Chemical bonding is related to the arrangement of electrons in compounds. In this chapter, we look at different types of chemical bonds and some of the unusual properties of compounds that result.

4.1 The Art of Deduction: Stable Electron Configurations

Learning Objective ❯ Determine the number of electrons in an ion.

In our discussion of the atom and its structure (Chapters 2 and 3), we followed the historical development of some of the more important atomic concepts. We could continue to look at chemistry in this manner, but that would require several volumes of print—and perhaps more of your time than you care to spend. We won't abandon the historical approach entirely but will emphasize another important aspect of scientific endeavor: deduction.

The art of deduction works something like this.

- **Fact:** Noble gases, such as helium, neon, and argon, are inert; they undergo few, if any, chemical reactions.
- **Theory:** The inertness of noble gases results from their electron configurations. Each (except helium) has an octet of electrons in its outermost shell.
- **Deduction:** Other elements that can alter their electron configurations to become like those of noble gases would become less reactive by doing so.

We can use an example to illustrate this deductive argument. Sodium has 11 electrons, one of which is in the third shell. Recall that electrons in the outermost shell are called **valence electrons**, while those in all the other shells are lumped together as **core electrons**. If the sodium atom got rid of its valence electron, its remaining core electrons would have the same electron configuration as an atom of the noble gas neon. Using main-shell configurations (Chapter 3), we can represent this as

The outermost shell is filled when it contains eight electrons, two in an *s* orbital and six in a *p* orbital. The first shell is an exception: It holds only two electrons in the 1*s* orbital.

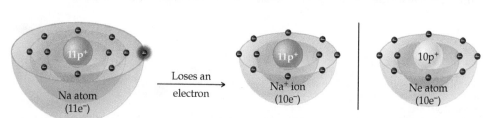

Na atom (11e⁻) — Loses an electron → Na⁺ ion (10e⁻) | Ne atom (10e⁻)

Similarly, if a chlorine atom gained an electron, it would have the same electron configuration as argon.

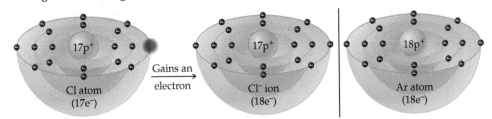

The sodium atom, having lost an electron, becomes positively charged. It has 11 protons (11+) and only 10 electrons (10−). It is symbolized by Na^+ and is called a *sodium ion*. The chlorine atom, having gained an electron, becomes negatively charged. It has 17 protons (17+) and 18 electrons (18−). It is symbolized by Cl^- and is called a *chloride ion*. Note that a positive charge, as in Na^+, indicates that one electron has been lost. Similarly, a negative charge, as in Cl^-, indicates that one electron has been gained.

It is important to note that even though Cl^- and Ar are **isoelectronic** (have the same electron configuration), they are *different* chemical species. In the same way, a sodium atom does not *become* an atom of neon when it loses an electron; the sodium ion is simply isoelectronic with neon.

Self-Assessment Questions

1. Which group of elements in the periodic table is characterized by an especially stable electron arrangement?
   a. 2A   **b.** 2B   **c.** 8A   **d.** 8B

2. The structural difference between a sodium atom and a sodium ion is that the sodium ion has one
   a. less proton than the sodium atom
   b. less electron than the sodium atom
   c. more proton and one less electron than the sodium atom
   d. more proton than the sodium atom

3. Which of the following are isoelectronic?
   a. K^+ and Ar   **b.** Mg^{2+} and Ar   **c.** Ne and Cl^- **d.** Xe and Kr

4. The anion Cl^- is isoelectronic with the cation
   a. Ca^{2+} **b.** Li^+ **c.** Mg^{2+} **d.** Na^+

Answers: 1, c; 2, b; 3, a; 4, a

1. My air purifier uses a negative ion generator. What is a negative ion? A negative ion is an atom or a group of atoms with one or more extra electrons. In a negative ion generator, a high voltage produces negative ions.

4.2 Lewis (Electron-Dot) Symbols

Learning Objective ❯ Write the Lewis symbol for an atom or ion.

In forming ions, the cores of sodium atoms and chlorine atoms do not change. It is convenient therefore to let the element symbol represent the *core* of the atom (nucleus plus inner electrons). The valence electrons are then represented by dots. The equations of the preceding section then can be written as follows:

$$Na\cdot \rightarrow Na^+ + 1\ e^-$$

and

$$\cdot \overset{..}{\underset{..}{Cl}}: \ + \ 1\ e^- \longrightarrow :\overset{..}{\underset{..}{Cl}}:^-$$

In these representations, the element symbol represents the core, and dots stand for valence electrons. These electron-dot symbols are usually called **Lewis symbols**.

▲ Electron-dot symbols are called *Lewis symbols* after G. N. Lewis, the famous American chemist (1875–1946) who invented them. Lewis also made important contributions to our understanding of thermodynamics, acids and bases, and spectroscopy.

Table 4.1	Lewis Symbols for Selected Main Group Elements

Group 1A	Group 2A	Group 3A	Group 4A	Group 5A	Group 6A	Group 7A	Noble Gases
H·							He:
Li·	·Be·	·B·	·C·	:N·	:O·	:F·	:Ne:
Na·	·Mg·	·Al·	·Si·	:P·	:S·	:Cl·	:Ar:
K·	·Ca·				:Se·	:Br·	:Kr:
Rb·	·Sr·				:Te·	:I·	:Xe:
Cs·	·Ba·						

Lewis Symbols and the Periodic Table

It is especially easy to write Lewis symbols for most of the main group elements. The number of valence electrons for most of these elements is equal to the group number (Table 4.1). Because of their more complicated electron configurations, elements in the central part of the periodic table (the transition metals) cannot easily be represented by electron-dot symbols.

In writing a Lewis symbol, only the *number* of dots is important. The dots need not be drawn in any specific positions, except that there should be no more than two dots on any given side of the chemical symbol (right, left, top, or bottom).

Example 4.1 Writing Lewis Symbols

Without referring to Table 4.1, write Lewis symbols for magnesium, oxygen, and phosphorus. You may use the periodic table.

Solution

Magnesium is in group 2A, oxygen is in group 6A, and phosphorus is in group 5A. The Lewis symbols, therefore, have two, six, and five dots, respectively. They are

$$·Mg· \quad :\ddot{O}: \quad :\ddot{P}·$$

■ EXERCISE 4.1

Without referring to Table 4.1, write Lewis symbols for each of the following elements. You may use the periodic table.

a. Ar **b.** Ca **c.** F **d.** N **e.** K **f.** S

Self-Assessment Questions

1. How many dots surround Be in the Lewis symbol for beryllium?
   a. 2 **b.** 4 **c.** 5 **d.** 9

2. How many dots surround F in the Lewis symbol for fluorine?
   a. 1 **b.** 5 **c.** 7 **d.** 9

3. Which of the following Lewis symbols is *incorrect*?
   a. ·C· **b.** :Cl· **c.** Li: **d.** :N·

4. Which of the following Lewis symbols is *incorrect*?
   a. ·As· **b.** :Ö· **c.** Rb· **d.** ·Si·

Answers: 1, a; 2, c; 3, c; 4, a

4.3 The Reaction of Sodium and Chlorine

Learning Objectives ❯ Distinguish between an ion and an atom. ❯ Describe the nature of the attraction that leads to formation of an ionic bond.

Sodium (Na) is a highly reactive metal. It is soft enough to be cut with a knife. When freshly cut, it is bright and silvery, but it dulls rapidly because it reacts with oxygen in the air. In fact, it reacts so readily in air that it is usually stored under oil or

(a)   (b)   (c)

◄ Figure 4.1 (a) Sodium, a soft, silvery metal, and chlorine, a greenish gas (b). The two react violently, to form sodium chloride (ordinary table salt), a white crystalline solid (c).

Q: *What kinds of particles, ions or molecules, make up sodium chloride?*

kerosene. Sodium reacts violently with water, too, becoming so hot that it melts. A small piece forms a spherical bead after melting and races around on the surface of the water as it reacts.

Chlorine (Cl_2) is a greenish-yellow gas. It is familiar as a disinfectant for drinking water and swimming pools. (The actual substance added is often a compound that reacts with water to form chlorine.) Chlorine is extremely irritating to the eyes and nose. In fact, it was used as a poison gas in World War I.

If a piece of sodium is dropped into a flask containing chlorine gas, a violent reaction ensues, producing sodium chloride, beautiful white crystals that you might sprinkle on your food at the dinner table. These white crystals are ordinary table salt. Sodium chloride has very few properties in common with either sodium or chlorine (Figure 4.1).

The Reaction of Sodium and Chlorine: Theory

A sodium atom achieves a filled valence shell by losing one electron. A chlorine atom achieves a filled valence shell by adding one electron. What happens when sodium atoms come into contact with chlorine atoms? The obvious: A chlorine atom takes an electron from a sodium atom.

Chlorine gas is composed of Cl_2 molecules, not separate Cl atoms. Each atom of the chlorine molecule takes an electron from a sodium atom. Two sodium ions and two chloride ions are formed.

$$Cl_2 + 2\,Na \rightarrow 2\,Cl^- + 2\,Na^+$$

2. Why does chlorine in a swimming pool have an odor, but chlorine in salt doesn't? Chlorine used in swimming pools is often the element, Cl_2, while the chlorine in salt exists as chlor*ide* ions, Cl^-. An element is chemically quite different from its ions.

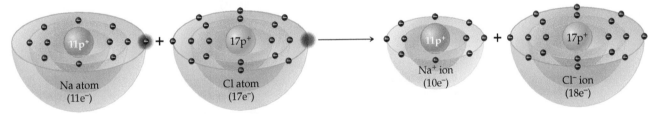

Na atom (11e⁻)   Cl atom (17e⁻)   Na⁺ ion (10e⁻)   Cl⁻ ion (18e⁻)

With Lewis symbols, this reaction is written as

$$Na\cdot \; + \; :\!\ddot{C}l\!\cdot \; \longrightarrow \; Na^+ \; + \; :\!\ddot{\underset{..}{C}l}\!:^-$$

Ionic Bonds

The Na^+ and Cl^- ions formed from sodium and chlorine atoms have opposite charges and are strongly attracted to one another. These ions arrange themselves in an orderly fashion. Each sodium ion attracts (and is attracted to) six chloride ions (above and below, front and back, left and right), as shown in Figure 4.2a. The arrangement is repeated many times in all directions (Figure 4.2b). The result is a **crystal** of sodium chloride. The orderly microscopic arrangement of the ions is reflected in the macroscopic shape, a cube, of a salt crystal (Figure 4.2c). Even the tiniest grain of salt has billions and billions of each type of ion. The forces holding the crystal together—the attractive forces between positive and negative ions—are called **ionic bonds**.

3. My father is on a low-sodium diet. What exactly does that mean? It means that he must restrict his intake of sodium *ions*. For many people, too many sodium ions in the body can increase blood pressure.

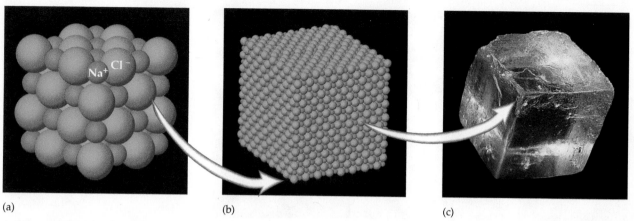

(a)   (b)   (c)

▲ **Figure 4.2** Molecular and macroscopic views of a sodium chloride crystal. (a) Each Na^+ ion (small purple spheres) is surrounded by six Cl^- ions (large green spheres), and each Cl^- ion by six Na^+ ions. (b) This arrangement repeats itself many, many times. (c) The highly ordered pattern of alternating Na^+ and Cl^- ions is observed in the macroscopic world as a crystal of sodium chloride.

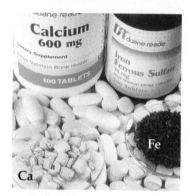

▲ **Figure 4.3** Forms of iron and calcium that are useful to the human body are the ions (usually Fe^{2+} and Ca^{2+}) in ionic compounds such as $FeSO_4$ and $CaCO_3$. The elemental forms (Fe and Ca) are chemically very different from the forms found in ionic compounds.

Atoms and Ions: Distinctively Different

Ions are emphatically different from the atoms from which they are made, much as a whole peach (an atom) and a peach pit (a positive ion) are different from one another. The names and symbols of an atom and its ion may look a lot alike, but the actual entities are very different (Figure 4.3). Unfortunately, the situation is confusing because people talk about needing iron to perk up "tired blood" and calcium for healthy teeth and bones. What they really need is iron(II) *ions* (Fe^{2+}) and calcium *ions* (Ca^{2+}). You wouldn't think of eating iron nails to get iron (although some enriched cereals do indeed have powdered iron added; the iron metal is readily converted to Fe^{2+} ions in the stomach). Nor would you eat highly reactive calcium metal.

Similarly, if you are warned to reduce your sodium intake, your doctor is not concerned that you are eating too much sodium metal—that would be exceedingly unpleasant—but that your intake of Na^+ *ions*—usually as sodium chloride—may be too high. Although the names are similar, the atom and the ion are quite different chemically. It is important to make careful distinctions and use precise terminology, as we shall do here.

Self-Assessment Questions

1. A potassium ion and an argon atom have the same
   a. electron configuration   **b.** net charge
   c. nuclear charge   **d.** properties

2. How many dots are shown on the Lewis symbol for chloride ion, and what is the ion's charge?
   a. five dots, no charge   **b.** six dots, + charge
   c. seven dots, − charge   **d.** eight dots, − charge

3. The bonding between K^+ ions and F^- ions in potassium fluoride is
   a. covalent   **b.** ionic   **c.** nonpolar   **d.** polar

Answers: 1, a; 2, d; 3, b

4.4 Using Lewis Symbols for Ionic Compounds

Learning Objectives ❯ Write symbols for common ions and determine their charges.
❯ Describe the relationship between the octet rule and the charge on an ion.

Potassium, a metal in the same family as sodium and therefore similar to sodium in properties, also reacts with chlorine. The reaction yields potassium chloride (KCl).

$$K\cdot \; + \; \cdot\overset{\cdot\cdot}{\underset{\cdot\cdot}{Cl}}: \longrightarrow K^+ + :\overset{\cdot\cdot}{\underset{\cdot\cdot}{Cl}}:^-$$

Potassium also reacts with bromine, a reddish-brown liquid in the same family as chlorine and therefore similar to chlorine in properties. The product, potassium bromide (KBr), is a stable, white, crystalline solid.

$$\text{K·} + \text{·}\ddot{\text{Br}}\text{:} \longrightarrow \text{K}^+ + \text{:}\ddot{\text{Br}}\text{:}^-$$

Example 4.2   Electron Transfer to Form Ions

Use Lewis symbols to show the transfer of electrons from sodium atoms to bromine atoms to form ions with noble gas configurations.

Solution
Sodium has one valence electron, and bromine has seven. Transfer of the single valence electron from sodium to bromine leaves each with a noble gas configuration.

$$\text{Na·} + \text{·}\ddot{\text{Br}}\text{:} \longrightarrow \text{Na}^+ + \text{:}\ddot{\text{Br}}\text{:}^-$$

■ EXERCISE 4.2A
Use Lewis symbols to show the transfer of electrons from lithium atoms to fluorine atoms to form ions with noble gas configurations.

■ EXERCISE 4.2B
Use Lewis symbols to show the transfer of electrons from rubidium atoms to iodine atoms to form ions with noble gas configurations.

Magnesium, a group 2A metal, is harder and less reactive than sodium. Magnesium reacts with oxygen, a group 6A element that is a colorless gas, to form a stable, white, crystalline solid called magnesium oxide (MgO).

$$\text{·Mg·} + \text{·}\ddot{\text{O}}\text{:} \longrightarrow \text{Mg}^{2+} + \text{:}\ddot{\text{O}}\text{:}^{2-}$$

Magnesium must give up two electrons and oxygen must gain two electrons for each to have the same configuration as the noble gas neon.

An atom such as oxygen, which needs two electrons to achieve a noble gas configuration, may react with potassium atoms, which have only one electron each to give. In this case, two atoms of potassium are needed for each oxygen atom. The product is potassium oxide (K$_2$O).

$$\begin{array}{l} \text{K·} \\ \text{K·} \end{array} + \text{·}\ddot{\text{O}}\text{:} \longrightarrow \begin{array}{l} \text{K}^+ \\ \text{K}^+ \end{array} + \text{:}\ddot{\text{O}}\text{:}^{2-}$$

Through this reaction, each potassium atom achieves the argon configuration. As before, oxygen ends up with the neon configuration.

When an Mg atom becomes an Mg^{2+} ion, its second shell becomes its outermost shell. The Mg^{2+} ion is isoelectronic with the Ne atom and has the same stable main-shell electron configuration: 2 8.

Example 4.3   Electron Transfer to Form Ions

Use Lewis symbols to show the transfer of electrons from magnesium atoms to nitrogen atoms to form ions with noble gas configurations.

Solution

$$\begin{array}{l} \text{·Mg·} \\ \text{·Mg·} \\ \text{·Mg·} \end{array} + \begin{array}{l} \text{·}\ddot{\text{N}}\text{·} \\ \text{·}\ddot{\text{N}}\text{·} \end{array} \longrightarrow \begin{array}{l} \text{Mg}^{2+} \\ \text{Mg}^{2+} \\ \text{Mg}^{2+} \end{array} + \begin{array}{l} \text{:}\ddot{\text{N}}\text{:}^{3-} \\ \text{:}\ddot{\text{N}}\text{:}^{3-} \end{array}$$

▲ It DOES Matter!

Loss of electrons is known as *oxidation*, and gain of electrons is called *reduction*. Oxidation by oxygen gas is both useful and destructive. Oxygen gas oxidizes fuels to produce energy, but it also oxidizes iron metal into familiar orange or red rust (Fe_2O_3), which causes billions of dollars of damage each year. We explore the concepts of oxidation and reduction in greater detail in Chapter 8.

Each of the three magnesium atoms gives up two electrons (a total of six), and each of the two nitrogen atoms acquires three electrons (a total of six). Notice that the total positive and negative charges on the products are equal (6+ and 6−). Magnesium reacts with nitrogen to yield magnesium nitride (Mg_3N_2).

■ EXERCISE 4.3
Use Lewis symbols to show the transfer of electrons from aluminum atoms to oxygen atoms to form ions with noble gas configurations.

Generally speaking, metallic elements in groups 1A and 2A (those from the left side of the periodic table) react with nonmetallic elements in groups 6A and 7A (those from the right side) to form ionic compounds. These products are stable crystalline solids.

The Octet Rule

Each atom of a metal tends to give up the electrons in its outer shell, and each atom of a nonmetal tends to take on enough electrons to complete its valence shell. The resulting ions have noble gas configurations. A set of eight valence electrons—an *octet*—is characteristic of all noble gases except helium. When atoms react with each other, they often tend to attain this stable noble-gas electron configuration. Thus, they are said to follow the **octet rule**, or the "rule of eight." (In the case of helium, a maximum of two electrons can occupy its single electron shell, and so hydrogen follows the "rule of two.")

In following the octet rule, atoms of group 1A metals give up one electron to form 1+ ions, those of group 2A metals give up two electrons to form 2+ ions, and those of group 3A metals give up three electrons to form 3+ ions. Group 7A nonmetal atoms take on one electron to form 1− ions, and group 6A atoms tend to pick up two electrons to form 2− ions. Atoms of B group metals can give up various numbers of electrons to form positive ions with various charges. These periodic relationships are summarized in Figure 4.4.

Table 4.2 lists symbols and names for some ions formed when atoms gain or lose electrons. (The ion names are explained in the next section.) You can calculate the charge on the negative ions in the table by subtracting 8 from the group number. For example, the charge on the oxide ion (oxygen is in group 6A) is 6 − 8 = −2. The nitride ion (nitrogen is in group 5A) has a charge of 5 − 8 = −3.

Example 4.4   Determining Formulas by Electron Transfer

What is the formula of the compound formed by the reaction of sodium and sulfur?

Solution
Sodium is in group 1A; the sodium atom has one valence electron. Sulfur is in group 6A; the sulfur atom has six valence electrons.

Na·   ·S̈·

▶ Figure 4.4 Periodic relationships of some simple ions. Many of the transition elements (B groups) can form different ions with different charges.

Q: *Can you write a formula for the simple ion formed from selenium (Se)? For the simple ion formed from indium (In)?*

1A	2A										3A	4A	5A	6A	7A	Noble gases
Li^+													N^{3-}	O^{2-}	F^-	
Na^+	Mg^{2+}	3B	4B	5B	6B	7B	8B		1B	2B	Al^{3+}		P^{3-}	S^{2-}	Cl^-	
K^+	Ca^{2+}						Fe^{2+} Fe^{3+}		Cu^+ Cu^{2+}	Zn^{2+}					Br^-	
Rb^+	Sr^{2+}								Ag^+						I^-	
Cs^+	Ba^{2+}															

Table 4.2 Symbols and Names for Some Simple (Monatomic) Ions

Group	Element	Name of Ion	Symbol for Ion
1A	Hydrogen	Hydrogen ion	H^+
	Lithium	Lithium ion	Li^+
	Sodium	Sodium ion	Na^+
	Potassium	Potassium ion	K^+
2A	Magnesium	Magnesium ion	Mg^{2+}
	Calcium	Calcium ion	Ca^{2+}
3A	Aluminum	Aluminum ion	Al^{3+}
5A	Nitrogen	Nitride ion	N^{3-}
6A	Oxygen	Oxide ion	O^{2-}
	Sulfur	Sulfide ion	S^{2-}
7A	Fluorine	Fluoride ion	F^-
	Chlorine	Chloride ion	Cl^-
	Bromine	Bromide ion	Br^-
	Iodine	Iodide ion	I^-
1B	Copper	Copper(I) ion (cuprous ion)	Cu^+
		Copper(II) ion (cupric ion)	Cu^{2+}
	Silver	Silver ion	Ag^+
2B	Zinc	Zinc ion	Zn^{2+}
8B	Iron	Iron(II) ion (ferrous ion)	Fe^{2+}
		Iron(III) ion (ferric ion)	Fe^{3+}

4. If there is iron in blood, why aren't we magnetic? Iron metal is magnetic, but compounds—such as the hemoglobin in blood—that have iron usually have iron(II) ions or iron(III) ions. The ions differ chemically and physically from the metal and are not magnetic.

Sulfur needs two electrons to gain an argon configuration, but sodium has only one to give. The sulfur atom therefore must react with two sodium atoms.

$$
\begin{array}{c}
Na\cdot \\
\quad\quad + \cdot\ddot{\underset{\cdot\cdot}{S}}\cdot \longrightarrow \\
Na\cdot
\end{array}
\quad
\begin{array}{c}
Na^+ \\
\quad\quad + :\ddot{\underset{\cdot\cdot}{S}}:^{2-} \\
Na^+
\end{array}
$$

The formula of the compound, called sodium sulfide, is Na_2S.

▪ **EXERCISE 4.4A**
What are the formulas of the compounds formed by the reaction of **(a)** calcium with fluorine and **(b)** lithium with oxygen?

▪ **EXERCISE 4.4B**
Use Figure 4.4 to predict the formulas of the two compounds that can be formed from iron (Fe) and chlorine.

Self-Assessment Questions

1. Which of the following pairs of elements would be most likely to form an ionic compound?
   a. Ca and Mg   **b.** Cd and Ca   **c.** K and S   **d.** Ne and Na

2. Sulfur forms a simple (monatomic) ion with a charge of
   a. 6−   **b.** 2−   **c.** 2+   **d.** 6+

3. Magnesium forms a simple (monatomic) ion with a charge of
   a. 2−   **b.** 2+   **c.** 4+   **d.** 8+

4. Mg and N react to form Mg_3N_2, an ionic compound. How many electrons are there in the valence shell of the N^{3-} ion?
   a. 2   **b.** 6   **c.** 8   **d.** 18

5. The formula of the ionic compound formed by lithium and oxygen is
   a. LiO   **b.** Li_2O **c.** LiO_2 **d.** Li_2O_3

6. The formula of the ionic compound formed by magnesium and bromine is
   a. MgBr   **b.** Mg_2Br **c.** $MgBr_2$ **d.** Mg_2Br_3

7. Only one of the following ions is likely to be formed in an ordinary chemical reaction; it is
   a. Ar^{3-} **b.** Br^- **c.** K^{2+} **d.** S^-

4.5 Formulas and Names of Binary Ionic Compounds

Learning Objective ❯ Name and write formulas for binary ionic compounds.

Names of simple positive ions (*cations*) are derived from those of their parent elements by the addition of the word *ion*. A sodium atom, on losing an electron, becomes a *sodium ion* (Na^+). A magnesium atom (Mg), on losing two electrons, becomes a *magnesium ion* (Mg^{2+}). When a metal forms more than one ion, the charges on the different ions are denoted by Roman numerals in parentheses. For example, Fe^{2+} is iron(II) ion and Fe^{3+} is iron(III) ion.

Names of simple negative ions (*anions*) are derived from those of their parent elements by changing the usual ending to *-ide* and adding the word *ion*. A chlor*ine* atom, on gaining an electron, becomes a chlor*ide ion* (Cl^-). A sul*fur* atom gains two electrons, becoming a sul*fide ion* (S^{2-}).

Simple ions of opposite charge can be combined to form **binary** (two-element) **ionic compounds**. To get the correct formula for a binary ionic compound, write each ion with its charge (positive ion to the left), then transpose the charge numbers (but not the plus and minus signs) and write them as subscripts. The process is best learned by practice, which is provided in the following examples and exercises and in the problems at the end of the chapter.

Example 4.5 Determining Formulas from Ionic Charges

Write the formulas for **(a)** calcium chloride and **(b)** aluminum oxide.

Solution

a. First, we write the symbols for the ions. (We write the charge on chloride ion explicitly as "1−" to illustrate the method. You may omit the "1" when you are comfortable with the process.)

$$Ca^{2+} \quad Cl^{1-}$$

We cross over the charge numbers (without the charges) as subscripts.

$$Ca^{2+} \qquad Cl^{1-}$$

Then we write the formula. The formula for calcium chloride is

$$Ca_1Cl_2 \quad \text{or} \quad \text{(dropping the ``1'') simply} \quad CaCl_2$$

b. We write the symbols for the ions.

$$Al^{3+} \quad O^{2-}$$

We cross over the charge numbers as subscripts.

$$Al^{3+} \qquad O^{2-}$$

We write the formula for aluminum oxide as

$$Al_2O_3$$

■ EXERCISE 4.5

Write the formulas for **(a)** potassium oxide, **(b)** calcium nitride, and **(c)** calcium sulfide.

The method just described, called the *crossover method,* works because it is based on the transfer of electrons and the conservation of charge. Two Al atoms lose three electrons each (a total of six electrons lost), and three O atoms gain two electrons each (a total of six electrons gained). The electrons lost must equal the electrons gained. Similarly, two Al^{3+} ions have six positive charges (three each), and three O^{2-} ions have six negative charges (two each). The net charge on Al_2O_3 is zero, just as it should be.

Now you are able to translate chemical words, such as aluminum oxide, into a chemical formula, Al_2O_3. You also can translate in the other direction, as shown in Example 4.6.

A Compound by Any Other Name ...

As you read labels on foodstuffs and pharmaceuticals, you will see some names that are beginning to sound familiar, and some that are confusing or mysterious. For example, why do we have two names for Fe^{2+}? Some names are historical: Iron, copper, gold, silver, and other elements have been known for thousands of years. In naming compounds of these elements, the ending -*ous* came to be used for the ion of smaller charge, and the ending -*ic* for the ion of larger charge. The modern system uses Roman numerals to indicate ionic charge. Although the new system is more logical and easier to apply, the old names persist, especially in everyday life and in some of the biomedical sciences.

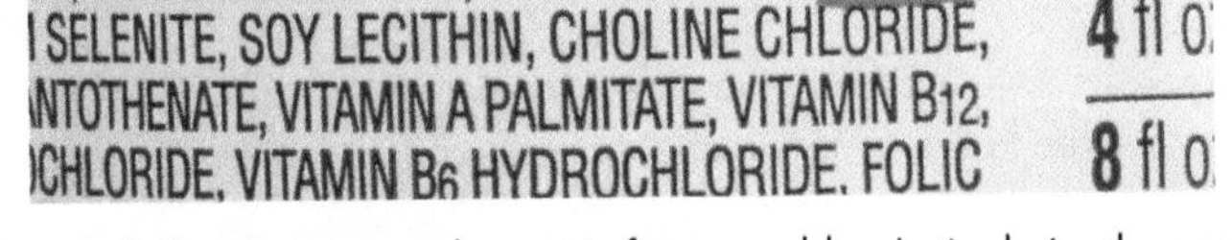

▲ Labels for dietary supplements often use older, Latin-derived names.

Example 4.6 Naming Ionic Compounds

What are the names of **(a)** MgS and **(b)** FeCl₃?

Solution

a. From Table 4.2, we can determine that MgS is made up of Mg^{2+} (magnesium ion) and S^{2-} (sulfide ion). The name is simply magnesium sulfide.

b. From Table 4.2, we can determine that the ions in $FeCl_3$ are

$$Fe^{3+} \quad Cl^-$$

How do we know the iron ion in $FeCl_3$ is Fe^{3+} and not Fe^{2+}? Because there are three Cl^- ions, each with a 1− charge, the single Fe ion must have a 3+ charge since the compound, $FeCl_3$, is neutral. The names of these ions are iron(III) ion (or ferric ion) and chloride ion. Therefore, the compound is iron(III) chloride (or, by the older system, ferric chloride).

■ EXERCISE 4.6
What are the names of **(a)** CaF_2 and **(b)** $CuBr_2$?

Self-Assessment Questions

1. The formula for the binary ionic compound of barium and sulfur is
   a. BaS   **b.** Ba_2S **c.** BaS_2 **d.** Ba_2S_3

2. Which of the following formulas is incorrect?
   a. AlF_3 **b.** K_2S **c.** MgF   **d.** NaI

3. Which of the following formulas is incorrect?
   a. $AlCl_3$ **b.** Al_3P_2 **c.** CaS   **d.** Cs_2S

4. The correct name for KCl is
   a. krypton chloride   **b.** krypton chlorine
   c. potassium chloride   **d.** potassium chlorine

5. The correct name for Al_2S_3 is
   a. aluminum sulfide   **b.** aluminum trisulfide
   c. antimony sulfide   **d.** antimony trisulfide

6. The correct name for LiI is
   a. indium lithide   **b.** iodine lithide
   c. lithium indide   **d.** lithium iodide

7. The correct name for $ZnCl_2$ is
   a. dichlorozirconium   **b.** zinc chloride
   c. zinc dichloride   **d.** zirconium chloride

Answers: 1, a; 2, c; 3, b; 4, c; 5, a; 6, d; 7, b

4.6 Covalent Bonds: Shared Electron Pairs

Learning Objectives ❯ Explain the difference between a covalent bond and an ionic bond. ❯ Name and write formulas for covalent compounds.

We might expect a hydrogen atom, with its one electron, to acquire another electron and achieve the configuration of the noble gas helium. In fact, hydrogen atoms do just that in the presence of atoms of a reactive metal such as lithium—that is, a metal that readily gives up an electron.

$$Li \cdot + H \cdot \longrightarrow Li^+ + H{:}^-$$

But what if there are no other kinds of atoms around, only hydrogen? One hydrogen atom can't gain an electron from another, for all hydrogen atoms have an equal attraction for electrons. Two hydrogen atoms can compromise, however, by *sharing a pair* of electrons.

$$H \cdot + \cdot H \longrightarrow H{:}H$$

By sharing electrons, the two hydrogen atoms form a hydrogen molecule. The bond formed when atoms share electrons is called a **covalent bond**. If one pair of electrons is shared, the bond is a **single bond**.

H:H

⌐—covalent bond (shared pair of electrons)

Let's consider chlorine next. A chlorine atom readily takes an extra electron from anything willing to give one up. But again, what if the only things around are other chlorine atoms? Chlorine atoms can also attain a more stable arrangement by sharing a pair of electrons.

$$:\ddot{\text{C}}\text{l}\cdot \; + \; \cdot\ddot{\text{C}}\text{l}: \longrightarrow :\ddot{\text{C}}\text{l}:\ddot{\text{C}}\text{l}:$$

The shared pair of electrons in the chlorine molecule is another example of a covalent bond; they are called a **bonding pair**. The electrons that stay on one atom and are not shared are called *nonbonding pairs*, or **lone pairs**.

$$:\ddot{\text{C}}\text{l}:\ddot{\text{C}}\text{l}:$$

For simplicity, the hydrogen molecule is often represented as H_2, and the chlorine molecule as Cl_2. In each case, the covalent bond between the atoms is understood. Sometimes the covalent bond is indicated by a dash: $H-H$ and $Cl-Cl$. Lone pairs of electrons often are not shown. Each chlorine atom in a chlorine molecule has eight electrons around it, an arrangement like that of the noble gas argon. Thus, the atoms involved in a covalent bond follow the octet rule by sharing electrons, just as those linked by an ionic bond follow it by giving up or accepting electrons.

Multiple Bonds

In some molecules, atoms must share more than one pair of electrons to follow the octet rule. In carbon dioxide (CO_2), for example, the carbon atom shares *two* pairs of electrons with each of the two oxygen atoms.

$$:\ddot{\text{O}}::\text{C}::\ddot{\text{O}}:$$

Note that each atom has an octet of electrons around it as a result of this sharing. We say that the atoms are joined by a **double bond**, a covalent linkage in which two atoms share two pairs of electrons. A double bond is indicated by a double dash between atoms ($O=C=O$).

Two atoms also can share three pairs of electrons. In the nitrogen (N_2) molecule, for example, each nitrogen atom shares three pairs of electrons with the other.

$$:\text{N}:::\text{N}:$$

The atoms are joined by a **triple bond**, a covalent linkage in which two atoms share three pairs of electrons ($N\equiv N$). Note that each of the nitrogen atoms has an octet of electrons around it.

Names of Covalent Compounds

Covalent, or *molecular*, compounds are those in which electrons are shared, not transferred. Such compounds generally have molecules that consist of two or more nonmetals. Many covalent compounds have common and widely used names. Examples are water (H_2O), ammonia (NH_3), and methane (CH_4).

For most other covalent compounds, the naming process is more systematic. The prefixes *mono-*, *di-*, *tri-*, and so on are used to indicate the number of atoms of each element in the molecule. A list of these prefixes for up to 10 atoms is given in Table 4.3. For example, the compound N_2O_4 is called *dinitrogen tetroxide*. (The ending vowel is often dropped from *tetra-* and other prefixes when they precede another vowel.) We often leave off the prefix *mono-* (NO is nitrogen oxide) but include it when we need to distinguish between two compounds of the same pair of elements (CO is carbon monoxide; CO_2 is carbon dioxide).

Covalent bonds are usually represented as dashes. The three kinds of covalent bonds are simply written as follows:

$H-Cl$ $O=C=O$ $N\equiv N$

Table 4.3	Prefixes That Indicate the Number of Atoms of an Element in a Covalent Compound
Prefix	**Number of Atoms**
Mono-	1
Di-	2
Tri-	3
Tetra-	4
Penta-	5
Hexa-	6
Hepta-	7
Octa-	8
Nona-	9
Deca-	10

Example 4.7 Naming Covalent Compounds

What are the names of **(a)** SCl_2 and **(b)** P_4S_3?

Solution

a. With one sulfur atom and two chlorine atoms, SCl_2 is sulfur dichloride.

b. With four phosphorus atoms and three sulfur atoms, P_4S_3 is tetraphosphorus trisulfide.

■ EXERCISE 4.7

What are the names of **(a)** BrF_3, **(b)** BrF_5, **(c)** N_2O, and **(d)** N_2O_5?

You can have fun with chemical names. Some compounds have strange—even funny—common names. Curious? Curium(III) chloride ($CmCl_3$) is curous chloride. Nickel(II) curate ($NiCmO_3$) is nickelous curate. Titanium(IV) chloride ($TiCl_4$) is titanic chloride. Some ions of uranium, such as UO_2^{2-}, UO_3^{2-}, $U_2O_7^{2-}$, are uranates. The hydrides of group 4 elements include methane (CH_4), silane (SiH_4), and germane (GeH_4). Is GeH_4 relevant?

Example 4.8 Formulas of Covalent Compounds

Write the formula for tetraphosphorus hexoxide.

Solution

The prefix *tetra-* indicates four phosphorus atoms, and *hex-* specifies six oxygen atoms. The formula is P_4O_6.

■ EXERCISE 4.8

Write the formulas for **(a)** phosphorus trichloride, **(b)** dichlorine heptoxide, **(c)** nitrogen triiodide, and **(d)** disulfur dichloride.

Self-Assessment Questions

1. A bond formed when two atoms share a pair of electrons is
   a. covalent b. ionic c. nonpolar d. polar

2. The bond in Br_2 is
   a. double covalent b. ionic
   c. single covalent d. triple covalent

3. The bond in N_2 is
   a. double covalent b. ionic
   c. single covalent d. triple covalent

4. The formula for phosphorus trichloride is
   a. KCl_3 b. K_3Cl c. PCl_3 d. P_3Cl

5. The formula for disulfur difluoride is
   a. SF_2 b. S_2F_2 c. SFe_2 d. S_2Fl_2

6. The correct name for N_2S_4 is
   a. dinitrogen disulfide b. dinitrogen tetrasulfide
   c. tetrasulfodinitrogen d. tetrasulfur dinitride

7. The correct name for I_2O_5 is
   a. diiodine pentoxide b. diiodopentoxide
   c. iridium pentoxide d. pentaoxodiiodine

Answers: 1, a; 2, c; 3, d; 4, c; 5, b; 6, b; 7, a

4.7 Unequal Sharing: Polar Covalent Bonds

Learning Objectives ❭ Classify a covalent bond as polar or nonpolar. ❭ Use electronegativities of elements to determine bond polarity.

So far, we have seen that atoms combine in two different ways. Atoms that are quite different in electron configuration (from opposite sides of the periodic table) react by the complete transfer of one or more electrons from one atom to another to form an ionic bond. Some identical nonmetal atoms (such as two chlorine atoms or two hydrogen atoms) combine by sharing a pair of electrons to form a covalent bond. Now let's consider bond formation between atoms that are different, but not different enough to form ionic bonds.

Hydrogen Chloride

Hydrogen and chlorine react to form a colorless gas called *hydrogen chloride*. This reaction may be represented as

$$\text{H} \cdot + \cdot \ddot{\underset{\cdot\cdot}{\text{C}}} \text{l} : \longrightarrow \text{H} : \ddot{\underset{\cdot\cdot}{\text{C}}} \text{l} :$$

Ignoring the lone pairs of electrons and using a dash to represent the covalent bond, we can write the hydrogen chloride molecule as H—Cl. Both hydrogen and chlorine need an electron to achieve a noble gas configuration—a helium configuration for hydrogen and an argon configuration for chlorine. They achieve these configurations by sharing a pair of electrons to form a covalent bond.

Example 4.9   Covalent Bonds from Lewis Symbols

Use Lewis symbols to show the formation of a covalent bond **(a)** between two fluorine atoms and **(b)** between a fluorine atom and a hydrogen atom.

Solution

$$:\ddot{\text{F}} \cdot \; + \; \cdot \ddot{\text{F}}: \; \longrightarrow \; :\ddot{\text{F}} : \ddot{\text{F}}: \quad \text{bonding pair}$$

$$\text{H} \cdot \; + \; \cdot \ddot{\text{F}}: \; \longrightarrow \; \text{H} : \ddot{\text{F}}: \quad \text{bonding pair}$$

■ EXERCISE 4.9
Use Lewis symbols to show the formation of a covalent bond between **(a)** two bromine atoms, **(b)** a hydrogen atom and a bromine atom, and **(c)** an iodine atom and a chlorine atom.

You might reasonably ask why a hydrogen molecule and a chlorine molecule react at all. Have we not just learned that these molecules form because the result is a stable arrangement of electrons? Yes, indeed, that is the case. But there is stable, and there is *more* stable. The chlorine molecule represents a more stable arrangement than two separate chlorine atoms. However, given the opportunity, a chlorine atom selectively forms a bond with a hydrogen atom rather than with another chlorine atom.

For convenience and simplicity, the reaction of hydrogen (molecule) and chlorine (molecule) to form hydrogen chloride is often represented as

$$\text{H}_2 + \text{Cl}_2 \longrightarrow 2\,\text{HCl}$$

The bonds between the atoms and the lone pairs on the chlorine atoms are not shown explicitly, but remember that they are there.

Each molecule of hydrogen chloride consists of one atom of hydrogen and one atom of chlorine. These unlike atoms share a pair of electrons. *Share*, however, does not necessarily mean "share equally." Chlorine atoms have a greater attraction for a shared pair of electrons than hydrogen atoms do. Chlorine is said to be more *electronegative* than hydrogen.

Electronegativity

The **electronegativity** of an element is a measure of the attraction of an atom of that element *in a molecule* for a pair of shared electrons. The atoms to the right in the periodic table are, in general, more electronegative than those to the left. The ones on the right are precisely the atoms that, in forming ions, tend to gain electrons and form negative ions. The ones on the left—metals—tend to give up electrons and become positive ions. Within a column, electronegativity tends to be higher at the top and lower at the bottom of the column.

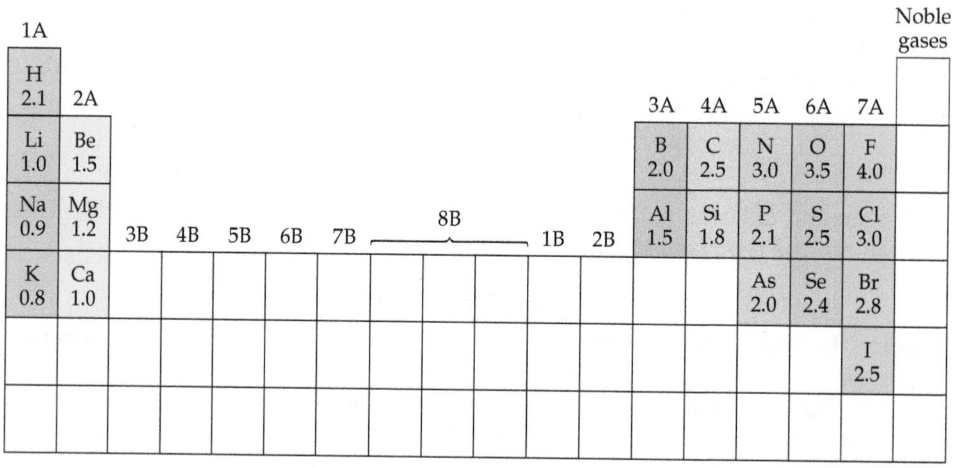

▶ **Figure 4.5** Pauling electronegativity values for several common elements.

Q: *Can you estimate a value for the electronegativity of germanium (Ge)? For the electronegativity of rubidium (Rb)?*

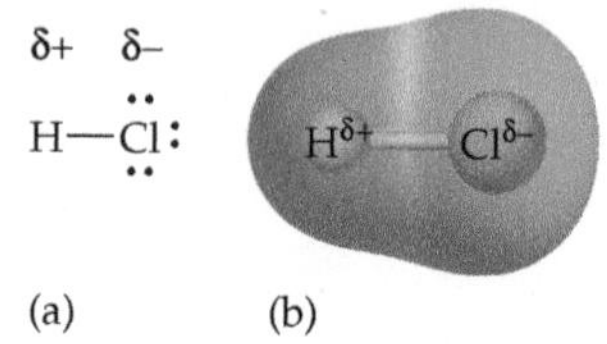

1A																	Noble gases
H 2.1	2A											3A	4A	5A	6A	7A	
Li 1.0	Be 1.5											B 2.0	C 2.5	N 3.0	O 3.5	F 4.0	
Na 0.9	Mg 1.2	3B	4B	5B	6B	7B	8B			1B	2B	Al 1.5	Si 1.8	P 2.1	S 2.5	Cl 3.0	
K 0.8	Ca 1.0													As 2.0	Se 2.4	Br 2.8	
																I 2.5	

δ+ δ−
H—Cl̈:

(a)   (b)

H^{δ+}   Cl^{δ−}

▲ **Figure 4.6** Representation of the polar hydrogen chloride molecule. (a) The electron-dot formula, with the symbols δ+ and δ− indicating the partial positive and partial negative charge, respectively. (b) An *electrostatic potential diagram* depicting the unequal distribution of electron density in the hydrogen chloride molecule.

▲ Chlorine hogs the electron blanket, leaving hydrogen partially, but positively, exposed.

The more electronegative an atom is, the greater its tendency to pull the electrons in the bond toward its end of the bond when it is involved in covalent bonding. The American chemist Linus Pauling (1901–1994) devised a scale of relative electronegativity values by assigning fluorine, the most electronegative element, a value of 4.0. Figure 4.5 displays the electronegativity values for some of the common elements that we will encounter in this text.

Chlorine (3.0) is more electronegative than hydrogen (2.1). In the hydrogen chloride molecule, the shared electrons are held more tightly by the chlorine atom. Thus, the chlorine end of the molecule is more negative than the hydrogen end. When the electrons in a covalent bond are not equally shared, the bond is said to be *polar*. The bond in a hydrogen chloride molecule is described as a **polar covalent bond**, whereas the bond in a hydrogen molecule or a chlorine molecule is a **nonpolar covalent bond**. A polar covalent bond is not an ionic bond. In an ionic bond, one atom completely loses an electron. In a polar covalent bond, the atom at the positive end of the bond (hydrogen in HCl) still has a fractional share in the bonding pair of electrons (Figure 4.6). To distinguish this kind of bond from an ionic bond or a nonpolar covalent bond, the following notation is used:

$$\overset{\delta+}{H}—\overset{\delta-}{Cl}$$

The line between the atoms represents the covalent bond, a pair of shared electrons. The δ+ and δ− (read "delta plus" and "delta minus") signify which end of the bond is partially positive and which is partially negative. (The word *partially* is used to distinguish these charges from the full charges on ions.)

We can use the electronegativity values for the two atoms joined by a bond to predict the type of bonding. When the electronegativity difference is zero or very small (<0.5), the bond is *nonpolar covalent*, with nearly equal sharing of the electrons. When the electronegativity difference is large (>2.0), complete electron transfer occurs and an *ionic* bond is formed, as in the case of sodium and chlorine. When the electronegativity difference is between 0.5 and 2.0, a *polar covalent* bond is formed.

Example 4.10 Using Electronegativities to Classify Bonds

Use data from Figure 4.5 to classify the bond between each of the following pairs of atoms as nonpolar covalent, polar covalent, or ionic:

a. H, H   **b.** O, H   **c.** C, H

Solution

a. Two H atoms have exactly the same electronegativity. The electronegativity difference is 0. The bond is nonpolar covalent.

b. The electronegativity difference is 3.5 − 2.1 = 1.4. The bond is polar covalent.

c. The electronegativity difference is 2.5 − 2.1 = 0.4. The bond is nonpolar covalent.

■ EXERCISE 4.10A
Use data from Figure 4.5 to classify the bond between each of the following pairs of atoms as nonpolar covalent, polar covalent, or ionic:

a. H, Br   b. Na, O   c. C, C

■ EXERCISE 4.10B
Use the periodic table to classify the following bonds as nonpolar covalent or polar covalent:

a. C—N   b. C—O   c. C=C

Self-Assessment Questions

1. When HCl is formed,
   a. a Cl atom gives one valence electron to an H atom
   b. an H atom gives one valence electron to a Cl atom
   c. a pair of valence electrons is shared, one each from the H atom and the Cl atom
   d. a pair of valence electrons is shared, none from the H atom and two from the Cl atom

2. Which of the following bonds is least polar?
   a. C—Br   b. C—Cl   c. C—F   d. H—H

3. Which of the following bonds is most polar?
   a. C—C   b. C—F   c. C—O   d. F—F

4. In a polar covalent bond, the atom with greater electronegativity bears a
   a. full negative charge   b. full positive charge
   c. partial negative charge   d. partial positive charge

5. For an ionic bond to exist between two atoms, their difference in electronegativity should be
   a. between 0 and 0.5   b. between 0.5 and 2.0
   c. greater than 2.0   d. zero

Answers: 1, c; 2, d; 3, b; 4, c; 5, c

4.8 Polyatomic Molecules: Water, Ammonia, and Methane

Learning Objective ❯ Predict the number of bonds formed by common nonmetals (the HONC rules).

To obtain an octet of electrons, an oxygen atom must share electrons with *two* hydrogen atoms, a nitrogen atom must share electrons with *three* hydrogen atoms, and a carbon atom must share electrons with *four* hydrogen atoms. In general, nonmetals tend to form a number of covalent bonds that is equal to eight minus the group number. Oxygen, which is in group 6A, forms $8 - 6 = 2$ covalent bonds in most molecules. Nitrogen, in group 5A, forms $8 - 5 = 3$ covalent bonds in most molecules. Carbon, in group 4A, forms $8 - 4 = 4$ covalent bonds in most molecules, including those of the great host of organic compounds (Chapter 9). The following simple guidelines—sometimes called the HONC rules—will enable you to write formulas for many molecules.

- Hydrogen forms 1 bond.
- Oxygen forms 2 bonds.
- Nitrogen forms 3 bonds.
- Carbon forms 4 bonds.

Water

Water is one of the most familiar chemical substances. The electrolysis experiment of Nicholson and Carlisle (Chapter 2) and the fact that both hydrogen and oxygen are diatomic (two-atom) gases indicate that the molecular formula for water is H_2O. To attain an octet, oxygen shares two pairs of electrons. Because a hydrogen atom shares only one pair of electrons, however, an oxygen atom must bond with two hydrogen atoms, forming a *polyatomic* molecule—a molecule containing more than two atoms.

$$\ddot{\text{O}}\!: \; + \; 2\,\text{H}\!\cdot \; \longrightarrow \; \text{H}\!:\!\ddot{\text{O}}\!: \quad \text{or} \quad \text{H}\!-\!\text{O}$$
$$\qquad\qquad\qquad\quad \text{H} \qquad\qquad |$$
$$\qquad\qquad\qquad\qquad\qquad\qquad \text{H}$$

This arrangement completes the valence shell octet of the oxygen atom, giving it the neon configuration. It also completes the outer shell of each hydrogen atom, giving each of these atoms the helium configuration. Oxygen has a higher electronegativity than does hydrogen, so the H—O bonds formed are *polar covalent*.

Ammonia

A nitrogen atom has five electrons in its valence shell. It can attain the neon configuration by sharing three pairs of electrons with *three* hydrogen atoms. The result is the compound ammonia.

$$\cdot\ddot{\text{N}}\cdot \; + \; 3\,\text{H}\!\cdot \; \longrightarrow \; \text{H}\!:\!\ddot{\text{N}}\!:\!\text{H} \quad \text{or} \quad \text{H}\!-\!\text{N}\!-\!\text{H}$$
$$\qquad\qquad\qquad\qquad \text{H} \qquad\qquad\quad |$$
$$\qquad\qquad\qquad\qquad\qquad\qquad\qquad \text{H}$$

In ammonia, the bond arrangement is that of a tripod (see Figure 4.10) with a hydrogen atom at the end of each leg and the nitrogen atom with its unshared pair of electrons at the top. (We will see why it has this shape in Section 4.11.) The electronegativity of N is 3.0, and that of H is 2.1, so all three N—H bonds are *polar covalent*.

Methane

A carbon atom has four electrons in its valence shell. It can achieve the neon configuration by sharing pairs of electrons with four hydrogen atoms, forming the compound methane.

$$\qquad\qquad\qquad\qquad\qquad \text{H} \qquad\qquad\quad \text{H}$$
$$\cdot\dot{\text{C}}\cdot \; + \; 4\,\text{H}\!\cdot \; \longrightarrow \; \text{H}\!:\!\ddot{\text{C}}\!:\!\text{H} \quad \text{or} \quad \text{H}\!-\!\text{C}\!-\!\text{H}$$
$$\qquad\qquad\qquad\qquad \text{H} \qquad\qquad\quad \text{H}$$

The methane molecule, as shown above, appears to be planar but actually is not—as we shall see in Section 4.11. The electronegativity difference between H and C is so small that the C—H bonds are considered nonpolar.

Self-Assessment Questions

1. When two H atoms each share an electron with an O atom to form H_2O, the bonding is
   a. diatomic
   b. ionic
   c. nonpolar covalent
   d. polar covalent

2. How many electrons are in the valence shell of the N atom in an ammonia molecule?
   a. 2
   b. 5
   c. 6
   d. 8

3. To gain an octet of electrons in forming methane, a carbon atom must share an electron with each of
   a. 2 H atoms
   b. 4 H atoms
   c. 6 H atoms
   d. 8 H atoms

Answers: 1, d; 2, d; 3, b

4.9 Polyatomic Ions

Learning Objective ❯ Recognize common polyatomic ions and be able to use them in naming and writing formulas for ionic compounds.

Many compounds contain both ionic and covalent bonds. Sodium hydroxide, commonly known as lye, consists of sodium ions (Na^+) and hydroxide ions (OH^-). The hydroxide ion contains an oxygen atom covalently bonded to a hydrogen atom,

Table 4.4 Some Common Polyatomic Ions

Charge	Name	Formula
1+	Ammonium ion	NH_4^+
	Hydronium ion	H_3O^+
1−	Hydrogen carbonate (bicarbonate) ion	HCO_3^-
	Hydrogen sulfate (bisulfate) ion	HSO_4^-
	Acetate ion	$CH_3CO_2^-$ (or $C_2H_3O_2^-$)
	Nitrite ion	NO_2^-
	Nitrate ion	NO_3^-
	Cyanide ion	CN^-
	Hydroxide ion	OH^-
	Dihydrogen phosphate ion	$H_2PO_4^-$
	Permanganate ion	MnO_4^-
2−	Carbonate ion	CO_3^{2-}
	Sulfate ion	SO_4^{2-}
	Chromate ion	CrO_4^{2-}
	Hydrogen (monohydrogen) phosphate ion	HPO_4^{2-}
	Oxalate ion	$C_2O_4^{2-}$
	Dichromate ion	$Cr_2O_7^{2-}$
3−	Phosphate ion	PO_4^{3-}

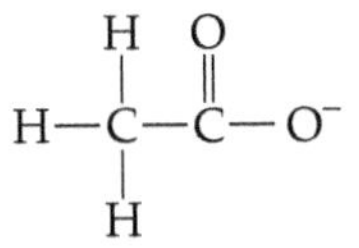

Acetate ion

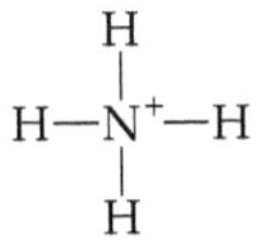

Ammonium ion

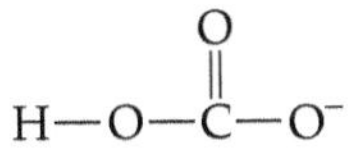

Hydrogen carbonate ion
(bicarbonate ion)

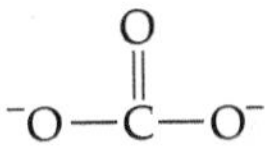

Carbonate ion    Nitrite ion

plus an "extra" electron. That extra electron gives hydroxide ion a negative charge and gives the O and the H atom each a filled shell.

$$e^- + \cdot\ddot{O}\cdot + \cdot H \longrightarrow :\ddot{O}:H^-$$

The formula for sodium hydroxide is NaOH. For each sodium ion, there is one hydroxide ion.

There are many groups of atoms that (like hydroxide ion) remain together through most chemical reactions. **Polyatomic ions** are charged particles containing two or more covalently bonded atoms. A list of common polyatomic ions is given in Table 4.4. You can use these ions, in combination with the simple ions in Table 4.2, to determine formulas for many ionic compounds.

Example 4.11   Formulas with Polyatomic Ions

What is the formula for ammonium sulfide?

Solution
Ammonium ion is found in Table 4.4. Sulfide ion is a sulfur atom (group 6A) with two additional electrons. The ions are

$$NH_4^+ \quad S^{2-}$$

Crossing over gives

The formula for ammonium sulfide is $(NH_4)_2S$. (Note the parentheses.)

■ EXERCISE 4.11A
What are the formulas for **(a)** calcium acetate, **(b)** potassium oxide, and **(c)** aluminum sulfate?

■ EXERCISE 4.11B
How many **(a)** sulfur atoms are in the formula for aluminum sulfate, how many and **(b)** how many carbon atoms are in the formula for calcium acetate?

Example 4.12 Naming Compounds with Polyatomic Ions

What are the names of **(a)** NaCN and **(b)** $Fe(OH)_2$?

Solution

As with compounds containing only monatomic ions, we name the cation and then the anion.

a. The cation is sodium ion, and the anion is cyanide ion (Table 4.4). The compound is sodium cyanide.

b. The cation is an iron ion, and the anion is hydroxide ion (Table 4.4). There are two hydroxide ions, each with a charge of $1-$, so the iron ion must be a $2+$ ion [iron(II)]. The compound is iron(II) hydroxide.

■ **EXERCISE 4.12A**

What are the names of **(a)** $CaCO_3$, **(b)** $Mg_3(PO_4)_2$, and **(c)** K_2CrO_4?

■ **EXERCISE 4.12B**

What are the names of **(a)** $(NH_4)_2SO_4$, **(b)** KH_2PO_4, and **(c)** $CuCr_2O_7$?

Self-Assessment Questions

1. Which of the following compounds incorporates a polyatomic ion?
   a. CO_2 **b.** $C_6H_{12}O_6$ **c.** K_2SO_3 **d.** $SrBr_2$

2. The formula for ammonium phosphate is
   a. NH_4PO_3 **b.** $NH_4(PO_4)_2$ **c.** $(NH_4)_2PO_4$ **d.** $(NH_4)_3PO_4$

3. The formula for sodium hydrogen carbonate is
   a. $NaHCO_3$ **b.** Na_2HCO_3 **c.** NaH_2CO_3 **d.** $NaHCO_4$

4. The formula for copper(I) hydrogen sulfate is
   a. $CuHSO_4$ **b.** Cu_2HSO_3 **c.** Cu_2HSO_4 **d.** $Cu(HSO_4)_2$

5. The formula for calcium nitrate is
   a. $CaNO_3$ **b.** Ca_2NO_3 **c.** $Ca(NO_3)_2$ **d.** $CaNO_4$

6. The correct name for NH_4HCO_3 is
   a. ammonium acetate   **b.** ammonium carbonate
   c. ammonium hydrogen carbonate   **d.** ammonium cyanide

Answers: 1, c; 2, d; 3, a; 4, a; 5, c; 6, c

4.10 Rules for Writing Lewis Formulas

Learning Objectives ❯ Write Lewis formulas for simple molecules and polyatomic ions.
❯ Identify free radicals.

As we have seen, electrons are transferred or shared in ways that leave most atoms with octets of electrons in their outermost shells. This section describes how to write **Lewis formulas** for molecules and polyatomic ions. To write a Lewis formula, we first put the atoms of the molecule or ion in their proper places, and then we place all the valence electrons so that each atom has a filled shell.

The *skeletal structure* of a molecule tells us the order in which the atoms are attached to one another. Drawing a skeletal structure takes some practice. However, if there is no experimental evidence, the following guidelines help us to devise likely skeletal structures:

- Hydrogen atoms form only single bonds. They are always at the end of a sequence of atoms. Hydrogen is often bonded to carbon, nitrogen, or oxygen.
- Oxygen tends to have two bonds, nitrogen usually has three bonds, and carbon has four bonds.
- Polyatomic molecules and ions often consist of a central atom surrounded by atoms of higher electronegativity. (Hydrogen is an exception; it is always on the outside, even when bonded to a more electronegative element.) The central atom of a polyatomic molecule or ion is often the *least* electronegative atom.

After choosing a skeletal structure for a polyatomic molecule or ion, we can use the following steps to write the Lewis formula:

1. Determine the total number of valence electrons. This total is the sum of the valence electrons for all the atoms in the molecule or ion. You must also account for the charge(s) on a polyatomic ion. For a polyatomic anion, *add* to its total number of valence electrons the number of negative charges. For a polyatomic cation, *subtract* the number of positive charges.

Examples:

$$N_2O_4 \text{ has } (2 \times 5) + (4 \times 6) = 34 \text{ valence electrons.}$$

$$NO_3^- \text{ has } [(1 \times 5) + (3 \times 6)] + 1 = 24 \text{ valence electrons.}$$

$$NH_4^+ \text{ has } [(1 \times 5) + (4 \times 1)] - 1 = 8 \text{ valence electrons.}$$

2. Write a reasonable skeletal structure and connect bonded pairs of atoms by a dash (one shared electron pair).
3. Place electrons in pairs around outer atoms so that each (except hydrogen) has an octet.
4. Subtract the number of electrons assigned so far (both in bonds and as lone pairs) from the total calculated in step 1. Any electrons that remain are assigned in pairs to the central atom(s).
5. If a central atom has fewer than eight electrons after step 4, one or more multiple bonds are likely. Move one or more lone pairs from an outer atom to the space between the atoms to form a double or triple bond. A deficiency of two electrons suggests a double bond, and a shortage of four electrons indicates a triple bond or two double bonds to the central atom.

Example 4.13 Writing Lewis Formulas

Write Lewis formulas for **(a)** methanol (CH_3OH), **(b)** the BF_4^- ion, and **(c)** carbon dioxide (CO_2).

Solution

a. We start by following the preceding rules:

1. The total number of valence electrons is $4 + (4 \times 1) + 6 = 14$.
2. The skeletal structure must have all the H atoms on the outside. That means the C and O atoms must be bonded to each other. A reasonable skeletal structure is

3. Now, we count five bonds with two electrons each, making a total of ten electrons. Thus, four of the 14 valence electrons are left to be assigned. They are placed (as two lone pairs) on the oxygen atom.

(The remaining steps are not necessary. Both carbon and oxygen now have octets of electrons.)

b. Again, we start by applying the preceding rules:

1. There are $3 + (4 \times 7) + 1 = 32$ valence electrons.
2. The skeletal structure is

$$
\begin{array}{c}
\text{F} \\
| \\
\text{F}-\text{B}-\text{F} \\
| \\
\text{F}
\end{array}
$$

3. Placing three lone pairs on each fluorine atom gives

$$
\left[
\begin{array}{c}
\ddot{\ddot{\text{F}}}\!\!: \\
| \\
:\!\ddot{\text{F}}-\text{B}-\ddot{\text{F}}\!\!: \\
| \\
:\!\ddot{\text{F}}\!\!:
\end{array}
\right]^{-}
$$

4. We have assigned 32 electrons. None remains to be assigned. Brackets and a negative sign are added to show that this is the structure for an anion, not a molecule. The charge is written outside the brackets to indicate the charge is on the ion as a whole, not necessarily on any particular atom.

c. Again, we start by applying the rules:

1. There are $4 + (2 \times 6) = 16$ valence electrons.
2. The skeletal structure is O—C—O.
3. We place three lone pairs on each oxygen atom.

$$:\ddot{\text{O}}-\text{C}-\ddot{\text{O}}:$$

4. We have assigned 16 electrons. None remains to be placed.
5. The central carbon atom has only four electrons. It needs to have two double bonds in order to achieve an octet. We move a lone pair from each oxygen atom to the space between the atoms to form a double bond on each side of the carbon atom.

$$:\ddot{\text{O}}=\text{C}=\ddot{\text{O}}:$$

■ **EXERCISE 4.13A**
Write Lewis formulas for **(a)** oxygen difluoride, OF_2, and **(b)** methyl chloride, CH_3Cl.

■ **EXERCISE 4.13B**
Write Lewis formulas for **(a)** the azide ion, N_3^-, and **(b)** the nitryl fluoride molecule, NO_2F (O—N—O—F skeleton).

The rules we have used here lead to the results for selected elements that are summarized in Table 4.5. Figure 4.7 relates the number of covalent bonds that a particular element forms to its position on the periodic table.

Odd-Electron Molecules: Free Radicals

There are some classes of molecules in which atoms do not conform to the octet rule. *Free radicals* are one such class. (See Problems 51 and 52 for two other types.) Molecules with odd numbers of valence electrons obviously cannot satisfy the octet rule. Examples of such molecules are nitrogen monoxide (NO, also called nitric oxide), with $5 + 6 = 11$ valence electrons; nitrogen dioxide (NO_2), with 17 valence electrons; and chlorine dioxide (ClO_2), which has 19 valence electrons.

An atom or molecule with unpaired electrons is called a **free radical**. Most free radicals are highly reactive and exist for only a very brief time before reacting with another species. Every atom or molecule with an odd number of electrons must have one unpaired electron. Filled shells and subshells contain all paired electrons, with two electrons in each orbital (Section 3.7). Therefore, we need only consider valence electrons to determine whether an atom or molecule is a free radical. Lewis

Table 4.5 Number of Bonds Formed by Selected Elements

Lewis Symbol	Bond Picture	Number of Bonds	Representative Molecules	Ball-and-Stick Models
H·	H—	1	H—H H—Cl	 HCl
He:		0	He	 He
·Ċ·	—Ċ—	4	H—C—H (with H above and below) H—C—F (with O above)	CH₄
·N̈·	—N—	3	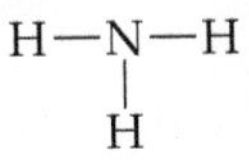 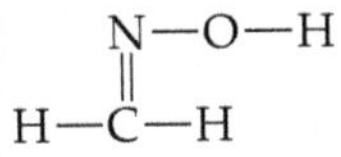 H—N—H (with H below) H—C—H (with N—O—H above)	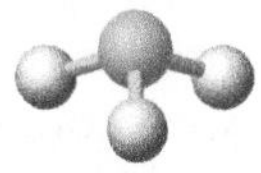 NH₃
·Ö:	—O—	2	H—O (with H below) H—C—H (with O above)	H₂O
·F̈:	—F	1	H—F F—F	 F₂
·C̈l:	—Cl	1	Cl—Cl 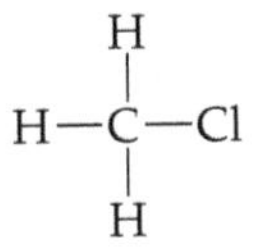 H—C—Cl (with H above and below)	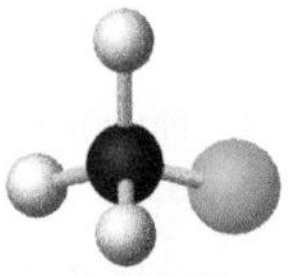 CH₃Cl

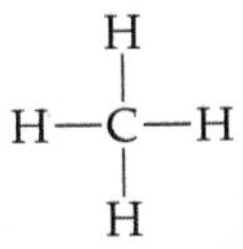

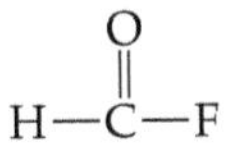

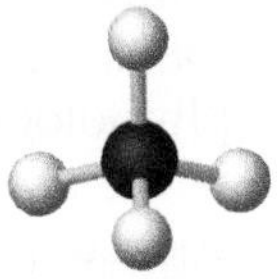

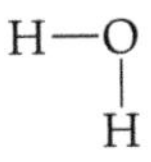

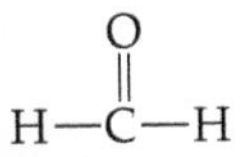

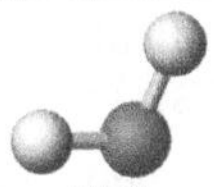

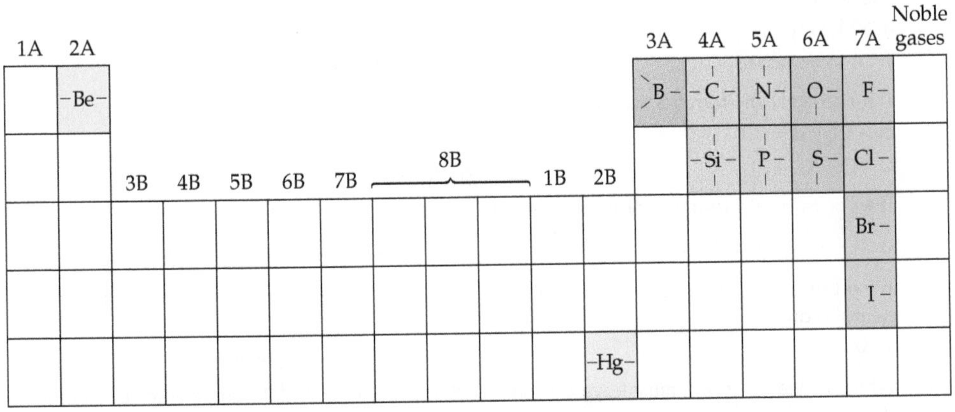

◀ **Figure 4.7** Covalent bonding of representative elements on the periodic table.

Q: *What is the relationship between an atom's position on the periodic table and the number of covalent bonds it tends to form? Why are the group 1A and most of the group 2A elements omitted from the table?*

formulas of NO, NO₂, and ClO₂ each have one atom with an unpaired electron. An atom having an unpaired electron cannot have an octet of electrons in its outer shell.

$$:N::O: \qquad :Ö:N::Ö: \qquad :Ö:Cl:Ö:$$

Nitrogen oxides are major components of smog (Chapter 13). Chlorine atoms from the breakdown of chlorofluorocarbons in the stratosphere lead to depletion of the ozone layer (Chapter 13). Some free radicals are quite stable, however, and have important functions in the body as well as in industrial processes (see the box on page 112).

Useful Applications of Free Radicals

The very reactive nature of free radicals does not preclude their importance and use in a variety of natural and industrial applications.

- Nitric oxide (NO) has been shown to be a signaling molecule in the human cardiovascular system. American scientists Robert F. Furchgott, Louis J. Ignarro, and Ferid Murad won the Nobel Prize in Physiology or Medicine in 1998 for that discovery. Interestingly, one of the physiological effects of sildenafil citrate (Viagra®) is the production of small quantities of NO in the bloodstream.

- Hydroxyl radicals (·OH) are produced in the body in the process of oxidation of foods and by radiation. The decomposition of hydrogen peroxide (HOOH) and other peroxides produces ·OH. These radicals inflict havoc on DNA and other essential substances and they have been implicated in the formation of cancerous cells due to their rapid reaction with DNA. Hydroxyl radicals are also play a role in air pollution (Chapter 13).

- Many plastics, including polyethylene and polyvinyl chloride (PVC), are made using free radicals to initiate the reactions. Liquid polyester resin is used to repair automobiles and to construct small boats and surfboards. The resin is converted to hard plastic by the addition of a free-radical catalyst called *methyl ethyl ketone peroxide.*

- The free radical chlorine dioxide (ClO_2) is widely used to bleach paper and other products, including flour. Unbleached flour (left) is a pale cream color; bleached flour (right) is whiter and is considered more attractive to consumers.

▲ Chlorine dioxide (ClO_2) is used to bleach flour. Unbleached flour (left) and bleached flour (right).

Self-Assessment Questions

1. How many lone pairs of electrons are there in the Lewis formula of CF_4?
   a. 4   **b.** 12   **c.** 14   **d.** 16

2. How many unshared electrons are there in the Lewis formula of H_2O_2?
   a. 3   **b.** 8   **c.** 14   **d.** 18

3. The Lewis formula for CCl_4 has
   a. 0 lone pairs   **b.** 1 double bond
   c. 4 ionic bonds   **d.** 24 unshared electrons

4. The correct Lewis formula for carbon dioxide is
   a. O—C—O   **b.** :O—C—O:
   c. :Ö—C—Ö: **d.** :Ö=C=Ö:

5. The correct Lewis formula for the Cl_2O molecule is
   a. :Cl—Cl—Ö: b. :Cl=O=Cl   c. :Ö—Cl—Ö: d. :Cl—Ö—Cl:

6. In the Lewis formula for CO_2, the number of lone pairs of electrons in the outer shell of the central atom is
   a. 0   **b.** 1   **c.** 2   **d.** 4

7. Which of the following must have a triple bond in order to complete an octet for each atom in its Lewis formula?
   a. F_2 **b.** HCN   **c.** HI   **d.** O_2

8. The Lewis formula for the SO_3^{2-} ion that follows the octet rule is

$$
\text{a.} \left[\begin{matrix} :\ddot{O}-S-\ddot{O}: \\ | \\ :\ddot{O}: \end{matrix} \right]^{2-}
\quad
\text{b.} \left[\begin{matrix} :\ddot{O}-S=\ddot{O}: \\ | \\ :\ddot{O}: \end{matrix} \right]^{2-}
\quad
\text{c.} \left[\begin{matrix} :\ddot{O}=S=\ddot{O}: \\ | \\ :\ddot{O}: \end{matrix} \right]^{2-}
\quad
\text{d.} \left[\begin{matrix} :\ddot{O}-S-\ddot{O}: \\ | \\ :\ddot{O}: \end{matrix} \right]^{2-}
$$

4.11 Molecular Shapes: The VSEPR Theory

Learning Objective   ❯ Predict the shapes of simple molecules from their Lewis formulas.

We have represented molecules in two dimensions on paper, but molecules have three-dimensional shapes that are important in determining their properties. For example, the shapes of the molecules that make up gasoline determine its octane rating (Chapter 15), and drug molecules must have the right atoms in the right places to be effective (Chapter 18). We can use Lewis formulas as part of the process of predicting molecular shapes. Figure 4.8 shows the shapes that we consider in this book.

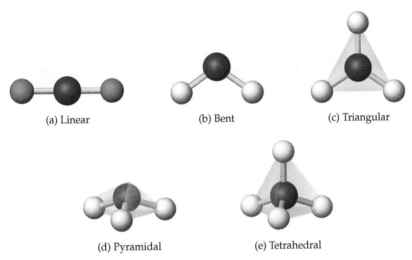

(a) Linear   (b) Bent   (c) Triangular

(d) Pyramidal   (e) Tetrahedral

▲ **Figure 4.8** Shapes of molecules. In a *linear* molecule (a), all the atoms are along a line; the bond angle is 180°. A *bent* molecule (b) has an angle less than 180°. Connecting the three outer atoms of a *triangular* molecule (c) with imaginary lines produces a triangle with an atom at the center. Imaginary lines connecting all four atoms of a *pyramidal* molecule (d) form a three-sided pyramid. Connecting the four outer atoms of a *tetrahedral* molecule (e) with imaginary lines produces a tetrahedron (a four-sided figure in which each side is a triangle) with an atom at the center.

We use the **valence shell electron pair repulsion (VSEPR) theory** to predict the arrangement of atoms about a central atom in a molecule. The basis of the VSEPR theory is that electron pairs arrange themselves about a central atom in a way that minimizes repulsions between these like-charged particles. This means that electron pairs (both lone pairs and shared pairs in bonds) will be as far apart as possible. In applying the VSEPR theory to predict molecular shapes, we will use the term *electron set* to refer to either a lone pair on a central atom or a bond—single, double, or triple—between the central atom and another atom. Table 4.6 presents the geometric shapes associated with the arrangement of two, three, or four electron sets about a central atom.

- When *two* electron sets are as far apart as possible, they are on opposite sides of the central atom at an angle of 180°.
- *Three* electron sets assume a triangular arrangement about the central atom, forming angles of separation of 120°.
- *Four* electron sets form a tetrahedral array around the central atom, giving a separation of about 109.5°.

We can determine the shapes of many molecules (and polyatomic ions) by following this simple procedure:

1. Draw a Lewis formula in which a shared electron pair (bonding pair) is indicated by a line. Use dots to show any unshared pairs (lone pairs) of electrons.

Table 4.6 Bonding and the Shapes of Molecules

Number of Bonded Atoms	Number of Lone Pairs	Number of Electron Sets	Molecular Shape	Examples of Molecules	Ball-and-Stick Models
2	0	2	Linear	$BeCl_2$ $HgCl_2$ CO_2 HCN	 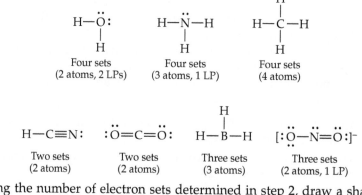BeCl₂
3	0	3	Triangular	BF_3 $AlBr_3$ CH_2O	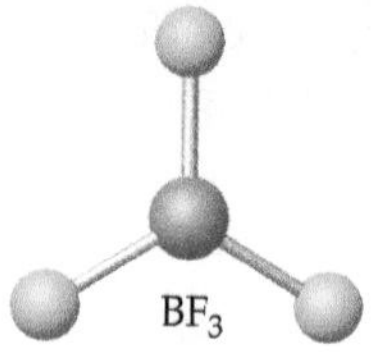 BF₃
4	0	4	Tetrahedral	CH_4 CBr_4 $SiCl_4$	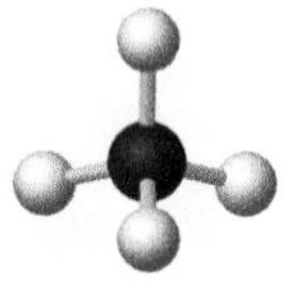 CH₄
3	1	4	Pyramidal	NH_3 PCl_3	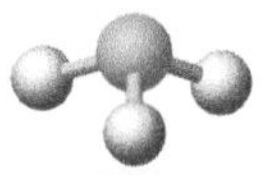 NH₃
2	2	4	Bent	H_2O H_2S SCl_2	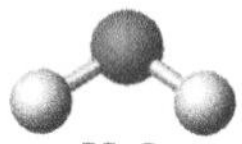 H₂O
2	1	3	Bent	SO_2 O_3	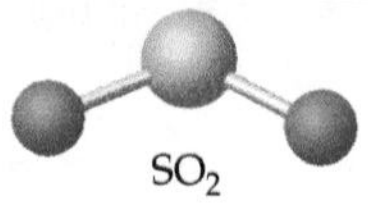 SO₂

2. To determine shape, count the number of electron sets around the *central* atom. Recall that a multiple bond counts only as one electron set. Examples are

$$H-\overset{\cdot\cdot}{\underset{\vert}{O}}:$$ H

Four sets
(2 atoms, 2 LPs)

$$H-\overset{\cdot\cdot}{\underset{\vert}{N}}-H$$ H

Four sets
(3 atoms, 1 LP)

$$H-\overset{\overset{H}{\vert}}{\underset{\vert}{C}}-H$$ H

Four sets
(4 atoms)

$$H-C\equiv N:$$

Two sets
(2 atoms)

$$:\overset{\cdot\cdot}{O}=C=\overset{\cdot\cdot}{O}:$$

Two sets
(2 atoms)

$$H-\overset{\overset{H}{\vert}}{\underset{\vert}{B}}-H$$

Three sets
(3 atoms)

$$[:\overset{\cdot\cdot}{\underset{\cdot\cdot}{O}}-N=\overset{\cdot\cdot}{O}:]^-$$

Three sets
(2 atoms, 1 LP)

3. Using the number of electron sets determined in step 2, draw a shape *as if* all the sets were bonding pairs and place these electron sets as far apart as possible (Table 4.6).

4. If there are *no* lone pairs, the shape from step 3 is the shape of the molecule. If there *are* lone pairs, remove them, leaving the bonding pairs exactly as they were. (This may seem strange, but it stems from the fact that *all* the sets determine the geometry, but only the arrangement of bonded atoms is considered in the shape of the molecule.)

Example 4.14 Shapes of Molecules

What are the shapes of **(a)** the H_2CO molecule and **(b)** the SCl_2 molecule?

Solution

a. We follow the preceding rules, starting with the Lewis formula.

1. The Lewis formula for H_2CO is

$$
\begin{array}{c}
H \\
| \\
C = \ddot{O} \\
| \\
H
\end{array}
$$

2. There are three sets of electrons: two C—H single bonds and one C=O double bond.

3. A triangular arrangement puts the three electron sets as far apart as possible.

$$
\begin{array}{c}
H \quad \overset{120°}{\searrow} \\
C = \ddot{O}: \\
H \nearrow
\end{array}
$$

4. All the electron sets are bonding pairs; the molecular shape is triangular, the same as the arrangement of the electron sets.

b. Again, we follow the rules, starting with the Lewis formula.

1. The Lewis formula for SCl_2 is

$$
\begin{array}{c}
:\ddot{S} - \ddot{C}l: \\
| \\
:\ddot{C}l:
\end{array}
$$

2. There are four sets of electrons on the sulfur atom.

3. A tetrahedral arrangement around the central atom puts the four sets of electrons as far apart as possible.

A tetrahedral arrangement with a bond angle of about 109.5°

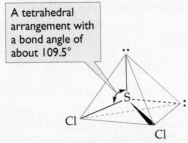

4. Two of the electron sets are bonding pairs and two are lone pairs. Ignore the lone pairs. The molecular shape is *bent*, with a bond angle of about 109.5°.

■ **EXERCISE 4.14A**

What are the shapes of **(a)** the PH_3 molecule and **(b)** the nitrate ion (NO_3^-)?

■ **EXERCISE 4.14B**

What are the shapes of **(a)** the carbonate ion (CO_3^{2-}) and **(b)** the hydrogen peroxide (H_2O_2) molecule?

Self-Assessment Questions

Match the formula in the left column with the molecular shape in the right column.

1. CS_2 **a.** bent

2. H_2S **b.** linear

3. PF_3 **c.** pyramidal

4. SiF_4 **d.** tetrahedral

Answers: 1, b; 2, a; 3, c; 4, d

4.12 Shapes and Properties: Polar and Nonpolar Molecules

Learning Objective ❯ Classify a simple molecule as polar or nonpolar from its shape and the polarity of its bonds.

Section 4.7 discussed polar and nonpolar bonds. A diatomic molecule is nonpolar if its bond is nonpolar, as in H_2 or Cl_2, and polar if its bond is polar, as in HCl. Recall from Section 4.7 that the partial charges in a polar bond are indicated by $\delta+$ and $\delta-$. In the case of a **dipole**, a molecule with a positive end and a negative end, the polarity is commonly indicated with an arrow with a plus sign at the tail end ($\longleftrightarrow$). The plus sign indicates the part of the molecule with a partial positive charge, and the head of the arrow signifies the end of the molecule with a partial negative charge.

$$H\text{—}H \quad \text{and} \quad Cl\text{—}Cl \qquad \overset{\delta+\quad\delta-}{H\text{—}Cl} \quad \text{or} \quad \overset{\longleftrightarrow}{H\text{—}Cl}$$

Nonpolar   Polar

For a molecule with three or more atoms, we must consider the polarity of the individual bonds as well as the overall geometry of the molecule to determine whether the molecule as a whole is polar. A **polar molecule** has separate centers of positive and negative charge, just as a magnet has north and south poles. Many properties of compounds—such as melting point, boiling point, and solubility—depend on the polarity of their molecules.

Methane: A Tetrahedral Molecule

There are four electron sets around the central carbon atom in methane, CH_4. Using the VSEPR theory, we would expect a tetrahedral arrangement and bond angles of 109.5° (Figure 4.9a). The actual bond angles are 109.5°, as predicted by the theory. All four electron sets are shared with hydrogen atoms and, therefore, occupy identical volumes. Each carbon-to-hydrogen bond is slightly polar (Figure 4.9b), but the methane molecule as a whole is symmetric. The slight bond polarities cancel out, leaving the methane molecule, as a whole, nonpolar (Figure 4.9c).

Ammonia: A Pyramidal Molecule

In ammonia, NH_3, the central nitrogen atom has three bonds and a lone pair around it. The N—H bonds of ammonia are more polar than the C—H bonds of methane. More important, the NH_3 molecule has a different geometry as a result of the lone pair on the nitrogen atom. The VSEPR theory predicts a tetrahedral arrangement of the four sets of electrons, giving bond angles of 109.5° (Figure 4.10a). However, the lone pair of electrons occupies a greater volume than a bonding pair, pushing the bonding pairs slightly closer together and resulting in actual bond angles of about 107°. The pyramidal geometry can be envisioned as a tripod with a hydrogen atom at the end of each leg and the nitrogen atom with its lone pair sitting at the top. Each nitrogen-to-hydrogen bond is somewhat polar (Figure 4.10b). The asymmetric structure makes the ammonia molecule polar, with a partial negative charge on the nitrogen atom and partial positive charges on the three hydrogen atoms (Figure 4.10c).

Water: A Bent Molecule

The O—H bonds in water are even more polar than the N—H bonds in ammonia because oxygen is more electronegative than nitrogen. (Recall that electronegativity increases from left to right in the periodic table.) Just because a molecule contains polar bonds, however, does not mean that the molecule as a whole is polar. If the atoms in the water molecule were in a straight line (that is, in a linear arrangement, as in CO_2), the two polar bonds would cancel one another and the molecule would be nonpolar.

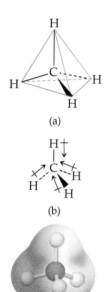

▲ **Figure 4.9** The methane molecule. In (a), black lines indicate covalent bonds; the red lines outline a tetrahedron; and all bond angles are 109.5°. The slightly polar C—H bonds cancel each other (b), resulting in a nonpolar, tetrahedral molecule (c).

Q: *How does the electrostatic potential diagram in (c) look different from the one in Figure 4.6?*

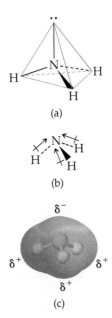

▲ Figure 4.10 The ammonia molecule. In (a), black lines indicate covalent bonds. The red lines outline a tetrahedron. The polar N—H bonds do not cancel each other completely in (b), resulting in a polar, pyramidal molecule (c).

Q: *How does the electrostatic potential diagram in Figure 4.10 (c) resemble the one in Figure 4.6?*

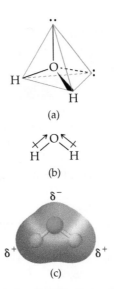

▲ Figure 4.11 The water molecule. In (a), black lines indicate covalent bonds, and the red lines outline a tetrahedron. The polar O—H bonds do not cancel each other in (b), resulting in a polar, bent molecule (c).

In its physical and chemical properties, however, water acts like a polar molecule. Molecules such as water and ammonia, in which the polar bonds do not cancel out, act as dipoles. Such molecules have a positive end and a negative end.

We can understand the dipole in the water molecule by using the VSEPR theory. The two bonds and two lone pairs should form a tetrahedral arrangement of electron sets (Figure 4.11a). Ignoring the lone pairs, the molecular shape has the atoms in a bent arrangement, with a bond angle of about 104.5° (instead of 109.5°). As with ammonia, the actual angle is slightly smaller than the predicted angle because of the greater volume of space occupied by the two lone pairs compared to the bonding pairs. The larger space occupied by the lone pairs reduces the space in which the bonding pairs reside, pushing them closer together. The two polar O—H bonds do not cancel each other (Figure 4.11b), making the bent water molecule polar (Figure 4.11c).

Self-Assessment Questions

1. Which of the following molecules is polar?
   a. Br_2 b. CH_4 c. CO_2 d. NH_3

2. Which of the following molecules is polar?
   a. C_2H_2 (linear)   b. Cl_2 c. CCl_4 d. PF_3

3. Which of the following molecules is polar?
   a. CF_4 b. C_2H_4 (planar)   c. NF_3 d. O_2

4. Which of the following molecules has polar bonds but is not polar?
   a. CCl_4 b. Cl_2 c. NCl_3 d. OF_2

Answers: 1, d; 2, d; 3, c; 4, a

John C. Warner, *Warner Babcock Institute for Green Chemistry*

Amy S. Cannon, *Beyond Benign*

Green Chemistry and Chemical Bonds

You learned in this chapter that atoms bond together to form compounds and these new compounds have properties that differ greatly from the component elements. In molecular compounds (molecules), atoms join by forming covalent bonds that cause the molecules to adopt specific geometric shapes (Sections 4.6, 4.7, 4.12). Each atom is held in a specific position relative to other atoms in the molecule. In ionic compounds, atoms are held together through ionic bonds (Section 4.3).

Molecular shape and composition of compounds control reactivity and interactions with other substances. As a chemist manipulates the geometry and composition of molecules, the properties can change drastically. A wonderful example of how shape impacts the design of molecules is seen in medicine. Within our bodies, biological molecules have particular shapes that are recognized by enzymes and other receptors, in the same way that a key matches a lock (Chapter 16). The molecule and the receptor fit together to form complexes through *noncovalent forces* (intermolecular forces, Section 6.3).

Medicinal chemists design new medicines and drug molecules (Chapter 18) so that they will resemble biological molecules and bind to enzymes or receptors in our body. But these molecule-receptor complexes must behave differently from the biological molecule. The binding triggers a response in our bodies and helps us to heal. Medicinal chemists use the shapes of molecules and forces between them to create new life-saving or life-changing medicines. Interaction between molecules caused by the geometric orientations of their atoms is called **molecular recognition**. The 1987 Nobel Prize in Chemistry was awarded to Donald J. Cram, Jean-Marie Lehn, and Charles J. Pedersen for pioneering work in this area. Scientists are now learning to use molecular recognition to control molecular properties and create not only new medicines but also new materials.

What does this have to do with green chemistry? The processes that chemists rely on to make materials often use large amounts of energy or highly reactive and toxic chemicals. New production methods that take advantage of molecular recogni-

tion typically use lower energy, solvent-free processes that do not require harsh conditions.

This way of making materials takes advantage of several of the twelve principles of green chemistry. Principles 3, 5, 6, and 8 focus on the choices we make as chemists as we design new molecules and materials. For example, using less hazardous chemicals to make new medicines means we can reduce the environmental impact of the manufacturing process for these compounds. Doing so ensures that they can change the lives of sick patients as well as provide safer workplaces for the workers making the new medicines.

Typical reactions carried out in laboratories use solvents that dissolve the molecules (solutes) (Section 5.5) and allow them to react to form new molecules. Many solvents can be hazardous to human health and the environment. Processes for making new noncovalent complexes that rely on molecular recognition often do not require solvents. This drastically reduces the environmental impact of these processes.

Many traditional processes require high temperatures, which translates to high energy use. Noncovalent complexes created through molecular recognition function in much the same way as molecules interact within our bodies at moderate temperatures. Therefore, these new approaches use very little energy, which benefits the environment and reduces the manufacturing cost. Also, many processes that generate new molecules and materials are quite complex. By understanding how molecules interact by shape and noncovalent forces, we can reduce the complexity in these processes and avoid the generation of waste and the reliance on hazardous materials.

By understanding molecular shape, the nature of chemical bonds, and how molecules interact with other molecules through noncovalent forces, chemists are able to design new medicines, molecules, and materials that benefit society and, at the same time, have minimal impact on the environment and human health. Green chemistry allows chemists to use these skills combined with new innovative techniques to design chemicals that do not harm our environment in the process.

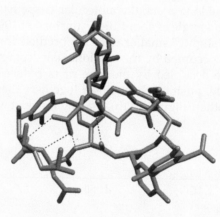

The antibiotic *vancomysin* carries out its function using molecular recognition. Vancomysin undergoes strong, selective hydrogen bonding with *peptides* (small protein chains) of bacteria, preventing formation of the cell wall.

A Chemical Vocabulary

Learning chemical symbolism is much like learning a foreign language. Once you have learned the basic "vocabulary," the rest is a lot easier. At first, the task is complicated because different chemical species or definitions sound a lot alike (sodium atoms versus sodium ions). Another complication is that we have several different ways to represent the *same* chemical species (Figure 4.12).

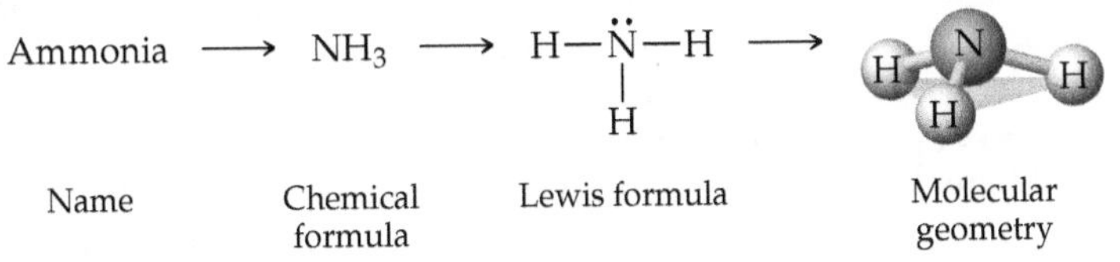

Ammonia $\longrightarrow$ NH_3 $\longrightarrow$ H—N̈—H $\longrightarrow$

Name   Chemical   Lewis formula   Molecular
formula   geometry

▲ **Figure 4.12** Several representations of the ammonia molecule.

In Chapter 1, we introduced symbols for the chemical elements. Chapter 3 discussed the structure of the nucleus and the symbolism for distinguishing different isotopes. This chapter covered chemical names and chemical formulas. Now you also know how to write Lewis symbols and formulas using dots to represent valence electrons and you can predict the shapes of thousands of different molecules with the VSEPR theory. In the next chapter, you will add the mathematics of chemistry to your toolbox.

CRITICAL THINKING EXERCISES

Apply knowledge that you have gained in this chapter and one or more of the FLaReS principles (Chapter 1) to evaluate the following statements or claims.

4.1 Some people believe that crystals have special powers. Crystal therapists claim that they can use quartz crystals to restore balance and harmony to a person's spiritual energy.

4.2 A "fuel-enhancer" device is being sold by an entrepreneur. The device contains a powerful magnet and is placed on the fuel line of an automobile. The inventor claims that the device "separates the positive and negative charges in the hydrocarbon fuel molecules, increasing their polarity and allowing them to react more readily with oxygen."

4.3 Sodium chloride (NaCl) is a metal–nonmetal compound held together by ionic bonds. A scientist has studied mercury(II) chloride ($HgCl_2$) and says that its atoms are held together by covalent bonds. The scientist says that since a solution of this substance in water does not conduct an electric current, it does not contain an appreciable amount of ions.

4.4 Another scientist, noting that the noble gas xenon does not contain any ions, states that xenon atoms must be held together by covalent bonds.

4.5 A web page claims, "Fifty years ago, the hydrogen bond angle in water was 108° and you rarely heard of anyone with cancer. Today, it's only 104° and, as a result, cancer is an epidemic!"

SUMMARY

Section 4.1—Outermost shell electrons are called valence electrons; those in all other shells are core electrons. The noble gases are inert because they (except He) have an octet of valence electrons. Atoms of other elements become more stable by gaining or losing electrons to attain an electron configuration that makes them isoelectronic with (having the same electron configuration as) a noble gas.

Section 4.2—The number of valence electrons for most main group elements is the same as the group number. Electron-dot symbols, or Lewis symbols, use dots singly or in pairs to represent valence electrons of an atom or ion.

Section 4.3—The element sodium reacts violently with elemental chlorine to give sodium chloride, or table salt. In this reaction, an electron is transferred from a sodium atom to a chlorine atom, forming ions.

The ions formed have opposite charges and are strongly attracted to one another; this attraction results in an ionic bond. The positive and negative ions arrange themselves in a regular array, forming a crystal of sodium chloride. The ions of an element have very different properties from the atoms of that element.

Section 4.4—Metal atoms tend to give up their valence electrons to become positively changed ions, and nonmetal atoms tend to accept (8 − group number) electrons to become negatively changed ions. In either case, the ions formed (except hydrogen ions and lithium ions) tend to have eight valence electrons. The formation of ions is thus said to follow the octet rule. The symbol for an ion is the element symbol with a superscript that indicates the number and type (+ or −) of charge. Some elements, especially the transition metals, can form ions of different charges. The formula of an ionic compound always has the same number of positive charges as negative charges.

Section 4.5—A binary ionic compound contains two different elements; it has a cation of a metal and an anion of a nonmetal. The formula of a binary ionic compound represents the numbers and types of ions in the compound. The formula is found by crossing over the charge numbers of the ions (without the plus and minus signs).

Binary ionic compounds are named by naming the cation first, and then putting an -ide ending on the stem of the anion name. Examples are calcium chloride, potassium oxide, aluminum nitride, and so on. Differently charged cations of a metal are named with Roman numerals to indicate the charge: Fe^{2+} is iron(II) ion and Fe^{3+} is iron(III) ion.

Section 4.6—Nonmetal atoms can bond by sharing one or more pairs of electrons, forming a covalent bond. A single bond is one pair of shared electrons; a double bond is two pairs; and a triple bond is three pairs. Shared pairs of electrons are called bonding pairs, and unshared pairs are called nonbonding pairs, or lone pairs. Most binary covalent compounds are named by naming the first element in the formula, followed by the stem of the second element with an -ide ending. Prefixes such as mono-, di-, tri-, and so on, are used to indicate the number of atoms of each element.

Section 4.7—Bonding pairs are shared equally when the two atoms are the same but may be unequally shared when the atoms are different. The electronegativity of an element is the attraction of an atom in a molecule for a bonding pair. Electronegativity generally increases toward the right and up on the periodic table, so fluorine is the most electronegative element. When electrons of a covalent bond are shared unequally, the more electronegative atom takes on a partial negative charge (δ−), the other atom takes on a partial positive charge (δ+), and the bond is said to be a polar covalent bond. The greater the difference in electronegativity, the more polar is the bond. A bonding pair shared equally is a nonpolar covalent bond.

Section 4.8—Carbon tends to form four covalent bonds, nitrogen three, and oxygen two; hydrogen can form only one bond. A water molecule has two bonding pairs (O—H bonds) and two lone pairs, an ammonia molecule has three bonding pairs (N—H bonds) and one lone pair, and a methane molecule has four bonding pairs (C—H bonds).

Section 4.9—A polyatomic ion is a charged particle containing two or more covalently bonded atoms. Compounds containing polyatomic ions are named, and their formulas written, in the same fashion as compounds containing monatomic ions, except that parentheses are placed around the formula for a polyatomic ion if there is more than one of it in the compound. Names of polyatomic ions often end in -ate or -ite.

Section 4.10—A Lewis formula shows the arrangement of atoms, bonds, and lone pairs in a molecule or polyatomic ion. To draw a Lewis formula, we (a) count the valence electrons; (b) draw a reasonable skeletal structure, showing the arrangement of atoms; (c) connect bonded atoms with a dash (one electron pair); (d) place electron pairs around outer atoms to give each an octet; and (e) place remaining electrons in pairs on the central atom. A multiple bond is included if there are not enough electrons to give each atom (except hydrogen) an octet. There are exceptions to the octet rule. Atoms and molecules with unpaired electrons are called free radicals. They are highly reactive and short-lived. Examples of free radicals are NO and ClO_2.

Section 4.11—The shape of a molecule can be predicted with the VSEPR theory, which assumes that sets of electrons (either lone pairs or electrons in a bond) around a central atom will get as far away from each other as possible. Two sets of electrons are 180° apart, three sets are about 120° apart, and four sets are about 109° apart. Once these angles have been established, we determine the shape of the molecule by examining only the bonded atoms. Simple molecules have shapes described as linear, bent, triangular, pyramidal, or tetrahedral.

Section 4.12—Like a polar bond, a polar molecule has separation between its centers of positive charge and negative charge. A molecule with nonpolar bonds is nonpolar. A molecule with polar bonds is nonpolar if its shape causes the polar bonds to cancel one another. If the polar bonds do not cancel, the molecule is polar or is said to be a dipole. The water molecule has polar O—H bonds and is bent, so it is polar.

Green chemistry Chemists manipulate the geometry and composition of molecules to change the properties of both molecules and materials. Typical methods for making these molecules and materials use highly reactive and toxic chemicals and high-energy processes. Greener approaches that take advantage of molecular recognition can instead use low energy, solvent-free processes that do not require harsh conditions.

Learning Objectives

❯ Determine the number of electrons in an ion. (4.1)   Problems 1–4

❯ Write the Lewis symbol for an atom or ion. (4.2)   Problems 7, 8

❯ Distinguish between an ion and an atom. (4.3)   Problems 1, 2, 59

❯ Describe the nature of the attraction that leads to formation of an ionic bond. (4.3)   Problems 41, 42

❯ Write symbols for common ions, and determine their charges. (4.4)   Problems 3, 11–16

❯ Describe the relationship between the octet rule and the charge on an ion. (4.4)	Problem 4
❯ Name and write formulas for binary ionic compounds. (4.5)	Problems 9, 10, 17–20, 55, 67
❯ Explain the difference between a covalent bond and an ionic bond. (4.6)	Problems 23–28, 41, 42
❯ Name and write formulas for covalent compounds. (4.6)	Problems 23–30
❯ Classify a covalent bond as polar or nonpolar. (4.7)	Problems 35–42
❯ Use electronegativities of elements to determine bond polarity. (4.7)	Problem 57
❯ Predict the number of bonds formed by common nonmetals (the HONC rules). (4.8)	Problems 5, 6
❯ Recognize common polyatomic ions and be able to use them in naming and writing formulas for compounds. (4.9)	Problems 21, 22, 65
❯ Write Lewis formulas for simple molecules and polyatomic ions. (4.10)	Problems 31–34, 56, 66
❯ Identify free radicals. (4.10)	Problems 49, 50
❯ Predict the shapes of simple molecules from their Lewis formulas. (4.11)	Problems 43–44
❯ Classify a simple molecule as polar or nonpolar from its shape and the polarity of its bonds. (4.12)	Problems 45–48
❯ Explain how shape and composition change the properties of molecules.	Problem 68
❯ Describe the concept of molecular recognition.	Problems 68, 69
❯ Explain the green chemistry advantages of using production methods based on molecular recognition.	Problems 70, 71

REVIEW QUESTIONS

1. How does sodium metal differ from sodium ions (in sodium chloride, for example) in properties?

2. What are the structural differences among chlorine atoms, chlorine molecules, and chloride ions? How do their properties differ?

3. What are the charges on simple ions formed from atoms of the following?
    a. group 1A elements
    b. group 6A elements
    c. group 5A elements
    d. group 2A elements

4. In what group of the periodic table would elements that form ions with the following charges likely be found?
    a. 2−   b. 3+
    c. 1+   d. 2+

5. How many covalent bonds do each of the following usually form? You may refer to the periodic table.
    a. H   b. Cl
    c. S   d. F
    e. N   f. P

6. Of the elements H, O, N, and C, which one(s) can readily form triple bonds?

PROBLEMS

Lewis Symbols for Elements

7. Write Lewis symbols for each of the following elements. You may use the periodic table.
    a. calcium   b. sulfur
    c. silicon

8. Write Lewis symbols for each of the following elements. You may use the periodic table.
    a. phosphorus   b. fluorine
    c. boron

Lewis Formulas for Ionic Compounds

9. Write Lewis formulas for each of the following.
    a. sodium iodide   b. potassium sulfide
    c. calcium chloride   d. aluminum fluoride

10. Write Lewis formulas for each of the following.
    a. lithium bromide
    b. strontium sulfide
    c. sodium nitride
    d. aluminum oxide

Names and Symbols for Simple Ions

11. Without referring to Table 4.2, supply a symbol given the name or a name given the symbol for each of the following ions:
    a. magnesium ion   b. Na^+
    c. oxide ion   d. Cl^-
    e. zinc ion   f. Cu^+

12. Without referring to Table 4.2, supply a symbol given the name or a name given the symbol for each of the following ions:
    a. sulfide ion
    b. K^+
    c. Br^-
    d. fluoride ion
    e. Ca^{2+}
    f. iron(III) ion

13. Refer to page 98; then use that information to name the following ions:
    a. Cr^{2+}
    b. Cr^{3+}
    c. Cr^{6+}

14. Refer to page 98; then use that information to name the following ions.
    a. Mo^{4+}
    b. Mo^{6+}

15. Refer to page 98; then write symbols for:
    a. vanadium(II) ion
    b. titanium(II) ion
    c. titanium(IV) ion

16. Refer to page 98; then write symbols for:
    a. manganese(II) ion
    b. manganese(III) ion
    c. manganese(VII) ion

Names and Formulas for Binary Ionic Compounds

17. Write a formula to match the name or a name to match the formula of the following binary ionic compounds:
    a. sodium iodide
    b. KCl
    c. copper(I) oxide
    d. MgF_2
    e. iron(II) bromide
    f. $FeBr_3$

18. Write a formula to match the name or a name to match the formula of the following binary ionic compounds:
    a. LiF
    b. calcium chloride
    c. MgS
    d. silver iodide
    e. CuO
    f. copper(I) sulfide

19. There are two common binary ionic compounds formed from chromium and oxygen. One of them contains chromium(III) ions; the other contains chromium(VI) ions. Write the formulas for the two compounds, and name them.

20. One of two binary ionic compounds is often added to toothpaste. One of these compounds contains sodium and fluorine; the other contains tin(II) ions and fluorine. Write the formulas for these two compounds, and name them.

Names and Formulas for Ionic Compounds with Polyatomic Ions

21. Supply a formula to match the name or a name to match the formula for the following:
    a. potassium hydroxide
    b. $MgCO_3$
    c. iron(III) cyanide
    d. iron(II) oxalate
    e. $CuSO_4$
    f. $Na_2Cr_2O_7$

22. Supply a formula to match the name or a name to match the formula for the following:
    a. $AgNO_2$
    b. lithium chromate
    c. $(NH_4)_2SO_3$
    d. magnesium hydrogen carbonate
    e. copper(I) phosphate
    f. $Al(MnO_4)_3$

Molecules: Covalent Bonds

23. Use Lewis symbols to show the sharing of electrons between a hydrogen atom and a fluorine atom.

24. Use Lewis symbols to show the sharing of electrons between two bromine atoms to form a bromine (Br_2) molecule. Label all electron pairs as bonding pairs (BPs) or lone pairs (LPs).

25. Use Lewis symbols to show the sharing of electrons between a phosphorus atom and hydrogen atoms to form a molecule in which phosphorus has an octet of electrons.

26. Use Lewis symbols to show the sharing of electrons between a silicon atom and hydrogen atoms to form a molecule in which silicon has an octet of electrons.

27. Use Lewis symbols to show the sharing of electrons between a carbon atom and chlorine atoms to form a molecule in which each atom has an octet of electrons.

28. Use Lewis symbols to show the sharing of electrons between a nitrogen atom and fluorine atoms to form a molecule in which each atom has an octet of electrons.

Names and Formulas for Covalent Compounds

29. Supply a formula for the name or a name for the formula for the following covalent compounds:
    a. dinitrogen tetroxide
    b. bromine trichloride
    c. OF_2
    d. nitrogen triiodide
    e. CBr_4
    f. N_2S_4

30. Supply a formula for the name or a name for the formula for the following covalent compounds:
    a. carbon disulfide
    b. chlorine trifluoride
    c. PF_5
    d. CI_4
    e. tricarbon dioxide
    f. P_4S_3

Lewis Formulas for Molecules and Polyatomic Ions

31. Write Lewis formulas that follow the octet rule for the following covalent molecules:
    a. SiH_4
    b. N_2F_4
    c. CH_5N
    d. H_2CO
    e. NOH_3
    f. H_3PO_3

32. Write Lewis formulas that follow the octet rule for the following covalent molecules:
    a. NH_2Cl
    b. C_2H_4
    c. H_2SO_4
    d. C_2N_2
    e. $COCl_2$
    f. SCl_2

33. Write Lewis formulas that follow the octet rule for the following ions:
    a. ClO^-
    b. HPO_4^{2-}
    c. BrO_3^-

34. Write Lewis formulas that follow the octet rule for the following ions:
    a. CN^-
    b. ClO_2^-
    c. HSO_4^-

Electronegativity: Polar Covalent Bonds

35. Classify the following covalent bonds as polar or nonpolar.
    a. H—O
    b. N—F
    c. Cl—B

36. Classify the following covalent bonds as polar or nonpolar.
    a. H—N
    b. O—Be
    c. P—F

37. Use the symbol ↔ to indicate the direction of the dipole in each polar bond in Problem 35.

38. Use the symbol $\leftrightarrow$ to indicate the direction of the dipole in each polar bond in Problem 36.

39. Use the symbols $\delta+$ and $\delta-$ to indicate partial charges, if any, on the following bonds.
    a. Si—O   b. F—F
    c. F—N

40. Use the symbols $\delta+$ and $\delta-$ to indicate partial charges, if any, on the following bonds.
    a. O—H   b. C—F
    c. C=C

Classifying Bonds

41. Classify the bonds in the following as ionic or covalent. For bonds that are covalent, indicate whether they are polar or nonpolar.
    a. K_2O b. BrCl
    c. MgF_2 d. I_2

42. Classify the bonds in the following as ionic or covalent. For bonds that are covalent, indicate whether they are polar or nonpolar.
    a. Na_2O b. $CaCl_2$
    c. NBr_3 d. CS_2

VSEPR Theory: The Shapes of Molecules

43. Use the VSEPR theory to predict the shape of each of the following molecules:
    a. silane (SiH_4)
    b. hydrogen selenide (H_2Se)
    c. phosphine (PH_3)
    d. silicon tetrafluoride (SiF_4)
    e. oxygen difluoride (OF_2)
    f. formaldehyde (H_2CO)

44. Use VSEPR theory to predict the shape of each of the following molecules:
    a. chloroform ($CHCl_3$)
    b. boron trichloride (BCl_3)
    c. carbon tetrafluoride (CF_4)
    d. sulfur difluoride (SF_2)
    e. nitrogen triiodide (NI_3)
    f. dichlorodifluoromethane (CCl_2F_2)

Polar and Nonpolar Molecules

45. The molecule BeF_2 is linear. Is it polar or nonpolar? Explain.

46. The molecule SF_2 is bent. Is it polar or nonpolar? Explain.

47. Look again at the molecules in Problem 43. For each one, are the bonds polar? What are the approximate bond angles? Is the molecule as a whole polar?

48. Look again at the molecules in Problem 44. For each one, are the bonds polar? What are the approximate bond angles? Is the molecule as a whole polar?

Molecules That Are Exceptions to the Octet Rule

49. Which of the following species (atoms or molecules) are free radicals?
    a. Br   b. F_2
    c. CCl_3

50. Which of the following species (atoms or molecules) are free radicals?
    a. S   b. NO_2
    c. N_2O_4

51. Free radicals are one class of molecules in which atoms do not conform to the octet rule. Another exception involves atoms with fewer than eight electrons, as seen in elements of group 3 and in beryllium. In some covalent molecules, these atoms can have six or four electrons, respectively. Write Lewis structures for the following covalent molecules:
    a. $AlBr_3$ b. BeH_2
    c. BH_3

52. Exceptions to the octet rule include molecules that have atoms with more than eight valence electrons, most typically 10 or 12. Atoms heavier than Si can expand their valence shell, meaning that they can accommodate the "extra" electrons in unoccupied, higher-energy orbitals. Draw Lewis structures for the following molecules or ions:
    a. XeF_4 b. I_3^-
    c. SF_4 d. KrF_2

ADDITIONAL PROBLEMS

53. Why does neon tend not to form chemical bonds?

54. Draw an electrostatic potential diagram of the H_2S molecule. Use the symbols $\delta+$ and $\delta-$ to indicate the polarity of the molecule.

55. The gas phosphine (PH_3) is used as a fumigant to protect stored grain and other durable produce from pests. Phosphine is generated where it is to be used by adding water to aluminum phosphide or magnesium phosphide. Give formulas for these two phosphides.

56. There are two different covalent molecules with the formula C_2H_6O. Write Lewis formulas for the two molecules.

57. Solutions of iodine chloride (ICl) are used as disinfectants. Is the compound ICl ionic, polar covalent, or nonpolar covalent?

58. Consider the hypothetical elements X, Y, and Z, which have the following Lewis symbols:

    $:\ddot{X}\cdot$ $:\ddot{Y}\cdot$ $:\dot{Z}\cdot$

    a. To which group in the periodic table would each element belong?
    b. Write the Lewis formula for the simplest compound each would form with hydrogen.
    c. Write Lewis formulas for the ions that would be formed when X reacted with sodium and when Y reacted with sodium.

59. Potassium is a soft, silvery metal that reacts violently with water and ignites spontaneously in air. Your doctor recommends that you take a potassium supplement. Would you take potassium metal? If not, what would you take?

60. What is wrong with the phrase "just a few molecules of potassium iodide"?

61. Use subshell notation to write an electron configuration for the most stable simple ion formed by each of the following elements.
    a. Ca   b. Rb
    c. S   d. I
    e. N   f. Se

62. Why is Na^+ smaller than Na? Why is Cl^- larger than Cl?

63. The halogens (F, Cl, Br, and I) tend to form only one single bond in binary molecules. Explain.

64. A science magazine for the general public contains this statement: "Some of these hydrocarbons are very light, like methane gas—just a single carbon molecule attached to three hydrogen molecules." Evaluate the statement, and correct any inaccuracies.

65. Sodium tungstate is Na_2WO_4. What is the formula for aluminum tungstate?

66. Scientists estimate that the atmosphere of Titan (a moon of Saturn) consists of about 98.4% nitrogen and 1.6% methane. They have also found traces of organic molecules with the molecular formulas C_2H_4, C_3H_4, C_4H_2, HCN, HC_3N, and C_2N_2. Write possible Lewis formulas for each of these molecules.

67. What is the formula for the compound formed by the imaginary ions Q^{2+} and ZX_4^{3-}?

68. Give two design criteria that chemists use to design new medicines.

69. What is the term for the science that explains how molecules interact through geometric orientation of atoms?

70. Give three ways that molecular recognition approaches can support greener methods for making molecules and materials.

71. How can an understanding of enzymes and biological receptors guide medicinal chemists?

 COLLABORATIVE GROUP PROJECTS

Prepare a PowerPoint, poster, or other presentation (as directed by your instructor) for presentation to the class. Projects 1 and 2 are best done by a group of four students.

1. Make a form like that in Problem 3, page 40, but replace the column headings "Word" and "Definition" with "Name" and "Lewis Formula." Student 1 should write the name from the list below in the first column of the form and its Lewis formula in the second column. Proceed as in Problem 3, page 40, ending by comparing the name in the last column with that in the first column. Discuss any differences in the two names. If the name in the last column differs from that in the first column, determine what went wrong in the process.
   a. bromide ion
   b. calcium fluoride
   c. phosphorus trifluoride
   d. carbon disulfide

2. Make a form like that in Problem 3, page 40, using the column headings "Name" and "Structure." Then student 1 should write a name from the list below in the first column of the form and its structure in the second column. Proceed as in Problem 3, page 40, ending by comparing the name in the last column with that in the first column. Discuss any differences in the two names. If the name in the last column differs from that in the first column, determine what went wrong in the process.
   a. ammonium nitrate   b. potassium phosphate
   c. lithium carbonate   d. copper(I) chloride

3. Starting with 20 balloons, blown up to about the same size and tied, tie two balloons together. Next, tie three balloons together. Repeat this with four, five, and six balloons. (*Suggestion*: Three sets of two balloons can be twisted together to form a six-balloon set, and so on.) Show how these balloon sets can be used to illustrate the VSEPR theory.

4. Prepare a brief biographical report on one of the following:
   a. Gilbert N. Lewis   b. Linus Pauling

5. There are several different definitions and scales for electronegativity. Search for information on these, and write a brief compare-and-contrast essay about two of them.

Chemical Accounting

Have You Ever Wondered?

1. How can a car make more pollution than the gasoline it uses?

2. What's the difference between 14K gold and 18K gold?

3. Does 2% milk have just 2% of the calories of whole milk?

4. What does a cholesterol level of 200 mean?

Learning Objectives

> Identify balanced and unbalanced chemical equations, and balance equations by inspection. (5.1)

> Determine volumes of gases that react, using a balanced equation for a reaction. (5.2)

> Calculate the formula mass, molecular mass, or molar mass of a substance. (5.3)

> Convert from mass to moles and from moles to mass of a substance. (5.4)

> Calculate the mass or number of moles of a reactant or product from the mass or number of moles of another reactant or product. (5.4)

> Calculate the concentration (molarity, percent by volume, or percent by mass) of a solute in a solution. (5.5)

> Calculate the amount of solute or solution given the concentration and the other amount. (5.5)

> Explain how the concept of atom economy can be applied to pollution prevention and environmental protection.

> Calculate the atom economy for chemical reactions.

Mass and Volume Relationships

We can look at or represent chemical phenomena on three levels:

1. Macro and tangible: for example, a sample of yellow powder or a blue solution in a beaker.
2. Particle (atom, molecule, or ion) and invisible: for example, a sulfur atom, a carbon dioxide molecule, or a chloride ion.
3. Symbolic and mathematical: for example, S, CO_2, Cl, or $d = m/V$.

Macro-level representations of chemicals are familiar from everyday life. It is easy to visualize salt crystals in a shaker, gold in jewelry, baking soda in a box, aspirin in tablets, and many other common substances, because they are tangible. We can see them and touch them.

Everything that burns fuel requires oxygen, and the human body is no exception. At the top of Mt. Everest, there is not enough oxygen in the air to keep people alive, so climbers making the ascent must bring oxygen with them. But how much oxygen should each climber bring? A knowledge of chemistry allows this question to be answered, thus promoting the safety of the climbers and the success of their venture.

The other representations were introduced in earlier chapters. You may have recognized the mathematical equation for density from Chapter 1. We employed symbols when discussing atoms in Chapters 2 and 3 and formulas in our discussion of molecules and ions in Chapter 4. In this chapter, we consider symbolic and mathematical descriptions of chemical changes.

Much chemistry can be discussed and understood with little or no mathematics, but the quantitative aspects can shed a great deal of light on properties of matter. In this chapter, we will consider some of the basic calculations used in chemistry and related fields such as biology and medicine. Chemists use many kinds of mathematics, from simple arithmetic to sophisticated calculus and complicated computer algorithms, but our calculations here will require at most a bit of algebra.

5.1 Chemical Sentences: Equations

Learning Objective ❯ Identify balanced and unbalanced chemical equations, and balance equations by inspection.

Chemistry is a study of matter and the changes it undergoes and of the energy that brings about these changes or is released when these changes happen. The symbols and formulas we have used to represent elements and compounds make up the letters (symbols) and words (formulas) of our chemical language. Using them, we can write sentences (chemical equations). A **chemical equation** uses symbols and formulas to represent the elements and compounds involved in the change.

At the macro level, we can describe a chemical reaction in words. For example,

Carbon reacts with oxygen to form carbon dioxide.

We can describe the same reaction symbolically.

$$C + O_2 \longrightarrow CO_2$$

The plus sign (+) indicates that carbon and oxygen are added together or combined in some way. The arrow ($\longrightarrow$) is read "yield(s)" or "react(s) to produce." Substances on the left of the arrow (C and O_2 in this case) are **reactants**, or *starting materials*. Those on the right (here, CO_2) are the **products** of the reaction. Reactants and products need not be written in any particular order in a chemical equation, except that all reactants must be to the left of the arrow and all products to the right. In other words, we could also write the preceding equation as

$$O_2 + C \longrightarrow CO_2$$

At the atomic or molecular level, the equation means that one carbon (C) atom reacts with one oxygen (O_2) molecule to produce one carbon dioxide (CO_2) molecule.

Sometimes, we indicate the physical states of the reactants and products by writing the initial letter of the state immediately following the formula: (g) indicates a gaseous substance, (l) a liquid, and (s) a solid. The label (aq) indicates that the substance is in an aqueous (water) solution. Using state labels, the above equation becomes

$$C(s) + O_2(g) \longrightarrow CO_2(g)$$

Balancing Chemical Equations

We can represent the reaction of carbon and oxygen to form carbon dioxide quite simply, but many other chemical reactions require more thought. For example, hydrogen reacts with oxygen to form water. Using formulas, we can represent this reaction as

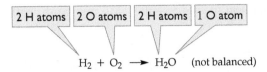

$H_2 + O_2 \longrightarrow H_2O$ (not balanced)

However, this representation shows two oxygen atoms in the reactants (as O_2), but only one in the product (in H_2O). Because matter is neither created nor destroyed in a chemical reaction (the law of conservation of mass, Section 2.2), the equation must be *balanced* to represent the chemical reaction correctly. That means the same number of each type of atom must appear on both sides of the arrow. To balance the oxygen atoms, we need only place the coefficient 2 in front of the formula for water.

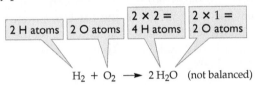

$H_2 + O_2 \longrightarrow 2 H_2O$ (not balanced)

This coefficient means that two molecules of water are produced. As is the case with a subscript 1, a coefficient of 1 is understood when there is no number in front of a formula. *Everything* in a formula is multiplied by the coefficient. In the preceding equation, adding the coefficient 2 before H_2O not only increases the number of oxygen atoms on the product side to two but also increases the number of hydrogen atoms to four.

But the equation is still not balanced. As we took care of the oxygen, we unbalanced the hydrogen. To balance the hydrogen, we place a coefficient 2 in front of H_2.

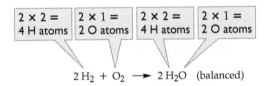

$2 H_2 + O_2 \longrightarrow 2 H_2O$ (balanced)

Now there are four hydrogen atoms and two oxygen atoms on each side of the equation. Atoms are conserved: The equation is balanced (Figure 5.1), and the law of conservation of mass is obeyed. Figure 5.2 illustrates two common pitfalls in the process of balancing equations, as well as the correct method. Remember not to

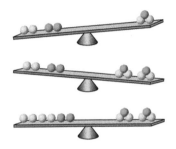

= hydrogen
= oxygen

▲ **Figure 5.1** To balance the equation for the reaction of hydrogen and oxygen to form water, the same number of each kind of atom must appear on each side (atoms are conserved). When the equation is balanced, there are four H atoms and two O atoms on each side.

Q: *Why can't you balance the equation by removing one of the oxygen atoms from the left side of the top balance?*

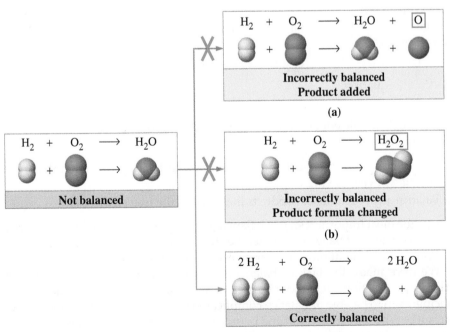

◀ **Figure 5.2** Balancing the equation for the reaction between hydrogen and oxygen to form water. (a) Incorrect. There is no atomic oxygen (O) as a product. Other products cannot be introduced simply to balance an equation. (b) Incorrect. The product of the reaction is water (H_2O), not hydrogen peroxide (H_2O_2). A formula can't be changed simply to balance an equation. (c) Correct. An equation can be balanced only by using the correct formulas and adjusting the coefficients.

add to or change chemical species on either side, but to use coefficients to equate the numbers of atoms of each type.

Example 5.1 Balancing Equations

Balance the following chemical equation, which represents the reaction that occurs when an airbag in a car deploys.

$$NaN_3 \longrightarrow Na + N_2$$

Solution

The sodium (Na) atoms are balanced, but the nitrogen atoms are not. To balance this equation, we can use the concept of the least common multiple. There are three nitrogen atoms on the left (reactant side) and two on the right (product side). The least common multiple of 2 and 3 is 6. To get *six* nitrogen atoms on each side, we need *three* N_2 and *two* NaN_3:

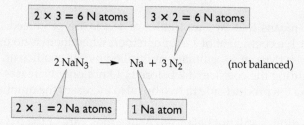

We now have *two* sodium atoms on the left. We can get two on the right by placing the coefficient 2 in front of Na.

$$2\,NaN_3 \longrightarrow 2\,Na + 3\,N_2 \quad \text{(balanced)}$$

Checking, we count two Na atoms and six N atoms on each side. The equation is balanced.

■ EXERCISE 5.1A

The reaction between hydrogen and nitrogen to give ammonia, called the *Haber process*, is typically the first step in the industrial production of nitrogen fertilizers.

$$H_2 + N_2 \longrightarrow NH_3$$

Balance the equation.

■ EXERCISE 5.1B

Iron ores such as Fe_2O_3 are *smelted* by reaction with carbon to produce metallic iron and carbon dioxide.

$$Fe_2O_3 + C \longrightarrow CO_2 + Fe$$

Balance the equation.

Although simple equations can be balanced by trial and error, a couple of strategies often help:

1. If an element occurs in just one substance on each side of the equation, try balancing that element *first*.
2. Balance any reactants or products that exist as the free element *last*.

Perhaps the most important step in balancing any equation is to check that the result you obtain is indeed balanced. Remember that for each element, the same number of atoms of the element must appear on each side of the equation.

We have made the task of balancing equations appear easy by considering fairly simple reactions. It is more important at this point for you to understand the principle than to be able to balance complicated equations. You should know what is meant by a balanced equation and be able to balance simple equations. It is crucial that you understand the information that is contained in balanced equations.

Self-Assessment Questions

1. Which of the following equations are balanced? (You need not balance the equations. Just determine whether they are balanced as written.)

   I. $Ca + 2 H_2O \longrightarrow Ca(OH)_2 + H_2$

   II. $4 LiH + AlCl_3 \longrightarrow 2 LiAlH_4 + 2 LiCl$

   III. $2 LiOH + CO_2 \longrightarrow Li_2CO_3 + H_2O$

   IV. $2 Sn + 2 H_2SO_4 \longrightarrow 2 SnSO_4 + SO_2 + 2 H_2O$

   a. I and II   **b.** I and III   **c.** II and III   **d.** II and IV

2. Consider the equation for the reaction of phosphine with oxygen to form tetraphosphorus decoxide and water:

   $$PH_3 + O_2 \longrightarrow P_4O_{10} + H_2O \quad \text{(not balanced)}$$

   When the equation is balanced, how many molecules of water are produced for each molecule of P_4O_{10} formed?

   a. 1   **b.** 4   **c.** 6   **d.** 12

Items 3–5 refer to the following equation for the reaction of calcium hydroxide $[Ca(OH)_2]$ with phosphoric acid (H_3PO_4).

$$Ca(OH)_2 + H_3PO_4 \longrightarrow H_2O + Ca_3(PO_4)_2 \quad \text{(not balanced)}$$

3. When the equation is balanced, how many H_2O molecules will be produced for each H_3PO_4 molecule that reacts?

   a. 1   **b.** 2   **c.** 3   **d.** 6

4. When the equation is balanced, how many H_3PO_4 molecules must react to produce one $Ca_3(PO_4)_2$ formula unit?

   a. 1   **b.** 2   **c.** 3   **d.** 6

5. When the equation is balanced, how many $Ca(OH)_2$ formula units are needed to react with six H_3PO_4 molecules?

   a. 1   **b.** 1.5   **c.** 6   **d.** 9

Just as a molecule is the smallest unit of a molecular compound, a *formula unit* is the smallest unit of an ionic compound.

Answers: 1, b; 2, c; 3, c; 4, b; 5, d

5.2 Volume Relationships in Chemical Equations

Learning Objective ❯ Determine volumes of gases that react, using a balanced equation for a reaction.

So far we have looked at chemical reactions in terms of individual atoms and molecules. In the real world, however, chemists work with quantities of matter that contain billions of billions of atoms. John Dalton postulated that atoms of different elements have different masses. Therefore, equal masses of different elements must contain different numbers of atoms. By analogy, a kilogram of golf balls contains a smaller number of balls than a kilogram of Ping-Pong balls, because a golf ball is heavier than a Ping-Pong ball. One could determine the number of balls in each case simply by counting them. For atoms, however, counting is not so straightforward. The smallest visible particle of matter contains more atoms than could be counted in ten lifetimes! Even so, we can determine the number of atoms in a substance, as you will learn in this chapter.

Studies of gases in the eighteenth century advanced our understanding of how to account for atoms involved in chemical reactions. The interesting nature and behavior of gases are explored in Chapter 6; here we focus on some historical experiments with gases that revealed how chemical equations can be balanced. Experiments with gases led French scientist Joseph Louis Gay-Lussac (1778–1850) to an approach to quantifying atoms. In 1808, he announced the results of some chemical reactions that he had carried out with gases and summarized these experiments in a new law. The **law of combining volumes** states that when all measurements are made at the same temperature and pressure, the volumes of gaseous reactants and products are in small whole-number ratios. One such experiment is illustrated in

▶ **Figure 5.3** Gay-Lussac's law of combining volumes. Three volumes of hydrogen gas react with one volume of nitrogen gas to yield two volumes of ammonia gas, when measured at the same temperature and pressure.

Q: *Can you sketch a similar figure for the reaction* $2 SO_2(g) + O_2(g) \longrightarrow 2 SO_3(g)$?

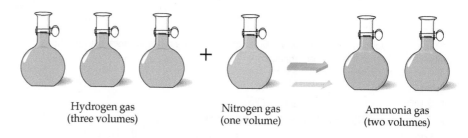

Hydrogen gas
(three volumes)

Nitrogen gas
(one volume)

Ammonia gas
(two volumes)

Figure 5.3. When hydrogen reacts with nitrogen to form ammonia, three volumes of hydrogen combine with one volume of nitrogen to yield two volumes of ammonia. The small whole-number ratio is 3:1:2.

Gay-Lussac thought there must be some relationship between the numbers of molecules and the volumes of gaseous reactants and products. But it was Amedeo Avogadro who first explained the law of combining volumes in 1811. **Avogadro's hypothesis**, based on a shrewd interpretation of experimental facts, was that equal volumes of all gases, when measured at the same temperature and pressure, contain the same number of molecules (Figure 5.4).

▶ **Figure 5.4** Avogadro's explanation of Gay-Lussac's law of combining volumes. Equal volumes of all the gases contain the same number of molecules.

Q: *Can you sketch a similar figure for the reaction* $2 NO(g) + O_2(g) \longrightarrow 2 NO_2(g)$?

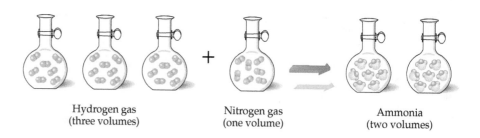

Hydrogen gas
(three volumes)

Nitrogen gas
(one volume)

Ammonia
(two volumes)

"Volumi eguali di gas nelle stesse condizioni di temperatura e di pressione contengono lo stesso numero di molecole."

▲ Amedeo Avogadro (1776–1856) and his hypothesis. The quotation reads, "Equal volumes of all gases at the same temperature and pressure contain the same number of molecules."

The equation for the combination of hydrogen and nitrogen to form ammonia is

$$3 H_2(g) + N_2(g) \longrightarrow 2 NH_3(g)$$

Note that the coefficients of the molecules correlate with the combining ratio of the gas volumes, 3:1:2 (Figure 5.3). The equation says that three H_2 molecules react with one N_2 molecule to produce two NH_3 molecules. The balanced equation provides the combining ratios. If you had 3 million H_2 molecules, you would need 1 million N_2 molecules to produce 2 million NH_3 molecules. According to the equation, three volumes of hydrogen react with one volume of nitrogen to produce two volumes of ammonia because each volume of hydrogen contains the same number of molecules as that same volume of nitrogen.

Example 5.2   Volume Relationships of Gases

What volume of oxygen is required to burn 0.556 L of propane in the following combustion reaction, assuming that both gases are measured at the same temperature and pressure?

$$C_3H_8(g) + 5 O_2(g) \longrightarrow 3 CO_2(g) + 4 H_2O(g)$$

Solution

The coefficients in the equation indicate that each volume of $C_3H_8(g)$ requires five volumes of O_2 gas. Thus, we use 5 L $O_2(g)$/1 L $C_3H_8(g)$ as a conversion factor to find the volume of oxygen required. (Conversion factors are explained in Section A.3 of the Appendix.)

$$? \text{ L } O_2(g) = 0.556 \text{ L } C_3H_8(g) \times \frac{5 \text{ L } O_2(g)}{1 \text{ L } C_3H_8(g)} = 2.78 \text{ L } O_2(g)$$

▪ EXERCISE 5.2A
Using the equation in Example 5.2, calculate the volume of $CO_2(g)$ produced when 0.492 L of propane is burned if the two gases are compared at the same temperature and pressure.

▪ EXERCISE 5.2B
If 10.0 L each of propane and oxygen are combined at the same temperature and pressure, which gas will be left over after reaction? What volume of that gas will remain?

Self-Assessment Questions

1. In the reaction $2 H_2(g) + O_2(g) \longrightarrow 2 H_2O(g)$, with all substances at the same temperature and pressure, the ratio of volumes, for H_2, O_2, and H_2O, respectively, is
   a. 1:0:1   b. 2:0:2   c. 1:1:1   d. 2:1:2

2. How many CO_2 molecules are produced in the following reaction if 50 O_2 molecules react?

$$2 C_8H_{18}(l) + 25 O_2(g) \longrightarrow 16 CO_2(g) + 18 H_2O(l)$$

   a. 25 molecules   b. 50 molecules   c. 32 molecules   d. 16 molecules

3. In the reaction $N_2(g) + 3 H_2(g) \longrightarrow 2 NH_3(g)$, with all substances at the same temperature and pressure, what volume of ammonia is produced when 4.50 L of nitrogen reacts with excess hydrogen?
   a. 3.00 L   b. 4.50 L   c. 6.75 L   d. 9.00 L

Answers: 1, d; 2, c; 3, d

5.3 Avogadro's Number and the Mole

Learning Objectives ❯ Calculate the formula mass, molecular mass, or molar mass of a substance.

Avogadro's hypothesis, which has been verified many times and in several ways over the years, states that equal volumes of gases at the same temperature and pressure contain equal numbers of molecules. This means that if we weigh equal volumes of different gases, the gases won't weigh the same. The ratio of their masses should be the same as the mass ratio of the molecules themselves.

Avogadro's Number: 6.02×10^{23}

Avogadro had no way of knowing how many molecules were in a given volume of gas. Scientists since his time have determined the number of atoms in various weighed samples of substances. Atoms are so incredibly small that these numbers are extremely large, even for tiny samples. Recall that the mass of a carbon-12 atom is exactly 12 atomic mass units (u) (Section 2.4, page 51) because the carbon-12 atom sets the standard for atomic mass. The number of carbon-12 atoms in a 12-g sample of carbon-12 is called **Avogadro's number** and has been determined experimentally to be 6.0221367×10^{23}. We usually round this number to three significant figures: 6.02×10^{23}.

The Mole: "A Dozen Eggs and a Mole of Sugar, Please"

We buy socks by the pair (2 socks), eggs by the dozen (12 eggs), and pencils by the gross (144 pencils). A dozen is the same number whether we are counting eggs or oranges. But a dozen eggs and a dozen oranges do not weigh the same. If an orange weighs five times as much as an egg, a dozen oranges will weigh five times as much as a dozen eggs.

▶ How big is Avogadro's number?

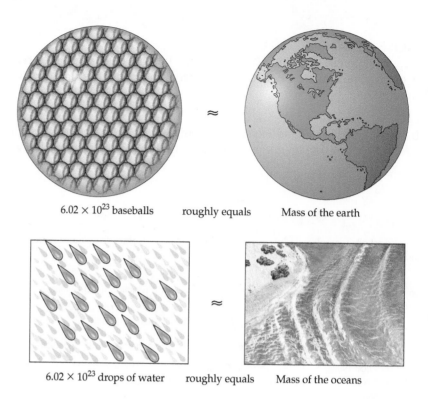

6.02 × 10²³ baseballs   roughly equals   Mass of the earth

6.02 × 10²³ drops of water   roughly equals   Mass of the oceans

Chemists count atoms and molecules by the *mole*. A single carbon atom is much too small to see or weigh, but a mole of carbon atoms fills a tablespoon and weighs 12 g. A mole of carbon and a mole of titanium each contain the same number of atoms. But a titanium atom has a mass four times that of a carbon atom, so a mole of titanium has a mass four times that of a mole of carbon.

A **mole (mol)** is an amount of substance that contains the same number of elementary units as there are atoms in exactly 12 g of carbon-12. That number is 6.02×10^{23}, Avogadro's number. The elementary units may be atoms (such as S or Ca), molecules (such as O_2 or CO_2), ions (such as K^+ or SO_4^{2-}), or any other kind of formula unit. A mole of NaCl, for example, contains 6.02×10^{23} NaCl formula units, which means that it contains 6.02×10^{23} Na^+ ions and 6.02×10^{23} Cl^- ions.

Formula Masses

Each element has a characteristic atomic mass. Because chemical compounds are made up of two or more elements, the masses of compounds are combinations of atomic masses. For any substance, the **formula mass** is the sum of the masses of the atoms represented in the formula. If the formula represents a molecule, the term *molecular mass* is often used. For example, because the formula CO_2 specifies one carbon atom and two oxygen atoms per molecule of carbon dioxide, the formula (or molecular) mass of carbon dioxide (CO_2) is the atomic mass of carbon plus twice the atomic mass of oxygen.

$$\text{Formula mass } CO_2 = 1 \times \text{atomic mass of C} + 2 \times \text{atomic mass of O}$$
$$= 1 \times 12.0 \, u + 2 \times 16.0 \, u = 44.0 \, u$$

Example 5.3 Calculating Molecular Masses

Calculate **(a)** the molecular mass of nitrogen dioxide (NO_2), an amber-colored gas that is a constituent of smog, and **(b)** the formula mass of ammonium sulfate $[(NH_4)_2SO_4]$, a fertilizer commonly used by home gardeners.

Solution

a. We start with the molecular formula: NO_2. Then, to determine the molecular mass, we simply add the atomic mass of nitrogen to twice the atomic mass of oxygen.

$$1 \times \text{atomic mass of N} = 1 \times 14.0 \text{ u} = 14.0 \text{ u}$$
$$2 \times \text{atomic mass of O} = 2 \times 16.0 \text{ u} = \underline{32.0 \text{ u}}$$
$$\text{Formula mass of } NO_2 = 46.0 \text{ u}$$

b. The formula $(NH_4)_2SO_4$ signifies two nitrogen atoms, eight hydrogen atoms, one sulfur atom, and four oxygen atoms. Combining the atomic masses, we have

$$(2 \times 14.0 \text{ u}) + (8 \times 1.01 \text{ u}) + (1 \times 32.0 \text{ u}) + (4 \times 16.0 \text{ u}) = 132.1 \text{ u}$$

■ **EXERCISE 5.3**

Calculate the formula mass of **(a)** sodium azide (NaN_3), used in automobile airbags, **(b)** phosphoric acid (H_3PO_4), used to flavor some cola drinks, **(c)** *para*-dichlorobenzene ($C_6H_4Cl_2$), used as a moth repellent, and **(d)** calcium dihydrogen phosphate $[Ca(H_2PO_4)_2]$, used as a mineral supplement in foods.

Percent Composition of a Compound from Formula Masses

A formula represents not only an atom ratio, but also a mass ratio. For example, the mass of 1.00 mol CO_2 is 44.0 g, of which 12.0 g is carbon and 32.0 g is oxygen. The composition of CO_2 can be expressed as percents by mass of carbon and of oxygen:

$$\% \text{ by mass C} = \frac{\text{mass C}}{\text{mass } CO_2} \times 100\% = \frac{12.0 \text{ g}}{44.0 \text{ g}} \times 100\% = 27.3\%$$

Because oxygen is the only other element in CO_2, its percent by mass is $100\% - 27.3\% = 72.7\%$ oxygen.

The idea of percent composition by mass is useful in several applications. Dietary sodium limits are usually indicated in milligrams of Na^+. We consume Na^+ mainly as sodium chloride. The American Heart Association (AHA) recommends a maximum intake of 2400 mg Na^+ per day. Example 5.4 shows how we can relate this amount to the NaCl in one teaspoon of table salt.

Example 5.4 Calculating Percent Composition from a Formula

What mass of Na^+ is present in one teaspoon (6.0 g) of NaCl? How does this compare to the maximum intake of 2400 mg Na^+ per day recommended by the AHA?

Solution

A mole of sodium chloride has one mole (23.0 g) Na^+ and one mole (35.5 g) Cl^-. The percent by mass of Na^+ is

$$\% \text{ by mass Na} = \frac{\text{mass Na}}{\text{mass NaCl}} \times 100\% = \frac{23.0 \text{ g}}{58.5 \text{ g}} \times 100\% = 39.3\%$$

So in 100 g of NaCl there are 39.3 g of Na^+. One teaspoon (6.0 g) of NaCl has

$$6.0 \text{ g NaCl} \times \frac{39.3 \text{ g Na}^+}{100 \text{ g NaCl}} = 2.4 \text{ g Na}^+$$

That is 2400 mg Na^+, the maximum recommended for one day's intake.

■ **EXERCISE 5.4**

Calculate the percent by mass of nitrogen in **(a)** KNO_3 and **(b)** $(NH_4)_2S$.

Many environmental pollutants are reported as elements even when the actual pollutant is a compound or a mixture of compounds. For example, nitrates (NO_3^-) in groundwater (Chapter 14) are reported as parts per million nitrogen, and carbon dioxide emissions (Chapter 13) often are reported as tons of carbon. The idea of percent by mass is useful in understanding these reported quantities.

Self-Assessment Questions

1. How many carbon-12 atoms are there in exactly 12 g of carbon-12?
   a. 1   **b.** 12   **c.** 144   **d.** 6.02×10^{23}

2. The mass of 1 mol of carbon-12 atoms is
   a. 12 g   **b.** 12.011 g   **c.** 12 u   **d.** 12.011 u

3. Which of the following has the smallest molecular mass?
   a. CH_4 **b.** HF   **c.** H_2O **d.** NH_3

4. How many moles of sulfur atoms are in 1 mol $Fe_2(SO_4)_3$?
   a. 1 mol   **b.** 3 mol   **c.** 15 mol   **d.** 17 mol

5. How many moles of hydrogen atoms are present in 2.00 mol of ammonia (NH_3)?
   a. 2.00 mol   **b.** 3.00 mol   **c.** 6.00 mol   **d.** 8.00 mol

6. Sodium chloride, by mass, is
   a. about 40% Na^+ and 60% Cl^- **b.** 50% Na^+ and 50% Cl^-
   c. about 60% Na^+ and 40% Cl^- **d.** 23.0% Na^+ and 35.5% Cl^-

Answers: 1, d; 2, a; 3, a; 4, b; 5, c; 6, a

5.4 Molar Mass: Mole-to-Mass and Mass-to-Mole Conversions

Learning Objectives ❯ Convert from mass to moles and from moles to mass of a substance. ❯ Calculate the mass or number of moles of a reactant or product from the mass or number of moles of another reactant or product.

The **molar mass** of a substance is just what the name implies: the mass of one mole of that substance. The molar mass is numerically equal to the atomic mass, molecular mass, or formula mass, but it is expressed in the unit *grams per mole* (g/mol). The atomic mass of sodium is 23.0 u, so its molar mass is 23.0 g/mol. The molecular mass of carbon dioxide is 44.0 u; its molar mass is 44.0 g/mol. The formula mass of ammonium sulfate is 132.1 u; its molar mass is 132.1 g/mol. We can use these facts, together with the definition of the mole, to write the following relationships.

$$1 \text{ mol Na} = 23.0 \text{ g Na}$$
$$1 \text{ mol CO}_2 = 44.0 \text{ g CO}_2$$
$$1 \text{ mol (NH}_4)_2\text{SO}_4 = 132.1 \text{ g (NH}_4)_2\text{SO}_4$$

These relationships supply the conversion factors we need to convert between mass in grams and amount in moles, as illustrated in the following examples.

Example 5.5 Conversions Involving Moles and Mass

a. What mass in grams of N_2 is 0.400 moles N_2? **(b)** Calculate the number of moles of Na in a 62.5 g sample of sodium metal.

Solution

a. The molecular mass of N_2 is $2 \times 14.0 \text{ u} = 28.0 \text{ u}$. The molar mass of N_2 is therefore 28.0 g/mol. Using this molar mass as a conversion factor (red), we have

$$? \text{ g N}_2 = 0.400 \text{ mol N}_2 \times \frac{28.0 \text{ g N}_2}{1 \text{ mol N}_2} = 11.2 \text{ g N}_2$$

b. The molar mass of Na is 23.0 g/mol. To convert from mass to moles, we must use the *inverse* of the molar mass as a conversion factor (1 mol Na/23.0 g Na) to cancel units of mass. When we start with grams, we must have grams in the denominator of our conversion factor (red).

$$? \text{ mol Na} = 62.5 \text{ g Na} \times \frac{1 \text{ mol Na}}{23.0 \text{ g Na}} = 2.72 \text{ mol Na}$$

■ EXERCISE 5.5A

Calculate the mass, in grams, of **(a)** 0.0728 mol silicon, **(b)** 55.5 mol H_2O, and **(c)** 0.0728 mol $Ca(H_2PO_4)_2$.

■ EXERCISE 5.5B

Calculate the amount, in moles, of **(a)** 3.71 g Fe, **(b)** 165 g C_4H_{10}, and **(c)** 0.100 g $Mg(NO_3)_2$.

Figure 5.5 shows one-mole samples of several different substances. Each container holds Avogadro's number of formula units of the substance. That is, there are just as many sugar molecules in the largest dish as there are helium atoms in the balloon.

◄ **Figure 5.5** One mole of each of several familiar substances. From left to right on the table are sugar, salt, carbon, and copper. Behind them, the balloon contains helium. Each container holds Avogadro's number of elementary units of the substance. There are 6.02×10^{23} molecules of sugar ($C_{12}H_{22}O_{11}$), 6.02×10^{23} formula units of NaCl, 6.02×10^{23} atoms of carbon, 6.02×10^{23} atoms of copper, and 6.02×10^{23} atoms of helium in the respective samples.

Q: How many Na^+ ions and how many Cl^- ions are there in the dish of salt? If the balloon was filled with oxygen gas (O_2), how many oxygen atoms would it contain?

Mole and Mass Relationships in Chemical Equations

Chemists, other scientists, and engineers are often confronted with questions such as "How much iron can be obtained from 1.0 ton of Fe_2O_3?" or "How much carbon dioxide is produced by burning 1000 g of propane?" There is no simple way to calculate the mass of one substance directly from the mass of another in the same reaction. Because chemical reactions involve atoms and molecules, quantities in reactions are calculated in moles of atoms, ions, or molecules. To do such calculations, it is necessary to convert grams of a substance to moles, as we did in Example 5.5. We also must write balanced equations to determine molar ratios.

Recall that chemical equations provide not only ratios of atoms and molecules but also mole ratios. For example, the equation

$$C + O_2 \longrightarrow CO_2$$

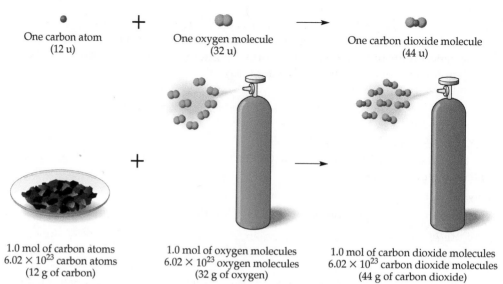

One carbon atom (12 u)   +   One oxygen molecule (32 u)   ⟶   One carbon dioxide molecule (44 u)

1.0 mol of carbon atoms
6.02×10^{23} carbon atoms
(12 g of carbon)

1.0 mol of oxygen molecules
6.02×10^{23} oxygen molecules
(32 g of oxygen)

1.0 mol of carbon dioxide molecules
6.02×10^{23} carbon dioxide molecules
(44 g of carbon dioxide)

▲ **Figure 5.6** We cannot weigh single atoms or molecules, but we can weigh equal numbers of these tiny particles.

▲ **It DOES Matter!**

If there is not enough oxygen gas to react completely with burning carbon, some of the carbon will be incompletely oxidized and deadly carbon monoxide will form. Most of the 65 deaths in the Midwestern ice storm in January–February 2009 were the result of burning fuels (charcoal, kerosene, or gasoline, in an electricity generator) indoors without adequate oxygen.

tells us that one C atom reacts with one O_2 molecule (two atoms) to form one CO_2 molecule (one C atom and two O atoms). The equation also means that 1 mol (6.02×10^{23} atoms) of carbon reacts with 1 mol (6.02×10^{23} molecules) of oxygen to yield 1 mol (6.02×10^{23} molecules) of carbon dioxide. Because the molar mass in grams of a substance is numerically equal to the formula mass of the substance in atomic mass units, the equation also tells us (indirectly) that 12.0 g (1 mol) C reacts with 32.0 g (1 mol) O_2 to yield 44.0 g (1 mol) CO_2 (Figure 5.6).

The important thing is to maintain the *ratio* of masses. For example, in the preceding reaction, the mass ratio of oxygen to carbon is 32.0:12.0, or 8.0:3.0. Thus, 8.0 g O and 3.0 g C will produce 11.0 g CO_2. In fact, to calculate the amount of oxygen needed to react with a given amount of carbon, we need only multiply the amount of carbon by the factor 32.0:12.0. The following examples illustrate these relationships.

CONCEPTUAL Example 5.6   Molecular, Molar, and Mass Relationships

Nitrogen monoxide (nitric oxide), an air pollutant discharged by internal combustion engines, combines with oxygen to form nitrogen dioxide, a yellowish-brown gas that irritates our respiratory systems and eyes. The equation for this reaction is

$$2\,NO + O_2 \longrightarrow 2\,NO_2$$

State the molecular, molar, and mass relationships indicated by this equation.

Solution

The molecular and molar relationships can be obtained directly from the equation; no calculation is necessary. The mass relationship requires a little calculation.

Molecular: Two molecules of NO react with one molecule of O_2 to form two molecules of NO_2.

Molar: 2 mol NO reacts with 1 mol O_2 to form 2 mol NO_2.

Mass: 60.0 g NO (2 mol NO × 30.0 g/mol) reacts with 32.0 g (1 mol O_2 × 32.0 g/mol) O_2 to form 92.0 g (2 mol NO_2 × 46.0 g/mol) NO_2.

▪ **EXERCISE 5.6**

Hydrogen sulfide, a gas that smells like rotten eggs, burns in air to produce sulfur dioxide and water according to the equation

$$2\,H_2S + 3\,O_2 \longrightarrow 2\,SO_2 + 2\,H_2O$$

State the molecular, molar, and mass relationships indicated by this equation.

Molar Relationships in Chemical Equations

The quantitative relationship between reactants and products in a chemical reaction is called **stoichiometry**. The ratio of moles of reactants and products is given by the coefficients in a balanced chemical equation. Consider the combustion of propane, the main component of bottled gas.

$$C_3H_8 + 5\,O_2 \longrightarrow 3\,CO_2 + 4\,H_2O$$

The coefficients in the balanced equation allow us to make statements such as

- 1 mol C_3H_8 reacts with 5 mol O_2.
- 3 mol CO_2 is produced for every 1 mol C_3H_8 that reacts.
- 4 mol H_2O is produced for every 3 mol CO_2 produced.

We can turn these statements into conversion factors known as stoichiometric factors. A **stoichiometric factor** relates the amounts, in *moles*, of any two substances involved in a chemical reaction. Note that we can set up stoichiometric factors for any two substances involved in a reaction. Also note that stoichiometric factors, because they come from the balanced equation for a reaction, involve small whole numbers. In the examples that follow, stoichiometric factors are shown in color.

Example 5.7 | Molar Relationships

When 0.105 mol of propane is burned in a plentiful supply of oxygen, how many moles of oxygen are consumed?

$$C_3H_8 + 5\,O_2 \longrightarrow 3\,CO_2 + 4\,H_2O$$

Solution

The equation tells us that 5 mol O_2 is required to burn 1 mol C_3H_8. From this relationship, we can construct conversion factors to relate moles of oxygen to moles of propane. The possible conversion factors are

$$\frac{1 \text{ mol } C_3H_8}{5 \text{ mol } O_2} \quad \text{and} \quad \frac{5 \text{ mol } O_2}{1 \text{ mol } C_3H_8}$$

Which one do we use? Only if we multiply the given quantity (0.105 mol C_3H_8) by the factor on the *right* will the answer be expressed in the units requested (moles of oxygen).

$$? \text{ mol } O_2 = 0.105 \text{ mol } \cancel{C_3H_8} \times \frac{5 \text{ mol } O_2}{1 \cancel{\text{ mol } C_3H_8}} = 0.525 \text{ mol } O_2$$

▪ **EXERCISE 5.7A**

Consider the combustion (burning) of propane presented in Example 5.7. **(a)** How many moles of CO_2 are formed when 0.529 mol C_3H_8 is burned? **(b)** How many moles of CO_2 are produced when 1.010 mol O_2 is consumed?

▪ **EXERCISE 5.7B**

For the combustion of propane in Example 5.7, suppose that 50.0 mol O_2 and 25.0 mol propane are combined. After reaction, which reactant will be used up, and how many moles of the other reactant will be left over? (*Hint:* Calculate the number of moles of propane that will react with the oxygen given. Is there enough propane?)

Mass Relationships in Chemical Equations

A chemical equation defines the stoichiometric relationship in terms of moles, but problems are seldom presented in terms of moles. Typically, you are given the mass (grams) of one substance and asked to calculate the mass of another substance that will react or can be produced. Such calculations involve several steps:

1. Write a balanced chemical equation for the reaction.
2. Determine the molar masses of the substances involved in the calculation.
3. Write down the given quantity and use the molar mass to convert this quantity to moles.
4. Use coefficients (stoichiometric relationship) from the balanced chemical equation to convert moles of the given substance to moles of the desired substance.
5. Use the molar mass to convert moles of the desired substance to grams of the desired substance.

If we know the quantity of any substance in an equation, we can determine the quantities of all the other substances. The conversion process is diagrammed in Figure 5.7. It is best learned by studying examples and working exercises.

▲ **Figure 5.7** We can use a chemical equation to relate the numbers of *moles* of any two substances represented in the equation. These substances may be a reactant and a product, two reactants, or two products. We cannot directly relate the mass of one substance to the mass of another substance involved in the same reaction. To obtain *mass* relationships, we must convert the mass of each substance to moles, relate moles of one substance to moles of the other through a stoichiometric factor, and then convert moles of the second substance to its mass.

Example 5.8   Mass Relationships

Calculate the mass of oxygen needed to react with 10.0 g of carbon in the reaction that forms carbon dioxide.

Solution

Step 1: The balanced equation is

$$C + O_2 \longrightarrow CO_2$$

Step 2: The molar masses are 12.0 g/mol for C and $2 \times 16.0 = 32.0$ g/mol for O_2.

Step 3: We convert the given mass of carbon to an amount in moles.

$$? \text{ mol C} = 10.0 \text{ g C} \times \frac{1 \text{ mol C}}{12.0 \text{ g C}} = 0.833 \text{ mol C}$$

Step 4: We use coefficients from the balanced equation to establish the stoichiometric factor (red) that relates the amount of oxygen to that of carbon.

$$0.833 \text{ mol C} \times \frac{1 \text{ mol O}_2}{1 \text{ mol C}} = 0.833 \text{ mol O}_2$$

Step 5: We convert from moles of oxygen to grams of oxygen.

$$0.833 \text{ mol O}_2 \times \frac{32.0 \text{ g O}_2}{1 \text{ mol O}_2} = 26.7 \text{ g O}_2$$

We can also combine the five steps into a single setup. Note that the units in the denominators of the conversion factors are chosen so that each cancels the unit in the numerator of the preceding term.

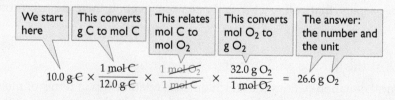

We start here	This converts g C to mol C	This relates mol C to mol O_2	This converts mol O_2 to g O_2	The answer: the number and the unit

$$10.0 \text{ g C} \times \frac{1 \text{ mol C}}{12.0 \text{ g C}} \times \frac{1 \text{ mol O}_2}{1 \text{ mol C}} \times \frac{32.0 \text{ g O}_2}{1 \text{ mol O}_2} = 26.6 \text{ g O}_2$$

(The answers are slightly different due to rounding in the intermediate steps.)

▪ EXERCISE 5.8A

Calculate the mass of oxygen (O_2) needed to react with 0.334 g nitrogen (N_2) in the reaction that forms nitrogen dioxide.

▪ EXERCISE 5.8B

Calculate the mass of carbon dioxide formed by burning 775 g each of **(a)** methane (CH_4) and **(b)** butane (C_4H_{10}) in oxygen gas. (*Hint:* The reaction in Example 5.7 may help in balancing the equations.)

1. How can a car make more pollution than the gasoline it uses? A mole of carbon (12 g) combines with oxygen from the atmosphere to form a mole of carbon dioxide (44 g). Gasoline is mostly carbon by weight, so the mass of carbon dioxide formed is greater than the mass of gasoline burned. Carbon dioxide is a major greenhouse gas (Chapter 13).

Self-Assessment Questions

1. The mass of 4.75 mol H_2SO_4 is
   a. 314 g
   b. 456 g
   c. 466 g
   d. 564 g

2. For which of the following would a 10.0-g sample contain the most moles?
   a. Cu
   b. Fe
   c. Si
   d. S

3. How many moles of CO_2 are there in 1 lb (453.6 g) CO_2?
   a. 0.0969 mol
   b. 9.20 mol
   c. 10.3 mol
   d. 14.2 mol

4. How many moles of benzene (C_6H_6) are there in a 7.81-g sample of benzene?
   a. 0.100 mol
   b. 1.00 mol
   c. 7.81 mol
   d. 610 mol

Items 5–7 refer to the equation $2\,H_2 + O_2 \longrightarrow 2\,H_2O$.

5. At the molar level, the equation means that
   a. 2 mol H reacts with 1 mol O to form 2 mol H_2O
   b. 4 mol H reacts with 2 mol O to form 4 mol H_2O
   c. 2 mol H_2 reacts with 1 mol O_2 to form 2 mol H_2O
   d. 2 mol O_2 reacts with 1 mol H_2 to form 2 mol H_2O

6. How many moles of water can be formed from 0.500 mol H_2?
   a. 0.500 mol
   b. 1.00 mol
   c. 2.00 mol
   d. 4.00 mol

7. How many moles of oxygen (O_2) are required to form 0.222 mol H_2O?
   a. 0.111 mol
   b. 0.222 mol
   c. 0.444 mol
   d. 1.00 mol

Answers: 1, c; 2, c; 3, c; 4, a; 5, c; 6, c; 7, a

Margaret Kerr, *Worcester State University*

Atom Economy

Imagine yourself in the future. Your job is related to environmental protection, which requires that you provide information to practicing chemists as they design new processes and reactions. Waste management is one of your top concerns. Although waste typically has been addressed after the production of desired commodities, you realize that a greener approach enables minimizing the waste from the start. What tools would you use in this job? What topics are important? How can chemists provide new products while protecting the environment?

Intrinsic in greener approaches to waste management is the concept of *atom economy*, a calculation of the number of atoms conserved in the desired product rather than in waste. In 1998, Barry Trost (Stanford University) won a Presidential Green Chemistry Challenge Award for his work in developing this concept. By calculating the number of atoms that will not become part of the desired product and, therefore, will enter the waste stream, chemists can precisely determine the minimum amount of waste that will be produced by chemicals used in a reaction before even running the reaction.

You have learned how to write and balance chemical equations (Section 5.1) and you also can calculate molar mass, convert from mass to moles, and determine the amount of product formed from given amounts of reactants (Sections 5.3, 5.4). Other ways of calculating the efficiency of a reaction has traditionally been expressed using *theoretical yield*, *experimental yield*, and *percent yield*. The theoretical yield is the maximum amount of desired product that can be produced by the amounts of reactants used. Under laboratory conditions, the theoretical yield of a reaction is not usually obtained. The actual amount of desired product collected is called the experimental yield. Chemists often express their experimental results in percent yield, which is simply the experimental yield divided by the theoretical yield, then multiplied by 100.

$$\% \text{ yield} = \frac{\text{experimental yield}}{\text{theoretical yield}} \times 100\%$$

A report of a 100% yield for a reaction seems good, but the percent yield considers only the desired product. Any other substance formed (for instance, a byproduct) is not counted in the percent yield. Byproducts often become part of the chemical waste stream. Some reactions actually produce more byproducts than desired products.

Atom economy is a better way to measure reaction efficiency. Percent atom economy (% A.E.) measures the proportion of the atoms in the reaction mixture that actually become part of the desired product. Reactant atoms that do not appear in the product are considered waste. The % A.E. is given by the following relationship:

$$\% \text{ A.E.} = \frac{\text{molar mass of desired product}}{\text{molar masses of all reactants}} \times 100\%$$

A reaction can have a poor atom economy even when the percent yield is near 100%.

Consider the following two ways to make ethyl bromide (C_2H_5Br), a compound used as a solvent, an anesthetic, a refrigerant, and a fumigant. First, ethyl bromide can be made using ethanol (C_2H_5OH) and phosphorus tribromide (PBr_3).

$$3\ C_2H_5OH + PBr_3 \rightarrow 3\ C_2H_5Br + H_3PO_3$$

In this reaction, a Br atom substitutes for the OH group of the alcohol. In reactions like this one, generally only one product is desired and all other products are not utilized. The wasted atoms in the preceding equation are shown in red.

We can calculate the atom economy for this reaction.

$$\% \text{ A.E.} = \frac{3 \times \text{molar mass } C_2H_5Br}{3 \times \text{molar mass } C_2H_5OH + \text{molar mass } PBr_3} \times 100\%$$

$$= \frac{3 \times 108.97 \text{ g/mol}}{(3 \times 46.07 \text{ g/mol}) + 270.69 \text{ g/mol}} \times 100\% = 79.9\%$$

These substitution reactions never have 100% atom economy because there is always a byproduct. This results in some atoms going into the waste stream.

Ethyl bromide can also be made using ethylene (C_2H_4) and hydrogen bromide:

$$C_2H_4 + HBr \rightarrow C_2H_5Br$$

In this reaction, all of the atoms in both reactants appear in the desired product C_2H_5Br and none go into the waste stream. The percent atom economy is 100%.

$$\% \text{ A.E.} = \frac{\text{molar mass } C_2H_5Br}{\text{molar mass } C_2H_4 + \text{molar mass } HBr} \times 100\%$$

$$= \frac{108.97 \text{ g/mol}}{28.05 \text{ g/mol} + 80.91 \text{ g/mol}} \times 100\% = 100\%$$

Because the concept of atom economy offers a way to predict waste, it can lead to innovative design processes that eliminate or minimize waste. By focusing on waste from the beginning of the reaction, we reduce or eliminate cleanup at the end.

5.5 Solutions

Learning Objectives ❯ Calculate the concentration (molarity, percent by volume, or percent by mass) of a solute in a solution. ❯ Calculate the amount of solute or solution given the concentration and the other amount.

Many chemical reactions take place in solutions. A **solution** is a homogeneous mixture of two or more substances. The substance being dissolved is the *solute*, and the substance doing the dissolving is the *solvent*. The solvent is usually present in greater quantity than the solute. There are many solvents: Kerosene dissolves grease; ethanol dissolves many drugs; isopentyl acetate, a component of banana oil, is a solvent for model airplane glue.

Water is no doubt the most familiar solvent, dissolving as it does many common substances such as sugar, salt, and ethanol. We focus our discussion here on **aqueous solutions**, those in which water is the solvent, and we take a more quantitative look at the relationship between solute and solvent.

Solution Concentrations

We say that some substances, such as sugar and salt, are *soluble* in water. Of course, there is a limit to the quantity of sugar or salt that we can dissolve in a given volume of water. Yet we still find it convenient to say that they are soluble in water because an appreciable quantity dissolves. Other substances, such as an iron nail or sand (silicon dioxide), we consider to be *insoluble* because their solubility in water is near zero. Such terms as *soluble* and *insoluble* are useful, but they are imprecise and must be used with care.

Two other roughly estimated but sometimes useful terms are *dilute* and *concentrated*. A **dilute solution** is one that contains a little bit of solute in lots of solvent. For example, a pinch of sugar in a cup of tea makes a dilute, faintly sweet, sugar solution. A **concentrated solution** is one with a relatively large amount of solute dissolved in a relatively small amount of solvent. Pancake syrup, with lots of sugar solute in a relatively small amount of water, is a concentrated, and very sweet, solution.

Scientific work generally requires more precise concentration units than "a pinch of sugar in a cup of tea." Further, quantitative work often requires the *mole* unit because substances enter into chemical reactions according to *molar* ratios.

Molarity

A concentration unit that chemists often use is *molarity*. For reactions involving solutions, the amount of solute is usually measured in moles and the quantity of solution in liters or milliliters. The **molarity (M)** is the amount of solute, in moles, per liter of solution.

$$\text{Molarity (M)} = \frac{\text{moles of solute}}{\text{liters of solution}}$$

▲ It DOES Matter!

The ethanol content of a beverage is almost always expressed by *volume* (see Example 5.13A). This may be done partly as a marketing ploy. Ethanol is about 20% less dense than water, so a beverage that is labeled "12% alcohol by volume" is only about 10% ethanol by weight. The higher percent by volume may make purchasers think they are getting "more for the money."

Example 5.9 | Solution Concentration: Molarity and Moles

Calculate the molarity of a solution made by dissolving 3.50 mol NaCl in enough water to produce 2.00 L of solution.

Solution

$$\text{Molarity (M)} = \frac{\text{moles of solute}}{\text{liters of solution}} = \frac{3.50 \text{ mol NaCl}}{2.00 \text{ L solution}} = 1.75 \text{ M NaCl}$$

We read 1.75 M NaCl as "1.75 molar sodium chloride."

■ EXERCISE 5.9A

Calculate the molarity of a solution that has 0.0500 mol NH_3 in 5.75 L of solution.

■ EXERCISE 5.9B

Calculate the molarity of a solution made by dissolving 0.750 mol H_3PO_4 in enough water to produce 775 mL of solution.

Usually, when preparing a solution, we must *weigh* the solute. Balances do not display units of moles, so we usually work with a given mass and divide by the molar mass of the substance, as illustrated in Example 5.10.

Example 5.10 | Solution Concentration: Molarity and Mass

What is the molarity of a solution in which 333 g potassium hydrogen carbonate is dissolved in enough water to make 10.0 L of solution?

Solution

First, we must convert grams of $KHCO_3$ to moles of $KHCO_3$.

$$333 \text{ g KHCO}_3 \times \frac{1 \text{ mol KHCO}_3}{100.1 \text{ g KHCO}_3} = 3.33 \text{ mol KHCO}_3$$

Next, we use this value as the numerator in the defining equation for molarity. The solution volume, 10.0 L, is the denominator.

$$\text{Molarity} = \frac{3.33 \text{ mol KHCO}_3}{10.0 \text{ L solution}} = 0.333 \text{ M KHCO}_3$$

■ EXERCISE 5.10A

Calculate the molarity of **(a)** 18.0 g H_2SO_4 in 2.00 L of solution and **(b)** 3.00 g KI in 2.39 L of solution.

■ EXERCISE 5.10B

Calculate the molarity of 0.206 g HF in 752 mL of solution (HF is used for etching glass).

Often, we need to know the *mass* of solute required to prepare a given volume of a solution of a particular molarity. In such calculations, we can use molarity as a conversion factor between moles of solute and liters of solution. For instance, in Example 5.11, the expression "0.15 M NaCl" means 0.15 mol NaCl per liter of solution, expressed as the conversion factor

$$\frac{0.15 \text{ mol NaCl}}{1 \text{ L solution}}$$

Example 5.11 | Solution Preparation: Molarity

What mass in grams of NaCl is required to prepare 0.500 L of typical over-the-counter saline solution (about 0.15 M NaCl)?

Solution

First, we use the molarity as a conversion factor to calculate moles of NaCl.

$$0.500 \text{ L solution} \times \frac{0.15 \text{ mol NaCl}}{1 \text{ L solution}} = 0.075 \text{ mol NaCl}$$

Then, we use the molar mass to calculate grams of NaCl.

$$0.75 \text{ mol NaCl} \times \frac{58.5 \text{ g NaCl}}{1 \text{ mol NaCl}} = 44 \text{ g NaCl}$$

■ EXERCISE 5.11
What mass in grams of potassium hydroxide is required to prepare **(a)** 2.00 L of 6.00 M KOH and **(b)** 100.0 mL of 1.00 M KOH?

Quite often, solutions of known molarity are available commercially. For example, concentrated hydrochloric acid is 12 M. How would you determine the *volume* of this solution that contains a certain number of moles of solute? We can again rearrange the definition of molarity to obtain the volume.

$$\text{Liters of solution} = \frac{\text{moles of solute}}{\text{molarity}}$$

Example 5.12 Moles from Molarity and Volume

Concentrated hydrochloric acid is 12.0 M HCl. What volume in milliliters of this solution contains 0.425 mol HCl?

Solution

$$\text{Liters of HCl solution} = \frac{\text{moles of solute}}{\text{molarity}} = \frac{0.425 \text{ mol HCl}}{12.0 \text{ M HCl}}$$

$$= \frac{0.425 \text{ mol HCl}}{12.0 \text{ mol HCl/L}} = 0.0354 \text{ L}$$

In this case, 0.0354 L (35.4 mL) of the solution contains 0.425 mol of the solute. Remember that molarity is moles per liter of *solution*, not per liter of solvent.

■ EXERCISE 5.12A
What volume in milliliters of 15.0 M aqueous ammonia (NH_3) solution contains 0.445 mol NH_3?

■ EXERCISE 5.12B
What mass in grams of HNO_3 is in 500 mL of acid rain that has a concentration of 2.00×10^{-5} M HNO_3?

Percent Concentrations

For many practical applications, including those in medicine and pharmacy, solution concentrations are often expressed in percentages. There are different ways to express percentages, depending on whether mass or volume is being measured. If both solute and solvent are liquids, **percent by volume** is often used because liquid volumes are easily measured.

$$\text{Percent by volume} = \frac{\text{volume of solute}}{\text{volume of solution}} \times 100\%$$

In calculating percent by volume, we can measure the solute and solution in any unit of volume as long as we use the same unit for both. For example, we can measure both volumes in milliliters or in gallons. Ethanol (CH_3CH_2OH) for medicinal

2. What's the difference between 14K gold and 18K gold? A karat (K) is a traditional way of expressing the concentration of gold. A 14K gold necklace contains 14 g of gold per 24 g of the necklace (58% gold by mass). An 18K gold ring contains 18 g of gold per 24 g of the ring (75% gold by mass). So what do you suppose is the percent by mass of gold in 24K gold?

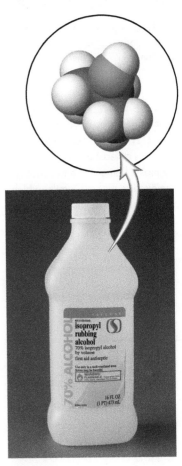

▲ Rubbing alcohol is a water–isopropyl alcohol solution that is 70% isopropyl alcohol [$(CH_3)_2CHOH$] by volume.

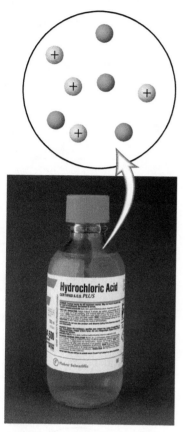

▲ "Reagent grade" concentrated hydrochloric acid is a 38% by mass solution of HCl in water.

3. Does 2% milk have just 2% of the calories of whole milk? No. Whole milk contains at least 3.25% butterfat by mass. Some of the butterfat is removed to make 2% milk, which is 2% butterfat by mass. Actually, 2% milk has about 75% of the calories of whole milk.

▲ **It Does Matter!**
An isotonic, or "normal," intravenous solution must have the proper concentration of solute to avoid damage to blood cells.

purposes is 95% by volume. That is, it consists of 95 mL CH_3CH_2OH per 100 mL of aqueous solution.

Example 5.13   Percent by Volume

Two-stroke engines use a mixture of 120 mL of oil dissolved in enough gasoline to make 4.0 L of fuel. What is the percent by volume of oil in this mixture?

Solution

$$\text{Percent by volume} = \frac{120 \text{ mL oil}}{4000 \text{ mL solution}} \times 100\% = 3.0\%$$

■ EXERCISE 5.13A
What is the volume percent of ethanol in a solution of 625 mL of an ethanol–water solution that contains 58.0 mL of water?

■ EXERCISE 5.13B
Determine the volume percent of toluene ($C_6H_5CH_3$) in a solution made by mixing 40.0 mL of toluene with 75.0 mL of benzene (C_6H_6). Assume that the volumes are additive.

Many commercial solutions are labeled with the concentration in **percent by mass**. For example, sulfuric acid is sold in several concentrations: 35.7% H_2SO_4 for use in storage batteries, 77.7% H_2SO_4 for the manufacture of phosphate fertilizers, and 93.2% H_2SO_4 for pickling steel. Each of these percentages is by mass: 35.7 g of H_2SO_4 per 100 g of sulfuric acid solution, and so on.

$$\text{Percent by mass} = \frac{\text{mass of solute}}{\text{mass of solution}} \times 100\%$$

As with percent by volume, we can express the masses of solute and solution in any mass unit, as long as we use the same unit for both.

Example 5.14   Percent by Mass

What is the percent by mass of NaCl if 25.5 g of it is dissolved in 425 g (425 mL) of water?

Solution
We use these values in the above percent-by-mass equation:

$$\text{Percent by mass} = \frac{25.5 \text{ g NaCl}}{(25.5 + 425) \text{ g solution}} \times 100\% = 5.66\% \text{ NaCl}$$

■ EXERCISE 5.14A
Hydrogen peroxide solution for home use is 3.0% by mass of H_2O_2 in water. What is the percent by mass of a solution of 9.40 g H_2O_2 dissolved in 335 g (335 mL) of water?

■ EXERCISE 5.14B
Sodium hydroxide (NaOH, lye) is used to make soap and is quite soluble in water. What is the percent by mass of NaOH in a solution that contains 1.00 kg NaOH in 950 mL water?

Example 5.15 Solution Preparation: Percent by Mass

Describe how to make 430 g of an aqueous solution that is 4.85% by mass $NaNO_3$.

Solution

We begin by rearranging the equation for percent by mass to solve for mass of solute.

$$\text{Mass of solute} = \frac{\text{percent by mass} \times \text{mass of solution}}{100\%}$$

Substituting, we have

$$\frac{4.85\% \times 430 \text{ g}}{100\%} = 20.9 \text{ g}$$

We would weigh out 20.9 g $NaNO_3$ and add enough water to make 430 g of solution.

▪ EXERCISE 5.15A

Describe how you would prepare 125 g of an aqueous solution that is 4.50% glucose by mass.

▪ EXERCISE 5.15B

Describe how you would prepare 1750 g of *isotonic saline*, a commonly used intravenous (IV) solution that is 0.89% sodium chloride by mass.

Note that for percent concentrations, the mass or volume of the solute needed doesn't depend on what the solute is. A 10% by mass solution of NaOH contains 10 g NaOH per 100 g of solution. Similarly, 10% HCl and 10% $(NH_4)_2SO_4$ and 10% $C_{110}H_{190}N_3O_2Br$ each contain 10 g of the specified solute per 100 g of solution. For *molar* solutions, however, the mass of solute in a solution of specified molarity is different for different solutes. A liter of 0.10 M solution requires 4.0 g (0.10 mol) NaOH, 3.7 g (0.10 mol) HCl, 13.2 g (0.10 mol) $(NH_4)_2SO_4$, or 166 g (0.10 mol) $C_{110}H_{190}N_3O_2Br$.

4. What does a cholesterol level of 200 mean? Concentrations of solutes in body fluids are often too low to be expressed conveniently as percentages. A common unit is milligrams (of solute) per deciliter of blood (or other fluid). A cholesterol level of 200 means 200 mg of cholesterol per dL (100 mL) of blood.

Self-Assessment Questions

1. In a solution of 85.0 g water and 5.0 g sucrose $(C_{12}H_{22}O_{11})$, the
   a. solute is sucrose and the solution is the solvent
   b. solute is sucrose and the solvent is water
   c. solute is water and sucrose is the solvent
   d. water and sucrose are both solutes

2. What is the molarity of a sodium hydroxide solution having 0.500 mol NaOH in 250 mL of solution?
   a. 0.00200 M   b. 0.200 M   c. 2.00 M   d. 8.00 M

3. How many moles of sugar are required to make 4.00 L of 0.600 M sugar solution?
   a. 1.20 mol   b. 2.40 mol   c. 24.0 mol   d. 6.67 mol

4. What mass of NaCl in grams is needed to prepare 2.500 L of a 0.800 M NaCl solution?
   a. 2.00 g   b. 4.00 g   c. 58.5 g   d. 117 g

5. What volume of 6.00 M HCl solution contains 1.50 mol HCl?
   a. 250 mL   b. 300 mL   c. 900 mL   d. 9.00 L

6. What is the percent by volume of ethanol in a solution made by adding 50.0 mL of pure ethanol to enough water to make 250 mL of solution?
   a. 16.7%   b. 20.0%   c. 25.0%   d. 80.0%

7. A solution contains 15.0 g sucrose and 60.0 g of water. What is the percent by mass of sucrose in the solution?
   a. 15.0%   b. 20.0%   c. 25.0%   d. 80.0%

8. What volume of water should be added to 23.4 g NaCl to make 100.0 mL of 4.00 M NaCl solution?
   a. 76.6 mL   b. 96.0 mL
   c. 100.0 mL   d. enough to make 100.0 mL of solution

Answers: 1. b; 2. c; 3. b; 4. d; 5. a; 6. b; 7. b; 8. d

CRITICAL THINKING EXERCISES

Apply knowledge that you have gained in this chapter and one or more of the FLaReS principles (Chapter 1) to evaluate the following statements or claims.

5.1 Suppose that someone has published a paper claiming to have established a new value for Avogadro's number. The author says that he has made some very careful laboratory measurements and his calculations indicate that the true value for Avogadro's number is 3.01875×10^{23}. Is this claim credible in your opinion? What questions would you ask the author about his claim?

5.2 A chemistry teacher asked her students, "What is the mass, in grams, of a mole of bromine?" One student answered 80; another said 160; and several others gave answers of 79, 81, 158, and 162. The teacher stated that all of these answers were correct. Do you believe her statement?

5.3 A website on fireworks provides directions for preparing potassium nitrate, KNO_3 (molar mass = 101 g/mol), using potassium carbonate (138 g/mol)

and ammonium nitrate (80 g/mol), according to the following equation:

$$K_2CO_3 + 2\,NH_4NO_3 \longrightarrow 2\,KNO_3 + CO_2 + H_2O + NH_3$$

The directions state: "Mix one kilogram of potassium carbonate with two kilograms of ammonium nitrate. The carbon dioxide and ammonia come off as gases, and the water can be evaporated, leaving two kilograms of pure potassium nitrate." Use information from this chapter to evaluate this statement.

5.4 A battery manufacturer claims that lithium batteries deliver the same power as batteries using nickel, zinc, or lead, but the lithium batteries are much lighter because lithium has a lower atomic mass than does nickel, zinc, or lead.

5.5 After working Problem 66 of Additional Problems, evaluate the claim that homeopathy is a valid alternative medical treatment.

SUMMARY

Section 5.1—A **chemical equation** is shorthand for a chemical change, using symbols and formulas instead of words: for example, $C + O_2 \longrightarrow CO_2$. Substances to the left of the arrow are starting materials, or **reactants**; those to the right of the arrow are **products**, or what the reaction produces. Physical states may be indicated with (s), (l), or (g). Because matter is conserved, a chemical equation must be balanced. It must have the same numbers and types of atoms on each side. Equations are balanced by placing coefficients in front of the formula for each reactant or product; we do *not* balance an equation by changing the formulas of reactants or products. The balanced equation $2\,NaN_3 \longrightarrow 2\,Na + 3\,N_2$ means that two formula units of NaN_3 react to give two atoms of Na and three molecules of N_2.

Section 5.2—Gay-Lussac's experiments led him to the **law of combining volumes**: At a given temperature and pressure, the volumes of gaseous reactants and products are in a small whole-number ratio (such as 1:1, 2:1, 4:3). **Avogadro's hypothesis** explained this law by stating that equal volumes of all gases contain the same number of molecules at fixed temperature and pressure.

Section 5.3—**Avogadro's number** is defined as the number of ^{12}C atoms in exactly 12 grams of ^{12}C, that is, 6.02×10^{23} atoms. A **mole (mol)** is the amount of a substance that contains Avogadro's number of elementary units—atoms, molecules, or formula units, depending on the substance. The **formula mass** is the sum of masses of the atoms represented in the formula of a substance. If the formula represents a molecule, the term *molecular mass* often is used. A formula represents a mass ratio as well as an atom ratio, and the

composition by mass of a compound may be calculated from the formula.

Section 5.4—The **molar mass** is the mass of one mole of a substance. Molar mass has the same number as formula mass, molecular mass, or atomic mass but is expressed in units of grams per mole (g/mol). Molar mass is used to convert from grams to moles of a substance, and vice versa. A balanced equation can be read in terms of atoms and molecules or in terms of moles. **Stoichiometry**, or mass relationships in chemical reactions, can be found by using **stoichiometric factors**, which relate moles of one substance to moles of another. Stoichiometric factors can be obtained without calculation, directly from the balanced equation. To evaluate mass relationships in chemical reactions, molar masses and stoichiometric factors are both used as conversion factors.

Section 5.5—A **solution** is a homogeneous mixture of two or more substances, often consisting of a solute dissolved in a solvent. A substance is soluble in a solvent if some appreciable quantity of the substance dissolves in the solvent. Any substance that does not dissolve significantly in a solvent is insoluble in that solvent. An **aqueous solution**, indicated by the label (aq), has water as the solvent. The concentration of a solution can be expressed in many ways. A **concentrated solution** has a relatively large amount of solute compared to solvent, and a **dilute solution** has only a little solute in a large amount of solvent. One quantitative unit of concentration is **molarity (M)**, moles of solute dissolved per liter of solution.

$$\text{Molarity (M)} = \frac{\text{moles of solute}}{\text{liters of solution}}$$

There are several ways to express concentration using percentages. Two important ones are *percent by volume* and *percent by mass*.

$$\text{Percent by volume} = \frac{\text{volume of solute}}{\text{volume of solution}} \times 100\%$$

$$\text{Percent by mass} = \frac{\text{mass of solute}}{\text{mass of solution}} \times 100\%$$

For each concentration unit, if we know two of the three terms in the equation, we can solve for the third.

Green chemistry Atom economy is an important component of green chemistry and waste prevention. By strategically designing reactions to maximize the number of atoms utilized, a chemist has the ability to reduce waste production.

Learning Objectives

❯ Identify balanced and unbalanced chemical equations, and balance equations by inspection. (5.1)	Problems 4, 11–16, 51–53, 62
❯ Determine volumes of gases that react, using a balanced equation for a reaction. (5.2)	Problems 2, 3, 17–22, 55
❯ Calculate the formula mass, molecular mass, or molar mass of a substance. (5.3)	Problems 27–34
❯ Convert from mass to moles and from moles to mass of a substance. (5.4)	Problem 71
❯ Calculate the mass or number of moles of a reactant or product from the mass or number of moles of another reactant or product. (5.4)	Problems 35–38, 54, 56–58, 62, 69
❯ Calculate the concentration (molarity, percent by volume, or percent by mass) of a solute in a solution. (5.5)	Problems 39–50, 60, 61
❯ Calculate the amount of solute or solution given the concentration and the other amount. (5.5)	Problems 59, 64, 65
❯ Explain how the concept of atom economy can be applied to pollution prevention and environmental protection.	Problems 73, 74
❯ Calculate the atom economy for chemical reactions.	Problems 72–76

REVIEW QUESTIONS

1. Define or illustrate each of the following.
   a. formula unit   b. formula mass
   c. mole   d. Avogadro's number
   e. molar mass   f. molar volume (of a gas)

2. Explain the difference between the atomic mass of chlorine and the formula mass of chlorine gas.

3. What is Avogadro's hypothesis? How does it explain Gay-Lussac's law of combining volumes?

4. Referring to the law of conservation of mass, explain why we must work with balanced chemical equations.

5. Define or explain and illustrate the following terms.
   a. solution   b. solvent
   c. solute   d. aqueous solution

6. Define or explain and illustrate the following terms.
   a. concentrated solution b. dilute solution
   c. soluble   d. insoluble

PROBLEMS

Interpreting Formulas

7. How many oxygen atoms does each of the following contain?
   a. $Al(H_2PO_4)_3$ b. $HOC_6H_4COOCH_3$
   c. $(BiO)_2SO_4$

8. How many carbon atoms does each of the following contain?
   a. $Fe_2(CO_3)_3$ b. $Al(CH_3COO)_3$
   c. $(CH_3)CCH(CH_3)_2$

9. How many atoms of each element (N, P, H, and O) does the notation $3\ (NH_4)_2HPO_4$ indicate?

10. How many atoms of each element (Fe, C, H, and O) does the notation $4\ Fe(HOOCCH_2COO)_3$ indicate?

Interpreting Chemical Equations

11. Consider the following equation. **(a)** Explain its meaning at the molecular level. **(b)** Interpret it in terms of moles. **(c)** State the mass relationships conveyed by the equation.
$$2\ H_2O_2 \longrightarrow 2\ H_2O + O_2$$

12. Express each chemical equation in terms of moles.
   a. $2\ Ca + O_2 \longrightarrow 2\ CaO$
   b. $CH_4 + 2\ O_2 \longrightarrow CO_2 + 2\ H_2O$

Balancing Chemical Equations

13. Balance the following equations.
   a. $Mg + O_2 \longrightarrow MgO$
   b. $C_3H_8 + O_2 \longrightarrow CO_2 + H_2O$
   c. $H_2 + Ta_2O_3 \longrightarrow Ta + H_2O$

14. Balance the following equations.
   a. $K + O_2 \longrightarrow K_2O_2$
   b. $FeCl_2 + Na_2SiO_3 \longrightarrow NaCl + FeSiO_3$
   c. $F_2 + AlCl_3 \longrightarrow AlF_3 + Cl_2$

15. Write balanced equations for the following processes.
   a. Nitrogen gas and oxygen gas react to form nitrogen oxide (NO).
   b. Ozone (O_3) decomposes into oxygen gas.
   c. Uranium(IV) oxide reacts with hydrogen fluoride (HF) to form uranium(IV) fluoride and water.

16. Write balanced equations for the following processes.
   a. Iron metal reacts with oxygen gas to form rust [iron(III) oxide].
   b. Calcium carbonate (the active ingredient in many antacids) reacts with stomach acid (HCl) to form calcium chloride, water, and carbon dioxide.
   c. Heptane (C_7H_{16}) burns in oxygen gas to form carbon dioxide and water.

Volume Relationships in Chemical Equations

17. Make a sketch similar to Figure 5.3 to show the reaction of hydrogen gas with oxygen gas to form steam [$H_2O(g)$] at 100 °C.

18. Make a sketch similar to Figure 5.3 to show that when hydrogen reacts with oxygen to form steam at 100 °C, each volume of gas—hydrogen, oxygen, or steam—contains the same number of molecules.

19. Consider the following equation, which represents the combustion (burning) of hexane (C_6H_{14}).

$$2\,C_6H_{14}(g) + 19\,O_2(g) \longrightarrow 12\,CO_2(g) + 14\,H_2O(g)$$

   a. What volume, in liters, of $CO_2(g)$ is formed when 20.6 L of $C_6H_{14}(g)$ is burned? Assume that both gases are measured under the same conditions.
   b. What volume, in milliliters, of $C_6H_{14}(g)$ has to burn to react with 29.0 mL $O_2(g)$? Assume that both gases are measured under the same conditions.

20. Consider the following equation, which represents the combustion of ammonia.

$$4\,NH_3(g) + 3\,O_2(g) \longrightarrow 2\,N_2(g) + 6\,H_2O(g)$$

   a. What volume, in liters, of $N_2(g)$ is formed when 125 L of $NH_3(g)$ is burned? Assume that both gases are measured under the same conditions.
   b. What volume, in liters, of $O_2(g)$ is required to form 36 L of $H_2O(g)$? Assume that both gases are measured under the same conditions.

21. Using the equation in Problem 19, determine the ratio of volume of $CO_2(g)$ formed to volume of $C_6H_{14}(g)$ that reacts, assuming that both gases are measured under the same conditions.

22. Using the equation in Problem 20, determine the ratio of volume of $H_2O(g)$ formed to volume of $NH_3(g)$ that reacts, assuming that both gases are measured under the same conditions.

Avogadro's Number

23. How many **(a)** sulfur *molecules* and how many **(b)** sulfur *atoms* are there in 1.00 mol S_8?

24. How many **(a)** magnesium ions and how many **(b)** nitride ions are there in 1.00 mol Mg_3N_2?

25. Choose one of the following to complete this statement correctly: One *mole* of bromine (Br_2) gas _____.
   a. has a mass of 79.9 g
   b. contains 6.02×10^{23} Br atoms
   c. contains 12.04×10^{23} Br atoms
   d. has a mass of 6.02×10^{23} g

26. **(a)** How many barium ions and how many nitrate ions are there in 1.00 mol $Ba(NO_3)_2$? **(b)** How many nitrogen atoms and how many oxygen atoms are there in 1.00 mol $Ba(NO_3)_2$?

Formula Masses and Molar Masses

You may round atomic masses to one decimal place.

27. Calculate the molar mass of each of the following compounds.
   a. $AgNO_3$ b. $Mg(ClO)_2$
   c. $Zn(IO_4)_2$ d. $CH_3(CH_2)_3COF$

28. Calculate the molar mass of each of the following compounds.
   a. Bi_2O_3 b. $FeSO_4$
   c. $Ca(CH_3COO)_2$ d. $(NH_4)_2Cr_2O_7$

29. Calculate the mass, in grams, of each of the following.
   a. 7.57 mol $BaSO_4$ b. 0.0472 mol $CuCl_2$
   c. 0.250 mol $C_{12}H_{22}O_{11}$

30. Calculate the mass, in grams, of each of the following.
   a. 4.61 mol PCl_3 b. 6.15 mol Cr_2O_3
   c. 0.158 mol IF_5

31. Calculate the amount, in moles, of each of the following.
   a. 6.63 g Sb_2S_3 b. 19.1 g MoO_3
   c. 434 g $AlPO_4$

32. Calculate the amount, in moles, of each of the following.
   a. 16.3 g SF_6 b. 25.4 g $Pb(C_2H_3O_2)_2$
   c. 15.6 g $CoCl_3$

33. Calculate the percent by mass of N in **(a)** $NaNO_3$ and **(b)** NH_4Cl.

34. Calculate the percent by mass of C, H, and O in glucose ($C_6H_{12}O_6$).

Mole and Mass Relationships in Chemical Equations

35. Consider the reaction for the combustion of butane (C_4H_{10}), a component of liquefied petroleum (LP) gas.

$$2\,C_4H_{10}(g) + 13\,O_2(g) \longrightarrow 8\,CO_2(g) + 10\,H_2O(g)$$

   a. How many moles of CO_2 are produced when 8.12 mol of butane are burned?
   b. How many moles of oxygen are required to burn 3.13 mol of butane?

36. Consider the reaction for the combustion of octane (C_8H_{18}).

$$2\,C_8H_{18} + 25\,O_2 \longrightarrow 16\,CO_2 + 18\,H_2O$$

   a. How many moles of H_2O are produced when 0.281 mol of octane is burned?
   b. How many moles of CO_2 are produced when 8.12 mol of oxygen reacts with octane?

37. What mass in grams **(a)** of ammonia can be made from 440 g H_2 and **(b)** of hydrogen is needed to react completely with 892 g N_2?

$$N_2 + H_2 \longrightarrow NH_3 \quad \text{(not balanced)}$$

38. Toluene (C_7H_8) and nitric acid (HNO_3) are used in the production of trinitrotoluene (TNT, $C_7H_5N_3O_6$), an explosive.

$$C_7H_8 + HNO_3 \longrightarrow C_7H_5N_3O_6 + H_2O \quad \text{(not balanced)}$$

What mass in grams **(a)** of nitric acid is required to react with 454 g C_7H_8 and **(b)** of TNT can be made from 829 g C_7H_8?

Molarity of Solutions

39. Calculate the molarity of each of the following solutions.
    a. 23.4 mol HCl in 10.0 L of solution
    b. 0.0875 mol Li_2CO_3 in 632 mL of solution

40. Calculate the molarity of each of the following solutions.
    a. 8.82 mol H_2SO_4 in 7.50 L of solution
    b. 1.22 mol C_2H_5OH in 96.3 mL of solution

41. What mass in grams of solute is needed to prepare **(a)** 3.50 L of 0.500 M NaOH and **(b)** 65.0 mL of 1.45 M $C_6H_{12}O_6$?

42. What mass in grams of solute is needed to prepare **(a)** 0.250 L of 0.167 M $K_2Cr_2O_7$ and **(b)** 625 mL of 0.0200 M $KMnO_4$?

43. What volume in liters of **(a)** 6.00 M NaOH contains 2.50 mol NaOH and **(b)** 0.0500 M KH_2AsO_4 contains 8.10 g KH_2AsO_4?

44. What volume in liters of **(a)** 0.250 M NaOH contains 1.05 mol NaOH and **(b)** 4.25 M $H_2C_2O_4$ contains 0.225 g $H_2C_2O_4$?

Percent Concentrations of Solutions

45. What is the percent by volume concentration of **(a)** 58.0 mL of water in 625 mL of an acetic acid–water solution and **(b)** 79.1 mL of methanol in 755 mL of a methanol–water solution?

46. What is the percent by volume concentration of **(a)** 35.0 mL of water in 725 mL of an ethanol–water solution and **(b)** 78.9 mL of acetone in 1550 mL of an acetone–water solution?

47. Describe how you would prepare 3375 g of an aqueous solution that is 8.2% NaCl by mass.

48. Describe how you would prepare 2.44 kg of an aqueous solution that is 16.3% KOH by mass.

49. Describe how you would prepare 2.00 L of an aqueous solution that is 2.00% acetic acid by volume.

50. Describe how you would prepare 500.0 mL of an aqueous solution that is 30.0% isopropyl alcohol by volume.

ADDITIONAL PROBLEMS

51. Both magnesium and aluminum react with hydrogen ions in aqueous solution to produce hydrogen. Why is it that only one of the following equations correctly describes the reaction?

$$Mg(s) + 2 H^+(aq) \longrightarrow Mg^{2+}(aq) + H_2(g)$$
$$Al(s) + 2 H^+(aq) \longrightarrow Al^{3+}(aq) + H_2(g)$$

52. Which of the following correctly represents the decomposition of potassium chlorate to produce potassium chloride and oxygen gas?
    a. $KClO_3(s) \longrightarrow KClO_3(s) + O_2(g) + O(g)$
    b. $2 KClO_3(s) \longrightarrow 2 KCl(s) + 3 O_2(g)$
    c. $KClO_3(s) \longrightarrow KClO(s) + O_2(g)$
    d. $KClO_3(s) \longrightarrow KCl(s) + O_3(g)$

53. Write a balanced chemical equation to represent **(a)** the decomposition, by heating, of solid mercury(II) nitrate to produce pure liquid mercury, nitrogen dioxide gas, and oxygen gas, and **(b)** the reaction of aqueous sodium carbonate with aqueous hydrochloric acid (hydrogen chloride) to produce water, carbon dioxide gas, and aqueous sodium chloride.

54. Joseph Priestley discovered oxygen in 1774 by heating "red calx of mercury" [mercury(II) oxide]. The calx decomposed to its elements. The equation is

$$HgO \longrightarrow Hg + O_2 \quad \text{(not balanced)}$$

What mass of oxygen is produced by the decomposition of 1.08 g HgO?

55. Consider 1.00 mol $H_2(g)$, 2.00 mol He(g), and 0.50 mol $C_2H_2(g)$ at the same temperature and pressure. **(a)** Do the three samples have the same number of atoms? **(b)** Which sample has the greatest mass?

56. What mass in grams of the magnetic oxide of iron (Fe_3O_4) can be made from 24.0 g of pure iron and an excess of oxygen? The equation is

$$Fe + O_2 \longrightarrow Fe_3O_4 \quad \text{(not balanced)}$$

57. When heated above ~900 °C, limestone (calcium carbonate) decomposes to quicklime (calcium oxide), which is used to make cement, and carbon dioxide. What mass in grams of quicklime can be produced from 4.72×10^9 g of limestone?

58. Ammonia reacts with oxygen to produce nitric acid (HNO_3) and water. What mass of nitric acid, in grams, can be made from 971 g of ammonia?

59. Hydrogen peroxide solution sold in drugstores is 3.0% H_2O_2 by mass dissolved in water. How many moles of H_2O_2 are in a typical 16-fl. oz. bottle of this solution? (1 fl. oz. = 29.6 mL; density = 1.00 g/mL)

60. What is the mass percent of **(a)** NaOH in a solution of 4.12 g NaOH in 100.0 g of water and **(b)** ethanol in a solution of 5.00 mL of ethanol (density = 0.789 g/mL) in 50.0 g of water?

61. What is the volume percent of **(a)** ethanol in 625 mL of an ethanol–water solution that contains 58.0 mL of water and **(b)** acetone in 1.25 L of an acetone–water solution that contains 10.00 mL of acetone?

62. Laughing gas (dinitrogen monoxide, N_2O, also called nitrous oxide) can be made by very carefully heating ammonium nitrate. The other product is water.
 a. Write a balanced equation for the process.
 b. Draw the Lewis structure for N_2O.
 c. What mass in grams of N_2O can be made from 48.0 g of ammonium nitrate?

63. In Table 1.6 we listed some multiplicative prefixes used with SI base units. In the 1990s, some new prefixes were recommended:

 zetta- (Z, 10^{21}) yotta- (Y, 10^{24})
 zepto- (z, 10^{-21}) yocto- (y, 10^{-24})

 a. What is the mass of 1.00 ymol of uranium in yoctograms?
 b. How many atoms are in 1.00 zmol of uranium?

64. What volume of 0.0859 M oxalic acid contains 31.7 g of oxalic acid ($H_2C_2O_4$)?

65. In tests for intoxication, blood alcohol levels are expressed as percents by volume. A blood alcohol level of 0.080% by volume means 0.080 mL of ethanol per 100 mL of blood and is considered proof of intoxication. If a person's total blood volume is 5.0 L, what volume of alcohol in the blood gives a blood alcohol level of 0.165% by volume?

66. Homeopathic remedies are prepared using a process of dilution, starting with a substance that causes symptoms of the illness being treated. Some homeopaths use a scale (X) in which the substance is diluted by a factor of ten at each stage. For example, for a 6X remedy, the original substance is diluted tenfold six times, for a total dilution of 10^6. (Many homeopathic remedies are diluted far more than six times.)
 a. If the original substance is in the form of a 1.00 M solution, what would be the yoctomolar concentration of a 24X remedy? (Few starting solutions are 1 M; most are far less concentrated.)
 b. How many molecules of the original substance remain in 1.00 L of a 24X remedy?

67. Evaluate this statement: "One cup of water has more molecules than there are cups of water in all of Earth's oceans" (1 cup = 236 mL = 236 cm³). For the volume of the oceans, see Problem 25, page 36.

68. If a Neanderthal excreted 500 mL of urine into the ocean 50,000 years ago, how many molecules in 500 mL of water you drink today are from that urine? Refer to Problem 67, and assume complete mixing of the waters of Earth over 50,000 years.

69. A truck carrying about 31,000 kg of sulfuric acid (H_2SO_4) is involved in an accident, spilling the acid. What mass of sodium bicarbonate ($NaHCO_3$) is needed to react with and neutralize the sulfuric acid? The products of the reaction are sodium sulfate (Na_2SO_4), water, and carbon dioxide.

70. Referring to Problem 69, determine the mass of sodium carbonate (Na_2CO_3) needed to neutralize the acid. (The products of the reaction are the same.)

71. How many moles of H_2O are in 1.00 L of water? ($d = 1.00$ g/mL)

72. Consider the following equation for the reaction of sodium azide that forms nitrogen gas in airbags. **(a)** What is the atom economy for the production of N_2? **(b)** What is the mass in grams of N_2 that is formed if 2.52 g of NaN_3 are reacted?

$$2\,NaN_3 \longrightarrow 2\,Na + 3\,N_2$$

73. Ethanol (C_2H_5OH) is a very important chemical. In addition to being widely used as an industrial solvent, a gasoline additive, and an alternative fuel, it is well-known as the alcohol in alcoholic beverages. A common name for ethanol is *grain alcohol* because it is formed by the fermentation of glucose ($C_6H_{12}O_6$) and other sugars in grains such as corn, wheat, and barley:

$$C_6H_{12}O_6 \longrightarrow C_2H_5OH + CO_2$$

The previous reaction has been carried out for many centuries and is one of the oldest manufacturing processes. In a more recent development, ethanol can be prepared by reacting ethylene (found in petroleum) with water:

$$C_2H_4 + H_2O \longrightarrow C_2H_5OH$$

 a. Write the *balanced* equation for each of the two reactions above.
 b. Calculate the %A.E. (for the product ethanol) for each of the two reactions.
 c. Explain how you can determine which reaction has the higher atom economy *without* doing the calculation in part (b) above.
 d. Is either method sustainable? Which one? Justify your answer.
 e. Given the results from parts (b) and (d) above, select one of the two methods as the best candidate overall for preparing ethanol. Justify your selection.

74. Formation of butene (C_4H_8) can be accomplished in several different ways. Two are shown below.

 Reaction A:

$$C_4H_9Br + NaOH \longrightarrow C_4H_8 + H_2O + NaBr$$

 Reaction B:

$$C_4H_6 + H_2 \longrightarrow C_4H_8$$

 Which reaction has a higher atom economy?

75. Consider the following equation for the formation of carbon dioxide (CO_2), a known greenhouse gas, from the combustion of hydrocarbons.

$$C_5H_{12} + O_2 \longrightarrow CO_2 + H_2O \text{ (not balanced)}$$

 a. What is the percent atom economy based on carbon dioxide as the target product?
 b. How many grams of CO_2 form if 10.0 g C_5H_{12} is burned?
 c. What is the percent yield of the reaction if 25.4 g CO_2 are formed at the end of the reaction? (Hint: Use the information in the Atom Economy essay for this calculation.)

76. Balance each reaction and calculate the percent atom economy based on the underlined molecule as your desired product.
 a. $CuCl_2(aq) + Na_2CO_3(aq) \longrightarrow \underline{CuCO_3}(s) + NaCl(aq)$
 b. $NH_3(g) + O_2(g) \longrightarrow \underline{NO}(g) + H_2O(g)$
 c. $KMnO_4(aq) + KOH(aq) + KI(aq) \longrightarrow \underline{K_2MnO_4}(aq) + KIO_3(aq) + H_2O(l)$

COLLABORATIVE GROUP PROJECTS

Prepare a PowerPoint, poster, or other presentation (as directed by your instructor) to share with the class.

1. Prepare a brief biographical report on Amedeo Avogadro.

2. In the view of many scientists, hydrogen holds great promise as a source of clean energy. A 2008 report by the U.S. National Research Council suggested that a government subsidy of roughly $4 billion per year through 2023 could make hydrogen cars competitive with petroleum-powered vehicles. Search the web to explore the proposals for using hydrogen as a fuel. Write a brief summary of what you find, and use an appropriate balanced equation to explain why hydrogen is considered a clean, renewable source. More discussion of hydrogen as a fuel is found in Chapter 15.

6

Gases, Liquids, Solids ...
and Intermolecular Forces

Learning Objectives

> Explain how the different properties of solids, liquids, and gases are related to the motion and spacing of atoms, molecules, or ions. (6.1)

> Identify some differences between ionic and molecular substances, and explain why these differences exist. (6.2)

> Classify forces between molecules as dipole–dipole forces, dispersion forces, or hydrogen bonds. (6.3)

> Explain why nonpolar solutes tend to dissolve in nonpolar solvents and polar and ionic solutes tend to dissolve in polar solvents. (6.4)

> List the five basic concepts of the kinetic–molecular theory of gases. (6.5)

> State the three simple gas laws, by name and mathematically. (6.6)

> Use any gas law to find the value of one variable if the other values are given. (6.6)

> State the ideal gas law, and use it to calculate one of the quantities if the others are given. (6.7)

> Describe how Green Chemistry Principle 3 must be considered in designing chemical reactions and processes.

> Identify the properties that make supercritical fluids applicable in greener chemical processes.

Have You Ever Wondered?

1. Why does Silly Putty® have such strange properties?

2. What does "10W40" on a bottle of motor oil mean?

3. What is it that keeps oil and water from mixing?

4. Why doesn't creamy Italian dressing separate like ordinary Italian dressing does?

5. How cold can it possibly get, and how hot can it possibly get?

6. Why are we supposed to measure bicycle tire pressure when tires are cold?

We introduced the three states of matter—gas, liquid, and solid—in Chapter 1. Water is the most familiar substance that we experience in all three states: as Earth's most common liquid, as a solid (ice), and as a gas (steam). Many other substances can exist in the three states, depending on conditions. An understanding of those conditions is important for our understanding of matter. The state that a substance exhibits depends on the physical properties of that substance, on the pressure, and especially on the temperature. When it is very cold, water exists as solid ice. When it is warmer, water is a liquid. At still higher temperatures, water boils and becomes steam.

Water is an unusual substance in a number of ways. It is the only common substance that exists in all three states—solid ice, liquid water, and gaseous steam—in Earth's biosphere. A small amount of solid water (left) can cool a relatively large amount of liquid water very quickly. Liquid water (center) is also a good cooling agent, and it dissolves many substances both ionic and covalent. Interestingly, the visible cloud often referred to as steam (top) is actually many microscopic droplets of liquid water; steam is an invisible gas. The properties mentioned here are largely due to the *intermolecular forces* that exist in water. We will learn about those forces in this chapter.

Chapter 4 described the forces called *chemical bonds* that bind atoms together within molecules. Chemical bonds are *intramolecular* forces that determine such molecular properties as geometry and polarity. Forces *between* molecules—*intermolecular* forces—determine the macroscopic physical properties of liquids and solids. Intermolecular forces are also related to the kinds of bonds found in substances. Figure 6.1 compares intermolecular and intramolecular forces. If there were no intermolecular attractive forces, there would be no liquids or solids—everything would be in a gaseous state.

The shape, size, and polarity of molecules determine how they interact with each other. The physical state of a material depends on the strength of the intermolecular forces that hold the molecules or ions together, relative to the thermal energy (temperature) that acts to separate them.

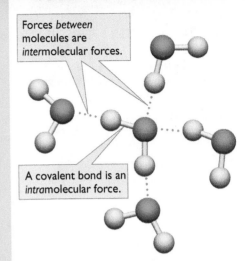

Forces *between* molecules are *intermolecular* forces.

A covalent bond is an *intramolecular* force.

▲ **Figure 6.1** Intramolecular and intermolecular forces. The gray "sticks" represent covalent bonds in water molecules—*intramolecular* forces, or pairs of shared electrons. The dotted red lines represent forces between water molecules—*intermolecular* forces.

6.1 Solids, Liquids, and Gases

Learning Objective ❯ Explain how the different properties of solids, liquids, and gases are related to the motion and spacing of atoms, molecules, or ions.

Most solids are highly ordered assemblies of atoms, molecules, or ions in close contact with one another, as suggested by Figure 6.2(a). This makes it difficult to compress solids. The motion of these particles is primarily vibration. Table salt (sodium chloride) is a typical crystalline solid. In this solid, ionic bonds hold the Na^+ and Cl^- ions in position and maintain the orderly arrangement (look again at Figure 4.2).

In liquids, the particles are still in close contact, but they are randomly arranged and are freer to move about [Figure 6.2(b)]. Like solids, liquids are difficult to compress, but they are able to flow and to conform to the shape of their container. To get a better image of a liquid at the molecular level, think of a box of marbles being shaken continuously. The marbles move back and forth, rolling over one another. The particles of a liquid (like the marbles) are not held in place as rigidly as the particles in a solid are. Even so, there must be some force attracting the particles in a liquid to one another. Otherwise, they would not stay close to one another.

In gases, the particles are separated by relatively great distances and are moving quite rapidly in random directions [Figure 6.2(c)]. In this state, the atoms or molecules have no interactions with one another. We will look more closely at gases in Section 6.5.

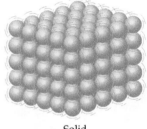

(a)   Solid

(b)   Liquid

(c)   Gas

▲ **Figure 6.2** Three states of matter. (a) Most solids have molecules (or atoms) that vibrate around fixed positions. (b) In liquids, the molecules are still close together but are free to move about like people in a crowded room. (c) Molecules of gases are widely spaced and move freely and randomly.

▲ Most solids are made up of highly ordered particles. Glass is an exception. The particles that make up glass (Chapter 12) are randomly arrayed.

1. Why does Silly Putty® **have such strange properties?** Although it appears to be a solid, Silly Putty® is actually a liquid—a very thick, slow-flowing (viscous) liquid.

▶ **Figure 6.3** Diagram of changes in state of a substance on heating or cooling.

Q: *What factors determine the actual temperatures at which the changes of state occur?*

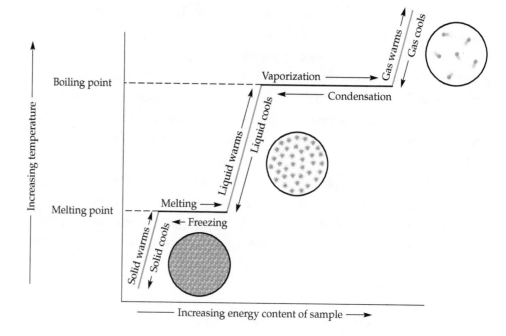

▲ The reverse of sublimation is *deposition*, a process that occurs on cold mornings. Water vapor deposits directly onto the grass as solid frost.

Most solids can be changed to liquids; that is, they can be *melted*. When a solid is heated, the thermal energy is absorbed by the particles of the solid. The energy causes the particles to vibrate more vigorously until, finally, the forces holding the particles in their regular arrangement are overcome. The solid becomes a liquid. The temperature at which this happens is the **melting point** of the solid. A high melting point indicates that the forces holding a solid together are very strong.

A liquid can change to a gas in a process called **vaporization**. Again, all that is needed to achieve this change is enough heat. Energy is absorbed by the liquid particles, which move faster and faster as a result. Finally, this increasingly violent motion overcomes the attractive forces holding the liquid particles close to one another and the particles fly apart. The liquid becomes a gas. The temperature at which this happens is the **boiling point** of the liquid.

Removing energy from the gas and slowing down the particles can reverse the sequence of changes. A gas changes to a liquid in a process called **condensation**; a liquid changes to a solid in a process called *freezing*. Figure 6.3 presents a diagram of the changes in state that occur as energy is added to or removed from a sample. Some substances go directly from the solid state to the gaseous state, a process called **sublimation**. For example, ice cubes left in a freezer for a long time shrink, and solid mothballs slowly disappear in a drawer or closet. In each case, the solid undergoes sublimation.

Self-Assessment Questions

1. Molecules are farthest apart in a(n)
   a. covalent solid   **b.** gas   **c.** ionic solid   **d.** liquid

2. Liquids are
   a. difficult to compress and have no definite shape
   b. difficult to compress and have no definite volume
   c. easy to compress and have a definite shape
   d. easy to compress and have no definite volume

3. When a liquid changes into a gas, the process is called
   a. condensation   **b.** fusion   **c.** gasification   **d.** vaporization

4. When a liquid changes into a solid, the process is called
   a. condensation   **b.** freezing   **c.** fusion   **d.** melting

5. When a solid changes directly into a gas, the process is called
   a. evaporation   **b.** fusion   **c.** sublimation   **d.** vaporization

Answers: 1, b; 2, a; 3, d; 4, b; 5, c

Doug Raynie, *South Dakota State University*

Supercritical Fluids

Many chemical reactions take place in solution (Section 5.5), and most chemical processes involve a separation of components at some stage. Water is an excellent solvent for many substances, but some substances do not dissolve in water under ordinary conditions. Chemists have traditionally used organic solvents such as benzene (C_6H_6), a cancer-causing aromatic hydrocarbon (Section 9.2), and methylene chloride (CH_2Cl_2), a toxic chlorinated hydrocarbon (Section 9.3), to dissolve nonpolar and slightly polar substances. Wouldn't it be nice to have a nontoxic, benign solvent that could be recycled readily?

Let's look again at the states of matter and changes of state (Section 6.1), particularly the change from liquid to gas. Have you ever used a pressure cooker, or tried to cook food while backpacking in the mountains? If you have, you've probably noticed that boiling point changes with pressure. In a pressure cooker, the increase in pressure lets us cook at higher temperatures. In the mountains, where the air pressure is lower, water boils at a lower temperature, so it takes longer to prepare a meal. This behavior is shown in the following graph called a *phase diagram*:

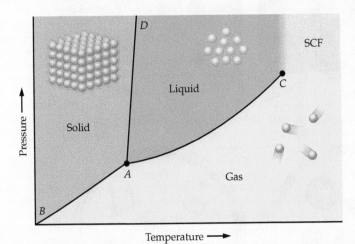

▲ A phase diagram shows the physical state of a material at given temperatures and pressures. As the temperature and pressure increase, the material shown in the graph changes from a solid to a liquid or gas. Above a certain temperature and pressure (the critical point C), the material is neither gas nor liquid but becomes a supercritical fluid.

The curve *AC* slopes upward, showing that the boiling point increases with increasing pressure. Notice that the line *AC* does not continue forever. Eventually, continued heating will take a substance

to point *C*, called the *critical point*. Above the critical point, matter exists as neither a gas nor a liquid but as a kind of a hybrid called a **supercritical fluid**. We can think of supercritical fluids as having properties of both gases and liquids. Most importantly, they can dissolve things as liquids do, but they flow rapidly like gases. We can vary these properties to make the fluid more liquid-like or more gas-like by changing the temperature or pressure.

The most commonly used supercritical fluid is carbon dioxide ($scCO_2$), an inexpensive, convenient-to-use, nonflammable, and nontoxic substance. Carbon dioxide becomes a supercritical fluid at temperatures greater than 31 °C and pressures greater than 73 atm. As a solvent, carbon dioxide (nonpolar) is a complement to water (polar), giving us two environmentally friendly solvents with different properties and uses. Individually or combined, these supercritical fluids can dissolve a wide range of chemical compounds. Also, because they can flow like gases, supercritical fluids can often make processes occur more quickly.

Supercritical water and $scCO_2$ are "generally regarded as safe" by the U.S. Food and Drug Administration and are often used in the food industry. For example, coffee is sometimes decaffeinated using $scCO_2$ extraction. After the extraction, the $scCO_2$ is decompressed and returned to a gaseous state, leaving the caffeine behind. The gaseous CO_2 is cooled and compressed to return it to a liquid form to be used again. This process is much greener than the older one using toxic methylene chloride, a liquid that had to be removed from the coffee by distillation. In the green chemistry essay "Green Dry Cleaning" in Chapter 21, you will see that carbon dioxide can also be used to replace perchloroethylene (C_2Cl_4), another toxic chlorinated hydrocarbon long used in dry cleaning.

Flavors and fragrances are often isolated using $scCO_2$. In the cosmetics industry, oils such as palm oil or jojoba oil are isolated from their plant sources using $scCO_2$. Supercritical fluids are used to clean or degrease precision parts in electronic instruments. In more specialized cases, chemical reactions are carried out using supercritical fluid solvents. The main drawback to the use of supercritical fluids is that special equipment is needed to control the temperatures and high pressures required for these processes.

Nearly all chemical processes require the separation of one chemical from a mixture of others. Water and $scCO_2$ give us a pair of inexpensive and safe solvents that dissolve a wide range of chemical compounds—an excellent application of Green Chemistry Principle 5, which urges the use of safer reaction conditions and less toxic solvents.

▲ It DOES Matter!

A salt lamp has a lightbulb mounted in a large piece of sodium chloride. Some vendors claim that the heat from the lamp causes negative ions to be emitted from the salt. But ionic compounds like sodium chloride have extremely high melting and boiling points, far above the temperature of an ordinary lightbulb. No significant amount of ions can be produced from such a lamp, and there is no conclusive evidence that such ions would be beneficial anyway.

6.2 Comparing Ionic and Molecular Substances

Learning Objective ❯ Identify some differences between ionic and molecular substances, and explain why these differences exist.

Recall that Figure 6.1 illustrates *intermolecular* forces. Ionic substances such as sodium chloride (recall Figure 4.2) are made of ions, not molecules, so "intermolecular forces" really doesn't apply to them. Nevertheless, there are attractive forces between ions, and we can compare them to the forces between molecules. First, let's consider some differences between ionic and molecular substances.

- Nearly all ionic compounds, such as $NaCl$, KBr, $CaCO_3$, and NH_4NO_3, are solids at room temperature. Some molecular substances are liquids or gases at room temperature, although many are solids. Ethane (CH_3CH_3), hydrogen sulfide (H_2S), and chlorine (Cl_2) are gases. Ethanol (CH_3CH_2OH), bromine (Br_2), and phosphorus trichloride (PCl_3) are liquids. Sulfur (S_8), glucose ($C_6H_{12}O_6$), and iodine (I_2) are solids.

- Ionic compounds generally have much higher melting points and boiling points than molecular compounds. High temperatures are necessary to overcome the strong ionic bonds (Section 4.3) in ionic compounds. Less energy is required to overcome the weak attractions between molecules (Section 6.3). For example, sodium chloride ($NaCl$) must be heated to 801 °C before it melts, but the molecular compound ethane (CH_3CH_3) melts at −184 °C.

- It generally takes ten to a hundred times as much energy to melt one mole of a typical ionic compound as it does to melt one mole of a typical molecular compound. To melt one mole of sodium chloride requires almost 30 kJ, while it takes only about 3 kJ to melt one mole of ethane.

▶ **Figure 6.4** (Left) The bulb lights because the solution of sodium chloride contains ions. The ions carry current, and the solution conducts electricity. (Right) A solution of methanol contains no ions and does not conduct electricity.

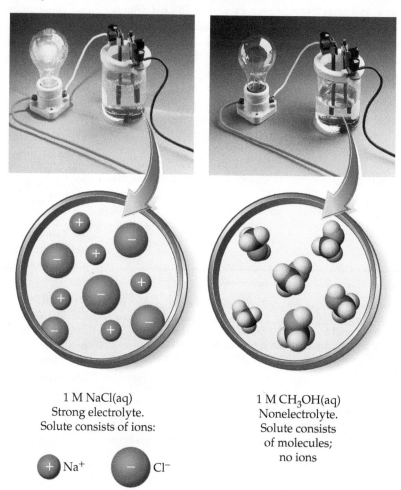

1 M NaCl(aq)
Strong electrolyte.
Solute consists of ions:

Na⁺   Cl⁻

1 M CH₃OH(aq)
Nonelectrolyte.
Solute consists
of molecules;
no ions

■ Many familiar ionic compounds dissolve in water; those that do form solutions that conduct electricity. The dissociated ions carry the electric current through the solution. Most molecular compounds, even those that dissolve in water, do not dissociate into ions and thus do not form conducting solutions. A solution of sodium chloride conducts electricity, as seen in Figure 6.4, while a solution of methanol (CH_3OH) does not.

■ As solids, most ionic compounds are crystalline, hard, and often quite brittle. Solid molecular compounds are usually much softer than ionic ones.

Next, we consider some other interactions that hold the particles of solids and liquids together.

Self-Assessment Questions

1. Which of the following is not composed of particles that exhibit intermolecular forces?
   a. Br_2 **b.** N_2 **c.** NaBr   **d.** NBr_3

2. Which of the following solids is likely to require the greatest input of energy to melt?
   a. O_2 **b.** N_2O **c.** KBr   **d.** Kr

Answers: 1, c; 2, c

6.3 Forces between Molecules

Learning Objective ❯ Classify forces between molecules as dipole–dipole forces, dispersion forces, or hydrogen bonds.

As we have noted, many substances, such as water and carbon dioxide, do not consist of ions but instead are molecular compounds. Molecular compounds are characterized by covalent bonds—*intra*molecular forces. For example, in a hydrogen chloride molecule, a covalent bond holds the hydrogen and chlorine *atoms* together. But what makes one HCl molecule interact with another? In this section, we examine several types of *inter*molecular forces—forces *between* molecules.

Dipole–Dipole Forces

Recall that the hydrogen chloride molecule is a *dipole*: a molecule with a positive end and a negative end (see Figure 4.6, page 104). When oppositely charged ends of two dipoles are brought close enough together, they attract one another. In solid HCl, the molecules line up so that the positive end of one molecule attracts the negative end of neighboring molecules, as suggested by Figure 6.5(a). If we heat the solid sufficiently, the orderly arrangement is undone and the solid melts. In the liquid state, the oppositely charged dipoles in the liquid still attract one another, but more randomly, as shown in Figure 6.5(b). These **dipole–dipole forces** occur

◀ **Figure 6.5** An idealized representation of dipole–dipole forces in (a) a solid and (b) a liquid. In a real liquid or solid, the interactions between particles are more complex.

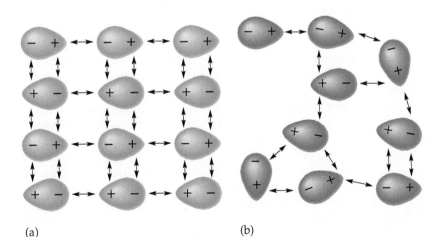

(a)   (b)

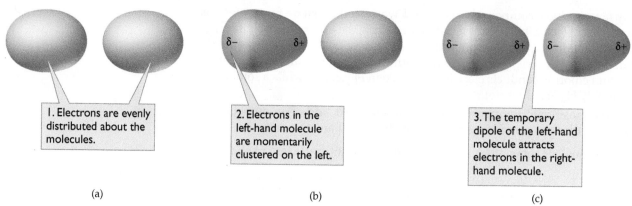

1. Electrons are evenly distributed about the molecules.

(a)

2. Electrons in the left-hand molecule are momentarily clustered on the left.

(b)

3. The temporary dipole of the left-hand molecule attracts electrons in the right-hand molecule.

(c)

▲ **Figure 6.6** Mechanism underlying dispersion forces.

Dispersion forces are weak for small, nonpolar molecules such as H_2, N_2, and CH_4. For molecules of similar size and shape, intermolecular forces range in strength from dispersion forces (the weakest) to dipole–dipole forces to hydrogen bonds (the strongest).

2. What does "10W40" on a bottle of motor oil mean? Oil must have the proper *viscosity* or thickness—which depends on the strength of its intermolecular forces—to lubricate an engine properly. High temperatures in the summer make the oil flow more easily, so a thicker oil (viscosity of 40) is needed. Lower temperatures require thinner oil (viscosity of 10). An oil labeled "10W40" has molecules with intermolecular forces that are about the same whether the oil is cold or hot, and such oil can be used in both summer and winter.

between any two polar molecules. Generally, these forces are much weaker than ionic bonds, but they are stronger than the forces between nonpolar molecules of comparable size. The more polar the molecules, the stronger are the dipole–dipole forces are.

Dispersion Forces

It is easy enough to understand how ions or polar molecules maintain contact with one another. After all, opposite charges attract. But how can we explain the fact that *nonpolar* substances can exist in the liquid and solid states? Even hydrogen (H_2) can exist as a liquid or a solid if the temperature is low enough (its melting point is −259 °C). Some force must be holding nonpolar molecules close to one another in the liquid and solid states.

Figure 6.6(a) suggests that the electrons in a covalent bond are evenly distributed between the two atoms sharing the bond. Recall, however, that electrons are *not* stationary but move continuously. Within a covalent bond, electrons are moving around their respective nuclei. On *average*, the two electrons in a nonpolar bond are between and equidistant from the two nuclei. But, at any given instant, it is possible for the electrons in one molecule to be at one end of that molecule [Figure 6.6(b)], causing a temporary negative charge at that end. This causes electrons in an adjacent molecule to move toward the opposite end of that molecule, as in Figure 6.6(c). Thus, at this instant, an attractive force is created between the electron-rich end of one molecule and the electron-poor end of the next.

These momentary, usually weak, attractive forces between molecules are called **dispersion forces**. Because the electrons are in constant motion, dispersion forces can be thought of as dipole–dipole forces in which the dipoles are constantly shifting. To a large extent, dispersion forces determine the physical properties of nonpolar compounds. However, dispersion forces do exist between *any* two particles, whether polar, nonpolar, or ionic.

Hydrogen Bonds

Certain polar molecules exhibit stronger attractive forces than would be expected from ordinary dipole–dipole interactions. These forces are strong enough to be given a special name, *hydrogen bonds*. The name is a bit misleading because it emphasizes only one component of the interactions. Not all compounds containing hydrogen exhibit this kind of attractive force. In most cases, the hydrogen atom *must* be attached to a small, very electronegative atom such as fluorine, oxygen, or nitrogen. The high electronegativity of such atoms gives rise to the great strength of hydrogen bonds. In hydrogen fluoride (HF), for example, the hydrogen–fluorine bond is strongly polar, with a negative fluorine end and a positive hydrogen end. Both hydrogen and fluorine are small atoms, and so the electrons on the fluorine end of one molecule can approach very closely to the hydrogen end of a second molecule. This unusually strong interaction between molecules that contain hydrogen bound to a small electronegative atom is called a **hydrogen bond**. Hydrogen bonds are often explicitly represented by *dotted* lines (see Figure 6.7) to emphasize that their strength is much greater than that of other intermolecular forces.

Water has both an unusually high melting point (0 °C) and an unusually high boiling point (100 °C) for a compound with such small molecules. These abnormal values are attributed to the water molecules' ability to form hydrogen bonds. Remember, however, that during melting and boiling, only the hydrogen bonds *between water molecules* are overcome. The covalent bonds between the hydrogen atoms and the oxygen atom in each water molecule remain intact. No chemical change occurs when there is a change in state because covalent bonds are much stronger than hydrogen bonds.

The unique properties of water resulting from hydrogen bonding are discussed in Chapter 14. Hydrogen bonding also plays an important role in biological molecules. The three-dimensional structures of proteins and enzymes and the arrangement of DNA (Chapter 16) are dependent on the presence and strength of hydrogen bonds.

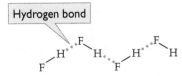

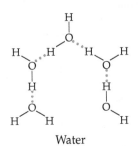

Water

▲ **Figure 6.7** Hydrogen bonding in hydrogen fluoride and in water. See also Figure 6.1.

Self-Assessment Questions

1. What intermolecular forces are most significant in accounting for the high boiling point of liquid water relative to other substances of similar molecular weight?
   a. dispersion forces
   b. dipolar attractions
   c. hydrogen bonds
   d. ionic bonds

2. Which one of the following interactions is the strongest?
   a. covalent bonds   **b.** dipole–dipole forces   **c.** dispersion forces   **d.** hydrogen bonds

3. In ethanol (CH_3CH_2OH), the attractions between neighboring molecules are
   a. covalent bonds and dispersion forces only
   b. covalent bonds and hydrogen bonds only
   c. covalent bonds only
   d. hydrogen bonds and dispersion forces only

4. The molecules of liquid water in a beaker are held to each other by
   a. covalent bonds
   b. intramolecular forces
   c. intermolecular forces
   d. ionic bonds

5. Of CH_3OH, H_2, HF, and H_2O, which molecule(s) can form hydrogen bonds?
   a. H_2 only
   b. H_2O only
   c. CH_3OH, HF, and H_2O
   d. all four

6. Which one of the following molecules does *not* form hydrogen bonds?
   a. ammonia (NH_3)
   b. chloroform ($CHCl_3$)
   c. methyl alcohol (CH_3OH)
   d. ethylene glycol ($HOCH_2CH_2OH$)

Answers: 1, c; 2, a; 3, d; 4, c; 5, c; 6, b

6.4 Forces in Solutions

Learning Objective ❭ Explain why nonpolar solutes tend to dissolve in nonpolar solvents and polar and ionic solutes tend to dissolve in polar solvents.

To complete our look at intermolecular forces, let's briefly examine the interactions that occur in solutions. A **solution** is an intimate, homogeneous mixture of two or more substances. Here *intimate* means that mixing occurs down to the level of individual ions and molecules, as suggested in Figure 6.8. For example, a sugar-in-water solution has separate sugar molecules randomly distributed among water molecules. *Homogeneous* means that all parts of the solution have the same distribution of components. A sugar solution is equally sweet at the top, bottom, and middle of the solution. The substance being dissolved, and usually present in a lesser amount, is called the **solute**. The substance doing the dissolving, and usually present in a greater amount, is the **solvent**. In a sugar-in-water solution, sugar is the solute and water is the solvent.

● = Solvent molecule
● = Solute molecule

▲ **Figure 6.8** In a solution, solute molecules (orange spheres) are randomly distributed among solvent molecules (purple spheres).

▶ **Figure 6.9** (a) Lawn mowers with two-cycle engines are fueled and lubricated with a solution of nonpolar lubricating oil in nonpolar gasoline. (b) In a salad dressing, polar vinegar and nonpolar olive oil are mixed. However, the two liquids do not form a solution and separate on standing. (c) Wine is a solution of polar ethyl alcohol in polar water.

Q: *What are some other examples of mixtures of polar and nonpolar substances?*

(a)   (b)   (c)

3. What is it that keeps oil and water from mixing? Oil molecules are nonpolar, and water molecules are very polar. The weak forces between oil and water molecule aren't strong enough to overcome the strong forces between the water molecules. Thus, oil and water don't mix.

4. Why doesn't creamy Italian dressing separate like ordinary Italian dressing does? Both kinds of dressings contain oil and vinegar. However, proteins (from egg yolk or other sources) are mixed into the creamy dressing. The protein molecules have both polar parts and nonpolar parts and keep tiny droplets of oil suspended in the vinegar.

Ordinarily, solutions form most readily when the substances involved have *similar* strengths of forces between their molecules (or atoms or ions). An old chemical adage is, "Like dissolves like." Nonpolar solutes dissolve best in nonpolar solvents. For example, oil and gasoline, both nonpolar, mix [Figure 6.9(a)], but oil and vinegar do not [Figure 6.9(b)]. Vinegar is mostly water, and the strong hydrogen bonds between water molecules do not allow nonpolar oil molecules (which have much weaker dispersion forces) to mix freely with them. On the other hand, both ethyl alcohol molecules and water molecules can form hydrogen bonds. Thus, ethyl alcohol readily dissolves in water [Figure 6.9(c)]. In general, a solute dissolves when attractive forces between it and the solvent overcome the attractive forces operating in the pure solute and in the pure solvent.

Why, then, does salt dissolve in water? Ionic solids are held together by strong ionic bonds. We have already seen that high temperatures are required to melt ionic solids and break these bonds. Yet if we simply place sodium chloride in water at room temperature, the salt dissolves. And when such a solid dissolves, its bonds *are* broken. The difference between the two processes is the difference between brute force and persuasion. In the melting process, we simply put in enough energy (as heat) to break the crystal down. In the dissolving process, we offer the ions an attractive alternative to their ionic interactions in the crystal.

When a salt crystal dissolves, water molecules first surround the crystal. The molecules that approach a negative ion align themselves so that the positive ends of their dipoles point toward the ion, as shown in Figure 6.10. The molecules that approach a positive ion align themselves so that the negative ends of their dipoles

▶ **Figure 6.10** An ionic solid (sodium chloride) dissolving in a polar solvent (water). The hydrogen ends of the water molecules surround the negatively charged chloride ions, while the oxygen ends of the water molecules surround the positively charged sodium ions.

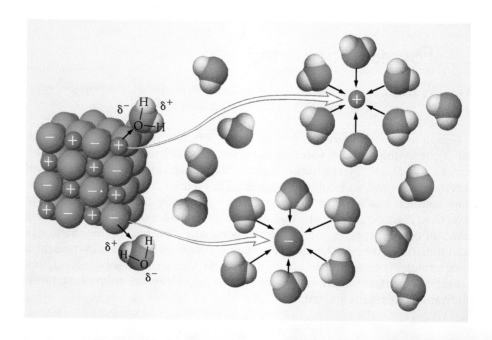

point toward the ion. Although the attraction between a dipole and an ion is not as strong as that between two ions, several water molecules surround each ion, and the many *ion–dipole* interactions overcome the ionic bonds.

In an ionic solid, the positive and negative ions are strongly bonded together in an orderly crystalline arrangement. In solution, cations and anions move about more or less independently, each surrounded by a cage of solvent molecules. Water—including the water in our bodies—is an excellent solvent for many ionic compounds. Water also dissolves many molecules that are polar covalent like itself. These solubility principles explain how nutrients reach the cells of our bodies (dissolved in blood, which is mostly water) and how many kinds of pollutants get into our water supplies.

Self-Assessment Questions

1. A solution is a mixture that is
   a. heterogeneous   b. homogeneous   c. homologous   d. humectic

2. Which of the following pairs of substances is *least likely* to form a solution?
   a. an ionic compound in a nonpolar solvent
   b. an ionic compound in a polar solvent
   c. a nonpolar compound in a nonpolar solvent
   d. a polar compound in a polar solvent

3. A positive test for iodine is the purple color of a solution of I_2 in hexane (C_6H_{14}). What type of solute–solvent interaction is most important in a solution of nonpolar I_2 in nonpolar C_6H_{14}?
   a. dipole–dipole forces
   b. dispersion forces
   c. ion–dipole interactions
   d. hydrogen bonds

4. What type of solute–solvent interaction is most important in a solution of calcium chloride ($CaCl_2$) in water?
   a. dipole–dipole forces
   b. ion–dipole interactions
   c. ion–dispersion forces
   d. ion–hydrogen bonds

5. What type of solute–solvent interaction is most important in a solution of acetic acid (CH_3COOH) in water?
   a. dipole–dipole forces
   b. dipole–hydrogen bonds
   c. hydrogen bonds
   d. ion–hydrogen bonds

6. Which of the following solutes will dissolve in octane (C_8H_{18}), a component of gasoline?
   a. $CH_3(CH_2)_4CH_3$
   b. $CaCl_2$
   c. KCl
   d. MgO

Answers: 1, b; 2, a; 3, b; 4, b; 5, c; 6, a

6.5 Gases: The Kinetic–Molecular Theory

Learning Objective ❯ List the five basic concepts of the kinetic–molecular theory of gases.

At the macroscopic level, gases may seem more difficult to understand than liquids and solids—perhaps because most gases are invisible, while we can see and feel liquids and solids. However, at the microscopic level, gases are more readily treated mathematically. Gas molecules are so far apart that intermolecular forces can be ignored. In liquids and solids, the intermolecular forces are stronger, although they vary depending on the type of molecules and the distance between them. This variation complicates any theoretical treatment.

Experiments with gases were instrumental in developing the concepts of Avogadro's number and of molar ratios in reactions. Let's look at the behavior of gases more closely, using a model known as the **kinetic–molecular theory** (Figure 6.11). There are five basic concepts of this theory.

1. Particles of a gas (usually *molecules*, but *atoms* in the case of noble gases) are in rapid, constant motion and move in straight lines.
2. The particles of a gas are tiny compared with the distances between them.

▲ **Figure 6.11** According to the kinetic–molecular theory, particles (molecules or atoms) of a gas are in constant, random motion. They move in straight lines and undergo collisions with each other and with the walls of the container.

3. Because the particles of a gas are so far apart, there is very little attraction between them.

4. Particles of a gas collide with one another. Energy is *conserved* in these collisions; energy lost by one particle is gained by the other.

5. Temperature is a measure of the average kinetic energy (energy of motion) of the gas particles.

Section 6.3 described how intermolecular forces hold molecules together in solids and liquids. In gases, the particles are separated by relatively great distances and are moving about randomly. Although these particles can collide, they seldom interact.

Self-Assessment Questions

1. Which of the following is *not* a concept of the kinetic–molecular theory of gases?
   a. Particles of a gas are in constant chaotic motion.
   b. The pressure and volume of a gas are inversely related.
   c. Temperature is a measure of the average kinetic energy of the gas particles.
   d. The particles are very small compared to the distances between them.

2. According to the kinetic–molecular theory of gases, a gas particle
   a. will collide with another gas particle with no loss of kinetic energy for either
   b. follows a well-defined pathway
   c. is tiny compared to the volume occupied by the gas
   d. repels another gas particle when the two come close together

3. In collisions between gas particles, the total energy
   a. decreases slightly
   b. decreases considerably
   c. increases slightly
   d. remains the same

Answers: 1, b; 2, c; 3, d

6.6 The Simple Gas Laws

Learning Objectives ❯ State the three simple gas laws, by name and mathematically. ❯ Use any gas law to find the value of one variable if the other values are given.

The behavior of gases can be described by mathematical relationships called *gas laws*. These equations use four variables to specify properties of a sample of gas: its amount in moles (n), its volume (V), its temperature (T), and its pressure (P). These variables are related through simple laws that show how one of the variables (for example, V) changes as a second variable (for example, P) changes and the other two (for example, n and T) remain constant.

Boyle's Law: Pressure and Volume

The first gas law was discovered by Robert Boyle in 1662. It describes the relationship between the pressure and the volume of a gas. **Boyle's law** states that *for a given amount of gas at a constant temperature, the volume of the gas varies inversely with its pressure.* That is, when the pressure in a closed container of gas increases, the volume decreases; when the pressure decreases, the volume increases.

A bicycle pump illustrates Boyle's law. When you push down on the plunger, you decrease the volume of the air in the pump. The pressure of the air increases, and the higher-pressure air flows into the bicycle tire.

Think of gases as pictured by the kinetic–molecular theory. A gas exerts a particular pressure because its molecules bounce against the container walls with a certain frequency and speed. If the volume of the container is increased while the amount of gas remains fixed, the number of molecules per unit volume decreases (Figure 6.12). The frequency with which molecules strike a unit area of the container

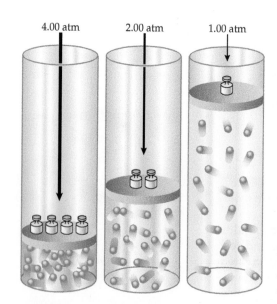

4.00 atm   2.00 atm   1.00 atm

▲ **Figure 6.12** The kinetic–molecular theory and Boyle's law. As the pressure is reduced from 4.00 atm to 2.00 atm and then to 1.00 atm, the volume of the gas doubles and then doubles again.

Q: *What would happen to the volume of the gas if the pressure were changed to 0.500 atm?*

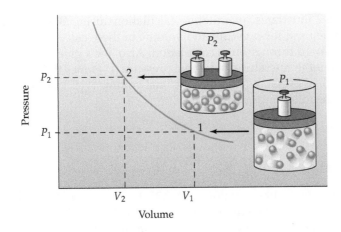

◀ **Figure 6.13** A graphic representation of Boyle's law. As the pressure is increased, the volume of a gas decreases. When the pressure is doubled ($P_2 = 2 \times P_1$), the volume of the gas decreases to one-half of its original value ($V_2 = \frac{1}{2} \times V_1$). The pressure–volume product is a constant ($PV = a$).

Q: *What would happen to the volume of the gas if the pressure were quadrupled?*

walls decreases, and the gas pressure decreases. Thus, as the volume of a gas is increased, its pressure decreases.

Mathematically, for a given amount of gas at a constant temperature, Boyle's law is written

$$V \propto \frac{1}{P}$$

where the symbol $\propto$ means "is proportional to." This relationship can be changed to an equation by inserting a proportionality constant, a.

$$V = \frac{a}{P}$$

Multiplying both sides of the equation by P, we get

$$PV = a \quad \text{(at constant temperature and amount of gas)}$$

Another way to state Boyle's law, then, is that for a given amount of gas at a constant temperature, the product of the pressure and the volume is a constant. This is an elegant and precise way of summarizing a lot of experimental data. If the product $P \times V$ is constant, then, when V increases, P must decrease, and vice versa. This relationship is illustrated in Figure 6.13 by a pressure–volume graph.

Boyle's law has a number of practical applications, which are perhaps best introduced through some examples. In Example 6.1, we see how to estimate an answer. Sometimes an estimate is all we need. Even when we need a quantitative answer, however, an estimate helps us determine whether or not the answer we get is reasonable.

Example 6.1 Boyle's Law: Pressure–Volume Relationships

A gas is enclosed in a cylinder fitted with a piston. The volume of the gas is 2.00 L at 0.524 atm. The piston is moved to increase the pressure to 5.15 atm. Which of the following is a reasonable value for the volume of the gas at the greater pressure?

    0.20 L   0.40 L   1.00 L   16.0 L

Solution
The pressure increase from 0.524 atm to 5.15 atm is almost tenfold. The volume should drop to about one-tenth of the initial value. Thus, we estimate a volume of 0.20 L. (The calculated value is 0.203 L.)

■ EXERCISE 6.1
Argon gas is enclosed in a 10.2-L tank at 1208 mmHg (*mmHg* is a pressure unit: 760 mmHg = 1 atm). Which of the following is a reasonable value for the pressure when the argon is transferred to a 30.0-L tank?

    300 mmHg   400 mmHg   3600 mmHg   12,000 mmHg

Example 6.2 illustrates quantitative calculations using Boyle's law. Note that any units can be used for pressure and volume in these calculations as long as the same units are used throughout a calculation. Also, for a given confined sample of a gas at a constant temperature, the initial pressure (P_1) times the initial volume (V_1) is equal to the final pressure (P_2) times the final volume (V_2). That is, Boyle's law can be written as the following equation.

$$P_1V_1 = a = P_2V_2$$

Example 6.2 Boyle's Law: Pressure–Volume Relationships

A cylinder of oxygen has a volume of 2.25 L. The pressure in the cylinder is 1470 pounds per square inch (psi) at 20 °C. What volume will the oxygen occupy at standard atmospheric pressure (14.7 psi), assuming no temperature change?

Solution

We find it helpful to first separate the initial and final conditions.

Initial	Final	Change
P_1 = 1470 psi	P_2 = 14.7 psi	↓ The pressure goes down; therefore,
V_1 = 2.25 L	V_2 = ?	↑ the volume goes up.

Next, we solve the equation $P_1V_1 = P_2V_2$ for the desired volume or pressure. In this case, we solve for V_2. Finally, we substitute the given values for P_1, V_1, and P_2.

$$V_2 = \frac{P_1V_1}{P_2}$$

$$V_2 = \frac{1470 \text{ psi} \times 2.25 \text{ L}}{14.7 \text{ psi}} = 225 \text{ L}$$

Because the final pressure (14.7 psi) is *less than* the initial pressure (1470 psi), we expect the final volume (225 L) to be *larger than* the original volume (2.25 L), and we see that it is.

■ **EXERCISE 6.2A**

A sample of air occupies 73.3 mL at 98.7 atm and 0 °C. What volume will the air occupy at 4.02 atm and 0 °C?

■ **EXERCISE 6.2B**

A sample of helium occupies 535 mL at 988 mmHg and 25 °C. If the sample is transferred to a 1.05-L flask at 25 °C, what will the gas pressure in the flask be?

Charles's Law: Temperature and Volume

In 1787, the French physicist Jacques Charles (1746–1823), a pioneer hot-air balloonist, studied the relationship between volume and temperature of gases. He found that when a fixed mass of gas is cooled at constant pressure, its volume decreases. When the gas is heated, its volume increases. Temperature and volume vary directly; that is, they rise or fall together. But this relationship is a bit more complex. If a quantity of gas that occupies 1.00 L is heated from 100 °C to 200 °C at constant pressure, the volume does not double but increases only to about 1.27 L. The relationship between temperature and volume is not as simple as it may seem at first.

For most measurements and quantities, "zero" means "none." A measured pressure of 0 atm means no measureable pressure, and it is not possible to have a lower pressure than 0 atm. On the other hand, zero degrees Celsius (0 °C) merely signifies the freezing point of water. Temperatures below 0 °C are often encountered. Decreasing the temperature of 1 L of a gas from 20 °C to 0 °C does not cause the volume to decrease to zero. Instead, the volume decreases only to about 0.92 L.

5. How cold can it possibly get, and how hot can it possibly get? At 0 K (absolute zero, −273.15 °C), molecular motion would stop. Because molecules cannot move any slower than "standing still," no lower temperature is possible. Theoretically, atoms can move almost as fast as the speed of light, so there is also an upper temperature limit; that limit is so high, however, that temperature ceases to have meaning.

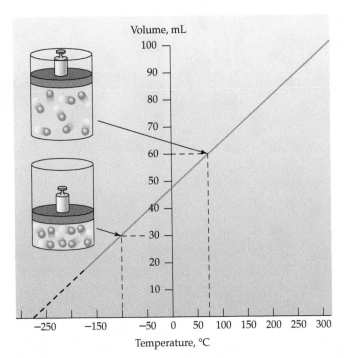

▲ **Figure 6.14** Charles's law relates gas volume to temperature at constant pressure. In the case shown, when the gas is at about 70 °C, its volume is 60 mL. As the temperature is lowered from about 70 °C to −100 °C, the volume drops to 30.0 mL. The volume continues to fall as the temperature is lowered. The extrapolated (dashed) line intersects the temperature axis (corresponding to a volume of zero) at about −273 °C.

Q: *What would be the approximate volume of the gas at a temperature of 150 °C?*

Charles noted that for each degree Celsius that the temperature rises, the volume of a gas increases by $\frac{1}{273}$ of its volume at 0 °C. A plot of volume against temperature is a straight line (Figure 6.14). We can extrapolate (extend) the line to the temperature at which the volume of the gas should become zero. This temperature is −273.15 °C. In 1848, William Thomson (Lord Kelvin) made this temperature the zero point on an absolute temperature scale now called the Kelvin scale. As noted in Chapter 1, the unit on this temperature scale is the kelvin (K).

A modern statement of **Charles's law** is that *the volume of a fixed amount of a gas at a constant pressure is directly proportional to its absolute temperature.* Mathematically, this relationship is expressed as

$$V = bT \quad \text{or} \quad \frac{V}{T} = b$$

where b is a proportionality constant. To keep V/T at a constant value, when the temperature increases, the volume must also increase. When the temperature decreases, the volume must decrease accordingly (Figure 6.15).

With a given sample of trapped gas at a constant pressure, the initial volume (V_1) divided by the initial absolute temperature (T_1) is equal to the final volume (V_2) divided by the final absolute temperature (T_2). We can therefore use the following equation to solve problems involving Charles's law.

$$\frac{V_1}{T_1} = \frac{V_2}{T_2}$$

The kinetic–molecular model readily explains the relationship between gas volume and temperature. When we heat a gas, the gas molecules absorb energy and move faster. These speedier molecules strike the walls of the container harder and more often. For the pressure to stay the same, the volume of the container must increase so that the increased molecular motion will be distributed over a greater space.

▶ **Figure 6.15** A dramatic illustration of Charles's law. (a) Liquid nitrogen (boiling point, −196 °C) cools the balloon and its contents to a temperature far below room temperature. (b) As the balloon warms back to room temperature, the volume of air increases proportionately (about fourfold).

(a)   (b)

Example 6.3 Charles's Law: Temperature–Volume Relationship

In a room at 27 °C, a balloon has a volume of 2.00 L. What would its volume be **(a)** in a sauna, where the temperature is 47 °C, and **(b)** outdoors, where the temperature is −23 °C? Assume that there is no change in pressure in either case.

Solution

First, and most important, we convert all temperatures to the Kelvin scale:

$$T(K) = t\,(°C) + 273$$

The initial temperature (T_1) in each case is $27 + 273 = 300$ K, and the final temperatures are **(a)** $47 + 273 = 320$ K and **(b)** $-23 + 273 = 250$ K.

a. We start by separating the initial from the final condition.

Initial	Final	Change
$T_1 = 300$ K	$T_2 = 320$ K	⇑
$V_1 = 2.00$ L	$V_2 = ?$	⇑

Solving the equation

$$\frac{V_1}{T_1} = \frac{V_2}{T_2}$$

for V_2, we have

$$V_2 = \frac{V_1 T_2}{T_1}$$

Substituting the known values gives

$$V_2 = \frac{2.00 \text{ L} \times 320 \text{ K}}{300 \text{ K}} = 2.13 \text{ L}$$

As expected, because the temperature increases, the volume must also increase.

b. We have the same initial conditions as in **(a)** but different final conditions.

Initial	Final	Change
$T_1 = 300$ K	$T_2 = 250$ K	⇓
$V_1 = 2.00$ L	$V_2 = ?$	⇓

Again, using Charles's law, we solve the equation for V_2 and substitute the known quantities.

$$V_2 = \frac{V_1 T_2}{T_1}$$

$$V_2 = \frac{2.00 \text{ L} \times 250 \text{ K}}{300 \text{ K}} = 1.67 \text{ L}$$

As expected, the volume decreases because the temperature decreases.

■ EXERCISE 6.3A
A sample of ethane gas occupies a volume of 16.8 L at 25 °C. What volume will this sample occupy at 109 °C? (Assume no change in pressure.)

■ EXERCISE 6.3B
At what Celsius temperature will the initial volume of ethane in Exercise 6.3A occupy 0.750 L? (Assume no change in pressure.)

Molar Volume

As Section 5.2 described, Amedeo Avogadro proposed a hypothesis to explain the volume ratios in which gases combine during chemical reactions. His hypothesis states that equal numbers of molecules of different gases at the same temperature and pressure occupy equal volumes. Thus, Avogadro's hypothesis relates an amount of gas (numbers of molecules, or moles) to the gas volume when temperature and pressure remain constant. We call the simple gas law implied by this relationship **Avogadro's law**: *At a fixed temperature and pressure, the volume of a gas is directly proportional to the amount of gas (that is, to the number of moles of gas, n, or to the number of molecules of gas).* If we double the number of moles of gas at a fixed temperature and pressure, the volume of the gas doubles. Mathematically, we can state Avogadro's law as

$$V \propto n \quad \text{or} \quad V = cn \quad \text{(where } c \text{ is a constant)}$$

A mole of gas contains Avogadro's number of molecules (or atoms if it is a noble gas). Furthermore, a gas sample consisting of Avogadro's number of molecules occupies the same volume (at a given temperature and pressure) regardless of the size or mass of the individual molecules. The volume occupied by 1 mole of gas is the **molar volume** of a gas.

Because the volume of a gas is altered by changes in temperature or pressure, a particular set of conditions has been chosen as the standard set for reference purposes. Standard pressure is 1 atmosphere (atm), which is the normal pressure of the air at sea level. Standard temperature is 0 °C, which is the freezing point of water. A mole of any gas at **standard temperature and pressure (STP)** occupies a volume of about 22.4 L, slightly more than a five-gallon water bottle (Figure 6.16). This is known as the *standard molar volume* of a gas. At a temperature of 0 °C and 1 atm pressure, a 22.4-L container holds one mole (28.0 g) of N_2, one mole (32.0 g) of O_2, one mole (44.0 g) of CO_2, and so on.

We can readily calculate the density (g/L) of a gas at STP. We begin with the molar mass of the gas (g/mol) and use the conversion factor 1 mol gas = 22.4 L. Because the conversion factor can be inverted, we can also use it to calculate molar mass from density.

▲ **Figure 6.16** An "empty" bottle from an office water cooler is not really empty. It holds five gallons of air, slightly less than 22.4 L— the volume of one mole of a gas at STP.

Q: *About how many C_2H_6 molecules would the bottle hold at STP?*

Example 6.4 Density of a Gas at STP

Calculate the density of **(a)** nitrogen gas and **(b)** methane (CH_4) gas, both at STP.

Solution

a. The molar mass of N_2 gas is 28.0 g/mol. We multiply by the conversion factor 1 mol N_2 = 22.4 L, arranged to cancel units of *moles*.

$$\frac{28.0 \text{ g } N_2}{1 \text{ mol } N_2} \times \frac{1 \text{ mol } N_2}{22.4 \text{ L } N_2} = 1.25 \text{ g/L}$$

b. The molar mass of CH_4 gas is (1×12.0) g/mol + (4×1.01) g/mol = 16.0 g/mol. Again, we use the conversion factor 1 mol CH_4 = 22.4 L.

$$\frac{16.0 \text{ g } CH_4}{1 \text{ mol } CH_4} \times \frac{1 \text{ mol } CH_4}{22.4 \text{ L } CH_4} = 0.714 \text{ g/L}$$

■ EXERCISE 6.4A

Calculate the density of xenon gas at STP.

■ EXERCISE 6.4B

Estimate the density of air at STP (assume that air is 78% N_2 and 22% O_2), and compare this value to the value you calculated for xenon in Exercise 6.4A.

Self-Assessment Questions

1. Gas pressure is caused by
   a. gas molecules colliding with each other
   b. gas molecules colliding with vessel walls
   c. gas molecules condensing to form a liquid
   d. measurement with a barometer

2. Boyle's law states that the pressure of a gas is inversely proportional to its
   a. amount
   b. mass
   c. temperature
   d. volume

3. A gas occupies 6.00 L at 2.00 atm pressure. At what pressure would the volume be 1.50 L if the temperature remains constant?
   a. 0.500 atm
   b. 8.00 atm
   c. 9.00 atm
   d. 12.00 atm

4. When the temperature is changed at constant pressure, the volume of a gas is halved. How is the final temperature related to the initial temperature?
   a. The Celsius temperature is doubled.
   b. The Celsius temperature is halved.
   c. The Kelvin temperature is doubled.
   d. The Kelvin temperature is halved.

5. One 1.00-L flask (Flask A) contains NO gas, and another 1.00-L flask (Flask B) contains NO_2 gas, both at STP. Flask A contains
   a. less mass and fewer particles than Flask B
   b. less mass but the same number of particles as Flask B
   c. less mass but more particles than Flask B
   d. more mass and more particles than Flask B

6. How many moles are there in 5.60 L of a gas at STP?
   a. 0.250 mol   b. 0.500 mol   c. 4.00 mol   d. 125 mol

6.7 The Ideal Gas Law

Learning Objective ❯ State the ideal gas law, and use it to calculate one of the quantities if the others are given.

Boyle's law, Charles's law, and Avogadro's law are useful when two variables of four (P, V, n, and T) can be held constant. Often, however, both the temperature and the pressure change at the same time. In such cases, the simple gas laws can be incorporated into a single relationship called the **combined gas law**. Mathematically, this law is written as

$$\frac{PV}{T} = k \quad \text{or} \quad PV = kT$$

where k is a constant. For comparing the same sample of gas under two different sets of conditions, the combined gas law can be written as

$$\frac{P_1 V_1}{T_1} = \frac{P_2 V_2}{T_2}$$

Because the amount of gas, n, may change as well, incorporating this variable gives an expression called the **ideal gas law**, which involves all four variables.

$$\frac{PV}{nT} = R \quad \text{or} \quad PV = nRT$$

In this equation, R is a constant (called the *gas constant*), which can be calculated from the fact that 1 mole of gas occupies 22.4 L at 273 K (0 °C) and 1 atm (Section 6.6). If P is in atmospheres, V in liters, and T in kelvins, then R has a value of

$$0.0821 \frac{\text{L} \cdot \text{atm}}{\text{mol} \cdot \text{K}}$$

The ideal gas equation can be used to calculate the value of any of the four variables—P, V, n, or T—if the other three values are known.

Example 6.5 Combined Gas Law

A balloon used for underwater salvage is inflated to 50.0 L at a depth of 200 ft, where the pressure is 6.89 atm and the temperature is 3 °C. The balloon rises to the surface (22 °C and 0.988 atm). What is the new volume of the balloon?

Solution
We start by solving the combined gas law equation for V_2.

$$\frac{P_1 V_1}{T_1} = \frac{P_2 V_2}{T_2}$$

$$V_2 = \frac{P_1 V_1 T_2}{T_1 P_2}$$

We have $T_1 = 3 + 273 = 276$ K, and $T_2 = 22.0 + 273 = 295$ K.

$$V_2 = \frac{6.89 \text{ atm} \times 50.0 \text{ L} \times 295 \text{ K}}{276 \text{ K} \times 0.988 \text{ atm}} = 373 \text{ L}$$

■ EXERCISE 6.5
What will be the final volume of a 425-mL sample of a gas initially at 22.0 °C and 760 mmHg pressure when the temperature is changed to 30.0 °C and the pressure to 360 mmHg?

6. Why is it recommended that bicycle tire pressure be measured when tires are cold? Tire pressure is measured when the tires are cold because a tire has nearly constant volume. According to the combined gas law, if the temperature increases (by friction from the road), the pressure increases, too. If the tire pressure were adjusted right after a long, hard bike ride, the tires might be soft and underpressurized the next morning.

Example 6.6 Ideal Gas Law

Use the ideal gas law to calculate (**a**) the volume occupied by 1.00 mol N_2 gas at 244 K and 1.00 atm pressure and (**b**) the pressure exerted by 0.500 mol O_2 gas in a 15.0-L container at 303 K.

Solution

a. We solve the ideal gas equation for V and substitute the known quantities.

$$V = \frac{nRT}{P}$$

$$V = \frac{1.00 \text{ mol}}{1.00 \text{ atm}} \times \frac{0.0821 \text{ L} \cdot \text{atm}}{\text{mol} \cdot \text{K}} \times 244 \text{ K} = 20.0 \text{ L}$$

b. Here we solve the ideal gas equation for P and substitute the known quantities.

$$P = \frac{nRT}{V}$$

$$P = \frac{0.500 \text{ mol}}{15.0 \text{ L}} \times \frac{0.0821 \text{ L} \cdot \text{atm}}{\text{mol} \cdot \text{K}} \times 303 \text{ K} = 0.829 \text{ atm}$$

■ **EXERCISE 6.6A**

Determine (**a**) the pressure exerted by 0.0450 mol O_2 gas in a 22.0-L container at 313 K and (**b**) the volume occupied by 0.400 mol N_2 gas at 298 K and 0.980 atm.

■ **EXERCISE 6.6B**

Determine the volume occupied by 132 g N_2 gas at 25 °C and 1.03 atm.

Self-Assessment Questions

1. In the ideal gas equation, $PV = nRT$, the variable n stands for
   a. a constant
   b. the number of atoms
   c. the number of moles
   d. the principal quantum number

2. At STP, 1.00 mole of an ideal gas occupies 22.4 L. What volume does 1.00 mole of an ideal gas occupy at 20 °C and 1.00 atm?
   a. 20.9 L   **b.** 22.4 L   **c.** 24.0 L   **d.** 448 L

3. The molar volume of an ideal gas at 2.00 atm and 546 K is
   a. 5.60 L   **b.** 22.4 L   **c.** 44.8 L   **d.** 89.6 L

Answers: 1, c; 2, c; 3, b

CRITICAL THINKING EXERCISES

Apply knowledge that you have gained in this chapter and one or more of the FLaReS principles (Chapter 1) to evaluate the following statements or claims.

6.1 Some tire stores claim that filling your car tires with pure, dry nitrogen is much better than using plain air. They make the following claims: (1) The pressure inside N_2-filled tires does not rise or fall with temperature changes. (2) Nitrogen leaks out of tires much more slowly than air because the N_2 molecules are bigger. (3) Nitrogen is not very reactive, and moisture and O_2 in air cause corrosion that shortens tire life by 25–30%.

6.2 A researcher claims to have discovered why the gecko can walk on walls and ceilings. His claim is

that the lizard's feet have many microscopic hair-like protrusions that get close enough to the wall or ceiling surface to allow intermolecular forces to "take over" and hold the gecko to the surface.

6.3 A microbrewery claims to have prepared "hydrogen beer." This beer is reportedly "carbonated" with H_2 gas instead of CO_2 gas. A chemist at the brewery claims that the H_2 gas molecules engage in hydrogen bonding with the water molecules in the beer, so that more gas can dissolve in the beer.

6.4 A student in an advanced chemistry course has been assigned to determine the density of the vapor from an unknown liquid. She claims that the density is 0.053 g/L.

SUMMARY

Section 6.1—When a substance is melted or vaporized, the forces that hold its particles (molecules, atoms, or ions) close to one another are overcome. Several properties are related to the strengths of those forces. The melting point of a solid is the temperature at which the forces holding the particles together in a regular arrangement are overcome. The reverse of the melting process, a liquid changing to a solid, is called *freezing*. Vaporization is the conversion of a liquid to a gas; the reverse process is called condensation. The temperature at which a substance vaporizes is called its boiling point. Some substances undergo sublimation, a conversion directly from the solid to the gaseous state.

Section 6.2—Ionic solids have very strong forces holding the ions to one another, so most ionic compounds have higher melting points and higher boiling points than molecular compounds.

Section 6.3—Dipole–dipole forces are due to the attraction of the positive end of one dipole for the negative end of another dipole. Nonpolar molecules also have forces between them. These dispersion forces result from electron motions within molecules, which cause tiny, short-lived dipoles. Dispersion forces are generally weak. An especially strong type of dipolar force occurs when the positive end of a dipole is a hydrogen atom attached to F, O, or N and the negative end is the F, O, or N atom. Such a force is called a hydrogen bond.

Section 6.4—A solution is a homogeneous mixture of two (or more) substances. The substance that is dissolved is called the solute, and the dissolving substance is called the solvent. Nonpolar solutes dissolve in nonpolar solvents. Polar and ionic solutes dissolve in polar solvents.

Section 6.5—The behavior of gases is explained using kinetic–molecular theory, which describes gas particles: (1) They move rapidly and constantly and in straight lines; (2) they are far apart; (3) there is little attraction between them; (4) when they collide, energy is conserved; (5) temperature is a measure of their average kinetic energy.

Section 6.6—Boyle's law says that the volume of a fixed amount of a gas varies inversely with pressure at constant temperature, or $P_1V_1 = P_2V_2$. Charles's law says that the volume of a fixed amount of a gas varies directly with absolute (Kelvin) temperature, or $V_1/T_1 = V_2/T_2$. Avogadro's law states that at constant temperature and pressure the volume of a gas is directly proportional to the number of moles of gas, $V = cn$. The molar volume of any gas is the volume occupied by 1 mole of the gas. At 0 °C and 1 atm, known as standard temperature and pressure (STP), the molar volume is 22.4 L for any gas. We can use that molar volume to convert from moles of gas to volume, and vice versa.

Section 6.7—The simple gas laws can be incorporated into a single relationship called the combined gas law. The ideal gas law shows the relationship among pressure (P), volume (V), number of moles (n), and absolute temperature (T): $PV = nRT$. When P is in atmospheres, V is in liters, n is moles of gas, and T is in kelvins, the value of the constant R is 0.0821 liter · atm/(mole · K).

Green chemistry While we are familiar with gases, liquids, and solids, a fourth phase of matter, supercritical fluid, exists at higher temperatures and pressures. Supercritical fluids have solubility properties similar to liquids, yet they flow like gases. The most common of these, $scCO_2$, is considered an environmentally friendly solvent and is replacing more toxic solvents in laboratories and industrial processes.

Learning Objectives

❭ Explain how the different properties of solids, liquids, and gases are related to the motion and spacing of atoms, molecules, or ions. (6.1)	Problems 1, 2, 4, 6
❭ Identify some differences between ionic and molecular substances, and explain why these differences exist. (6.2)	Problems 10–12
❭ Classify forces between molecules as dipole–dipole forces, dispersion forces, or hydrogen bonds. (6.3)	Problems 3, 7–10
❭ Explain why nonpolar solutes tend to dissolve in nonpolar solvents and polar and ionic solutes tend to dissolve in polar solvents. (6.4)	Problems 11, 12
❭ List the five basic concepts of the kinetic–molecular theory of gases. (6.5)	Problem 38
❭ State the three simple gas laws, by name and mathematically. (6.6)	Problem 38
❭ Use any gas law to find the value of one variable if the other values are given. (6.6)	Problems 5, 13–26
❭ State the ideal gas law, and use it to calculate one of the quantities if the others are given. (6.7)	Problems 27–34
❭ Describe how Green Chemistry Principle 3 must be considered in designing chemical reactions and processes.	Problems 49–51
❭ Identify the properties that make supercritical fluids applicable in greener chemical processes.	Problems 49, 50

REVIEW QUESTIONS

1. In what ways are liquids and solids similar? In what ways are they different?
2. Define each of the following terms.
   a. melting   **b.** vaporization
   c. condensation   **d.** freezing
3. List four types of interactions between the particles of a substance in the liquid and solid states. Give an example of each type.
4. In which process is energy absorbed by the substance undergoing the change of state?
   a. melting or freezing
   b. condensation or vaporization

5. In the combined gas law, is the volume of a gas directly proportional or inversely proportional to the pressure? Is the volume directly or inversely proportional to the absolute temperature?
6. Label each arrow with the correct term from Question 2 that identifies the process.

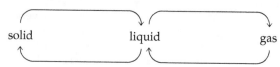

 PROBLEMS

Intermolecular Forces

7. For which of the following would hydrogen bonding be an important intermolecular force?

   a. H—S—H

   b. H—C—N—H (with H's on C and N)

   c. H—C—F (with H's on C)

   d. H—C—O—H

   e. H—C—C—H (ethane structure)

8. In which of the following are dispersion forces the only type of intermolecular force: N_2, NH_3, NCl_3?
9. In which of the following substances are dipole–dipole forces an important intermolecular force: Br_2, HBr, $NaBr$?
10. Which of the following have ionic bonds: N_2, NBr_3, $NaBr$?
11. Hexane (C_6H_{14}) is a nonpolar solvent. Would you expect KNO_3 to dissolve in hexane? Explain.
12. Which of the following would you expect to dissolve in water and which in carbon tetrachloride (CCl_4)?
    a. NaCl   **b.** C_5H_{12}
    c. C_8H_{18} **d.** Li_2CO_3

Boyle's Law

13. A sample of helium occupies 1820 mL at 719 mmHg. Assume that the temperature is held constant and determine **(a)** the volume of the helium at 752 mmHg and

(b) the pressure, in mmHg, if the volume is changed to 345 mL.

14. A decompression chamber used by deep-sea divers has a volume of 10.1 m³ and operates at an internal pressure of 4.25 atm. What volume, in cubic meters, would the air in the chamber occupy if it were at 1.00 atm pressure, assuming no temperature change?

15. Oxygen used in respiratory therapy is stored at room temperature under a pressure of 150 atm in a gas cylinder with a volume of 60.0 L.
    a. What volume would the oxygen occupy at 0.925 atm? Assume no temperature change.
    b. If the oxygen flow to the patient is adjusted to 6.00 L/min at room temperature and 0.925 atm, how long will the tank of gas last?

16. The pressure within a 4.50-L balloon is 1.10 atm. If the volume of the balloon increases to 9.95 L, what will the final pressure within the balloon be if the temperature does not change?

Charles's Law

17. A balloon is filled with helium. Its volume is 5.90 L at 26 °C. What will its volume be at 78 °C, assuming no pressure change?

18. A gas at a temperature of 100 °C occupies a volume of 154 mL. What will the volume be at 10 °C, assuming no change in pressure?

19. A sample of gas at STP is to be heated at constant pressure until its volume triples. What will the final gas temperature be?

20. A 567-mL sample of a gas at 305 °C and 1.20 atm is cooled at constant pressure until its volume becomes 425 mL. What is the final gas temperature?

Molar Volume and Gas Densities

21. What is the volume of each of the following samples of gas at STP?
    a. 1.00 mol Kr   **b.** 1.75 mol H_2
    c. 0.225 mol C_2H_4

22. What is the mass in grams of one molar volume of each of the gases in Problem 21?

23. Calculate the density, in grams per liter, of radon (Rn) gas at STP.

24. Calculate the density, in grams per liter, of carbon dioxide (CO_2) gas at STP.

25. Calculate the molar mass of **(a)** a gas that has a density of 2.12 g/L at STP and **(b)** an unknown liquid, whose vapor has a density of 2.97 g/L at STP.

26. Calculate the molar mass of **(a)** a gas that has a density of 1.98 g/L at STP and **(b)** an unknown liquid for which 3.33 L of its vapor at STP weighs 10.88 g.

The Ideal Gas Law

27. Will the volume of a fixed amount of a gas increase, decrease, or remain unchanged with
    a. an increase in pressure at constant temperature?
    b. a decrease in temperature at constant pressure?
    c. a decrease in pressure coupled with an increase in temperature?

28. Will the pressure of a fixed amount of a gas increase, decrease, or remain unchanged with
    a. an increase in temperature at constant volume?
    b. a decrease in volume at constant temperature?
    c. an increase in temperature coupled with a decrease in volume?

29. According to the kinetic–molecular theory, **(a)** what change in temperature occurs if the particles of a gas begin to move more slowly, on average, and **(b)** what change in pressure occurs when the particles of a gas strike the walls of the container less often?

30. For each of the following, indicate whether a given gas will have the same or different densities in the two containers. If the densities are different, in which container is the density greater?
    a. Containers A and B have the same volume and are at the same temperature, but the gas in A is at a higher pressure.
    b. Containers A and B are at the same pressure and temperature, but the volume of A is greater than that of B.
    c. Containers A and B are at the same pressure and volume, but the gas in A is at a higher temperature.

31. Calculate **(a)** the volume, in liters, of 0.00600 mol of a gas at 31 °C and 0.870 atm and **(b)** the pressure, in atmospheres, of 0.0108 mol $CH_4(g)$ in a 0.265-L flask at 37 °C.

32. Calculate **(a)** the volume, in liters, of 1.12 mol $H_2S(g)$ at 62 °C and 1.38 atm and **(b)** the pressure, in atmospheres, of 4.64 mol $CO(g)$ in a 3.96-L tank at 29 °C.

33. How many moles of $Kr(g)$ are there in 0.555 L of the gas at 0.918 atm and 25 °C?

34. How many grams of $CO(g)$ are there in 74.5 mL of the gas at 0.933 atm and 30 °C?

ADDITIONAL PROBLEMS

35. What mass of $He(g)$ will occupy the same volume at STP as 0.75 mol H_2 at STP? (Hint: It is not necessary to find the volume of the H_2 at STP.)

36. How many liters of hydrogen gas (at STP) are produced from the electrolysis of 1.00 L $H_2O(l)$? (Hint: 1.00 L H_2O weighs 1.00 kg.)

37. Which of the following will *not* result in an increase in the volume of a gas?
    a. an increase in temperature
    b. an increase in pressure
    c. a decrease in temperature
    d. a threefold increase in pressure together with a twofold reduction in Kelvin temperature

38. What are the five basic postulates of kinetic-molecular theory? Which postulate best explains why a gas can be compressed?

39. Which of the following gases has the greatest density at STP? Explain how this question may be answered *without* calculating the densities.
    a. BF_3 b. SO_3
    c. OF_2 d. PF_3

40. Choose the answer that correctly completes the statement: At 0 °C and 0.500 atm, 4.48 L $NH_3(g)$ **(a)** contains 0.20 mol NH_3; **(b)** has a mass of 3.40 g; **(c)** contains 6.02×10^{22} molecules; **(d)** contains 0.40 mol NH_3

41. Look again at Figure 6.15. If the balloon has a volume of a 1.50 L at 20 °C, what will its final volume be in part (a), assuming that the air in the balloon reaches the temperature of the liquid nitrogen? You may ignore the stretching forces in the rubber.

42. Butane (C_4H_{10}), a gas at room temperature, is compressed to a liquid and used as a fuel in cigarette lighters and camping stoves. If the 5.00 mL of liquid butane ($d = 0.601$ g/mL at 20 °C) in a lighter vaporizes, about what volume will the gas occupy at STP?

43. Three 2.00-L flasks, labeled X, Y, and Z, each at 758 mmHg and 21 °C, contain neon (Flask X), argon (Flask Y), and krypton (Flask Z). **(a)** Which flask holds the most atoms of gas? **(b)** In which flask does the gas have the greatest density? **(c)** If Flask X is heated and Flask Y is cooled, which of the flasks will have the highest pressure? **(d)** If the temperature of Flask X is lowered and that of Flask Z is raised, which of the three flasks will contain the largest number of moles of gas?

44. A 14.4-g sample of an unknown gas has a volume of 8.00 L at 760 mmHg and 25 °C. What is the molar mass of the gas?

45. Another simple gas law, sometimes called *Amontons's law*, states that pressure of a fixed amount of gas in a constant volume is proportional to its Kelvin temperature. Use this relationship to answer the following question. If a

basketball is inflated to an internal pressure of 1.32 atm at 25 °C and then taken outside, where the temperature is 10 °C, what will be the final pressure in the ball?

46. What is the volume **(a)** in cubic meters and **(b)** in liters of a room that is 4.6 m × 4.9 m × 3 m? **(c)** What mass in kg of $CO_2(g)$ at STP will the room hold?

47. A gas at 750 mmHg and 27 °C has a density of 2.32 g/L. Which of the following could it be: CO_2, Kr, H_2S, or C_4H_{10}?

48. The density (mass per unit volume) of air in the atmosphere is proportional to the atmospheric pressure. At sea level, mean atmospheric pressure is 760 mmHg. Boyle's law, which relates the pressure of a given amount of gas to its volume, indicates that density decreases with altitude in the atmosphere. As altitude increases, there is less mass of air above a given point; thus, less pressure is exerted. About half the mass of the atmosphere lies below an altitude of about 5.5 km, about 95% of the mass lies below 25 km, and 99% below 30 km. What is the approximate pressure at an altitude of **(a)** 5.5 km, **(b)** 25 km, and **(c)** 30 km?

49. Which of the following properties must be considered when selecting a solvent for a chemical process?
 a. Solute and solvent polarity
 b. Ease of isolation of solute
 c. Flammability
 d. Toxicity
 e. All of the above

50. Many of the Presidential Green Chemistry Challenge Awards have involved the use of liquid or supercritical carbon dioxide. What properties of $scCO_2$ support its use in greener chemical processing?

51. Give two examples of solvents previously used in industrial processes that have been replaced by $scCO_2$.

52. In addition to Green Chemistry Principles 3 and 5, how else might the use of an environmentally friendly solvent like $scCO_2$ impact green chemistry?

 COLLABORATIVE GROUP PROJECTS

Prepare a PowerPoint, poster, or other presentation (as directed by your instructor) to share with the class.

1. Look ahead to Table 9.3 (page 234) and consider this series of compounds: methane (CH_4), ethane (CH_3CH_3), propane ($CH_3CH_2CH_3$), butane ($CH_3CH_2CH_2CH_3$), and pentane ($CH_3CH_2CH_2CH_2CH_3$). For each compound: **(a)** Indicate whether its molecules are polar or nonpolar. **(b)** Indicate the predominant type of intermolecular forces in the liquid state. **(c)** Calculate the molar mass. **(d)** Convert each boiling point from Celsius degrees to kelvins. **(e)** Plot a graph of boiling point (in K) versus molar mass. **(f)** Is there any discernable relationship between molar mass and boiling point?

2. Consider this series of compounds: methane (CH_4), fluoromethane (CH_3F), chloromethane (CH_3Cl), bromomethane

(CH_3Br), and iodomethane (CH_3I). Repeat parts **(a)** through **(e)** of Project 1 for these compounds. Boiling points may be found in a printed reference work, such as the *CRC Handbook* or *Merck Index*, or on a Web site such as that of the National Institute for Standards and Technology (NIST). Is there any discernable relationship between molar mass and boiling point? How does the graph for these compounds differ from that in Project 1? Suggest a reason for the difference.

3. Most ionic compounds are solids, but *ionic liquids* have recently been made and have found many uses. Search the Web for information on ionic liquids. In particular, find out why they are liquids rather than solids, and report on some of their current and potential applications.

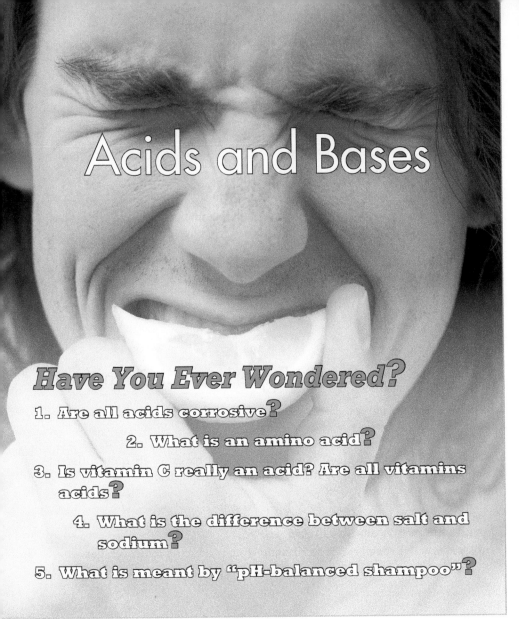

Acids and Bases

Have You Ever Wondered?

1. **Are all acids corrosive?**

2. **What is an amino acid?**

3. **Is vitamin C really an acid? Are all vitamins acids?**

4. **What is the difference between salt and sodium?**

5. **What is meant by "pH-balanced shampoo"?**

Please pass the protons

Have you ever tasted a lemon or a grapefruit? Or felt a burning sensation on your arm after using a cleaning solution containing ammonia? These are but two examples of acids (citric acid in lemons and grapefruit) and bases (ammonia in cleaning solutions) we encounter in our daily lives. Other familiar acids are vinegar (acetic acid), vitamin C (ascorbic acid), and battery acid (sulfuric acid). Some familiar bases are drain cleaner (sodium hydroxide), baking soda (sodium bicarbonate), and antacids.

From "acid indigestion" to "acid rain," the word *acid* appears frequently in the news and in advertisements. Air and water pollution often involve acids

The chemical substances we call acids and bases are all around us. Acids are used in steel production and metal plating, as well as in chemical analysis. Acids are even found in the food we eat. Pancakes and muffins rise because of acids and bases in the ingredients, and the tart taste of fruit comes from the different acids in its flesh. Although the items described and shown here are dramatically different, the acids in them have something in common. All of them can provide hydrogen (hydronium) ions.

and bases. Acid rain, for example, is a serious environmental problem. In arid areas, alkaline (basic) water is sometimes undrinkable.

Did you know that our senses recognize four tastes related to acid–base chemistry? Acids taste sour, bases taste bitter, and the compounds formed when acids react with bases (salts) taste salty. The sweet taste is more complicated. To taste sweet, a compound must have both an acidic part and a basic part, plus just the right geometry to fit the sweet-taste receptors of our taste buds.

In this chapter, we discuss some of the chemistry of acids and bases. You use them every day. Your body processes them continuously. You will probably hear and read about them as long as you live. What you learn here can help you gain a better understanding of these important classes of compounds.

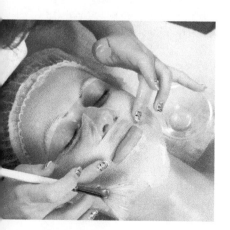

▲ Many skin-peel preparations used by cosmetologists contain alpha-hydroxy acids such as glycolic acid or lactic acid.

7.1 Acids and Bases: Experimental Definitions

Learning Objectives ❯ Distinguish between acids and bases using their chemical and physical properties. ❯ Explain how an acid–base indicator works.

Acids and bases are chemical opposites, and so their properties are quite different—often opposite. Let's begin by listing a few of these properties.
An *acid* is a compound that

- tastes sour.
- causes litmus indicator dye to turn red.
- dissolves active metals such as zinc and iron, producing hydrogen gas.
- reacts with bases to form water and ionic compounds called *salts*.

A *base* is a compound that

- tastes bitter.
- causes litmus indicator dye to turn blue.
- feels slippery on the skin.
- reacts with acids to form water and salts.

1. Are all acids corrosive? It is clear from Table 7.1 that *acid* does not necessarily mean "corrosive." Many acids are harmless enough to be included in foods we eat, and some are necessary to life.

We can identify foods that are acidic by their sour taste. Vinegar and lemon juice are examples. Vinegar is a solution of acetic acid (about 5%) in water. Lemons, limes, and other citrus fruits contain citric acid. Lactic acid gives yogurt its tart taste, and phosphoric acid is often added to carbonated drinks to impart tartness. The bitter taste of tonic water, on the other hand, comes in part from quinine, a base. Figure 7.1 shows some common acids and bases.

▶ **Figure 7.1** Some common acids (left), bases (center), and salts (right). Acids, bases, and salts are components of many familiar consumer products.

Q: *How would each of the three classes of compounds affect the indicator dye litmus? (See Figure 7.2.)*

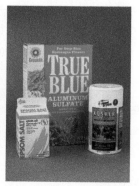

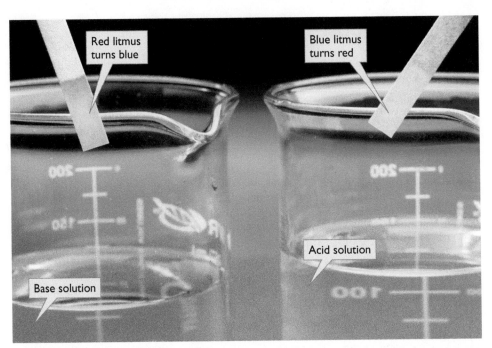

▲ Figure 7.2 Strips of paper impregnated with litmus dye (extracted from a fungus) are often used to distinguish between acids and bases. The sample on the left turns litmus blue and is therefore basic. The sample on the right turns litmus red and is acidic.

▲ It DOES Matter!!
Hydrangea is one of many types of flowers that may show different colors depending on the acidity of the soil in which it is grown. Some varieties are blue (top) when planted in slightly acidic soil and pink (bottom) when planted in more basic soil.

A litmus test is a common way to identify a substance as an acid or a base. Litmus (Figure 7.2) is an **acid–base indicator**, one of many such compounds. If you dip a strip of neutral (violet-colored) litmus paper into an unknown solution and the strip turns pink, the solution is acidic. If it turns blue, the solution is basic. If the strip does not turn pink or blue, the solution is neither acidic nor basic. Many substances, such as those that give the colors to grape juice, red cabbage, blueberries, and many flower petals, are acid–base indicators.

Self-Assessment Questions

1. Which of the following is *not* a property of acids?
   a. feel slippery on the skin
   b. react with Zn to form hydrogen gas
   c. taste sour
   d. turn litmus red

2. Which of the following is *not* a property of bases?
   a. feel slippery on the skin
   b. react with salts to form acids
   c. taste bitter
   d. turn litmus blue

3. In general, when an acid and a base are mixed,
   a. a new acid and a salt are formed
   b. a new base and a salt are formed
   c. no reaction occurs
   d. a salt and water are formed

4. A common substance that contains lactic acid is
   a. salad oil
   b. soap
   c. vinegar
   d. yogurt

5. The sour taste of grapefruit is due to
   a. acetic acid
   b. ammonia
   c. carbonic acid
   d. citric acid

▲ You can make your own indicator dye. Chop about 2 cups of red cabbage. Cover with boiling water. Stir. After about 10 min, filter out the solids with a coffee filter. Use about 50 mL of the liquid to test various household chemicals (vinegar, baking soda, ammonia, and so on) for pH. The indicator changes from red at about pH 2 to purple at pH 4, violet at pH 6, blue at pH 8, blue-green at pH 10, and greenish-yellow at pH 12. Other plant materials that contain indicators include blackberries, black raspberries, red radish peels, red rose petals, and turmeric.

Answers: 1, a; 2, b; 3, d; 4, d; 5, d

7.2 Acids, Bases, and Salts

Learning Objectives ❯ Identify Arrhenius and Brønsted–Lowry acids and bases.
❯ Write a balanced equation for a neutralization or an ionization.

Acids and bases have certain characteristic properties. But why do they have these properties? We use several different theories to explain these properties.

The Arrhenius Theory

▲ Swedish chemist Svante Arrhenius (1859–1927) proposed the theory that acids, bases, and salts in water are composed of ions. He also was the first to relate carbon dioxide in the atmosphere to the greenhouse effect (Chapter 13).

Svante Arrhenius developed the first successful theory of acids and bases in 1887. According to Arrhenius's concept, an **acid** is a molecular substance that breaks up in aqueous solution into hydrogen ions (H^+) and anions. (Because a hydrogen ion is a hydrogen atom from which the sole electron has been removed, H^+ ions are also called *protons*.) The acid is said to *ionize*. For example, nitric acid ionizes in water.

$$HNO_3(aq) \longrightarrow H^+(aq) + NO_3^-(aq)$$

In water, then, the properties of acids are those of the H^+ ion. It is the hydrogen ion that turns litmus red, tastes sour, and reacts with active metals and bases. Table 7.1 lists some common acids. Notice that each formula contains one or more hydrogen atoms. Chemists often indicate an acid by writing the formula with the H atom(s) first. HCl, H_2SO_4, and HNO_3 are acids; NH_3 and CH_4 are not. The formula $HC_2H_3O_2$ (acetic acid) indicates that one H atom ionizes when this compound is in aqueous solution, and three do not.

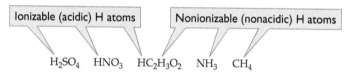

An Arrhenius **base** is defined as a substance that releases hydroxide ions (OH^-) in aqueous solution. Some bases are ionic solids that contain OH^-, such as sodium hydroxide (NaOH) and calcium hydroxide [$Ca(OH)_2$]. These compounds simply release hydroxide ions into the solution when the solid is dissolved in water:

$$NaOH(s) \xrightarrow{H_2O} Na^+(aq) + OH^-(aq)$$

We write H_2O over the arrow to indicate that it is a solvent, not a reactant.

Other bases are molecular substances such as ammonia that ionize to produce OH^- when placed in water (see page 181).

Experimental evidence indicates that the properties of bases in water are due to OH^-. Table 7.2 lists some common bases. Most of these are ionic compounds containing positively changed metal ions, such as Na^+ or Ca^{2+}, and negatively charged hydroxide ions. When these compounds dissolve in water, they all provide OH^- ions, and thus they are all bases. The properties of bases are those of hydroxide ions, just as the properties of acids are those of hydrogen ions.

Table 7.1	Some Common Acids		
Name	**Formula**	**Acid Strength**	**Common Uses/Notes**
Sulfuric acid	H_2SO_4	Strong	Battery acid; ore processing, fertilizer manufacturing, oil refining
Hydrochloric acid	HCl	Strong	Cleaning of metals and bricks, removing scale from boilers
Phosphoric acid	H_3PO_4	Moderate	Used in colas and rust removers
Lactic acid	$CH_3CHOHCOOH$	Weak	Yogurt; acidulant (food additive to increase tartness), lotion additive
Acetic acid	CH_3COOH	Weak	Vinegar; acidulant
Boric acid	H_3BO_3	Very weak	Antiseptic eyewash, roach poison
Hydrocyanic acid	HCN	Very weak	Plastics manufacture; extremely toxic

Table 7.2 | Some Common Bases

Name	Formula	Classification	Common Uses/Notes
Sodium hydroxide	NaOH	Strong	Acid neutralization; soap making
Potassium hydroxide	KOH	Strong	Making liquid soaps and biodiesel fuels
Lithium hydroxide	LiOH	Strong	Alkaline storage batteries
Calcium hydroxide	$Ca(OH)_2$	Strong[a]	Plaster, cement; soil neutralizer
Magnesium hydroxide	$Mg(OH)_2$	Strong[a]	Antacid, laxative
Ammonia	NH_3	Weak	Fertilizer, household cleansers

[a]Although these bases are classified as strong, they are not very soluble in water. Calcium hydroxide is only slightly soluble, and magnesium hydroxide is practically insoluble.

Arrhenius further proposed that the essential reaction between an acid and a base, **neutralization**, is the combination of H^+ and OH^- to form water. The cation that was originally associated with the OH^- combines with the anion that was associated with the H^+ to form an ionic compound, a **salt**.

$$\text{An acid} + \text{a base} \longrightarrow \text{a salt} + \text{water}$$

CONCEPTUAL Example 7.1 | Ionization of Acids and Bases

Write equations showing **(a)** the ionization of nitric acid (HNO_3) in water and **(b)** the ionization of solid potassium hydroxide (KOH) in water.

Solution

a. An HNO_3 molecule ionizes to form a hydrogen ion and a nitrate ion. Because this reaction occurs in water, we can use the label "(aq)" to indicate that the substances involved are in aqueous solution.

$$HNO_3(aq) \longrightarrow H^+(aq) + NO_3^-(aq)$$

b. Potassium hydroxide (KOH), an ionic solid, simply dissolves in the water, forming separate $K^+(aq)$ and $OH^-(aq)$ ions.

$$KOH(s) \xrightarrow{H_2O} K^+(aq) + OH^-(aq)$$

■ **EXERCISE 7.1A**
Write equations showing **(a)** the ionization of HBr (hydrobromic acid) in water and **(b)** the ionization of solid calcium hydroxide in water.

■ **EXERCISE 7.1B**
Historically, formulas for carboxylic acids (compounds containing a —COOH group; see Chapter 9) are often written with the ionizable hydrogen *last*. For example, instead of writing the formula for acetic acid as $HC_2H_3O_2$, it can be written as CH_3COOH. Write an equation showing the ionization of CH_3COOH in water.

2. What is an amino acid? An amino acid is a molecule that contains both —COOH, which is acidic, and —NH_2 (an *amino group*; see Sections 9.8 and 9.9), which is basic. Amino acids undergo acid-base reactions with one another and link together to form the proteins in living tissue.

Limitations of the Arrhenius Theory

The Arrhenius theory is limited in several ways.

■ A simple free proton does not exist in water solution. The H^+ ion has such a high positive charge density that it is immediately attracted to a lone pair of electrons on an O atom of an H_2O molecule, forming a *hydronium ion*, H_3O^+.

$$H:\overset{..}{\underset{..}{O}}: + H^+ \longrightarrow \left[H:\overset{..}{\underset{H}{O}}:H \right]^+$$

Water Hydronium ion

■ It does not explain the basicity of ammonia and related compounds. Ammonia seems out of place in Table 7.2 because it contains no hydroxide ions.

■ It applies only to reactions in aqueous solution.

As with many scientific theories, a better one based on newer data has supplanted Arrhenius's theory.

The Brønsted–Lowry Acid–Base Theory

The shortcomings of the Arrhenius theory were largely overcome by a theory proposed in 1923, by J. N. Brønsted in Denmark and T. M. Lowry in Great Britain, who were working independently. In the Brønsted–Lowry theory,

■ an acid is a *proton donor*, and
■ a base is a *proton acceptor*.

The theory portrays the ionization of hydrogen chloride in this way:

$$HCl(aq) + H_2O \longrightarrow H_3O^+(aq) + Cl^-(aq)$$

Here, water is a reactant. The acid molecules donate hydrogen ions (protons) to the water molecules, so the acid (HCl) acts as a proton donor.

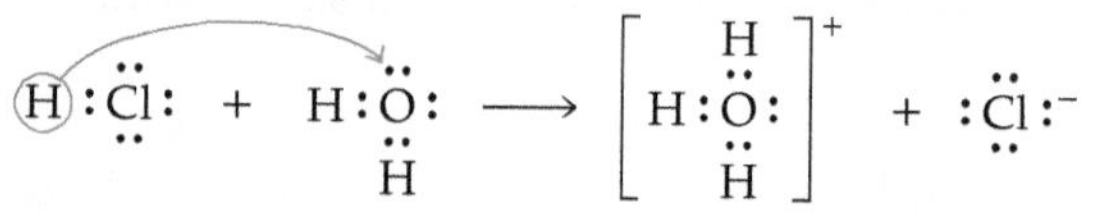

Acid
(proton donor)

Hydrochloric acid

The HCl molecule donates a proton to a water molecule, producing a hydronium ion and a chloride ion and forming a solution called *hydrochloric acid*. Other acids react similarly; they donate hydrogen ions to water molecules to produce hydronium ions. If we let HA represent any acid, the reaction is written as

$$HA(aq) + H_2O \longrightarrow H_3O^+(aq) + A^-(aq)$$

Even when the solvent is something other than water, the acid acts as a proton donor, transferring H^+ ions to the solvent molecules.

In water, an H^+ ion is associated with several H_2O molecules—for example, four H_2O molecules in the ion $H(H_2O)_4^+$, or $H_9O_4^+$. For most purposes, we simply use H^+ and ignore the associated water molecules. However, keep in mind that the notation H^+ is a simplification of the real situation: Protons in water actually exist associated with water molecules.

CONCEPTUAL Example 7.2 | Brønsted–Lowry Acids

Write an equation showing the reaction with water of HNO_3 as a Brønsted–Lowry acid. What is the role of water in the reaction?

Solution

As a Brønsted–Lowry acid, HNO_3 donates a proton to a water molecule, forming a hydronium ion and a nitrate ion.

$$HNO_3(aq) + H_2O \longrightarrow H_3O^+(aq) + NO_3^-(aq)$$

The water molecule accepts a proton from HNO_3. Water is a Brønsted–Lowry base in this reaction.

■ EXERCISE 7.2A

Write an equation showing the reaction with water of HBr as a Brønsted–Lowry acid.

■ EXERCISE 7.2B

Write an equation showing the reaction of methanol (CH_3OH) with $HClO_4$ as a Brønsted–Lowry acid.

Where does the OH^- come from when bases such as ammonia (NH_3) are dissolved in water? The Arrhenius theory proved inadequate in answering this question, but the Brønsted–Lowry theory explains how ammonia acts as a base in water.

Ammonia is a gas at room temperature. When it is dissolved in water, some of the ammonia molecules react as shown by the following equation.

$$NH_3(aq) + H_2O \longrightarrow NH_4^+(aq) + OH^-(aq)$$

An ammonia molecule accepts a proton from a water molecule; NH_3 acts as a Brønsted–Lowry base. (Recall that the N atom of ammonia has a lone pair of electrons, which it can share with a proton.) The water molecule acts as a proton donor—an acid. The ammonia molecule accepts the proton and becomes an ammonium ion. When a proton leaves a water molecule, it leaves behind the electron pair that it shared with the O atom. The water molecule becomes a negatively charged hydroxide ion.

In general, then, *a base is a proton acceptor* (Figure 7.3). This definition includes not only hydroxide ions but also neutral molecules such as ammonia and *amines* (organic compounds such as CH_3NH_2 that are derived from ammonia). It also includes other negative ions such as the oxide (O^{2-}), carbonate (CO_3^{2-}), and bicarbonate (HCO_3^-) ions. The idea of an acid as a proton donor and a base as a proton acceptor greatly expands our concept of acids and bases.

Acid   Base

◀ **Figure 7.3** A Brønsted–Lowry acid is a proton donor. A base is a proton acceptor.

Q: *Can you write an equation in which the acid is represented as HA and the base as :B⁻?*

Salts

Salts, formed from the neutralization reactions of acids and bases, are ionic compounds composed of cations and anions. These ions can be simple ions, such as sodium ion (Na^+) and chloride ion (Cl^-), or polyatomic ions, such as ammonium ion (NH_4^+), sulfate ion (SO_4^{2-}), and acetate ion (CH_3COO^-). Sodium chloride, ordinary table salt, is probably the most familiar salt.

Salts that conduct electricity when dissolved in water are called *electrolytes*. Various electrolytes, in certain amounts, are critical for many bodily functions including nerve conduction, heartbeat, and fluid balance. Medical blood tests often check levels of Na^+, K^+, Cl^-, HCO_3^-, and other electrolyte ions (Chapter 19).

There are many common salts with familiar uses. Sodium chloride and calcium chloride are used to melt ice on roads and sidewalks in winter. Copper(II) sulfate is used to kill tree roots in sewage lines. We will encounter many other examples in later chapters as dietary minerals (Chapter 17), fertilizers (Chapter 20), and more. Table 7.3 lists some salts used in medicine.

Table 7.3   Some Salts with Present or Past Uses in Medicine

Name	Formula	Uses
Silver nitrate	$AgNO_3$	Germicide and antiseptic
Stannous fluoride [tin(II) fluoride]	SnF_2	Toothpaste additive to prevent dental cavities
Calcium sulfate (plaster of Paris)	$(CaSO_4)_2 \cdot H_2O$[a]	Plaster casts
Magnesium sulfate (Epsom salts)	$MgSO_4 \cdot 7H_2O$[a]	Laxative, foot baths
Potassium permanganate	$KMnO_4$	Cauterizing agent, antiseptic
Ferrous sulfate [iron(II) sulfate]	$FeSO_4$	Prescribed for iron deficiency (anemia)
Zinc sulfate	$ZnSO_4$	Skin treatment (eczema)
Barium sulfate	$BaSO_4$	Provides the contrast material in "barium cocktail" given for gastrointestinal X-rays
Mercurous chloride [mercury(I) chloride; calomel]	Hg_2Cl_2	Laxative; no longer used

[a] These compounds are hydrates, substances containing water molecules combined in a definite ratio as an integral part of the compound.

Irv Levy, *Gordon College*

Sustainability: It's Basic (and Acidic)

Green chemistry is a part of sustainable chemistry. Sustainability, often defined as "meeting the needs of the present generation without compromising the ability of future generations to meet their needs," is much in the news these days. Green chemistry is one of the critical means of attaining sustainability. Understanding of acids and bases has led to greener, more sustainable methods for producing consumer products. Two important examples are soap and renewable biofuels.

Soap traditionally has been made from fats left from cooking meats and from vegetable oils. Fats and oils contain substances composed of three long chains of carbon atoms connected to a central set of three carbon atoms, an arrangement called a *triglyceride* (Chapter 16). To make soap, the fats are heated and mixed with lye solution (aqueous sodium hydroxide—a base). Each mole of triglyceride reacts with three moles of base to produce three moles of soap and one mole of the byproduct glycerol (also called glycerin). Soaps are salts (Section 7.2) of carboxylic acids that usually have a long chain of carbon atoms. An example of a typical soap is sodium palmitate. Its chemical formula is shown here.

$$CH_3(CH_2)_{14}COO^-Na^+$$

The byproduct glycerol has a number of uses, including as a moisturizing ingredient in soap. Chemists at Gordon College (Wenham, MA) found that adding glycerol to the fats and oils traditionally used in soap-making decreased the quantity of starting materials required for soap production. Much more glycerol byproduct is produced industrially than can be used by the soap industry, however, so the search continues for other green uses for glycerol.

The chemistry of biodiesel fuel production (also see Chapter 15) is much like that of soap-making. In both processes, bases are used and glycerol is formed. With the use of methanol (CH_3OH) in place of water and a catalytic amount of base, though, the triglycerides are converted to compounds called *esters* (Section 9.7). An example of a typical biodiesel molecule is shown here.

$$CH_3(CH_2)_{14}COOCH_3$$

Although the long chains of carbon atoms in biodiesel often are the same as in soap molecules, biodiesel

▲ Biodiesel is made from waste fats and oils used in cooking. In the past, those wastes would require disposal; now, they are useful. Biodiesel is an excellent example of sustainable chemistry.

molecules have a different group on one end of the chain. Compare these compounds to a typical diesel molecule from petroleum that does not contain any atoms other than carbon and hydrogen.

$$CH_3(CH_2)_{14}CH_3$$

What do soap, biodiesel, and glycerol have to do with sustainability and green chemistry? The first principle of green chemistry encourages the prevention of waste. Sometimes wastes also are harmful to the environment. Wouldn't it be better to redirect apparently useless materials into something useful?

Consider this: Each year billions of gallons of fats and oils are used to fry foods. Fryer oils degrade fairly quickly in commercial kitchens. For many years the used oils were carted off by disposal companies as waste. Today, much of that used oil is converted into biodiesel fuel, providing an alternative fuel that doesn't deplete fossil petroleum reserves. This approach satisfies the green chemistry principle of using renewable resources while providing new use for what was once considered waste. And it gets better! Petroleum diesel fuel is hazardous to humans and toxic to the environment. Biodiesel is much safer.

Acids also are involved in green processes such as cleaning. For example, polylactic acid (PLA) is a type of biodegradable and renewable plastic made from chemicals derived from corn (see green chemistry essay, Chapter 10). PLA plastic, made by companies such as NatureWorks, is found in many consumer materials, such as plastic cups. Research at Simmons College in Boston has led to a new way to convert used PLA cups into an antimicrobial cleaning solution containing lactic acid ($CH_3CHOHCOOH$). The shredded plastic is mixed with alcohol and base to break down the polymer to sodium lactate ($CH_3CHOHCOONa$). The basic sodium lactate solution is neutralized with acid to form the lactic acid cleaner, which is useful for wiping away soap scum.

In the quest for sustaisnability, acids and bases are an essential part of the toolbox that will continue to be used as chemists search for better ways to prevent waste and use renewable starting materials. You might argue that sustainability is basic—not to mention acidic.

Self-Assessment Questions

For Questions 1–5, match each formula with the compound's application.

1. CH_3COOH
2. H_3BO_3
3. HCl
4. H_2SO_4
5. NaOH

(a) battery acid
(b) soap making
(c) antiseptic eyewash
(d) remove boiler scale
(e) vinegar

6. Which of the following equations best represents what happens when hydrogen bromide dissolves in water?

a. $2\ HBr \xrightarrow{H_2O} Br_2 + H_2$

b. $HBr(g) \xrightarrow{H_2O} H(aq) + Br(aq)$

c. $HBr \longrightarrow H^+(aq) + Br^-(aq)$

d. $HBr(g) + H_2O \longrightarrow Br^-(aq) + H_3O^+(aq)$

For Questions 7–10, match each term with the correct definition.

7. Arrhenius acid
8. Arrhenius base
9. Brønsted acid
10. Brønsted base

(a) proton acceptor
(b) proton donor
(c) produces H^+ in water
(d) produces OH^- in water

Answers: 1, e; 2, c; 3, d; 4, a; 5, b; 6, d; 7, c; 8, d; 9, b; 10, a

7.3 Acidic and Basic Anhydrides

Learning Objective ❯ Identify acidic anhydrides and basic anhydrides, and write equations showing their reactions with water.

Certain metal and nonmetal oxides are well known for their ability to produce or to neutralize acids or bases. For example, nitrogen dioxide (NO_2) and sulfur dioxide (SO_2) are notorious for producing acid rain. Calcium oxide (quicklime, CaO) is widely used to neutralize acidic soils. In the Brønsted–Lowry view, many metal oxides act directly as bases because the oxide ion can accept a proton. These metal oxides also react with water to form metal hydroxides, compounds that are bases in the Arrhenius sense. And many nonmetal oxides react with water to form acids.

Nonmetal Oxides: Acidic Anhydrides

Many acids are made by reacting nonmetal oxides with water. For example, sulfur trioxide reacts with water to form sulfuric acid.

$$SO_3 + H_2O \longrightarrow H_2SO_4$$

Similarly, carbon dioxide reacts with water to form carbonic acid.

$$CO_2 + H_2O \longrightarrow H_2CO_3$$

In general, nonmetal oxides react with water to form acids.

$$\text{Nonmetal oxide} + H_2O \longrightarrow \text{acid}$$

Nonmetal oxides that act in this way are called **acidic anhydrides**. *Anhydride* means "without water." These reactions explain why rainwater is acidic (Section 7.8).

CONCEPTUAL **Example 7.3**   Acidic Anhydrides

Give the formula for the acid formed when sulfur dioxide reacts with water.

Solution

The formula for the acid, H_2SO_3, is obtained by adding the two H atoms and one O atom of water to SO_2. The equation for the reaction is simply

$$SO_2 + H_2O \longrightarrow H_2SO_3$$

▲ It DOES Matter!

Slaked lime is inexpensive, easily made from cheap raw materials, and low in toxicity. These properties make it the most widely used base for neutralizing acids. It is an ingredient in such diverse materials as bricklayer's mortar, plaster, glues, and even pickles and corn tortillas. The whitewash made famous in Mark Twain's *Adventures of Tom Sawyer* was a simple mixture of slaked lime and water.

■ EXERCISE 7.3A

Give the formula for the acid formed when selenium dioxide (SeO_2) reacts with water.

■ EXERCISE 7.3B

Give the formula for the acid formed when dinitrogen pentoxide (N_2O_5) reacts with water. (*Hint:* Two molecules of acid are formed.)

Metal Oxides: Basic Anhydrides

Just as acids can be made from nonmetal oxides, many common hydroxide bases can be made from metal oxides. For example, calcium oxide reacts with water to form calcium hydroxide ("slaked lime").

$$CaO + H_2O \longrightarrow Ca(OH)_2$$

Another example is the reaction of lithium oxide with water to form lithium hydroxide.

$$Li_2O + H_2O \longrightarrow 2\,LiOH$$

In general, metal oxides react with water to form bases (Figure 7.4). These metal oxides are called **basic anhydrides**.

$$\text{Metal oxide} + H_2O \longrightarrow \text{base}$$

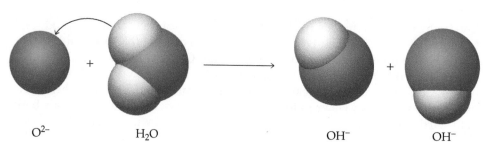

$$O^{2-} \qquad\qquad H_2O \qquad\qquad\qquad OH^- \qquad\qquad OH^-$$

▲ Figure 7.4 Metal oxides are basic because the oxide ion reacts with water to form two hydroxide ions.

Q: *Can you write an equation that shows how solid sodium oxide (Na_2O) reacts with water to form sodium hydroxide?*

CONCEPTUAL **Example 7.4** | Basic Anhydrides

Give the formula for the base formed by the addition of water to barium oxide (BaO).

Solution

Again, we add the atoms of a water molecule to BaO. Because a barium ion has a 2+ charge, the formula for the base has *two* hydroxide (1–) ions.

$$BaO + H_2O \longrightarrow Ba(OH)_2$$

■ EXERCISE 7.4A

Give the formula for the base formed by the addition of water to strontium oxide (SrO).

■ EXERCISE 7.4B

What base is formed by the addition of water to potassium oxide (K_2O)? (*Hint:* Two moles of base are formed for each mole of potassium oxide.)

1. Selenic acid (H_2SeO_4) is an extremely corrosive acid that when heated is capable of dissolving gold. It is quite soluble in water. The anhydride of selenic acid is
   a. SeO
   b. SeO_2
   c. SeO_3
   d. SeO_4

2. Zinc hydroxide [$Zn(OH)_2$] is used as an absorbent in surgical dressings. The anhydride of zinc hydroxide is
   a. ZnO
   b. ZnOH
   c. ZnO_2
   d. Zn_2O_3

Answers: 1, c; 2, a

7.4 Strong and Weak Acids and Bases

Learning Objective ❯ Define and identify strong and weak acids and bases.

When gaseous hydrogen chloride (HCl) reacts with water, it reacts completely to form hydronium ions and chloride ions.

$$HCl + H_2O \longrightarrow H_3O^+ + Cl^-$$

For many purposes, we simply write this reaction as the ionization of HCl and use (aq) to indicate a solution in water.

$$HCl(aq) \longrightarrow H^+(aq) + Cl^-(aq)$$

Most acids do not ionize completely, however. The poisonous gas hydrogen cyanide (HCN) also ionizes in water to produce hydrogen ions and cyanide ions. But HCN ionizes only to a slight extent. In a solution that has 1 mol of HCN in 1 L of water, only one HCN molecule in 40,000 ionizes to produce a hydrogen ion.

$$HCN(aq) \rightleftharpoons H^+(aq) + CN^-(aq)$$

We represent this slight ionization by using a double arrow. The opposite-pointing arrows indicate that the reaction is reversible; the ions can also combine to form HCN molecules. A short arrow points to the right and a longer arrow points to the left to indicate that most of the HCN remains intact as HCN molecules.

Clearly, acids can be classified according to their extent of ionication.

▪ An acid such as HCl that ionizes completely in (reacts completely with) water is called a **strong acid**.
▪ An acid such as HCN that ionizes only slightly in water is a **weak acid**.

There are only a few strong acids. The first two acids listed in Table 7.1 (sulfuric and hydrochloric) are the common ones. The other strong acids are nitric acid (HNO_3), hydrobromic acid (HBr), hydroiodic acid (HI), and perchloric acid ($HClO_4$). Most acids are weak acids.

Bases are also classified as strong or weak.

▪ A **strong base** is completely ionized in water.
▪ A **weak base** is only slightly ionized in water.

Perhaps the most familiar strong base is sodium hydroxide (NaOH), commonly called *lye*. It exists as sodium ions and hydroxide ions even in the solid state. Other strong bases include potassium hydroxide (KOH) and the hydroxides of all the other group 1A metals. Except for $Be(OH)_2$, the hydroxides of group 2A metals are also strong bases. However, $Ca(OH)_2$ is only slightly soluble in water, and $Mg(OH)_2$ is nearly insoluble. The concentration of hydroxide ions in a solution of $Ca(OH)_2$ or $Mg(OH)_2$ is, therefore, not very high.

The word *strong* does not refer to the *amount* of acid or base in a solution. As mentioned in Section 5.5, a solution that contains a relatively large amount of an acid or a base, whether strong or weak, as the solute in a given volume of solution is called a *concentrated* solution. A solution with only a little solute in that same volume of solution is a *dilute* solution.

3. Is vitamin C really an acid? Are all vitamins acids?
Yes, vitamin C is a complex organic compound known as *ascorbic acid*. Some, but not all, vitamins are acids (including folic acid and niacin). Like most acids, these vitamins are weak acids. Not only are they not corrosive but they are necessary to health.

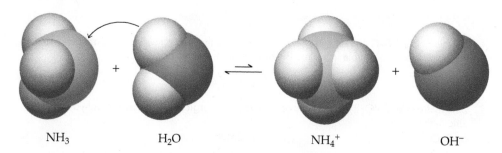

$$NH_3 \qquad\qquad H_2O \qquad\qquad\qquad NH_4^+ \qquad\qquad OH^-$$

▲ **Figure 7.5** Ammonia is a base because it accepts a proton from water. A solution of ammonia in water contains ammonium ions and hydroxide ions. Only a small fraction of the ammonia molecules react, however; most remain unchanged. Ammonia is therefore a *weak* base.

Q: *Amines are related to ammonia; in an amine, one or more of the H atoms of NH_3 is replaced by a carbon-containing group. Amines react in the same way as ammonia does. Can you write an equation that shows how the amine CH_3NH_2 reacts with water? One product is hydroxide ion.*

The most familiar weak base is ammonia (NH_3). It reacts with water to a slight extent to produce ammonium ions (NH_4^+) and hydroxide ions (Figure 7.5).

$$NH_3 + H_2O \rightleftharpoons NH_4^+ + OH^-$$

In its reaction with HCl (page 180), water acts as a base (proton acceptor). In its reaction with NH_3, water acts as an acid (proton donor). A substance such as water that can either donate a proton or accept a proton is said to be *amphiprotic* (see also Additional Problem 65).

Self-Assessment Questions

For Questions 1–7, select the correct classification (more than one substance may fit into a given classification).

1. $Ca(OH)_2$
2. HCN
3. HF
4. HNO_3
5. H_3PO_4
6. KOH
7. NH_3

(a) strong acid
(b) strong base
(c) weak acid
(d) weak base

8. Acetic acid reacts with water to form
   a. $CH_3COO^+ + H_2O$
   c. $CH_3COO^- + H_3O^-$
   b. $CH_3COOH + OH^-$
   d. $CH_3COO^+ + OH^-$

9. Ammonia reacts with water to form
   a. $NH_3 + H_2O$
   c. $NH_2^- + H_3O^+$
   b. $NH_4^+ + OH^-$
   d. $NH_3 + OH^-$

Answers: 1, b; 2, c; 3, c; 4, a; 5, c; 6, b; 7, d; 8, c; 9, b

7.5 Neutralization

Learning Objective ❯ Identify the reactants and predict the products in a neutralization reaction.

When an acid reacts with a base, the products are water and a salt. If a solution containing hydrogen ions (an acid) is mixed with another solution containing exactly the same amount of hydroxide ions (a base), the resulting solution does not change the color of litmus, dissolve zinc or iron, or feel slippery on the skin. It is no longer either acidic or basic. It is neutral. As was mentioned earlier, the reaction of an acid with a base is called *neutralization* (Figure 7.6).

$$H^+ + OH^- \longrightarrow H_2O$$

(a)

(b)

(c)

◀ Figure 7.6 The amount of acid (or base) in a solution is determined by careful neutralization. Here a 5.00-mL sample of vinegar, some water, and a few drops of phenolphthalein (an acid–base indicator) are placed in a flask (a). A solution of 0.1000 M NaOH is added to the flask slowly from a buret (a device for precise measurement of volumes of solutions) (b). As long as the acid is in excess, the solution is colorless. When the acid has been neutralized and a tiny excess of base is present, the phenolphthalein indicator turns pink (c).

Q: *Can you write an equation for the reaction of acetic acid (CH$_3$COOH), the acid in vinegar, with aqueous NaOH?*

If sodium hydroxide is neutralized by hydrochloric acid, the products are water and sodium chloride (ordinary table salt)

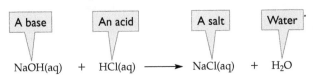

$$NaOH(aq) + HCl(aq) \longrightarrow NaCl(aq) + H_2O$$

| A base | An acid | A salt | Water |

Example 7.5 Neutralization Reactions

Potassium nitrate, a component of black powder gunpowder and some fertilizers, was obtained from the late Middle Ages through the nineteenth century by precipitation from urine. Commonly called *saltpeter*, it can be prepared by the reaction of nitric acid with potassium hydroxide. Write the equation for this neutralization reaction.

Solution

The OH$^-$ from the base and the H$^+$ from the acid combine to form water. The cation of the base (K$^+$) and the anion of the acid (NO$_3^-$) form a solution of the salt (potassium nitrate, KNO$_3$).

$$KOH(aq) + HNO_3(aq) \longrightarrow KNO_3(aq) + H_2O(l)$$

■ **EXERCISE 7.5A**
Countertop spills of lye solutions (aqueous sodium hydroxide) can be neutralized with vinegar (aqueous acetic acid; see Table 7.1). Write the equation for the neutralization reaction.

■ **EXERCISE 7.5B**
A toilet-bowl cleaner contains hydrochloric acid. An emergency first-aid treatment for accidental ingestion is a teaspoon of milk of magnesia (magnesium hydroxide). Write the equation for the neutralization reaction between magnesium hydroxide and hydrochloric acid. (*Hint:* Be sure to write the correct formulas for the reactants and the salt before attempting to balance the equation.)

4. What is the difference between salt and sodium? A salt is any ionic compound formed by reacting an acid and a base. In everyday life, *salt* usually means table salt—sodium chloride (NaCl). Sodium is a highly reactive metal element. Sodium ions are essential for life, but you wouldn't want to eat pure sodium. It reacts violently with water.

Self-Assessment Questions

1. When equal amounts of acids and bases are mixed,
   a. the acid becomes stronger
   b. the base becomes stronger
   c. no reaction occurs
   d. they neutralize each other

2. What amount in moles of hydrochloric acid is needed to neutralize 1.5 mol of sodium hydroxide?
   a. 1 mol
   b. 1.5 mol
   c. 3.0 mol
   c. 4.5 mol

3. What amount in moles of hydrochloric acid is needed to neutralize 2.4 mol of calcium hydroxide?
   a. 1.2 mol   **b.** 2.4 mol
   c. 3.0 mol   **d.** 4.8 mol

4. What amount in moles of sodium hydroxide is needed to neutralize 1.5 mol of phosphoric acid?
   a. 0.5 mol   **b.** 3.0 mol
   c. 4.5 mol   **d.** 6.0 mol

Answers: 1, d; 2, b; 3, d; 4, c

Table 7.4	Relationship between pH and Concentration of H⁺ Ion
Concentration of H⁺(mol/L)	**pH**
1×10^{-0}	0
1×10^{-1}	1
1×10^{-2}	2
1×10^{-3}	3
1×10^{-4}	4
1×10^{-5}	5
1×10^{-6}	6
1×10^{-7}	7
1×10^{-8}	8
1×10^{-9}	9
1×10^{-10}	10
1×10^{-11}	11
1×10^{-12}	12
1×10^{-13}	13
1×10^{-14}	14

The relationship between pH and [H⁺] is perhaps easier to see when the equation is written in the following form. $[H^+] = 10^{-pH}$

7.6 The pH Scale

Learning Objectives ❯ Describe the relationship between the pH of a solution and its acidity or basicity. ❯ Find the molar concentration of hydrogen ion, [H⁺], from a pH value or the pH value from [H⁺].

In solutions, the concentrations of ions are expressed in moles per liter (molarity; see Section 5.5). Because hydrogen chloride is completely ionized in water, a 1 molar solution of hydrochloric acid (1 M HCl), for example, contains 1 mol H^+ ions per liter of solution. Likewise, 1 L of 3 M HCl contains 3 mol H^+ ions, and 0.500 L of 0.00100 M HCl contains 0.500 L × 0.00100 mol/L = 0.000500 mol H^+ ions.

We can describe the acidity of a particular solution in moles per liter: The hydrogen ion concentration of a 0.00100 M HCl solution is 1×10^{-3} mol/L. However, exponential notation isn't very convenient. More often, the acidity of this solution is reported simply as pH 3.

We usually use the **pH** scale, first proposed in 1909 by the Danish biochemist S. P. L. Sørensen, to describe the degree of acidity or basicity. Most solutions have a pH that lies in the range from 0 to 14. The neutral point on the scale is 7, with values below 7 indicating increasing acidity and those above 7 increasing basicity. Thus, pH 6 is slightly acidic, whereas pH 12 is strongly basic (Figure 7.7).

The numbers on the pH scale are directly related to the hydrogen ion concentration. We might expect pure water to be completely in the form of H_2O molecules, but it turns out that about 1 out of every 500 million water molecules splits into H^+ and OH^- ions. This gives a concentration of hydrogen ion and of hydroxide ion in pure water of 0.0000001 mol/L, or 1×10^{-7} M. Can you see why 7 is the pH of pure water? It is simply the power of 10 for the molar concentration of H^+, with the negative sign removed. (The H in pH stands for "hydrogen," and the p for "power.") Thus, pH is defined as the negative logarithm of the molar concentration of hydrogen ion (refer to Table 7.4):

$$pH = -\log[H^+]$$

The brackets around H^+ mean "molar concentration."

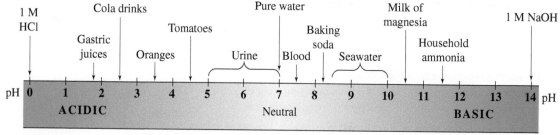

▲ **Figure 7.7** The pH scale. A change in pH of one unit means a tenfold change in the hydrogen ion concentration.

Q: Are tomatoes more acidic or less acidic than oranges? About how many times more (or less) acidic?

Table 7.5	Approximate pH Values of Some Common Solutions
Solution	**pH**
Hydrochloric acid (4%)	0
Gastric juice	1.6–1.8
Soft drink	2.0–4.0
Lemon juice	2.1
Vinegar (4%)	2.5
Urine	5.5–7.0
Rainwater[a]	5.6
Saliva	6.2–7.4
Milk	6.3–6.6
Pure water	7.0
Blood	7.4
Fresh egg white	7.6–8.0
Bile	7.8–8.6
Milk of magnesia	10.5
Washing soda	12.0
Sodium hydroxide (4%)	13.0

[a] Saturated with carbon dioxide from the atmosphere but unpolluted.

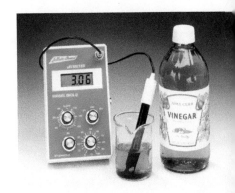

▲ A pH meter is a device for determining pH quickly and accurately.

Q: *Is the solution in the beaker more basic or less basic than household ammonia? (Refer to Figure 7.7.)*

Although pH is an acidity scale, note that its value goes down when acidity goes up. Not only is the relationship an inverse one, but it is also logarithmic. A decrease of 1 pH unit represents a tenfold increase in acidity, and when pH goes down by 2 units, acidity increases by a factor of 100. This relationship may seem strange at first, but once you understand the pH scale, you will appreciate its convenience.

Table 7.4 summarizes the relationship between hydrogen ion concentration and pH. A pH of 4 means a hydrogen ion concentration of 1×10^{-4} mol/L, or 0.0001 M. If the concentration of hydrogen ions is 0.01 M, or 1×10^{-2} M, the pH is 2. Typical pH values for various common solutions are listed in Table 7.5.

5. What is meant by "pH-balanced shampoo"? Shampoo on either end of the pH scale would damage hair (and probably skin as well!). Most shampoos are formulated to be neutral (pH 7) or slightly basic.

Example 7.6 pH from Hydrogen Ion Concentration

What is the pH of a solution that has a hydrogen ion concentration of 1×10^{-5} M?

Solution
The hydrogen ion concentration is 1×10^{-5} M. The exponent is −5; the pH is, therefore, the negative of this exponent: −(−5) or 5.

▪ EXERCISE 7.6A
What is the pH of a solution that has a hydrogen ion concentration of 1×10^{-9} M?

▪ EXERCISE 7.6B
What is the pH of a solution that is 0.010 M HCl? (*Hint:* HCl is a strong acid.)

Example 7.7 Finding Hydrogen Ion Concentration from pH

What is the hydrogen ion concentration of a solution that has a pH of 4?

Solution
A pH value of 4 means that the exponent of 10 is −4. The hydrogen ion concentration is, therefore, 1×10^{-4} M.

▪ EXERCISE 7.7A
What is the hydrogen ion concentration of a solution that has a pH of 2?

▪ EXERCISE 7.7B
What is the hydrogen ion concentration of a HI solution that has a pH of 3? (*Hint:* HI is a strong acid.)

CONCEPTUAL Example 7.8 — Estimating pH from Hydrogen Ion Concentration

Which of the following is a reasonable pH for a solution that is 8×10^{-4} M in H^+?

  a. 2.9   **b.** 3.1   **c.** 4.2   **d.** 4.8

Solution
The $[H^+]$ is greater than 1×10^{-4} M, and so the pH must be less than 4. That rules out answers (c) and (d). The $[H^+]$ is less than 10×10^{-4} (or 1×10^{-3} M), and so the pH must be greater than 3. That rules out answer (a). The only reasonable answer is (b), a value between 3 and 4.

    (With a scientific calculator, you can calculate the actual pH, usually with the following keystrokes: ⑧ (exp) ④ (±) (log) This gives a value of -3.1 for the log of 8×10^{-4}. Because pH is the *negative* log of the H^+ concentration, the pH value is 3.1.)

▪ EXERCISE 7.8
Which of the following is a reasonable pH for a solution that is 2×10^{-10} M in H^+?

  a. 2.0   **b.** 8.7   **c.** 9.7   **d.** 10.2

    It's not obvious right away, but every aqueous solution contains *both* hydrogen ions and hydroxide ions. An acidic solution contains more H^+ ions than OH^- ions. For example, a solution with a pH of 4 is 1×10^{-4} M in H^+ ions but only 1×10^{-10} M in OH^- ions. On the other hand, a basic solution contains more OH^- ions than H^+ ions. A solution with a pH of 12 is 1×10^{-12} M in H^+ ions and 1×10^{-2} M in OH^- ions. And a neutral solution contains equal concentrations of H^+ ions and OH^- ions; both are 1×10^{-7} M.

CONCEPTUAL Example 7.9 — Hydrogen and Hydroxide Ions in Acids and Bases

Classify the three aqueous solutions shown below as acidic, basic, or neutral. (Water molecules are not shown.)

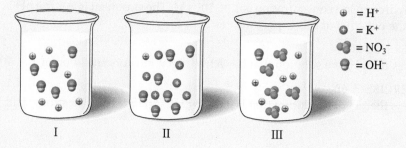

Solution
Beaker I contains equal numbers of OH^- ions and H^+ ions—six of each—so that solution is neutral. Beaker II contains more OH^- ions (seven) than H^+ ions (one), so its solution is basic. Beaker III contains six H^+ ions and one OH^- ion; the solution is acidic.

▪ EXERCISE 7.9
What is the formula of the compound that was dissolved in Beaker III of Example 7.9? What is the formula of the compound that was dissolved in Beaker II?

Self-Assessment Questions

1. The hydrogen ion concentration, [H$^+$], of a 0.0010 M HNO$_3$ solution is
   a. 1.0×10^{-4} M
   b. 1.0×10^{-3} M
   c. 1.0×10^{-2} M
   d. 10 M

2. What is the pH of a solution that has a hydrogen ion concentration of 1.0×10^{-11} M?
   a. 1.0
   b. 3
   c. 10
   d. 11

3. Swimming pool water with a pH of 8 has a hydrogen ion concentration of
   a. 8.0 M
   b. 8.0×10^{-8} M
   c. 1.0×10^{-8} M
   d. 1.0×10^8 M

4. The pH of pure water is
   a. 0
   b. 1
   c. 7
   d. 10
   e. 14

5. Which of the following is a reasonable pH for 0.15 M HCl?
   a. 0.15
   b. 0.82
   c. 8.24
   d. 13.18

6. Which of the following is a reasonable pH for 0.15 M NaOH?
   a. 0.15
   b. 0.82
   c. 8.24
   d. 13.18

7. Physiological pH (7.4) is the average pH of blood. Which of the following is a reasonable hydrogen ion concentration of a solution at physiological pH?
   a. −7.4 M
   b. 0.6 M
   c. 6×10^{-7} M
   d. 1×10^{-8} M
   e. 4×10^{-8}

7.7 Buffers and Conjugate Acid–Base Pairs

Learning Objectives ❯ Write the formula for the conjugate base of an acid or for the conjugate acid of a base. ❯ Describe the action of a buffer.

In the Brønsted–Lowry theory, a pair of compounds or ions that differ by one proton (H$^+$) is called a **conjugate acid–base pair**. HF and F$^-$ are a conjugate acid-base pair, as are NH$_3$ and NH$_4{}^+$. When a base (for example, NH$_3$) accepts a proton, it becomes an acid because it now has a proton that it can donate. NH$_4{}^+$ is an acid; it can donate its "extra" proton. Similarly, when an acid (for example, HF) donates a proton, it becomes a base, because it can now accept a proton. F$^-$ is a base; it can accept a proton.

CONCEPTUAL Example 7.10 Conjugate Acid–Base Pairs

What is the conjugate base **(a)** of HBr and **(b)** of HNO$_3$? What is the conjugate acid **(c)** of OH$^-$ and **(d)** of HSO$_4{}^-$?

Solution
a. Removing a proton from HBr leaves Br$^-$; the conjugate base of HBr is Br$^-$.
b. Removing a proton from HNO$_3$ leaves NO$_3{}^-$; the conjugate base of HNO$_3$ is NO$_3{}^-$.
c. Adding a proton to OH$^-$ gives H$_2$O; the conjugate acid of OH$^-$ is H$_2$O.
d. Adding a proton to HSO$_4{}^-$ gives H$_2$SO$_4$; the conjugate acid of HSO$_4{}^-$ is H$_2$SO$_4$.

■ EXERCISE 7.10
What is the conjugate base **(a)** of HCN and **(b)** of H$_3$O$^+$? What is the conjugate acid **(c)** of SO$_4{}^{2-}$ and **(d)** of HCO$_3{}^-$?

Buffer Solutions

A **buffer solution** maintains an almost constant pH when small amounts of a strong acid or a strong base are added to it. Buffer solutions have many important applications in industry, in the laboratory, and in living organisms because some chemical reactions consume acids, others produce acids, and many are catalyzed by acids[1]. A buffer solution consists of a weak acid and its conjugate base (for example, $HC_2H_3O_2$ and $C_2H_3O_2^-$) or a weak base and its conjugate acid (for example, NH_3 and NH_4^+).

Consider the equation for the ionization of acetic acid, in which the double arrow indicates the slight extent to which the acid ionizes.

$$HC_2H_3O_2(aq) \rightleftharpoons H^+(aq) + C_2H_3O_2^-(aq)$$

If we add sodium acetate to a solution of acetic acid, we are adding the conjugate base of acetic acid—that is, acetate ion—thus forming a buffer solution. If we add a little strong base to this solution, it will react with the weak acid.

$$OH^- + HC_2H_3O_2 \longrightarrow H_2O + C_2H_3O_2^-$$

Do you see that the solution no longer contains the strong base? Instead, it has a little more weak base and a little less weak acid than it did before the strong base was added. The pH remains very nearly constant. Likewise, if a little strong acid is added, it will react with the weak base.

$$H^+ + C_2H_3O_2^- \longrightarrow HC_2H_3O_2$$

The strong acid is consumed, a weak acid is formed, and the solution pH increases slightly. This behavior of buffered solutions contrasts sharply with that of unbuffered solutions, in which any added strong acid or base changes the pH greatly.

A dramatic and essential example of the action of buffers is found in our blood. Blood must maintain a pH very close to 7.4 or it cannot carry oxygen from the lungs to cells. The most important buffer for maintaining acid–base balance in the blood is the carbonic acid–bicarbonate ion (H_2CO_3/HCO_3^-) buffer.

Self-Assessment Questions

1. Which of the following pairs is a conjugate acid–base pair?
   a. CH_3COOH and OH^-
   b. HCN and CN^-
   c. HCN and OH^-
   d. HCl and OH^-

2. Which of the following is *not* a conjugate acid–base pair?
   a. CH_3COO^- and CH_3COOH
   b. F^- and HF
   c. H_2O and H_3O^+
   d. NH_3 and H_3O^+

3. A buffer solution is made from formic acid ($HCOOH$) and sodium formate ($HCOONa$). Added acid will react with
   a. $HCOO^-$
   b. $HCOOH$
   c. Na^+
   d. OH^-

4. Which of the following pairs could form a buffer?
   a. C_6H_5COOH and C_6H_5COONa
   b. HCl and $NaCl$
   c. HCl and $NaOH$
   d. NH_3 and NO_3^-

Answers: 1, b; 2, d; 3, a; 4, a

7.8 Acids and Bases in Industry and in Daily Life

Learning Objective ❯ Describe everyday uses of acids and bases and how they affect daily life.

Acids and bases play an important role in our bodies, in medicine, in our homes, and in industry, they are useful products in many ways, As industrial by-products, they can damage the environment. Their use requires caution, and their misuse can be dangerous to human health.

---

[1] A *catalyst* is a substance or mixture that speeds up a reaction. Unlike a reactant, a catalyst can be recovered unchanged after the reaction is complete, and ordinarily it can be reused. For example, the breakdown of some flavoring components of fruits is catalyzed by acid, and the formation of biodiesel fuel from waste oil is catalyzed by a strong base such as sodium hydroxide.

Acid Rain

Carbon dioxide is the anhydride of carbonic acid (Section 7.3). Raindrops falling through the air absorb CO_2, which is converted to H_2CO_3 in the drops. Rainwater is thus a dilute solution of carbonic acid, a weak acid. Rain saturated with carbon dioxide has a pH of 5.6. In many areas of the world, particularly those downwind from industrial centers, rainwater is much more acidic, with a pH as low as 3 or less. Rain with a pH below 5.6 is called **acid rain**.

Acid rain is due to acidic pollutants in the air. As we shall see in Chapter 13, several air pollutants are acid anhydrides. These include sulfur dioxide (SO_2),

mainly from the burning of high-sulfur coal in power plants and metal smelters, and nitrogen dioxide (NO_2) and nitric oxide (NO), from automobile exhaust fumes.

Some acid rain is due to natural pollutants, such as those resulting from volcanic eruptions and lightning. Volcanoes give off sulfur oxides and sulfuric acid, and lightning produces nitrogen oxides and nitric acid from nitrogen, oxygen, and water in the air.

Acid rain is an important environmental problem that involves both air pollution (Chapter 13) and water pollution (Chapter 14). It can have serious effects on plant and animal life.

Antacids: A Basic Remedy

The stomach secretes hydrochloric acid to aid in the digestion of food. Sometimes overindulgence or emotional stress leads to *hyperacidity* (too much acid is secreted). Hundreds of brands of antacids (Figure 7.8) are sold in the United States to treat this condition. Despite the many brand names, there are only a few different antacid ingredients, all of which are bases. Common ingredients are sodium bicarbonate, calcium carbonate, aluminum hydroxide, magnesium carbonate, and magnesium hydroxide. Even a single brand name often encompasses a variety of products. For example, there are more than a dozen varieties of Alka-Seltzer®.

Sodium bicarbonate ($NaHCO_3$), commonly called *baking soda*, was one of the first antacids and is still used occasionally. It is the principal antacid in most forms of Alka-Seltzer for heartburn relief. The bicarbonate ions react with the acid in the stomach to form carbonic acid, which then breaks down to carbon dioxide and water.

$$HCO_3^-(aq) + H^+(aq) \longrightarrow H_2CO_3(aq)$$

$$H_2CO_3(aq) \longrightarrow CO_2(g) + H_2O(l)$$

The $CO_2(g)$ is largely responsible for the burps that bicarbonate-containing antacids produce. Overuse of sodium bicarbonate can make the blood too alkaline,

You can make your own aspirin-free "Alka-Seltzer." Simply place half a teaspoon of baking soda in a glass of orange juice. (What is the acid and what is the base in this reaction?)

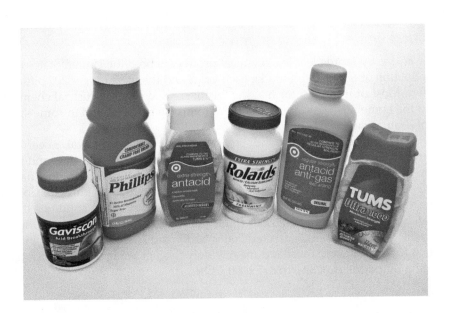

◀ **Figure 7.8** Claims that antacids are "fast acting" are almost meaningless because most common acid–base reactions are almost instantaneous. Some tablets may dissolve a little more slowly than others. You can speed their action by chewing them.

Why Doesn't Stomach Acid Dissolve the Stomach?

We know that strong acids are corrosive to skin. Look back at Table 7.1 and you will see that the gastric juice in your stomach is extremely acidic. Gastric juice is a solution containing about 0.5% hydrochloric acid. Why doesn't the acid in your stomach destroy your stomach lining? The cells that line the stomach are protected by a layer of mucus, a viscous solution of a sugar–protein complex called *mucin* and other substances in water. The mucus serves as a physical barrier, but its role is broader than that. The mucin acts like a sponge that soaks up bicarbonate ions from the cells lining the stomach and hydrochloric acid from within the stomach. The bicarbonate ions neutralize the acid within the mucus.

It used to be thought that stomach acid was the cause of ulcers, but it is now known that the acid plays only a minor role in ulcer formation. Research has shown that most ulcers develop as a result of infection with a bacterium called *Helicobacter pylori* (*H. pylori*) that damages the mucus, exposing cells in the stomach lining to the harsh stomach acid. Other agents, such as aspirin and alcohol, may be contributing factors to the development of ulcers. Treatment usually involves antibiotics that kill *H. pylori*.

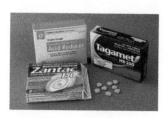

▲ Drugs such as ranitidine (Zantac™), famotidine (Pepcid AC™), cimetidine (Tagamet HB™), and omeprazole (Prilosec) are not antacids. Rather than neutralizing stomach acid, these drugs act on cells in the lining of the stomach, reducing the amount of acid that is produced.

a condition called **alkalosis**. Also, antacids that contain sodium ion are not recommended for people with hypertension (high blood pressure).

Calcium carbonate ($CaCO_3$) is safe in small amounts, but regular use can cause constipation. Also, taking large amounts of calcium carbonate can actually result in increased acid secretion after a few hours. Tums® and many store brands of antacids have calcium carbonate as the only active ingredient.

Aluminum hydroxide [$Al(OH)_3$], like calcium carbonate, can cause constipation. There is also some concern that antacids containing aluminum ions can deplete the body of essential phosphate ions. Aluminum hydroxide is the active ingredient in Amphojel®.

A suspension of magnesium hydroxide [$Mg(OH)_2$] in water is sold as *milk of magnesia*. Magnesium carbonate ($MgCO_3$) is also used as an antacid. These magnesium compounds act as antacids in small doses, but as laxatives in large doses.

Many antacid products have a mixture of antacids. Rolaids® and Mylanta® contain calcium carbonate and magnesium hydroxide. Maalox® liquid has aluminum hydroxide and magnesium hydroxide. These products balance the tendency of magnesium compounds to cause diarrhea with that of aluminum and calcium compounds to cause constipation.

Although antacids are generally safe for occasional use, they can interact with other medications. Anyone who has severe or repeated attacks of indigestion should consult a physician. Self-medication can sometimes be dangerous.

Acids and Bases in Industry and at Home

Sulfuric acid is by far the leading chemical product in both the United States (average production of about 40 billion kg each year) and the world (over 200 billion kg annually). Most of it is used for making fertilizers and other industrial chemicals. Around the home, we use sulfuric acid in automobile batteries and in some special kinds of drain cleaners.

Hydrochloric acid is used in industry to remove rust from metal, in construction to remove excess mortar from bricks and etch concrete for painting, and in the home to remove lime deposits from fixtures and toilet bowls. The product used in the home is often called *muriatic acid*, an old name for hydrochloric acid. Concentrated solutions (about 38% HCl) cause severe burns, but dilute solutions can be used safely in the home if handled carefully. Yearly production of hydrochloric acid is more than 4 billion kg in the United States and about 20 billion kg worldwide.

Lime (CaO) is the cheapest and most widely used commercial base. It is made by heating limestone ($CaCO_3$) to drive off CO_2.

$$CaCO_3(s) + heat \longrightarrow CaO(s) + CO_2(g)$$

Yearly production of calcium oxide is about 22 billion kg in the United States and about 280 billion kg worldwide. Adding water to lime forms calcium hydroxide $[Ca(OH)_2]$, or slaked lime, which is generally safer to handle. Slaked lime is used in agriculture and to make mortar and cement.

Sodium hydroxide (NaOH, lye) is the strong base most often used in the home. It is employed in products such as Easy Off® for cleaning ovens, in products such as Drano® for unclogging drains, and to make both commercial and homemade soaps. Yearly U.S. production of sodium hydroxide is about 9 billion kg.

Ammonia (NH_3) is produced in huge volume, mainly for use as fertilizer. Yearly U.S. production is nearly 11 billion kg. Ammonia is used around the home in a variety of cleaning products (Chapter 21).

Acids and Bases in Health and Disease

When they are misused, acids and bases can be damaging to human health. Concentrated strong acids and bases are corrosive poisons (Chapter 22) that can cause serious chemical burns. Once the chemical agents are removed, these injuries resemble burns caused by heat and are often treated in the same way. Besides being a strong acid, sulfuric acid is also a powerful dehydrating agent that can react with water in the cells.

Strong acids and bases, even in dilute solutions, break down, or *denature*, the protein molecules in living cells, much as cooking does. Generally, the fragments are not able to carry out the functions of the original proteins. If exposure to the acid or base is sustained, this fragmentation continues until the tissue has been completely destroyed.

Acids and bases affect human health in more subtle ways. A delicate balance between acids and bases must be maintained in the blood, other body fluids, and cells. If the acidity of the blood changes too much, the blood loses its capacity to carry oxygen. In living cells, proteins function properly only at an optimal pH. If the pH changes too much in either direction, the proteins can't carry out their functions. Fortunately, the body has a complex but efficient mechanism for maintaining a proper acid–base balance.

▲ **It DOES Matter!**
The proper pH is as important for plant growth as fertilizer is. Soil that is "sour," or too acidic, is "sweetened" by adding slaked lime (calcium hydroxide). A few plants, such as blueberries and citrus fruit, require acidic soil, and an acid such as vinegar may have to be periodically added to the soil they grow in.

▲ **Safety Alert**
Concentrated acids and bases can cause severe burns and are especially damaging to the eyes. Use great care in working with them. Always follow directions carefully. Wear chemical-splash safety goggles to protect your eyes and clothing that will protect your skin and clothes.

Self-Assessment Questions

1. Which of the following is a common ingredient in antacids?
   a. $CaCO_3$
   b. $Ca(OH)_2$
   c. HCl
   d. KOH

2. When a person with excess stomach acid takes an antacid, the pH of the person's stomach changes
   a. from a low value to a value nearer 7
   b. from 7 to a much higher value
   c. from a low value to an even lower value
   d. from a high value to a lower value

3. The leading chemical product of U.S. industry is
   a. ammonia
   b. lime
   c. pesticides
   d. sulfuric acid

4. The acid used in automobile batteries is
   a. citric acid
   b. hydrochloric acid
   c. nitric acid
   d. sulfuric acid

5. The base often used in soap making is
   a. $Ca(OH)_2$
   b. $Mg(OH)_2$
   c. NaOH
   d. NH_3

Answers: 1, a; 2, a; 3, d; 4, d; 5, c

CRITICAL THINKING EXERCISES

Apply knowledge that you have gained in this chapter and one or more of the FLaReS principles (Chapter 1) to evaluate the following statements or claims.

7.1 A television advertisement claimed that the antacid Maalox neutralizes stomach acid faster and, therefore, relieves heartburn faster than Pepcid AC®, a drug that inhibits the release of stomach acid. To illustrate this claim, two flasks of acid were shown. In one, Maalox rapidly neutralized the acid. In the other, Pepcid AC did not neutralize the acid.

7.2 Some people claim that putting salt on grapefruit takes away a little of the acidity.

7.3 Testifying in a court case, a witness makes the following statement: "Although runoff from our plant did appear to contaminate a stream, the pH of the stream before the contamination was 6.4, and after contamination it was 5.4. So the stream is now only slightly more acidic than before."

7.4 A Jamaican fish recipe calls for adding the juice of several limes to the fish, but no heat is used to cook the fish. The directions state that the lime juice in effect "cooks" the fish.

7.5 An advertisement claims that vinegar in a glass-cleaning product will remove the spots left on glasses by tap water. The spots are largely calcium carbonate deposits.

SUMMARY

Section 7.1—Acids taste sour, turn litmus red, and react with active metals to form hydrogen. Bases taste bitter, turn litmus blue, and feel slippery to the skin. Acids and bases react to form salts and water. An acid–base indicator such as litmus has different colors in acid and in base and is used to determine whether solutions are acidic or basic.

Section 7.2—According to Arrhenius's definition, an *acid* produces hydrogen ions (H^+, also called protons) in aqueous solution, and a *base* produces hydroxide ions (OH^-). Neutralization is the combination of H^+ and OH^- to form water. The anion and cation that were associated with H^+ and OH^- ions combine to form an ionic salt. In the more general Brønsted–Lowry acid–base theory, an acid is a proton donor and a base is a proton acceptor. When a Brønsted–Lowry acid dissolves in water, the H_2O molecules pick up H^+ to form hydronium ions (H_3O^+). A Brønsted–Lowry base in water accepts a proton from a water molecule, forming OH^-.

Section 7.3—Some nonmetal oxides (such as CO_2 and SO_3) are acidic anhydrides in that they react with water to form acids. Some metal oxides (such as Li_2O and CaO) are basic anhydrides; they react with water to form bases.

Section 7.4—A strong acid is one that ionizes completely in water to form H^+ ions and anions. A weak acid ionizes only slightly in water; most of the acid exists as intact molecules. Common strong acids are sulfuric, hydrochloric, and nitric acids. Likewise, a strong base is completely ionized in water, and a weak base is only slightly ionized. Sodium hydroxide and potassium hydroxide are common strong bases.

Section 7.5—The reaction between an acid and a base is called *neutralization*. In aqueous solution, it is the combination of H^+ and OH^- that forms water. The other anions and cations form an ionic salt.

Section 7.6—The pH scale indicates the degree of acidity or basicity; pH is defined as pH = $-\log[H^+]$, where $[H^+]$ is the molar concentration of hydrogen ion. A pH of 7 ($[H^+] = 1 \times 10^{-7}$ M) is neutral; pH values lower than 7 represent increasing acidity, and pH values greater than 7 represent increasing basicity. A change in pH of one unit represents a tenfold change in $[H^+]$.

Section 7.7—A pair of compounds or ions that differ by one proton (H^+) is called a conjugate acid–base pair. A buffer solution is a mixture of a weak acid and its conjugate base or a weak base and its conjugate acid. A buffer maintains a nearly constant pH when a small amount of a strong acid or a strong base is added.

Section 7.8—An antacid is a base such as sodium bicarbonate, magnesium hydroxide, aluminum hydroxide, or calcium carbonate that is taken to relieve hyperacidity. Overuse of some antacids can make the blood too alkaline (basic), a condition called alkalosis. Acid rain is rain with a pH less than 5.6. The acidity is due to sulfur oxides and nitrogen oxides from natural sources as well as industrial air pollution and automobile exhaust fumes. Acid rain can have serious effects on plant and animal life. Sulfuric acid is the number one chemical produced in the United States and is used for making fertilizers and other industrial chemicals. Hydrochloric acid is used for rust removal and etching mortar and concrete. Lime (calcium oxide) is made from limestone and is the cheapest and most widely used base. It is an ingredient in plaster and cement and is used in agriculture. Sodium hydroxide is used to make many industrial products, as well as soap. Ammonia is a weak base produced mostly for use as fertilizer. Concentrated strong acids and bases are corrosive poisons that can cause serious burns. Living cells have an optimal pH that is necessary for the proper functioning of proteins.

Green chemistry Base is used to convert renewable fats and oils into products such as soaps and biofuels. Treatment with acid can decompose special plastics (such as polylactic acid, PLA) into a useful antimicrobial cleaner. Application of the Twelve Principles of Green Chemistry can guide us to find practical uses for materials that were once considered waste.

Learning Objectives

❯ Distinguish between acids and bases using their chemical and physical properties. (7.1)	Problems 1, 26, 27
❯ Explain how an acid–base indicator works. (7.1)	Problem 2
❯ Identify Arrhenius and Brønsted–Lowry acids and bases. (7.2)	Problems 4, 12–22, 59
❯ Write a balanced equation for a neutralization or an ionization. (7.2)	Problems 8, 39–46, 60, 67
❯ Identify acidic and basic anhydrides, and write equations showing their reactions with water. (7.3)	Problems 7, 29, 30
❯ Define and identify strong and weak acids and bases. (7.4)	Problems 5, 9, 10, 31–38, 61
❯ Identify the reactants and predict the products in a neutralization reaction. (7.5)	Problems 43–46
❯ Describe the relationship between the pH of a solution and its acidity or basicity. (7.6)	Problems 47–54
❯ Find the molar concentration of hydrogen ion, $[H^+]$, from a pH value or the pH value from $[H^+]$. (7.6)	Problems 49–54
❯ Write the formula for the conjugate base of an acid or for the conjugate acid of a base. (7.7)	Problems 55, 56
❯ Describe the action of a buffer. (7.7)	Problem 65
❯ Describe everyday uses of acids and bases and how they affect daily life. (7.8)	Problems 11, 57, 58
❯ Write equations for the production of soap and of biofuel.	Problem 73
❯ Describe ways by which acids and bases can contribute to greener production of consumer products.	Problems 71, 72, 74

REVIEW QUESTIONS

1. Define the following terms, and give an example of each.
   a. acid   **b.** base   **c.** salt

2. Describe the effect on litmus and the action on iron or zinc of a solution that has been neutralized.

3. List four general properties **(a)** of acidic solutions and **(b)** of basic solutions.

4. Can a substance be a Brønsted–Lowry acid if it does not contain H atoms? Are there any characteristic atoms that must be present in a Brønsted–Lowry base?

5. Both strong bases and weak bases have properties characteristic of hydroxide ions. How do strong bases and weak bases differ?

6. What is meant by a proton in acid–base chemistry? How does it differ from a nuclear proton (Chapter 3)?

7. What is an acidic anhydride? A basic anhydride?

8. Describe the neutralization of an acid or a base.

9. Magnesium hydroxide is completely ionic, even in the solid state, yet it can be taken internally as an antacid. Explain why taking it does not cause injury although taking sodium hydroxide would.

10. What are the effects of strong acids and strong bases on the skin?

11. What is alkalosis? What antacid ingredient might cause alkalosis if taken in excess?

12. According to the Arrhenius theory, all acids have one element in common. What is that element? Are all compounds containing that element acids? Explain.

PROBLEMS

Acids and Bases: The Arrhenius Theory

13. Write an equation that represents how perchloric acid ($HClO_4$) behaves as an Arrhenius acid.

14. Write an equation that represents how dihydrogen phosphate ion ($H_2PO_4^-$) behaves as an Arrhenius acid. (Be sure to include the correct charges for ions.)

15. Write an equation showing that rubidium hydroxide ($RbOH$) acts as an Arrhenius base in water.

16. Write an equation showing that calcium hydroxide acts as an Arrhenius base in water.

Acids and Bases: The Brønsted–Lowry Acid–Base Theory

17. Use the Brønsted–Lowry definitions to identify the first compound in each equation as an acid or a base. (*Hint:* What is produced by the reaction?)
    a. $(CH_3)_2NH + H_2O \longrightarrow (CH_3)_2NH_2^+ + OH^-$
    b. $C_6H_5NH_2 + H_2O \longrightarrow C_6H_5NH_3^+ + OH^-$
    c. $C_6H_5CH_2NH_2 + H_2O \longrightarrow C_6H_5CH_2NH_3^+ + OH^-$

18. Use the Brønsted–Lowry definitions to identify the first compound in each equation as an acid or a base.
    a. $CH_3NH_2 + H_2O \longrightarrow CH_3NH_3^+ + OH^-$
    b. $H_2O_2 + H_2O \longrightarrow H_3O^+ + HO_2^-$
    c. $NH_2Cl + H_2O \longrightarrow NH_3Cl^+ + OH^-$

19. Write the equation that shows hydrogen chloride gas reacting as a Brønsted–Lowry acid in water. What is the name of the acid formed?

20. Write the equation that shows hydrogen iodide gas reacting as a Brønsted–Lowry acid in water. Based on the answer to Problem 19, suggest a name for the acid formed.

21. Write the equation that shows how ammonia acts as a Brønsted–Lowry base in water.

22. Hydroxylamine ($HONH_2$) is not an Arrhenius base, even though it contains OH, but it *is* a Brønsted–Lowry base. Write an equation that shows how hydroxylamine acts as a Brønsted–Lowry base in water.

Acids and Bases: Names and Formulas

23. For the following acids and bases, supply a formula to match the name or a name to match the formula.
    a. HCl
    b. strontium hydroxide
    c. KOH
    d. boric acid

24. For the following acids and bases, supply a formula to match the name or a name to match the formula.
    a. rubidium hydroxide
    b. $Al(OH)_3$
    c. hydrocyanic acid
    d. HNO_3

25. Name the following, and classify each as an acid or a base.
    a. H_3PO_4
    b. CsOH
    c. H_2CO_3

26. Name the following, and classify each as an acid or a base.
    a. $Mg(OH)_2$
    b. NH_3
    c. CH_3COOH

27. When an acid name ends in -*ic acid*, there is often a related acid whose name ends in -*ous acid*. The formula of the -*ous* acid has one less oxygen atom than that of the -*ic* acid. With this information, write formulas for (a) nitrous acid and (b) phosphorous acid.

28. Refer to Problem 27 and Table 7.1. Tellurium is chemically similar to sulfur. Use this information to write the formulas for (a) telluric acid and (b) tellurous acid.

Acidic and Basic Anhydrides

29. Give the formula for the compound formed when (a) sulfur trioxide reacts with water and (b) magnesium oxide reacts with water. In each case, is the product an acid or a base?

30. Give the formula for the compound formed when (a) potassium oxide reacts with water and (b) carbon dioxide reacts with water. In each case, is the product an acid or a base?

Strong and Weak Acids and Bases

31. When 1.0 mol of hydrogen iodide (HI) gas is dissolved in a liter of water, the resulting solution contains 1.0 mol of hydronium ions and 1.0 mol of iodide ions. Classify HI as a strong acid, a weak acid, a weak base, or a strong base.

32. Thallium hydroxide (TlOH) is a water-soluble ionic compound. Classify TlOH as a strong acid, a weak acid, a weak base, or a strong base.

33. Methylamine (CH_3NH_2) gas reacts slightly with water to form relatively few hydroxide ions and methylammonium ions ($CH_3NH_3^+$). Classify CH_3NH_2 as a strong acid, a weak acid, a weak base, or a strong base.

34. When 1 mol of hydrogen sulfide (H_2S) gas is dissolved in a liter of water, the resulting solution contains about 0.0004 mol of H^+ ions and about 3×10^{-11} mol of OH^- ions. Classify H_2S as a strong acid, a weak acid, a weak base, or a strong base.

35. Identify each of the following substances as a strong acid, a weak acid, a strong base, a weak base, or a salt.
    a. LiOH
    b. HBr
    c. HNO_2
    d. $CuSO_4$

36. Identify each of the following substances as a strong acid, a weak acid, a strong base, a weak base, or a salt.
    a. K_3PO_4
    b. $CaBr_2$
    c. $Mg(OH)_2$
    d. $BaCO_3$

37. Which of the following aqueous solutions has the highest concentration of H^+ ions? Which has the lowest?
    a. 0.10 M HNO_3
    b. 0.10 M NH_3
    c. 0.10 M CH_3COOH

38. Consider 0.10 M solutions of acetic acid, ammonia, hydrochloric acid, and sodium hydroxide. Rank these solutions in order of increasing pH.

Ionization of Acids and Bases

39. Write equations showing the ionization of the following as Arrhenius acids or bases.
    a. HNO_2
    b. $Ba(OH)_2$
    c. HBr

40. Write equations showing the ionization of the following as Arrhenius acids or bases.
    a. HI
    b. LiOH
    c. $HClO_2$

41. Write equations showing the ionization of the following as Brønsted–Lowry acids in water.
    a. HClO
    b. HNO_2
    c. H_2S

42. Write equations showing the ionization of the following as Brønsted–Lowry acids in water.
    a. HI
    b. $HClO_3$
    c. $CFH_2CHOHCOOH$

Neutralization

43. Write equations for the reaction (a) of potassium hydroxide with hydrochloric acid and (b) of lithium hydroxide with nitric acid.

44. Write equations for the reaction (a) of 1 mol of calcium hydroxide with 2 mol of hydrochloric acid and (b) of 1 mol of sulfuric acid with 2 mol of potassium hydroxide.

45. Write the equation for the reaction of 1 mol of sulfurous acid (H_2SO_3) with 1 mol of magnesium hydroxide.

46. Write the equation for the reaction of 1 mol of phosphoric acid with 1 mol of aluminum hydroxide.

The pH Scale

47. Indicate whether each of the following pH values represents an acidic, basic, or neutral solution.
    a. 4
    b. 7
    c. 3.5
    d. 9

48. Lime juice is quite sour. Which of the following is a reasonable pH for lime juice?
    a. 2
    b. 6
    c. 7.8
    d. 12

49. What is the pH of a solution that has a hydrogen ion concentration of 1.0×10^{-5} M?

50. What is the pH of a solution that has a hydrogen ion concentration of 1.0×10^{-9} M?

51. What is the hydrogen ion concentration of a solution that has a pH of 3?

52. What is the hydrogen ion concentration of a solution that has a pH of 11?

53. Milk of magnesia has a hydrogen ion concentration between 1.0×10^{-10} M and 1.0×10^{-11} M. What two whole-number values is the pH of milk of magnesia between?

54. Oven cleaner has a pH between 13 and 14. What two whole-number values of x should be used in 1.0×10^{-x} M to express the range of hydrogen ion concentration?

Conjugate Acid–Base Pairs

55. In the following reaction in aqueous solution, identify (a) which of the reactants is the acid and which is the base, (b) the conjugate base of the acid, and (c) the conjugate acid of the base.

$$HNO_3 \,(aq) + NH_3(aq) \longrightarrow NO_3^- \,(aq) + NH_4^+ \,(aq)$$

56. In the following reaction in aqueous solution, identify (a) which of the reactants is the acid and which is the base, (b) the conjugate base of the acid, and (c) the conjugate acid of the base.

$$CH_3CH_2COOH + H_2O \longrightarrow CH_3CH_2COO^- + H_3O^+$$

Antacids

57. Mylanta liquid has 200 mg of $Al(OH)_3$ and 200 mg of $Mg(OH)_2$ per teaspoonful. Write the equation for the neutralization of stomach acid [represented as HCl(aq)] by each of these substances.

58. What is the Brønsted–Lowry base in each of the following compounds, which are ingredients in antacids?
    a. $NaHCO_3$
    b. $Mg(OH)_2$
    c. $MgCO_3$
    d. $CaCO_3$

ADDITIONAL PROBLEMS

59. According to the Arrhenius theory, is every compound that contains OH a base? Explain.

60. Lime deposits on brass faucets are mostly $CaCO_3$. The deposits can be removed by soaking the faucets in hydrochloric acid. Write an equation for the reaction that occurs.

61. The conjugate base of a very weak acid is a strong base, and the conjugate base of a strong acid is a weak base. (a) Is Cl^- ion a strong base or a weak base? (b) Is CN^- a strong base or a weak base?

62. Strontium iodide can be made by the reaction of solid strontium carbonate ($SrCO_3$) with an acid. Identify the acid, and write the balanced equation for the reaction.

63. The pOH is related to $[OH^-]$ just as pH is related to $[H^+]$. What is the pOH (a) of a solution that has a hydroxide ion concentration of 1.0×10^{-3} M? (b) Of a 0.01 M KOH solution?

64. Rank 0.1 M solutions of (a) acetic acid ($HC_2H_3O_2$), (b) ammonia (NH_3), (c) nitric acid (HNO_3), (d) sodium chloride (NaCl), and (e) sodium hydroxide (NaOH) from the highest pH to the lowest pH.

65. Human blood contains buffers that minimize changes in pH. One blood buffer is the hydrogen phosphate ion (HPO_4^{2-}). Like water, HPO_4^{2-} is amphiprotic. That is, it can act either as a Brønsted–Lowry acid or as a Brønsted–Lowry base. Write equations that illustrate the reaction with water of HPO_4^{2-} as an acid and as a base.

66. Three varieties of Tums have calcium carbonate as the only active ingredient: Regular Tums tablets have 500 mg; Tums E-X, 750 mg; and Tums ULTRA, 1000 mg. How many regular Tums would you have to take to get the same quantity of calcium carbonate as you would get with two Tums E-X? With two Tums ULTRA tablets?

67. The active ingredient in the antacid Basaljel is a gel of solid aluminum carbonate. Write the equation for the neutralization of aluminum carbonate by stomach acid (aqueous HCl).

68. Milk of magnesia has 400 mg of $Mg(OH)_2$ per teaspoon. Calculate the mass of stomach acid that can be neutralized by 1.00 teaspoon of milk of magnesia, assuming that the stomach acid is 0.50% HCl by mass.

69. When a well is drilled into rock that contains sulfide minerals, some of the minerals may dissolve in the well water, yielding "sulfur water" that smells like rotten eggs. The water from these wells feels slightly slippery, contains HS^- ions, and turns litmus paper blue. From this information, write an equation representing the reaction of HS^- ions with water.

70. Sulfuric acid is produced from elemental sulfur by a three-step process: (1) Sulfur is burned to produce sulfur dioxide. (2) Sulfur dioxide is oxidized to sulfur trioxide using oxygen and a vanadium (V) oxide catalyst. (3) Finally, the sulfur trioxide is reacted with water to produce 98% sulfuric acid. Write equations for the three reactions.

71. The pH of soap is sometimes adjusted by adding citric acid before the raw soap is formed into bars. Would citric acid increase or decrease the pH of the finished soap?

72. Write an equation to show soap [as $CH_3(CH_2)_{14}COO^-Na^+$] acting as a base with sulfuric acid.

73. Write an equation for the neutralization reaction of a fatty acid ($HC_{16}H_{31}O_2$) with potassium hydroxide (KOH) in water. Is the product of this reaction a fuel or a soap?

74. Most soaps have a bitter taste and a slippery feel. What does this hint indicate about the pH of most soaps?

COLLABORATIVE GROUP PROJECTS

Prepare a PowerPoint, poster, or other presentation (as directed by your instructor) to share with the class.

1. Prepare a brief report on one of the following acids or bases. List sources (including local sources for the acid or base, if available) and commercial uses.
    a. ammonia
    b. hydrochloric acid
    c. phosphoric acid
    d. nitric acid
    e. sodium hydroxide
    f. sulfuric acid

2. Examine the labels of at least five antacid preparations. Make a list of the ingredients in each. Look up the properties (medical use, side effects, toxicity, and so on) of each ingredient on the Web or in a reference book such as *The Merck Index*.

3. Examine the labels of at least five toilet-bowl cleaners and five drain cleaners. Make a list of the ingredients in each. Look up the formulas and properties of each ingredient on the Web or in a reference book such as *The Merck Index*. Which ingredients are acids? Which are bases?

4. A web page on making biodiesel claims that any water in the waste oil must be removed before starting the reaction.

Oxidation and Reduction

Have You Ever Wondered?

1. **Why do AA and D batteries have the same voltage?**

2. **Why does it hurt my teeth when I bite on aluminum foil?**

3. **Why does a battery go dead?**

4. **Why are some batteries rechargeable, but others aren't?**

5. **Why does steel rust, while aluminum doesn't?**

6. **Does hydrogen have a promising future as a fuel?**

Learning Objectives

> Identify an oxidation–reduction reaction. (8.1)

> Classify a particular change within a redox reaction as either oxidation or reduction. (8.1)

> Identify the oxidizing agent and the reducing agent in a redox reaction. (8.2)

> Balance redox equations. (8.3)

> Identify and write the half-reactions in an electrochemical cell. (8.3)

> Describe the reactions that occur when iron rusts. (8.4)

> Explain why an explosive reaction is so energetic. (8.4)

> Write equations for reactions in which oxygen is an oxidizing agent. (8.5)

> List some of the common oxidizing agents encountered in daily life. (8.5)

> Identify some common reducing agents. (8.6)

> Write the overall equations for the metabolism of glucose and for photosynthesis. (8.7)

> Distinguish between the objectives of chemists producing industrial chemicals and those of chemists producing specialty chemicals.

> Explain how green chemistry can be applied to the design of new catalysts.

Burn and Unburn From a simple campfire to the most advanced electric battery, from the trees in a rainforest that consume carbon dioxide and make oxygen to the people hurrying along a city street, we depend on an important group of reactions called *oxidation–reduction reactions*, or *redox reactions* (a shortening of *reduction–oxidation*). These reactions are extremely diverse: charcoal burns, iron rusts, bleach removes stains, the food we eat is converted to energy for our brain and muscles, and plants use the sun's energy to produce food.

We see the long-term product of automotive steel and our atmosphere above: rust. The orange color is from iron(III) oxide. Steel is mostly iron, and iron undergoes an undesirable oxidation-reduction (redox) reaction in the presence of air and water. That reaction costs almost $10 billion every year, as engineers and manufacturers look for ways to minimize or prevent that redox reaction. Other redox reactions are desirable, or even necessary, to life itself. In this chapter, we will examine the nature of redox reactions, and we will look at some of their applications in life and in modern technology.

Oxidation and reduction always occur together. They are opposite aspects of a single process, a redox reaction. You can't have one without the other (Figure 8.1). When one substance is oxidized, another is reduced. However, it is sometimes convenient to discuss only a part of the process—the oxidation part or the reduction part.

Reduced forms of matter—foods, coal, and gasoline—are high in energy. *Oxidized* forms—carbon dioxide and water—are low in energy. The energy in foods and fossil fuels is released when these materials are oxidized. In this chapter, we examine the processes of oxidation and reduction in some detail to better understand the chemical reactions that keep us alive and maintain our civilization.

▲ **Figure 8.1** Oxidation and reduction always occur together. Pictured here on the left is a reaction called the ammonium dichromate volcano. In the reaction, the ammonium ion (NH_4^+) is oxidized and the dichromate ion ($Cr_2O_7^{2-}$) is reduced. Considerable heat and light are evolved. The equation for the reaction is

$$(NH_4)_2Cr_2O_7 \longrightarrow Cr_2O_3 + N_2 + 4\,H_2O$$

The water is driven off as vapor, and the nitrogen gas escapes, leaving pure Cr_2O_3 as the visible product (right).

8.1 Oxidation and Reduction: Three Views

Learning Objectives ❯ Identify an oxidation–reduction reaction. ❯ Classify a particular change within a redox reaction as either oxidation or reduction.

The term *oxidation* stems from the early recognition of oxygen's involvement in oxide formation; *reduction* originally meant removal of oxygen from an oxide. When oxygen combines with other elements or compounds, the process is called **oxidation**. The substances that combine with oxygen are said to have been *oxidized*. Originally, the term *oxidation* was limited to reactions involving combination with oxygen. As chemists came to realize that combination with chlorine (or bromine or another active nonmetal) was not all that different from combination with oxygen, they broadened the definition of oxidation to include reactions involving these other substances—as we shall shortly see.

Reduction is the opposite of oxidation. When hydrogen burns, it combines with oxygen to form water.

$$2\,H_2 + O_2 \longrightarrow 2\,H_2O$$

The hydrogen is oxidized in this reaction, but at the same time the oxygen is reduced. Whenever oxidation occurs, reduction must also occur. Oxidation and reduction always happen at the same time and in exactly equivalent amounts.

Because oxidation and reduction are chemical opposites and constant companions, their definitions are linked. We can view oxidation and reduction in at least three different ways (Figure 8.2).

◀ **Figure 8.2** Three different views of oxidation and reduction.

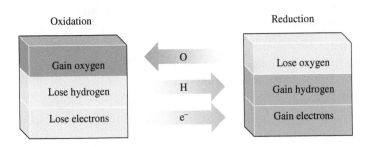

1. *Oxidation* is a gain of oxygen atoms.
   Reduction is a loss of oxygen atoms.

At high temperatures (such as those in automobile engines), nitrogen, which is normally quite unreactive, combines with oxygen to form nitric oxide.

$$N_2 + O_2 \longrightarrow 2\ NO$$

Nitrogen gains oxygen atoms; there are no O atoms in the N_2 molecule and one O atom in each of the NO molecules. Therefore, nitrogen is oxidized.

Now consider what happens when methane is burned to form carbon dioxide and water. Both carbon and hydrogen gain oxygen atoms, and so both elements are oxidized.

This C atom has no O atom attached

This C atom has two O atoms attached

$$CH_4 + 2\ O_2 \longrightarrow CO_2 + 2\ H_2O$$

These H atoms have no O atoms attached

These H atoms are attached to an O atom

When lead dioxide is heated at high temperatures, it decomposes as follows:

$$2\ PbO_2 \longrightarrow 2\ PbO + O_2$$

This Pb atom has two O atoms attached

This Pb atom has only one O atom attached

The lead dioxide loses oxygen, so it is reduced.

CONCEPTUAL Example 8.1 Redox Processes—Gain or Loss of Oxygen Atoms

In each of the following changes, is the reactant undergoing oxidation or reduction? (These are not complete chemical equations.)

a. $Pb \longrightarrow PbO_2$ **b.** $SnO_2 \longrightarrow SnO$

c. $KClO_3 \longrightarrow KCl$ **d.** $Cu_2O \longrightarrow 2\ CuO$

Solution

a. Lead gains oxygen atoms (it has none on the left and two on the right); it is oxidized.

b. Tin loses an oxygen atom (it has two on the left and only one on the right); it is reduced.

c. There are three O atoms on the left and none on the right. The compound loses oxygen; it is reduced.

d. The two copper atoms on the left share a single oxygen atom, that is, half an oxygen atom each. On the right, each Cu atom has an O atom all its own. Cu has gained oxygen; it is oxidized.

■ EXERCISE 8.1

In each of the following changes, is the reactant undergoing oxidation or reduction? (These are not complete chemical equations.)

a. $3 Fe \longrightarrow Fe_3O_4$

b. $NO \longrightarrow NO_2$

c. $CrO_3 \longrightarrow Cr_2O_3$

d. $C_3H_6O \longrightarrow C_3H_6O_2$

A second view of oxidation and reduction involves hydrogen atoms.

2. *Oxidation* is a loss of hydrogen atoms.

   Reduction is a gain of hydrogen atoms.

   Look once more at the burning of methane:

$$CH_4 + 2 O_2 \longrightarrow CO_2 + 2 H_2O$$

The oxygen gains hydrogen to form water, so the oxygen is reduced. Methane loses hydrogen and is oxidized. (We see that the carbon and hydrogens of CH_4 also gain oxygen, so our two views of oxidation and reduction are consistent with one another.)

Methyl alcohol (CH_3OH), when passed over hot copper gauze, forms formaldehyde and hydrogen gas.

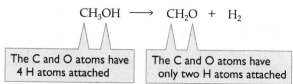

Because the methyl alcohol loses hydrogen, it is oxidized in this reaction.

Methyl alcohol can be made by reaction of carbon monoxide with hydrogen.

$$CO + 2 H_2 \rightarrow CH_3OH$$

Because the carbon monoxide gains hydrogen atoms, it is reduced.

Biochemists often find the gain or loss of hydrogen atoms a useful way to look at oxidation–reduction processes. For example, a substance called NAD^+ is changed to NADH in a variety of biochemical redox reactions. The actual molecules are rather complex, but we can write the equation for the oxidation of ethyl alcohol to acetaldehyde, one step in the metabolism of the alcohol, as follows.

$$CH_3CH_2OH + NAD^+ \longrightarrow CH_3CHO + NADH + H^+$$

We can see that ethyl alcohol is oxidized (loses hydrogen) and NAD^+ is reduced (gains hydrogen).

CONCEPTUAL Example 8.2   Redox Processes—Gain or Loss of Hydrogen Atoms

In each of the following changes, is the reactant undergoing oxidation or reduction? (These are not complete chemical equations.)

a. $C_2H_6O \longrightarrow C_2H_4O$

b. $C_2H_2 \longrightarrow C_2H_6$

Solution

a. There are six H atoms in the reactant on the left and only four in the product on the right. The reactant loses H atoms; it is oxidized.

b. There are two H atoms in the reactant on the left and six in the product on the right. The reactant gains H atoms; it is reduced.

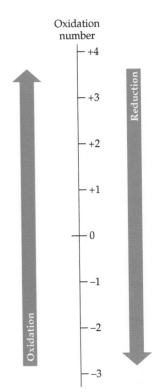

▲ **Figure 8.3** An increase in oxidation number means a loss of electrons and is therefore oxidation. A decrease in oxidation number means a gain of electrons and is therefore reduction.

Q: *Manganese's oxidation number changes from +4 in MnO_2 to +7 in MnO_4^-. Is it oxidized or reduced? Sulfur's oxidation number changes from 0 in S_8 to −2 in S^{2-}. Is it oxidized or reduced?*

■ **EXERCISE 8.2**

In each of the following changes, is the reactant undergoing oxidation or reduction? (These are not complete chemical equations.)

a. $C_3H_6O \longrightarrow C_3H_8O$

b. $C_3H_6 \longrightarrow C_3H_4$

A third view of oxidation and reduction involves gain or loss of electrons.

3. *Oxidation* is a loss of electrons.

Reduction is a gain of electrons.

When magnesium metal reacts with chlorine, magnesium ions and chloride ions are formed.

$$Mg + Cl_2 \longrightarrow Mg^{2+} + 2Cl^-$$

Because the magnesium atom loses electrons, it is oxidized, and because the chlorine atoms gain electrons, they are reduced.

It is easy to see that when magnesium atoms become Mg^{2+} ions, they lose electrons, and that when chlorine atoms become Cl^- ions, they must gain electrons. But which is oxidation and which is reduction? Perhaps Figure 8.3 can help. The charge on a simple ion is often referred to as its *oxidation number*. An increase in oxidation number (increase in positive charge) is oxidation; a decrease in oxidation number is reduction. The charge on an Mg atom is zero, therefore, conversion to Mg^{2+} is an increase in oxidation number (oxidation). For Cl atoms, the charge is also zero, and a change to Cl^- is a decrease in oxidation number (reduction).

This view of oxidation and reduction as a gain or loss of electrons is especially useful in electrochemistry (Section 8.3).

CONCEPTUAL Example 8.3 | Redox Processes—Gain or Loss of Electrons

In each of the following changes, is the reactant undergoing oxidation or reduction? (These are not complete chemical equations.)

a. $Zn \longrightarrow Zn^{2+}$

b. $Fe^{3+} \longrightarrow Fe^{2+}$

c. $S^{2-} \longrightarrow S$

d. $AgNO_3 \longrightarrow Ag$

Solution

a. In forming a 2+ ion, a Zn atom loses two electrons. Its oxidation number increases from 0 to +2. Zinc is oxidized.

b. To change from a 3+ ion to a 2+ ion, Fe gains an electron. Its oxidation number decreases from +3 to +2. The Fe^{3+} ion is reduced.

c. To change from a 2− ion to an atom with no charge, S loses two electrons. Its oxidation number increases. Sulfide ion is oxidized.

d. To answer this question, you must recognize that $AgNO_3$ is an ionic compound consisting of Ag^+ and NO_3^- ions. In changing from Ag^+ to Ag, silver gains an electron. Its oxidation number decreases. Silver ion is reduced.

■ **EXERCISE 8.3**

In each of the following changes, is the reactant undergoing oxidation or reduction? (These are not complete chemical equations.)

a. $Cr^{6+} \rightarrow Cr^{3+}$

b. $Sn^{2+} \longrightarrow Sn^{4+}$

c. $MnO_4^{2-} \longrightarrow MnO_4^-$

d. $Ti \rightarrow TiO_2$

Why do we have different ways to look at oxidation and reduction? Oxidation as a gain of oxygen is historical and specific, but the definition in terms of electrons applies more broadly. Which one should we use? Ordinarily, the definitions are consistent with one another, so we use the most convenient one. For the combustion (burning) of carbon,

$$C + O_2 \longrightarrow CO_2$$

Two mnemonics:
        LEO the lion says GER.
Loss of
   Electrons is
      Oxidation.
Gain of
   Electrons is
      Reduction.
         OIL RIG
Oxidation
   Is
      Loss of electrons.
Reduction
   Is
      Gain of electrons.

it is most convenient to see that carbon is oxidized by gaining oxygen atoms. Similarly, for the reaction

$$CH_2O + H_2 \longrightarrow CH_4O$$

it is easy to see that the reactant CH_2O gains hydrogen atoms and is thereby reduced. Finally, in the case of the reaction

$$3\,Sn^{2+} + 2\,Bi^{3+} \longrightarrow 3\,Sn^{4+} + 2\,Bi$$

it is clear that tin is oxidized because it loses electrons, increasing its oxidation number from +2 to +4. Similarly, we see that bismuth is reduced because it gains electrons, decreasing its oxidation number from +3 to 0.

Self-Assessment Questions

1. Which of the following is *not* one of the ways we can view oxidation?
   a. electrons gained   b. electrons lost
   c. hydrogen atoms lost   d. oxygen atoms gained

2. Which of the following partial equations represents an oxidation of nitrogen?
   a. $NH_3 \rightarrow NH_4^+$ b. $N_2O_4 \rightarrow NI_3$ c. $NO_3^- \rightarrow NO$ d. $NO_2 \rightarrow N_2O_5$

3. When CrO_4^- reacts to form Cr^{3+}, the chromium in CrO_4^- is
   a. reduced; it loses electrons
   b. reduced; it loses oxygen
   c. oxidized; its oxidation number increases
   d. oxidized; it gains positive charge

4. Which of the following partial equations best represents a reduction of molybdenum?
   a. $MoO_2 + H_2O \rightarrow H_2MoO_3$ b. $MoO_2 + 4\,H_2 \rightarrow Mo + 2\,H_2O$
   c. $2\,MoO_2 + O_2 \rightarrow 2\,MoO_3$ d. $MoO_2 + 4\,H^+ \rightarrow Mo^{4+} + 2\,H_2O$

5. According to the following partial equation, Cl_2 is

$$3\,Cl_2 + 2\,Al \rightarrow 2\,AlCl_3$$

   a. both oxidized and reduced   b. neither oxidized nor reduced
   c. oxidized, only   d. reduced only

6. According to the following partial equation, manganese

$$Mn \rightarrow Mn^{2+} + 2\,e^-$$

   a. gains electrons and is oxidized   b. gains electrons and is reduced
   c. loses electrons and is oxidized   d. loses electrons and is reduced

7. When an element is oxidized, its oxidation number
   a. decreases, as electrons are gained   b. decreases, as electrons are lost
   c. increases, as electrons are gained   d. increases, as electrons are lost

Answers: 1, a; 2, d; 3, b; 4, b; 5, d; 6, c; 7, d

8.2 Oxidizing and Reducing Agents

Learning Objective ❯ Identify the oxidizing agent and the reducing agent in a redox reaction.

Oxidation and reduction occur together. However, in looking at oxidation–reduction reactions, we often find it convenient to focus on the role played by a particular reactant. For example, in the reaction

$$CuO + H_2 \longrightarrow Cu + H_2O$$

we see that copper oxide is reduced and hydrogen is oxidized. We can conclude that if one substance is oxidized, the other must *cause* it to be oxidized. In the above reaction, CuO causes H_2 to be oxidized. Therefore, CuO is called the **oxidizing agent**. Conversely, H_2 causes CuO to be reduced, so H_2 is the **reducing agent**. Each oxidation–reduction reaction has an oxidizing agent and a reducing agent among the reactants. The reducing agent is the substance being oxidized; the oxidizing agent is the substance being reduced.

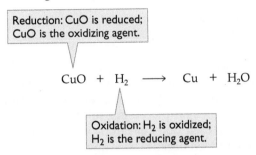

Reduction: CuO is reduced; CuO is the oxidizing agent.

$$CuO + H_2 \longrightarrow Cu + H_2O$$

Oxidation: H_2 is oxidized; H_2 is the reducing agent.

CONCEPTUAL Example 8.4 Oxidizing and Reducing Agents

Identify the oxidizing agents and reducing agents in the following reactions.

a. $2C + O_2 \longrightarrow 2CO$
b. $N_2 + 3H_2 \longrightarrow 2NH_3$
c. $SnO + H_2 \longrightarrow Sn + H_2O$
d. $Mg + Cl_2 \longrightarrow Mg^{2+} + 2Cl^-$

Solution

We can determine the answers by applying the three definitions of oxidation and reduction.

a. C gains oxygen and is oxidized, so it must be the reducing agent. O_2 is therefore the oxidizing agent.
b. N_2 gains hydrogen and is reduced, so it is the oxidizing agent. H_2 therefore is the reducing agent.
c. SnO loses oxygen and is reduced, so it is the oxidizing agent. H_2 is therefore the reducing agent.
d. Mg loses electrons and is oxidized, so it is the reducing agent. Cl_2 is therefore the oxidizing agent.

▪ **EXERCISE 8.4**

Identify the oxidizing agents and reducing agents in the following reactions.

a. $Se + O_2 \longrightarrow SeO_2$
b. $2K + Br_2 \longrightarrow 2K^+ + 2Br^-$
c. $CH_3CN + 2H_2 \longrightarrow CH_3CH_2NH_2$
d. $V_2O_5 + 2H_2 \longrightarrow V_2O_3 + 2H_2O$

Self-Assessment Questions

1. A reducing agent
   a. gains electrons
   b. gains protons
   c. loses electrons
   d. loses protons

2. Which substance is the oxidizing agent in the following reaction?
   $$Cu(s) + 2Ag^+(aq) \rightarrow Cu^{2+}(aq) + 2Ag(s)$$
   a. Ag
   b. Ag^+
   c. Cu
   d. Cu^{2+}

3. In the following reaction, the reducing agent is
   $$Al(s) + Cr^{3+}(aq) \rightarrow Al^{3+}(aq) + Cr(s)$$
   a. Al(s)
   b. $Al^{3+}(aq)$
   c. $Cr^{3+}(aq)$
   d. Cr(s)

4. What is the oxidizing agent in the following reaction?
   $$Zn(s) + 2Tl^+(aq) \rightarrow Zn^{2+}(aq) + 2Tl(s)$$
   a. Tl(s)
   b. $Tl^+(aq)$
   c. Zn(s)
   d. $Zn^{2+}(aq)$

5. What is the reducing agent in the following reaction?
   $$12H^+(aq) + 2IO_3^-(aq) + 10Fe^{2+}(aq) \rightarrow 10Fe^{3+}(aq) + I_2(s) + 6H_2O(l)$$
   a. $Fe^{2+}(aq)$
   b. $H^+(aq)$
   c. $I_2(s)$
   d. $IO_3^-(aq)$

Answers: 1, c; 2, b; 3, a; 4, b; 5, a

8.3 Electrochemistry: Cells and Batteries

Learning Objectives ❯ Balance redox equations. ❯ Identify and write the half-reactions in an electrochemical cell.

We saw in Chapter 3 that electricity can produce chemical change, a process called *electrolysis*. For example, an electric current passed through molten sodium chloride produces sodium metal and chlorine gas. Here we focus on the reverse process, in which chemical change produces electricity.

An electric current in a wire is simply a flow of electrons. Oxidation–reduction reactions in which electrons are transferred from one substance to another can be used to produce electricity. This is what happens in dry cell and storage batteries.

When a coil of copper wire is placed in a solution of silver nitrate (Figure 8.4a), the copper atoms give up their outer electrons to the silver ions. (We can omit the nitrate ions from the equation because they do not change.) The copper metal dissolves, going into solution as copper(II) ions that color the solution blue. The silver ions come out of solution as beautiful needles of silver metal (Figure 8.4b). The copper is oxidized; the silver ions are reduced.

▶ **Figure 8.4** A coil of copper wire is immersed in a colorless solution of Ag^+ ions (a). As the reaction progresses, the more active copper displaces the less active silver from solution, producing needle-like crystals of silver metal (b) and a blue solution of Cu^{2+} ions. The equation for the reaction is $2Ag^+(aq) + Cu(s) \longrightarrow 2Ag(s) + Cu^{2+}(aq)$.

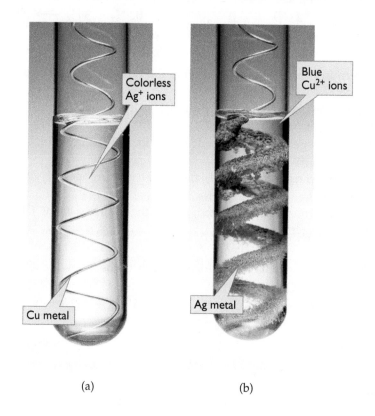

(a)   (b)

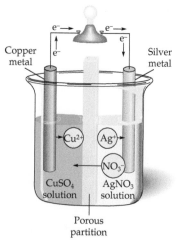

Copper metal   Silver metal

▲ **Figure 8.5** A simple electrochemical cell. The half-reactions are
Oxidation (anode):

$$Cu(s) \longrightarrow Cu^{2+}(aq) + 2 e^-$$

Reduction (cathode):

$$Ag^+(aq) + e^- \longrightarrow Ag(s)$$

Q: *To balance the equation for the overall reaction, you need to add a coefficient of 2 before Ag^+ and $Ag(s)$. Why?*

Because the reaction involves only the transfer of electrons, it can occur even when the silver ions are separated from the copper metal. If we place the reactants in separate compartments and connect them with a wire, the electrons will flow through the wire to get from the copper metal to the silver ions. This flow of electrons constitutes an electric current, and it can be used to run a motor or light a lamp.

In the **electrochemical cell** pictured in Figure 8.5, there are two separate compartments. One contains copper metal in a blue solution of copper(II) sulfate, and the other contains silver metal in a colorless solution of silver nitrate. Copper atoms give up electrons much more readily than silver atoms do, so electrons flow away from the copper compartment and toward the silver. The copper metal slowly dissolves as copper atoms give up electrons to form copper(II) ions. The electrons flow through the wire to the silver compartment, where silver ions pick them up to become silver atoms.

As time goes by, the copper bar slowly disappears and the silver bar gets bigger. The blue solution becomes darker blue as Cu atoms are converted to Cu^{2+} ions. Those Cu^{2+} ions give the left compartment a positive charge, so (negative) nitrate ions move from the right compartment, through the porous partition, into the copper sulfate solution. (That is why the partition is porous. If the nitrate ions were unable to move through it, the cell would not work.) For each copper atom that gives up two electrons, two silver ions each pick up one electron, and two nitrate ions move from the right compartment to the left compartment.

The two pieces of metal where electrons are transferred are called **electrodes**. The electrode where oxidation occurs is called the **anode**. The one where reduction occurs is the **cathode**. In our example cell, copper gives up electrons, it is oxidized, and the copper bar is therefore the anode. Silver ions gain electrons and are reduced, so the silver bar is the cathode.

Electrochemical reactions are often represented as two *half-reactions*. The following representation shows the two half-reactions for the copper–silver cell and their addition to give the overall cell reaction.

Oxidation: $Cu(s) \longrightarrow Cu^{2+}(aq) + 2\,e^-$
Reduction: $\underline{2\,Ag^+(aq) + 2\,e^- \longrightarrow 2\,Ag(s)}$
Overall reaction: $Cu(s) + 2\,Ag^+(aq) \longrightarrow Cu^{2+}(aq) + 2\,Ag(s)$

Note that the electrons cancel when the two half-reactions are added.

CONCEPTUAL Example 8.5   Oxidation and Reduction Half-Reactions

Represent the following reaction as two half-reactions, and label them as an oxidation half-reaction and a reduction half-reaction.

$$Mg + Cl_2 \longrightarrow Mg^{2+} + 2\,Cl^-$$

Solution

Magnesium is oxidized from Mg to Mg^{2+}, a process that involves loss of two electrons from the Mg atom. The oxidation half-reaction is therefore

$$\text{Oxidation}: \quad Mg \longrightarrow Mg^{2+} + 2\,e^-$$

The reduction half-reaction involves chlorine. Each of the two Cl atoms in the Cl_2 molecule must gain an electron to form a Cl^- ion. The reduction half-reaction is therefore

$$\text{Reduction}: \quad Cl_2 + 2\,e^- \longrightarrow 2\,Cl^-$$

■ EXERCISE 8.5

Represent the following reaction as two half-reactions, and label them as an oxidation half-reaction and a reduction half-reaction.

$$2\,Co + 3\,S \rightarrow 2\,Co^{3+} + 3\,S^{2-}$$

Example 8.6   Balancing Redox Equations

Balance the following half-reactions, and combine them to give a balanced overall reaction.

$$Sn^{2+} \longrightarrow Sn^{4+}$$
$$Bi^{3+} \longrightarrow Bi$$

Solution

Atoms are balanced in both half-reactions, but electric charge is not. To balance charge in the first half-reaction, we add two electrons on the right side.

$$Sn^{2+} \longrightarrow Sn^{4+} + 2\,e^-$$

The second half-reaction requires three electrons on the left side.

$$Bi^{3+} + 3\,e^- \longrightarrow Bi$$

1. Why do AA and D batteries have the same voltage? Cell voltage depends almost entirely on the overall cell reaction. Cells with the same cell reaction will have virtually the same voltage. However, a larger cell (D or flashlight battery) contains more reactants and will last longer in a particular device than would a smaller cell (AA or penlight battery).

2. Why does it hurt my teeth when I bite on aluminum foil? If you have an amalgam (metal) filling, aluminum touching the metal can cause a redox reaction in which the aluminum is oxidized. Only a small voltage is produced, but it can be enough to irritate the tooth's nerve causing a lot of discomfort!

Before we can combine the two, however, we must set electron loss equal to electron gain. Electrons lost by the substance being oxidized must be gained by the substance being reduced. To make electron loss and gain equal, we multiply the first half-reaction by 3 and the second by 2.

$$3 \times (Sn^{2+} \longrightarrow Sn^{4+} + 2\,e^-) \quad = \quad 3\,Sn^{2+} \qquad \longrightarrow 3\,Sn^{4+} + 6\,e^-$$
$$2 \times (Bi^{3+} + 3\,e^- \longrightarrow Bi) \quad = \quad 2\,Bi^{3+} + 6\,e^- \longrightarrow 2\,Bi$$
$$\overline{3\,Sn^{2+} + 2\,Bi^{3+} \longrightarrow 3\,Sn^{4+} + 2\,Bi}$$

Note that both atoms and charges balance in the overall reaction.

■ EXERCISE 8.6A
Balance the following half-reactions, and combine them to give a balanced overall reaction.

$$Fe \longrightarrow Fe^{3+}$$
$$Mg^{2+} \longrightarrow Mg$$

■ EXERCISE 8.6B
Balance the following half-reactions, and combine them to give a balanced overall reaction.

$$Pb \longrightarrow Pb^{2+}$$
$$Ag(NH_3)_2{}^+ \longrightarrow Ag + 2\,NH_3$$

Photochromic Glass

Eyeglasses with photochromic lenses eliminate the need for sunglasses because the lenses darken when exposed to bright light. This response to light is the result of oxidation–reduction reactions. Ordinary glass is a complex matrix of silicates (Chapter 12) that is transparent to visible light. Photochromic lenses have silver chloride (AgCl) and copper(I) chloride (CuCl) crystals uniformly embedded in the glass. Silver chloride is susceptible to oxidation and reduction by light. First, the light displaces an electron from a chloride ion.

$$Cl^- \xrightarrow{\text{oxidation}} Cl + e^-$$

The electron then reduces a silver ion to a silver atom.

$$Ag^+ + e^- \xrightarrow{\text{reduction}} Ag$$

Clusters of silver atoms block the transmittance of light, causing the lenses to darken. This process occurs quite quickly. The degree of darkening depends on the intensity of the light.

To be useful in eyeglasses, the photochromic process must be reversible. The darkening process is reversed by the copper(I) chloride. When the lenses are removed from light, the chlorine atoms formed by the exposure to light are reduced by the copper(I) ions, which are oxidized to copper(II) ions.

$$Cl + Cu^+ \longrightarrow Cu^{2+} + Cl^-$$

The copper(II) ions then oxidize the silver atoms.

$$Cu^{2+} + Ag \longrightarrow Cu^+ + Ag^+$$

The net effect is that the silver and chlorine atoms are converted to their original oxidized and reduced states, and the lenses become transparent once more.

▲ Photochromic glass darkens in the presence of light.

Dry Cells

The familiar *dry cell* (Figure 8.6) is used in flashlights and some small portable devices. It has a cylindrical zinc case that acts as the anode. A carbon rod in the center of the cell is the cathode. The space between the cathode and the anode contains a moist paste of graphite powder (carbon), manganese dioxide (MnO_2), and ammonium chloride (NH_4Cl). The anode reaction is the oxidation of the zinc cylinder to zinc ions. The cathode reaction involves reduction of manganese dioxide. A simplified version of the overall reaction is

$$Zn + 2\,MnO_2 + H_2O \longrightarrow Zn^{2+} + Mn_2O_3 + 2\,OH^-$$

The ordinary dry cell has largely been replaced by the alkaline cell, which is similar but contains potassium hydroxide instead of ammonium chloride. Alkaline cells are more expensive than zinc–carbon dry cells, but they last longer—both in storage and in use.

Lead Storage Batteries

Although we often refer to dry cells as batteries, a **battery** is actually a collection of electrochemical cells. The 12-volt (V) storage battery used in automobiles, for example, is a series of six 2-V cells. Each cell (Figure 8.7) contains a pair of electrodes, one lead and the other lead dioxide, in a chamber filled with sulfuric acid. Lead–acid batteries have been known for 150 years. They are used mainly in automobiles. Three hundred million of them are made per year.

An important feature of the lead storage battery is that it can be recharged. It discharges as it supplies electricity when the ignition is turned on to start a car or when the motor is off and the lights are on. It is recharged when the car is moving and an electric current created by the mechanical action of the car is supplied to the battery. The net reaction during discharge is

$$Pb + PbO_2 + 2\,H_2SO_4 \longrightarrow 2\,PbSO_4 + 2\,H_2O$$

The reaction during recharge is the reverse.

$$2\,PbSO_4 + 2\,H_2O \longrightarrow Pb + PbO_2 + 2\,H_2SO_4$$

Lead storage batteries are durable, but they are heavy, contain corrosive sulfuric acid, and lead is a toxic environmental problem.

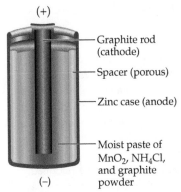

▲ **Figure 8.6** Cross section of a zinc–carbon cell. The half-reactions are

Oxidation (anode):

$$Zn(s) \longrightarrow Zn^{2+}(aq) + 2\,e^-$$

Reduction (cathode):

$$2MnO_2(s) + H_2O + 2\,e^- \longrightarrow$$
$$Mn_2O_3(s) + 2\,OH^-(aq)$$

▲ **It DOES Matter!**
Batteries labeled "Heavy Duty" or "Super" may be ordinary dry cells and may not have the longer shelf life and operating life of alkaline cells. Usually, alkaline cells are labeled as such and are only slightly higher in cost, making them a better buy.

3. Why does a battery go dead? When one or more of the reactants (zinc and MnO_2 in a dry cell) is essentially used up, the cell can no longer provide useful energy.

◀ **Figure 8.7** One cell of a lead-storage battery has two anode plates and two cathode plates. Six such cells make up the common 12-V car battery. The half-reactions are

Oxidation (anode):

$$Pb(s) + SO_4{}^{2-}(aq) \longrightarrow$$
$$PbSO_4(s) + 2\,e^-$$

Reduction (cathode):

$$PbO_2(s) + 4\,H^+(aq) +$$
$$SO_4{}^{2-}(aq) + 2\,e^- \longrightarrow$$
$$PbSO_4(s) + 2\,H_2O$$

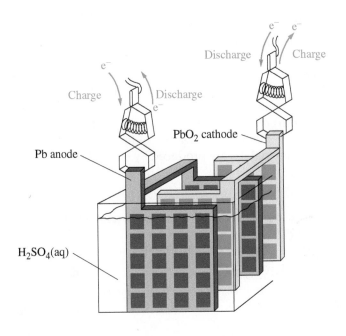

4. Why are some batteries rechargeable, but others aren't? A rechargeable battery uses a *reversible* redox reaction. The normal, forward reaction provides electrical energy. Applying electrical energy in the opposite direction using a charger reverses the reaction, and the starting materials are reformed. Not all redox reactions can be reversed in this manner.

Other Batteries

Much current battery technology involves the use of lithium, which has an extraordinarily low density and provides a higher voltage than other metals. Lithium cells make today's lightweight laptop computers possible. Lithium–SO_2 cells are used in submarines and rockets; lithium–iodine cells are used in pacemakers; and lithium–FeS_2 batteries are used in cameras, radios, and compact disc players.

Lithium cells provide so much energy and have such a compact volume that there have been incidents when the cells burst or even caught fire while being rapidly charged or discharged. Several manufacturers recalled millions of computer and telephone batteries between 2005 and 2011 because of the potential for such incidents.

The rechargeable NiCad cell (Cd anode, NiO cathode) has long been popular for portable radios and cordless tools. Its biggest competitor is the nickel–metal hydride cell, in which cadmium is replaced by a hydrogen-absorbing nickel alloy, such as $ZrNi_2$ or $LaNi_5$.

The button batteries used in hearing aids and hand calculators formerly contained mercury (zinc anode, HgO cathode), but these cells are gradually being phased out and replaced with zinc–air cells. Tiny silver oxide cells (zinc anode, Ag_2O cathode) are used mainly in watches and cameras.

Fuel Cells

An interesting kind of battery is the fuel cell. In a **fuel cell**, the oxidizing agent (usually oxygen) and the reducing agent are supplied continuously to the cell. Unlike other cells, a fuel cell does not "go dead" as long as the reactants are supplied. Moreover, when fossil fuels such as coal are burned to generate electricity, at most 35–40% of the energy from the combustion is actually harnessed. In a fuel cell, the fuel is oxidized and oxygen is reduced with 70–75% efficiency. As we shall see in Chapter 15, most present-day fuel cells use hydrogen as the fuel with platinum, nickel, or rhodium electrodes, in a solution of potassium hydroxide.

Electrolysis

Dry cells and fuel cells produce electricity from chemical reactions. Sometimes, we can reverse the process. In electrolysis (discussed briefly in Section 3.1), electricity supplied externally causes a chemical reaction to occur. The charging reaction of the lead storage cell shown in Figure 8.7 is one type of electrolysis. The car's alternator provides electric current, causing lead(II) sulfate to be converted back to lead metal and PbO_2. Other rechargeable cells undergo the reverse of their electricity-producing reaction when they are recharged.

Electrolysis is very important in industry. About 1% of all of the electricity in the United States is used to convert aluminum oxide to the aluminum metal we use for pots, foil, and cans. Chrome plating is performed by passing electricity through a solution of chromium ions (Cr^{6+}); electrons convert the ions to shiny chromium metal. Crude copper metal is purified by electrolysis, which converts the copper metal at the anode into copper(II) ions and then deposits nearly pure copper metal at the cathode. Many other materials—including sodium hydroxide, chlorine bleach, and magnesium metal—are produced by electrolysis.

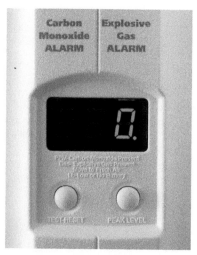

▲ Some carbon monoxide detectors use an electrochemical cell in which carbon monoxide is oxidized to carbon dioxide at the anode, and oxygen is consumed at the cathode. Sulfuric acid serves as the electrolyte. The cell produces current related to the CO concentration in the air, and the current triggers an alarm or produces a readout of the CO concentration.

Self-Assessment Questions

1. In the electrochemical cell whose overall reaction is represented by the following equation, the negative electrode is

$$Zn(s) + Cu^{2+}(aq) \rightarrow Zn^{2+}(aq) + Cu(s)$$

   a. Cu(s)   **b.** Cu^{2+}(aq)   **c.** Zn(s)   **d.** Zn^{2+}(aq)

2. In one kind of electrochemical cell, the anode is ____ and the cathode is ____.

   a. Zn, MnO_2 **b.** Zn, C   **c.** C, Zn   **d.** C, MnO_2

3. In an electrochemical cell composed of two half-cells, ions flow from one half-cell to another through
   a. electrodes
   b. an external conductor
   c. a porous partition
   d. a voltmeter

4. For the following reaction, the oxidation half-reaction is

$$Mg + CuO \rightarrow MgO + Cu$$

   a. $Cu^{2+} + 2\,e^- \rightarrow CuO$
   b. $CuO \rightarrow Cu^{2+} + 2\,e^-$
   c. $Mg^{2+} + 2\,e^- \rightarrow MgO$
   d. $Mg \rightarrow Mg^{2+} + 2\,e^-$

5. In a lead storage battery, the product of both cathode and anode half-reactions is
   a. H_2SO_4
   b. Pb
   c. PbO_2
   d. $PbSO_4$

6. The fluid in the chamber of a lead storage battery is
   a. hydrochloric acid
   b. hydrofluoric acid
   c. methanol
   d. sulfuric acid

7. The overall electricity-producing reaction in the H_2/O_2 fuel cell is

$$2\,H_2(g) + O_2(g) \rightarrow 2\,H_2O(g)$$

   The half-reaction at the cathode is
   a. $H_2 \rightarrow 2\,H^+ + 2\,e^-$
   b. $2\,H^+ + 2\,e^- \rightarrow H_2$
   c. $O_2(g) + 4\,H^+ + 4\,e^- \rightarrow 2\,H_2O$
   d. $2\,H_2O \rightarrow O_2(g) + 4\,H^+ + 4\,e^-$

Answers: 1, c; 2, b; 3, c; 4, d; 5, d; 6, d; 7, c

8.4 Corrosion and Explosion

Learning Objectives ❯ Describe the reactions that occur when iron rusts. ❯ Explain why an explosive reaction is so energetic.

You might think *corrosion* and *explosion* have little in common except that they rhyme. However, both processes involve redox reactions. Corrosion of metals is of great economic importance. In the United States alone, corrosion costs about $276 billion a year. Perhaps 20% of all the iron and steel produced in the United States each year goes to replace corroded items. Explosions can bring economic benefit when used in mining and road building. Or they can cause enormous loss in war and accidents.

The Rusting of Iron

In moist air, iron is oxidized, particularly at a nick or scratch.

$$Fe(s) \longrightarrow Fe^{2+}(aq) + 2\,e^-$$

As iron is oxidized, oxygen is reduced.

$$O_2(g) + 2\,H_2O(l) + 4\,e^- \longrightarrow 4\,OH^-(aq)$$

The net result, initially, is the formation of insoluble iron(II) hydroxide, which appears dark green or black.

$$2\,Fe(s) + O_2(g) + 2\,H_2O(l) \longrightarrow 2\,Fe(OH)_2(s)$$

This product is usually further oxidized to iron(III) hydroxide.

$$4\,Fe(OH)_2(s) + O_2(g) + 2\,H_2O(l) \longrightarrow 4\,Fe(OH)_3(s)$$

Iron(III) hydroxide $\left[Fe(OH)_3\right]$, sometimes written as $Fe_2O_3 \cdot 3\,H_2O$, is the familiar iron rust.

Oxidation and reduction often occur at separate points on the metal's surface. Electrons are transferred through the iron metal. The circuit is completed by an electrolyte in aqueous solution. In the Snow Belt, this solution is often the slush from road salt and melting snow. The metal is pitted in an anodic area, where iron is oxidized to Fe^{2+}. These ions migrate to the cathodic area, where they react with hydroxide ions formed by the reduction of oxygen.

$$Fe^{2+}(aq) + 2\,OH^-(aq) \longrightarrow Fe(OH)_2(s)$$

As noted previously, the iron(II) hydroxide is then oxidized to $Fe(OH)_3$, or rust. This process is diagrammed in Figure 8.8. Note that the anodic area is protected from oxygen by a water film, while the cathodic area is exposed to air.

▶ **Figure 8.8** The corrosion of iron requires water, oxygen, and an electrolyte.

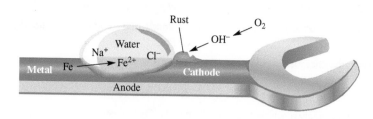

5. Why does steel rust, while aluminum doesn't? Both steel (iron) and aluminum undergo oxidation. But the product from iron flakes off, exposing a fresh iron surface that will rust again. The aluminum oxide formed when aluminum "rusts" adheres strongly to the surface of the metal, protecting it from further oxidation.

Protection of Aluminum

Aluminum is more reactive than iron, yet corrosion is not a serious problem with aluminum. We use aluminum foil, we cook with aluminum pots, and we buy beverages in aluminum cans. Even after many years, they do not corrode. How is this possible?

The aluminum at the surface reacts with oxygen in the air to form a thin layer of oxide. Instead of being porous and flaky like iron oxide, however, aluminum oxide is hard and tough and adheres strongly to the surface of the metal, protecting if from further oxidation.

Nonetheless, corrosion can sometimes be a problem with aluminum. Certain substances, such as salt, can interfere with the protective oxide coating on aluminum, allowing the metal to oxidize. This problem has caused mag wheels on automobiles to crack, and some planes with aluminum landing gear have had wheels shear off.

Silver Tarnish

▲ Silver tarnish (Ag_2S) is readily removed from silver metal brought into contact with aluminum metal in a baking soda solution. Working in a sink, add about 1 cup of baking soda to 1 gal of hot water. Immerse a piece of aluminum and then the tarnished silver object so it touches the aluminum.

Q: To what is the Ag_2S converted? To what is the Al converted?

The tarnish on silver results from oxidation of the silver surface by hydrogen sulfide (H_2S) in the air or from food. It produces a film of black silver sulfide (Ag_2S) on the metal surface. You can use silver polish to remove the tarnish, but in doing so, you also lose part of the silver. An alternative method involves the use of aluminum metal.

$$3\,Ag^+(aq) + Al(s) \longrightarrow 3\,Ag(s) + Al^{3+}(aq)$$

This reaction also requires an electrolyte, and sodium bicarbonate ($NaHCO_3$) is usually used. The tarnished silver is placed in contact with aluminum metal (often in the form of foil) and covered with a hot solution of sodium bicarbonate. The silver ions are reduced to silver metal at the expense of the cheaper metal.

Explosive Reactions

Corrosive reactions are often quite slow. A chemical explosion (that is, not one based on nuclear fission or fusion) is usually an extremely rapid redox reaction, often accompanied by a considerable increase in volume. The redox reaction often involves a compound of nitrogen, such as nitroglycerin (the active ingredient in dynamite), ammonium nitrate (NH_4NO_3, a common fertilizer), or trinitrotoluene (TNT). These compounds can decompose readily, yielding nitrogen gas as one of the products.

Explosive mixtures are used for mining, earthmoving projects, and the demolition of buildings. *ANFO* (*Ammonium Nitrate mixed with Fuel Oil*) is an inexpensive and effective explosive, widely used for mining salt, coal, and other minerals. When ANFO explodes, ammonium ion is the reducing agent and nitrate ion is the oxidizing agent. The fuel oil provides additional oxidizable material. Using $C_{17}H_{36}$ as the formula for a typical molecule in fuel oil, we can write the equation for the explosive reaction.

$$52\,NH_4NO_3(s) + C_{17}H_{36}(l) \longrightarrow 52\,N_2(g) + 17\,CO_2(g) + 122\,H_2O(g)$$

Notice that the starting materials, 53 mol of a solid and a liquid, generate 191 mol of gaseous products. This reaction produces a huge volume increase, which becomes part of the explosive force.

Unfortunately, ANFO has also been used in terrorist attacks around the world. Ammonium nitrate is a widely used fertilizer, and fuel oil is used in many home furnaces. The fact that both these materials are readily accessible to potential terrorists is cause for some concern.

Self-Assessment Questions

1. What type of reaction is the corrosion of iron?
   a. acid–base
   b. addition
   c. oxidation–reduction
   d. neutralization

2. Corrosion of aluminum is not as big a problem as corrosion of iron because aluminum
   a. forms an oxide layer that adheres to the metal's surface
   b. is less reactive than Fe
   c. needs water to corrode
   d. has a higher oxidation number

3. Silver tarnish is mainly
   a. AgCl
   b. Ag_2O
   c. Ag_2S
   d. Fe_2O_3

4. In a typical explosive reaction, which of the following usually occurs?
   a. Gases are converted from one form to another.
   b. Liquids or solids are converted to aqueous solutions.
   c. Liquids or solids are converted to gases.
   d. Nitrogen nuclei are split.

5. Black powder is a mixture of charcoal (carbon), potassium nitrate, and sulfur. The oxidizing agent in black powder is
   a. charcoal
   b. nitroglycerin
   c. potassium nitrate
   d. sulfur

Answers: 1, c; 2, a; 3, c; 4, c; 5, c

8.5 Oxygen: An Abundant and Essential Oxidizing Agent

Learning Objectives ❯ Write equations for reactions in which oxygen is an oxidizing agent. ❯ List some of the common oxidizing agents encountered in daily life.

Oxygen itself is the most common oxidizing agent. Many other oxidizing agents—sometimes called *oxidants*—are important in the laboratory, in industry, and in the home. They are used as antiseptics, disinfectants, and bleaches and play a role in many chemical syntheses.

Oxygen: Occurrence and Properties

Certainly one of the most important elements on Earth, oxygen is one of about two dozen elements essential to life. Making up one-fifth of the air, it oxidizes the wood in our campfires and the gasoline in our automobiles. It even "burns" the food we eat to give us the energy to move and to think. It is found in most compounds that are important to living organisms. Foodstuffs—carbohydrates, fats, and proteins—all contain oxygen. The human body is approximately 65% water (by mass). Because water is 89% oxygen by mass and many other compounds in your body also contain oxygen, almost two-thirds of your body mass is oxygen.

The structure and chemistry of Earth are discussed in Chapter 12, of the atmosphere in Chapter 13, and of water in Chapter 14.

▲ It DOES Matter!

Physical activity under conditions in which plenty of oxygen is available to body tissues is called *aerobic* exercise. When the available oxygen is insufficient, the exercise is called *anaerobic*, and it often leads to weakness and pain resulting from "oxygen debt." (See Chapter 19.)

Oxygen comprises about half of the accessible portion of Earth by mass. It occurs in all three subdivisions of Earth's outermost structure. Oxygen occurs as O_2 molecules in the atmosphere (the gaseous mass surrounding Earth). In the hydrosphere (the oceans, seas, rivers, and lakes), oxygen is combined with hydrogen in water. In the lithosphere (the outer solid portion of the Earth's crust), oxygen is combined with silicon (sand is SiO_2), aluminum (in clays), and other elements.

The atmosphere is about 21% elemental oxygen (O_2) by volume. The rest is about 78% nitrogen (N_2) and 1% argon (Ar), both of which are quite unreactive. The free, uncombined oxygen in the air is taken into our lungs, passes into our bloodstreams, is carried to our body tissues, and reacts with the food we eat. This is the process that provides us with all our energy.

Fuels such as natural gas, gasoline, and coal also need oxygen to burn and release their stored energy. Oxidation, or combustion, of these fossil fuels currently supplies about 86% of the energy that turns the wheels of civilization.

Pure oxygen is obtained by liquefying air and then letting the nitrogen and argon boil off. Nitrogen boils at $-196\,°C$, argon at $-186\,°C$, and oxygen at $-183\,°C$. About 20 billion kg of oxygen is produced annually in the United States, but most of it is used directly by industry, much of it in steel plants. About 1% is compressed into tanks for use in welding, hospital respirators, and other purposes.

Not everything that oxygen does is desirable. In addition to causing corrosion (Section 8.4), it promotes food spoilage and wood decay.

Oxygen: Reactions with Other Elements

Many oxidation reactions involving atmospheric oxygen are quite complicated, but we can gain some understanding by looking at some of the simpler ones. For example, as we have seen, oxygen combines with many metals to form metal oxides and with nonmetals to form nonmetal oxides.

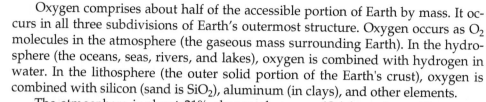

Example 8.7 | Writing Equations: Reaction of Oxygen with Other Elements

Magnesium combines readily with oxygen when ignited in air. Write the equation for this reaction.

Solution

Magnesium is a group 2A metal. Oxygen occurs as diatomic molecules (O_2). The two react to form MgO. The reaction is

$$Mg(s) + O_2(g) \longrightarrow MgO(s) \quad \text{(not balanced)}$$

To balance the equation, we need 2 MgO and 2 Mg.

$$2\,Mg(s) + O_2(g) \longrightarrow 2\,MgO(s)$$

■ **EXERCISE 8.7**

Write equations for the following reactions.

a. Zinc burns in air to form zinc oxide (ZnO).

b. Selenium (Se) burns in air to form selenium dioxide.

▲ Fuels burn more rapidly in pure oxygen than in air. Huge quantities of liquid oxygen are used to burn the fuels that blast rockets into orbit.

Oxygen: Reactions with Compounds

Oxygen reacts with many compounds, oxidizing one or more of the elements in the compound. As we have seen, combustion of a fuel is oxidation and produces oxides. There are many other examples. Hydrogen sulfide, a gaseous compound with a rotten-egg odor, burns to produce oxides of hydrogen (water) and of sulfur (sulfur dioxide).

$$2\,H_2S(g) + 3\,O_2(g) \longrightarrow 2\,H_2O(l) + 2\,SO_2(g)$$

Example 8.8 Writing Equations: Reaction of Oxygen with Compounds

Carbon disulfide, a highly flammable liquid, combines readily with oxygen, burning with a blue flame. What products are formed? Write the equation.

Solution

Carbon disulfide is CS_2. The products are oxides of carbon (carbon dioxide) and of sulfur (sulfur dioxide). The balanced equation is

$$CS_2(g) + 3 O_2(g) \longrightarrow CO_2(g) + 2 SO_2(g)$$

▪ EXERCISE 8.8A

When heated in air, lead sulfide (PbS) combines with oxygen to form lead(II) oxide (PbO) and sulfur dioxide. Write a balanced equation for the reaction.

▪ EXERCISE 8.8B

Write a balanced equation for the combustion (reaction with oxygen) of ethanol (C_2H_5OH).

Ozone: Another Form of Oxygen

In addition to diatomic O_2, oxygen also has a triatomic form (O_3) called *ozone*. Ozone is a powerful oxidizing agent and a harmful air pollutant. It can be extremely irritating to both plants and animals and is especially destructive to rubber. On the other hand, a layer of ozone in the upper stratosphere serves as a shield that protects life on Earth from ultraviolet radiation from the sun (Chapter 13). Ozone clearly illustrates that the same substance can be extremely beneficial or quite harmful, depending on the context.

Other Common Oxidizing Agents

Oxidizing agents used around the home include antiseptics, disinfectants, and bleaches. Many others are used in workplaces and in laboratories.

Disinfectants and antiseptics are alike in that both are materials used to destroy microorganisms (that is, they are germicidal), but antiseptics are applied mainly to living tissue and disinfectants to nonliving things. A good example of a disinfectant is chlorine, which is used to kill disease-causing microorganisms in drinking water and some swimming pools. The actual disinfecting agent is hypochlorous acid (HOCl), formed by the reaction of chlorine with water.

$$Cl_2(g) + H_2O(l) \longrightarrow HOCl(aq) + HCl(aq)$$

In recent years, concern has been raised over by-products that form when chlorine is used to disinfect water containing certain impurities. Although chlorine kills harmful microorganisms, it can also oxidize certain small molecules to form harmful by-products, such as chloroform.

Swimming pools are often chlorinated with calcium hypochlorite $[Ca(OCl)_2]$. Because calcium hypochlorite is alkaline, it also raises the pH of the water. (When a pool becomes too alkaline, the pH is lowered by adding hydrochloric acid. Swimming pools are usually maintained at pH 7.2–7.8.)

Hydrogen peroxide (H_2O_2) is a common oxidizing agent that has the advantage of being converted to water in most reactions. Pure hydrogen peroxide is a syrupy liquid. It is available (in laboratories) as a dangerous 30% solution that has powerful oxidizing power or as a 3% solution (sold in stores) for various uses around the home. When combined with a specially designed catalyst, hydrogen peroxide can be used to oxidize colored compounds and water impurities.

As a dilute aqueous solution, hydrogen peroxide is used to bleach hair (which gave rise to the phrase "peroxide blonde"). Dilute H_2O_2 is used medically to clean and deodorize wounds and ulcers.

Iodine is used as an antiseptic, either in an alcoholic solution (called *tincture of iodine*) or in Lugol's iodine solution (which contains no alcohol).

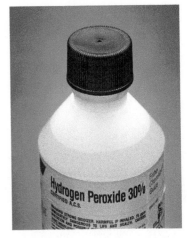

▲ Hydrogen peroxide is a powerful oxidizing agent. Dilute solutions are used as disinfectant and to bleach hair.

⚠ **SAFETY ALERT**

Strong oxidizing agents such as 30% aqueous hydrogen peroxide can cause severe burns. In general, strong oxidizing agents are corrosive, and many are highly toxic. They can also initiate a fire or increase the severity of a fire when brought into contact with combustible materials.

Solutions of potassium permanganate ($KMnO_4$), a common laboratory oxidizing agent, are good disinfectants. Such solutions are a deep purplish pink. Highly diluted solutions are pale pink (called "pinky water" in India) and are used in developing countries to disinfect foods. Their use is limited because the permanganate ion is reduced to brown manganese dioxide, leaving a brown stain on the treated substance.

▲ Pure water (left) has little effect on a dried tomato sauce stain. Sodium hypochlorite bleach (right) removes the stain by oxidizing the colored tomato pigments to colorless products.

An oxidizing agent sometimes used in the laboratory is potassium dichromate ($K_2Cr_2O_7$). It is an orange substance that turns green when it is reduced to chromium(III) compounds. One of the compounds that potassium dichromate oxidizes is ethyl alcohol. The early Breathalyzer test for intoxication made use of a dichromate solution. The exhaled breath of the person being tested was mixed with the acidic dichromate, and the degree of color change indicated the level of alcohol.

Ointments for treating acne often contain 5–10% benzoyl peroxide, a powerful antiseptic and also a skin irritant. It causes old skin to slough off and be replaced by new, fresher-looking skin. When used on areas exposed to sunlight, however, benzoyl peroxide may promote skin cancer.

Bleaches are oxidizing agents, too. A **bleach** removes unwanted color from fabrics or other material. Most bleaches work by oxidizing carbon-carbon double bonds in the colored substances to single bonds. This renders the stain colorless or nearly so. Almost any oxidizing agent could do the job, but some might be unsafe to use, or harmful to fabrics, or perhaps too expensive.

Bleaches (Chapter 21) are usually sodium hypochlorite (NaOCl) in aqueous solution (in laundry products such as Purex® and Clorox®), often called *chlorine bleaches*, or calcium hypochlorite [$Ca(OCl)_2$], known as *bleaching powder*. The powder is usually preferred for large industrial operations, such as the whitening of paper or fabrics. Nonchlorine bleaches, often called *oxygen bleaches*, contain sodium percarbonate (a combination of Na_2CO_3 and H_2O_2) or sodium perborate (a combination of $NaBO_2$ and H_2O_2).

Stain removal is more complicated than bleaching. A few stain removers are oxidizing agents, but some are reducing agents, some are solvents or detergents, and some have quite different action. Stains often require rather specific stain removers.

Self-Assessment Questions

1. When CH_4 is burned in plentiful air, the products are
   a. $C + H_2$ **b.** $CH_2 + H_2O$ **c.** $CO_2 + H_2$ **d.** $CO_2 + H_2O$

2. When sulfur burns in plentiful air, the product is
   a. CO_2 **b.** H_2S **c.** H_2SO_4 **d.** SO_2

3. Which of the following is a common oxidizing agent?
   a. HCl   **b.** H_2O_2 **c.** NaOH   **d.** NaCl

4. Which of the following is a common oxidizing agent?
   a. Cl_2 **b.** H_2 **c.** HCl   **d.** KOH

5. The main active ingredient in common household bleach, often called *chlorine bleach*, is
   a. HCl   **b.** NaOCl   **c.** NaOH   **d.** NaCl

6. Bleach for hair usually contains
   a. ammonia   **b.** hydrochloric acid
   c. hydrogen peroxide   **d.** sodium hypochlorite

7. Many disinfectants are
   a. oxidizing agents   **b.** reducing agents
   c. strong acids   **d.** strong bases

Answers: 1, d; 2, d; 3, b; 4, a; 5, b; 6, c; 7, a

8.6 Some Common Reducing Agents

Learning Objective ❯ Identify some common reducing agents.

In every reaction involving oxidation, the oxidizing agent is reduced, and the substance undergoing oxidation acts as a reducing agent. Let's now consider reactions in which the purpose of the reaction is reduction.

Metals

Most metals occur in nature as compounds. To prepare the free metals, the compounds must be reduced. Metals are often freed from their ores by using coal or *coke* (elemental carbon obtained by heating coal to drive off volatile matter). Tin(IV) oxide is one of the many ores that can be reduced with coal or coke.

$$SnO_2(s) + C(s) \longrightarrow Sn(s) + CO_2(g)$$

Sometimes a metal can be obtained by heating its ore with a more active metal. Chromium oxide, for example, can be reduced by heating it with aluminum.

$$Cr_2O_3(s) + 2\,Al(s) \longrightarrow Al_2O_3(s) + 2\,Cr(s)$$

Antioxidants

In food chemistry, certain reducing agents are called **antioxidants**. Ascorbic acid (vitamin C) can prevent the browning of fruit (such as sliced apples or pears) by inhibiting air oxidation. Vitamin C is water soluble, but tocopherol (vitamin E) and beta-carotene (a precursor of vitamin A) are fat-soluble antioxidants. All these vitamins are believed to retard various oxidation reactions that are potentially damaging to vital components of living cells (Chapter 17).

Hydrogen as a Reducing Agent

Hydrogen is an excellent reducing agent that can free many metals from their ores, but it is generally used to produce more expensive metals, such as tungsten (W).

$$WO_3(s) + 3\,H_2(g) \longrightarrow W(s) + 3\,H_2O(l)$$

Hydrogen can be used to reduce many kinds of chemical compounds. Ethylene, for example, can be reduced to ethane.

$$C_2H_4(g) + H_2(g) \longrightarrow C_2H_6(g)$$

The reaction requires a **catalyst**, a substance that increases the rate of a chemical reaction without itself being used up. (Catalysts lower the *activation energy*—the minimum energy needed to get a reaction started; they are further explored in Chapter 15.) Nickel is the catalyst used in this case.

Hydrogen also reduces nitrogen, from air, in the industrial production of ammonia.

$$N_2(g) + 3\,H_2(g) \longrightarrow 2\,NH_3(g)$$

Ammonia is the source of most nitrogen fertilizers in modern agriculture. The reaction that produces ammonia employs an iron catalyst.

A stream of pure hydrogen burns quietly in air with an almost colorless flame, but when a mixture of hydrogen and oxygen is ignited by a spark or a flame, an explosion results. The product in both cases is water.

$$2\,H_2(g) + O_2(g) \longrightarrow 2\,H_2O(l)$$

Certain metals, including platinum and palladium, have an unusual affinity for hydrogen. They absorb large volumes of the gas. Palladium can absorb up to 900 times its own volume of hydrogen. It is interesting to note that hydrogen and oxygen can be mixed at room temperature with no perceptible reaction. If a piece of platinum gauze is added to the mixture, however, the gases react violently. The platinum acts as a catalyst. The heat from the initial reaction heats up the platinum, making it glow; it then ignites the hydrogen–oxygen mixture, causing an explosion.

Nickel, platinum, and palladium are often used as catalysts for reactions involving hydrogen. These metals have the greatest catalytic activity when they are finely divided and have lots of active surface area. Hydrogen adsorbed on the surface of these metals is more reactive than ordinary hydrogen gas.

Catalysts are an important area of research in green chemistry. Chemists are able to develop more energy-efficient and sustainable processes by designing catalysts that enable chemical reactions to occur at lower temperatures or pressures.

▲ **It DOES Matter!**
In making a black-and-white photograph, silver bromide in the film is exposed to light. The silver ions so exposed can then be reduced to black silver metal, forming a photographic negative.

A nickel catalyst is used in converting unsaturated fats to saturated fats (Chapter 17). Unsaturated fats ordinarily react very slowly with hydrogen, but in the presence of nickel metal, the reaction proceeds readily. The nickel increases the rate of the reaction, but it does not increase the amount of product formed.

Colin P. Horwitz, *GreenOx Catalysts, Inc.*

Green Oxidation Catalysts

A catalyst provides a pathway for chemicals (reactants) to combine in a more effective manner than is possible without it. Catalysis is also central to green chemistry (Green Chemistry Principle 9). Catalysts increase efficiency and efficacy of chemical and energy resources and reduce reaction time, which also lead to cost savings.

Catalysts are widely used in oxidation reactions, especially those reactions that produce industrial and specialty chemicals. Industrial chemicals are produced on a scale of millions of tons per year and generally cost less than $0.50/lb. They are often building blocks for more sophisticated chemicals. On the other hand, specialty chemicals are produced on a smaller scale. They generally are more complex than industrial chemicals and have higher value in the marketplace.

There is great reliance on catalysts in the production of industrial chemicals because they must be made cheaply. For example, to produce terephthalic acid, *p*-xylene is oxidized with oxygen using a Co/Mn/Br catalyst. The terephthalic acid can then be converted to polyethylene terephthalate (PET), the major component of soft-drink bottles.

Another example is the oxidation of propylene to propylene oxide. Attempts to make this process greener began in the early 1990s and included using hydrogen peroxide, H_2O_2, as the oxidizing agent (Section 8.5). A titanium silicalite, TS-1, was the catalyst. Green benefits of this catalyst include the fact that Ti is both earth-abundant and nontoxic (see the Green Chemistry essay in Chapter 2). This research resulted in the HPPO process, which uses hydrogen peroxide and propylene oxide and is much greener than currently used methods. The propylene is oxidized under mild reaction conditions in aqueous methanol, and high selectivity for product over byproducts is reported. The methanol also is recycled. This process received a 2010 Presidential Green Chemistry Challenge Award and is being commercialized by a BASF–Dow Chemical Company partnership.

The complexity of specialty chemicals makes their synthesis challenging. Many reactions are based on oxidation, and a need for efficient routes has led to the development of an array of catalytic and noncatalytic methods. These approaches have often relied on chemical reagents that lead to the desired product but are environmentally harmful. A classic example of a noncatalytic method is the dichromate oxidation of an alcohol to an aldehyde.

$$3\ C_2H_6O + Cr_2O_7^{2-} + 8\ H^+ \rightarrow 3\ C_2H_4O + 2\ Cr^{3+} + 7\ H_2O$$

In this reaction, Cr^{6+} in the dichromate ion, $Cr_2O_7^{2-}$, is reduced to Cr^{3+}, and the alcohol is oxidized to an aldehyde. Although the product is formed, Cr^{6+} is a likely carcinogen, the noncatalytic reaction produces lots of waste, and the atom economy (see the Green Chemistry essay in Chapter 5) is poor.

There are many opportunities to employ green chemistry through the development of catalysts that make oxidations like the example above unnecessary. Many oxidation catalysts rely on transition metals (Section 3.8) attached to organic molecules. Catalyst design can be difficult because the organic part can become a target for oxidation during reactions. When this happens, complex protection schemes for the organic portion or high quantities of catalyst are required.

Professor Terry Collins at Carnegie Mellon University took a unique design approach in which weak links in the organic framework were replaced with more robust ones. An earth-abundant and nontoxic element, iron, was chosen as the metal, and the organic portions were designed to bind strongly to iron. The organic parts also contain biochemically common elements, C, H, N, and O. The resulting catalysts are soluble in water and can survive thousands of catalytic cycles. Also, the greener oxidant hydrogen peroxide, H_2O_2, can be used, which leads to oxidation products with low or no toxicity. The design process has yielded an expanding family of iron-based TAML® catalysts that can rapidly oxidize and thus destroy pollutants in water. This work garnered Collins a 1997 Presidential Green Chemistry Challenge Award.

Recent work with the TAML® catalysts has shown that they are effective at levels as low as a single part per million, are efficient users of H_2O_2, function in water over a wide pH range, and offer an alternative to other processes that also use H_2O_2 but much less efficiently. In some applications, the temperature of the reaction can be lowered, which saves energy, and the amounts of chemicals can be decreased because of the efficiency of the TAML® catalyst.

Using a catalyst can also allow a reaction to occur using milder reactants, such as oxygen or hydrogen peroxide instead of chlorine for oxidizing stains on clothes or destroying harmful microorganisms in drinking water.

A Closer Look at Hydrogen

Hydrogen is an especially vital element because it and oxygen are the components of water. By mass, hydrogen makes up only about 0.9% of the Earth's crust and oceans. However, because it has such a low atomic mass, it ranks third in abundance by number of atoms. A random sample of 10,000 atoms from this portion of Earth would have 1510 hydrogen atoms.

Unlike oxygen, hydrogen is rarely found as a free, uncombined element on Earth. Most of it is combined with oxygen in water. Some is combined with carbon in petroleum and natural gas, which are mixtures of hydrocarbons. Nearly all compounds derived from plants and animals contain hydrogen.

Because hydrogen has the lowest atomic number ($Z = 1$) and the smallest atoms of any element, it is first in the periodic table. However, it is difficult to know exactly where to place it. Hydrogen is usually shown as the first member of group 1A because it has the same valence electronic structure (ns^1) as alkali metals. Like the atoms of elements in group 1A, a hydrogen atom can lose an electron to form a 1+ ion; but, unlike the other group 1A elements, hydrogen is not a metal. Like the atoms of group 7A elements, a hydrogen atom can pick up an electron to become a 1− ion; but, unlike the other group 7A elements, hydrogen is not a halogen. We place hydrogen in group 1A in the periodic table on the inside front cover, but you should keep in mind that it is a unique element, and is in a class by itself.

Small amounts of elemental hydrogen can be made for laboratory use by reacting zinc with hydrochloric acid (Figure 8.9).

$$Zn(s) + 2\,HCl(aq) \longrightarrow ZnCl_2(aq) + H_2(g)$$

Hydrogen ranks low in abundance by mass on Earth. If we look beyond our home planet, however, hydrogen becomes much more significant. The sun, for example, is made up largely of hydrogen. The planet Jupiter is also mainly hydrogen. In fact, the universe is about 72% by mass H, 26% He, and 1% O.

◄ **Figure 8.9** Hydrogen gas can be prepared in the laboratory by the reaction of zinc metal with hydrochloric acid.

Commercial quantities of hydrogen are obtained as by-products of petroleum refining or from the reaction of natural gas with steam. About 8 billion kg of hydrogen is produced each year in the United States. At present, hydrogen is used mainly to make ammonia and methanol. Its possible use as a fuel in the future is discussed in Chapter 15.

Hydrogen is a colorless, odorless gas and the lightest of all substances. Its density is only one-fourteenth that of air, and for this reason it was once used in lighter-than-air craft (Figure 8.10). Unfortunately, hydrogen can be ignited by a spark, as occurred in 1937 when the German airship *Hindenburg* was destroyed in a disastrous fire and explosion while landing in Lakehurst, New Jersey. The use of hydrogen in airships was discontinued after that, and the industry never recovered. Today, the few airships that are still in service are filled with nonflammable helium, but they are used mainly in advertising.

▲ **Figure 8.10** Hydrogen is the most buoyant gas, but it is highly flammable. The disastrous fire that destroyed the hydrogen-filled German airship *Hindenburg* led to the replacement of hydrogen by nonflammable helium, which buoys the Goodyear blimp.

Q: *What is the equation for the reaction pictured on the left? Would a similar reaction occur if lightning struck the Goodyear blimp? Explain.*

6. Does hydrogen have a promising future as a fuel? Gram for gram, hydrogen provides more energy than any other chemical fuel. Also, when hydrogen is oxidized by oxygen, the product is ordinary water. Unfortunately, it takes more energy to produce hydrogen than we get from burning the hydrogen. Until we can use renewable energy to generate hydrogen, its future as a fuel will remain in question.

Self-Assessment Questions

1. Which of the following is a common reducing agent?
   a. Cl_2 **b.** F_2 **c.** H_2 **d.** I_2

2. Which of the following is a common reducing agent?
   a. C **b.** Cl_2 **c.** F_2 **d.** I_2

3. All the following metals are used as catalysts for reactions involving hydrogen gas *except*
   a. aluminum **b.** nickel **c.** palladium **d.** platinum

4. A catalyst changes the rate of a chemical reaction by
   a. changing the products of the reaction
   b. changing the reactants involved in the reaction
   c. increasing the frequency of molecular collisions
   d. lowering the activation energy

5. By number of atoms, what is the rank of hydrogen in abundance in the accessible portion of Earth?
   a. first **b.** second **c.** tenth **d.** third

6. Hydrogen gas can be produced by reacting an active metal such as zinc with
   a. an acid **b.** ammonia
   c. an oxidizing agent **d.** a reducing agent

7. Although helium gas is twice as dense as hydrogen gas, modern blimps are filled with helium because hydrogen is
   a. highly flammable **b.** more expensive
   c. rarer **d.** toxic

Answers: 1. c; 2, a; 3, a; 4, d; 5, d; 6, a; 7, a

8.7 Oxidation, Reduction, and Living Things

Learning Objective ❯ Write the overall equations for the metabolism of glucose and for photosynthesis.

Perhaps the most important oxidation–reduction processes are the ones that maintain life on this planet. We obtain energy for all our physical and mental activities by metabolizing food in a process called *cellular respiration*. The process has many steps, but eventually the food we eat is converted mainly into carbon dioxide, water, and energy.

Bread and many of the other foods we eat are largely made up of carbohydrates, composed of carbon, hydrogen, and oxygen (Chapter 17). If we represent carbohydrates with the simple example of glucose ($C_6H_{12}O_6$), we can write the overall equation for their metabolism as follows.

$$C_6H_{12}O_6 + 6\,O_2 \longrightarrow 6\,CO_2 + 6\,H_2O + \text{energy}$$

This process occurs constantly in animals, including humans. The carbohydrate is oxidized in the process.

Meanwhile, plants need carbon dioxide, water, and energy from the sun to produce carbohydrates. The process by which plants synthesize carbohydrates is called **photosynthesis** (Figure 8.11). The overall chemical equation is

$$6\,CO_2 + 6\,H_2O + \text{energy} \longrightarrow C_6H_{12}O_6 + 6\,O_2$$

◀ **Figure 8.11** Photosynthesis occurs in green plants. The chlorophyll pigments that catalyze the photosynthesis process give the green color to much of the land area of Earth.

Notice that this process in plant cells is exactly the reverse of the process going on inside animals. In food metabolism in animals, we focus on an oxidation process. In photosynthesis, we focus on a reduction process.

The carbohydrates produced by photosynthesis are the ultimate source of all our food because fish, fowl, and other animals either eat plants or eat other animals that eat plants. Note that the photosynthesis process not only makes carbohydrates but also yields free elementary oxygen (O_2). In other words, photosynthesis does not just provide the food we eat, it also provides the oxygen we breathe.

There are many oxidation reactions that occur in nature (with oxygen being reduced in the process). The net photosynthesis reaction is unique in that it is a natural reduction of carbon dioxide (with oxygen being oxidized). Many processes in nature use oxygen. Photosynthesis is the only natural process that produces it.

Self-Assessment Questions

1. The main process by which animals obtain energy from food is
   a. acidification
   b. cellular respiration
   c. photosynthesis
   d. reduction of CO_2

2. The only natural process that produces O_2 is
   a. acidification of carbonates
   b. photosynthesis
   c. oxidation of CO_2
   d. reduction of metal oxide

CRITICAL THINKING EXERCISES

Apply knowledge that you have gained in this chapter and one or more of the FLaReS principles (Chapter 1) to evaluate the following statements or claims.

8.1 Over the years, some people have claimed that someone has invented an automobile engine that burns water instead of gasoline. They say that we have not heard about it because the oil companies have bought the rights to the engine from the inventor so that they can keep it from the public and people will continue to burn gasoline in their cars.

8.2 In January 2011, Italian scientists claimed to have constructed an apparatus to produce energy. The apparatus uses hydrogen and nickel and is supposed to give several hundred times as much energy as would be obtained by merely burning the hydrogen.

8.3 A Web site claims that electricity can remove rust. The procedure is described as follows: Connect a wire to the object to be derusted, and immerse in a bath of sodium carbonate (washing soda) solution.

Immerse a second wire in the bath. Connect the wires to a battery so that the object to be derusted is the cathode. The site claims that hydrogen gas is produced at the cathode and oxygen at the anode. The hydrogen then changes the rust back to iron metal.

8.4 A friend claims that an automobile can be kept free of rust simply by connecting the negative pole of the car's battery to the car's body. He reasons that this action makes the car the cathode, and oxidation does not occur at the cathode. He claims that for years he has kept his car from rusting by doing this.

8.5 A salesman claims that your tap water is contaminated. As evidence, he connects a battery to a pair of "special electrodes" and dips the electrodes in a glass of your tap water. Within a few minutes, white and brown "gunk" appears in the water. The salesman sells a special purifying filter that he claims will remove the contaminants and leave the water pure and clear.

SUMMARY

Section 8.1—Oxidation and reduction are processes that occur together. They may be defined in three ways. Oxidation occurs when a substance gains oxygen atoms or loses hydrogen atoms or loses electrons. Reduction is the opposite of oxidation; it occurs when a substance loses oxygen atoms or gains hydrogen atoms or gains electrons. We usually use the definition that is most convenient for the situation.

Section 8.2—In an oxidation–reduction (or redox) reaction, the substance that causes oxidation is the oxidizing agent. The substance that causes reduction is the reducing agent. In a redox reaction, the oxidizing agent is reduced, and the reducing agent is oxidized.

Section 8.3—A redox reaction involves a transfer of electrons. That transfer can be made to take place in an electrochemical cell, which has two solid electrodes where the electrons are transferred. The electrode where oxidation occurs is the anode, and the one where reduction occurs is the cathode. Electrons are transferred from anode to cathode through a wire; their flow is an electric current. When the oxidation half-reaction is added to the reduction half-reaction, the electrons in the half-reactions cancel and we get the overall cell reaction. Knowing this, we can balance many redox reactions.

A dry cell (flashlight battery) has a zinc case and a central carbon rod and contains a paste of manganese dioxide with graphite powder and ammonium chloride. Alkaline cells are similar but contain potassium hydroxide instead of ammonium chloride. A battery is a series of connected cells. An automobile's lead storage battery contains six cells.

Each cell contains lead and lead dioxide electrodes in sulfuric acid, and the battery can be recharged. A fuel cell generates electricity by oxidizing a fuel in a cell to which the fuel and oxygen are supplied continuously.

Section 8.4—Corrosion of metals is ordinarily an undesirable redox reaction. When iron corrodes, the iron is first oxidized to Fe^{2+} ions, and oxygen gas is reduced to hydroxide ions. The $Fe(OH)_2$ that forms is further oxidized to $Fe(OH)_3$, or rust. Oxidation and reduction often occur in separate places on the metal surface, and an electrolyte (such as salt) on the surface can intensify the corrosion reaction. Aluminum corrodes, but the oxide layer is tough and adherent and protects the underlying metal. Silver corrodes in the presence of sulfur compounds, forming black silver sulfide, which can be removed electrochemically. An explosive reaction is a redox reaction that occurs rapidly and with a considerable increase in volume (due to the formation of gases).

Section 8.5—Oxygen is an oxidizing agent that is essential to life. It makes up about one-fifth of the air and about two-thirds of our body mass. Our food is "burned" in oxygen as we breathe, and fuels such as coal react with oxygen when they burn and release most of the energy used in civilization. Pure oxygen is obtained from liquefied air, and most of it is used in industry. Oxygen reacts with metals and nonmetals to form oxides. It reacts with many compounds to form oxides of the elements in the compound. Ozone, O_3, is a form of oxygen that is an air pollutant in the lower atmosphere but provides a shield from ultraviolet radiation in the upper atmosphere. Other oxidizing agents include hydrogen peroxide, potassium dichromate, benzoyl peroxide, and chlorine. A **bleach** is an oxidizing agent that removes unwanted color from fabric or other material.

Section 8.6—Most metals are reducing agents. An **antioxidant** is a reducing agent that retards damaging oxidation reactions in living cells. Vitamins C and E and beta-carotene are antioxidants. Common reducing agents include carbon, hydrogen, and active metals. Carbon in the form of coal or coke is often used as a reducing agent to obtain metals from their oxides. Active metals such as aluminum are also used for this purpose. Hydrogen can free many metals from their ores. Some reactions of hydrogen require a **catalyst**, which speeds up a reaction without itself being used up. Formation of ammonia from hydrogen and nitrogen uses a catalyst.

Hydrogen is a vital element because it is a component of water and of living tissue. Because it has the lowest atomic number and the smallest atoms, its behavior is unique among the elements. Hydrogen is produced in petroleum refining or from the reaction of natural gas with steam; it is used to make ammonia and methanol. Hydrogen was once used for lighter-than-air craft but its flammability caused it to be replaced by helium.

Section 8.7—Oxidation of carbohydrates and other substances in foods produces the energy humans and other animals need to survive. The reduction of carbon dioxide in **photosynthesis** is the most important reduction process on Earth. We could not exist without it. Photosynthesis provides the food we eat and the oxygen we breathe.

Green chemistry When a chemist needs to use an oxidation reaction to produce a chemical, it is important to find a catalyst that makes the reaction proceed efficiently so that energy and chemical resources are used wisely. To further the principles of green chemistry, the catalyst should be composed of nontoxic and earth-abundant elements.

Learning Objectives

❯ Identify an oxidation–reduction reaction. (8.1)	Problems 13–16
❯ Classify a particular change within a redox reaction as either oxidation or reduction. (8.1)	Problems 1, 4, 13, 14, 41–43, 47, 50, 54
❯ Identify the oxidizing agent and the reducing agent in a redox reaction. (8.2)	Problems 17–22, 27–36, 39, 48, 49
❯ Balance redox equations. (8.3)	Problems 25, 26, 51
❯ Identify and write the half-reactions in an electrochemical cell. (8.3)	Problems 2, 3, 5–8, 15, 16, 23, 24
❯ Describe the reactions that occur when iron rusts. (8.4)	Problem 9
❯ Explain why an explosive reaction is so energetic. (8.4)	
❯ Write equations for reactions in which oxygen is an oxidizing agent. (8.5)	Problems 37, 38
❯ List some of the common oxidizing agents encountered in daily life. (8.5)	Problems 10, 11
❯ Identify some common reducing agents. (8.6)	Problems 29–36
❯ Write the overall equations for the metabolism of glucose and for photosynthesis. (8.7)	Problems 12, 46, 53
❯ Distinguish between the objectives of chemists producing industrial chemicals and those of chemists producing specialty chemicals.	Problem 55
❯ Explain how green chemistry can be applied to the design of new catalysts.	Problems 56–58

 # REVIEW QUESTIONS

1. What happens to the oxidation number of one of its elements when a compound is oxidized? When it is reduced?

2. What is an electrochemical cell? A battery?

3. What is the purpose of a porous partition between the two electrode compartments in an electrochemical cell?

4. What is a half-reaction? How are half-reactions combined to give an overall cell reaction?

5. From what material is the case of a zinc–carbon dry cell made? What purpose does this material serve? What happens to it as the cell discharges?

6. How does an alkaline cell differ from a zinc–carbon dry cell?

7. What happens when a lead storage battery is charged?

8. Describe what happens when a lead storage battery discharges.

9. Describe what happens when iron corrodes. How does road salt intensify this process?

10. Describe how a bleaching agent, such as hypochlorite (ClO^-), works.

11. How does silver tarnish? How can the tarnish be removed without the loss of silver?

12. Relate the chemistry of photosynthesis to the chemical process that provides energy for your heartbeat.

PROBLEMS

Recognizing Oxidation and Reduction

13. Indicate whether the reactant in each of the following partial equations is being oxidized or reduced. Explain.
   a. $Fe \rightarrow Fe^{3+}$
   b. $H_2O \rightarrow O_2$
   c. $Sr \rightarrow Sr^{2+}$
   d. $P_4 \rightarrow 4\ P^{3-}$
   e. $CH_4O \rightarrow CH_2O$

14. In which of the following changes is the reactant undergoing oxidation? Explain.
   a. $C_2H_4 \rightarrow C_2H_6$
   b. $CrO_3 \rightarrow Cr$
   c. $Fe^{3+} \longrightarrow Fe^{2+}$
   d. $C_{27}H_{33}N_9O_{15}P_2 \longrightarrow C_{27}H_{35}N_9O_{15}P_2$
   e. $2\ Cl^- \rightarrow Cl_2$

15. Write a balanced oxidation half-reaction similar to $Na \longrightarrow Na^+ + e^-$ for each of the following metals.
   a. Ca
   b. Al
   c. Cu (two different equations)

16. Write a balanced reduction half-reaction similar to $Cl_2 + 2\ e^- \longrightarrow 2\ Cl^-$ for each of the following nonmetals.
   a. I_2
   b. N_2
   c. S_8

Oxidizing Agents and Reducing Agents

17. Identify the oxidizing agent and the reducing agent in each reaction.
   a. $3\ C + Fe_2O_3 \longrightarrow 3\ CO + 2\ Fe$
   b. $P_4 + 5\ O_2 \longrightarrow P_4O_{10}$
   c. $C + H_2O \longrightarrow CO + H_2$
   d. $H_2SO_4 + Zn \longrightarrow ZnSO_4 + H_2$

18. Identify the oxidizing agent and the reducing agent in each reaction.
   a. $CuS + H_2 \longrightarrow Cu + H_2S$
   b. $4\ K + CCl_4 \longrightarrow C + 4\ KCl$
   c. $C_3H_4 + 2\ H_2 \longrightarrow C_3H_8$
   d. $Fe^{3+} + Ce^{3+} \longrightarrow Fe^{2+} + Ce^{4+}$

19. Look again at Figure 8.4. What is the reducing agent?

20. What is the oxidizing agent in Figure 8.4?

21. Look again at Figure 8.6. Identify the oxidizing and reducing agents.

22. Look again at Figure 8.7. **(a)** Is SO_4^{2-} the oxidizing agent, the reducing agent, both, or neither? **(b)** When the cell is being charged, the discharge half-reactions are reversed. During charging, is Pb^{2+} being oxidized, reduced, both, or neither?

Half-Reactions

23. Separate the following redox reactions into half-reactions, and label each half-reaction as oxidation or reduction.
   a. $Fe(s) + 2\ H^+(aq) \longrightarrow Fe^{2+}(aq) + H_2(g)$
   b. $2\ Al(s) + 3\ Cr^{2+}(aq) \longrightarrow 3\ Cr(s) + 2\ Al^{3+}(aq)$

24. Separate the following redox reactions into half-reactions, and label each half-reaction as oxidation or reduction.
   a. $2\ Al(s) + 6\ H^+(aq) \longrightarrow 2\ Al^{3+}(aq) + 3\ H_2(g)$
   b. $2\ Cu^+(aq) + Mg(s) \longrightarrow Mg^{2+}(aq) + 2\ Cu(s)$

25. Label each of the following half-reactions as oxidation or reduction, and then combine them to obtain a balanced overall redox reaction.
   a. $2\ H_2O_2 \longrightarrow 2\ O_2 + 4\ H^+ + 4\ e^-$ and
      $Fe^{3+} + e^- \longrightarrow Fe^{2+}$
   b. $WO_3 + 6\ H^+ + 6\ e^- \longrightarrow W + 3\ H_2O$ and
      $C_2H_6O \longrightarrow C_2H_4O + 2\ H^+ + 2\ e^-$

26. Label each of the following half-reactions as oxidation or reduction, and then combine them to obtain a balanced overall redox reaction.
   a. $2\ I^- \longrightarrow I_2 + 2\ e^-$ and $Cl_2 + 2\ e^- \longrightarrow 2\ Cl^-$
   b. $HNO_3 + H^+ + e^- \longrightarrow NO_2 + H_2O$ and
      $SO_2 + 2\ H_2O \longrightarrow H_2SO_4 + 2\ H^+ + 2\ e^-$

Oxidation and Reduction: Chemical Reactions

27. In the following reactions, which substance is oxidized? Which is the oxidizing agent?
   a. $2\ HNO_3 + SO_2 \longrightarrow H_2SO_4 + 2\ NO_2$
   b. $2\ CrO_3 + 6\ HI \longrightarrow Cr_2O_3 + 3\ I_2 + 3\ H_2O$

28. In the following reactions, which element is oxidized and which is reduced?
   a. $CH_3CHO + H_2O_2 \rightarrow CH_3COOH + H_2O$
   b. $5\ C_2H_6O + 4\ MnO_4^- + 12\ H^+ \longrightarrow$
      $5\ C_2H_4O_2 + 4\ Mn^{2+} + 11\ H_2O$

29. Ethylene (C_2H_4) reacts with hydrogen to form ethane (C_2H_6). Is the ethylene oxidized or reduced? Explain.

30. Unsaturated vegetable oils react with hydrogen to form saturated fats. A typical reaction is

$$C_{57}H_{104}O_6 + 3\ H_2 \longrightarrow C_{57}H_{110}O_6$$

   Is the unsaturated oil oxidized or reduced? Explain.

31. Tantalum, a metal used in electronic devices such as cellular phones and computers, can be manufactured by the reaction of its oxide with molten sodium metal.

$$Ta_2O_5 + 10\ Na \rightarrow 2\ Ta + 5\ Na_2O$$

   Which substance is reduced? Which is the reducing agent?

32. To test for iodide ions (for example, in iodized salt), a solution is treated with chlorine to liberate iodine.

$$2\ I^- + Cl_2 \longrightarrow I_2 + 2\ Cl^-$$

   Which substance is oxidized? Which is reduced?

33. In the Fukushima nuclear reactor that failed in March 2011, zirconium metal reacted with steam to produce hydrogen gas.

$$Zr + 2\ H_2O \longrightarrow ZrO_2 + 2\ H_2$$

   What substance was oxidized in the reaction? What was the oxidizing agent?

34. Unripe grapes are exceptionally sour because of a high concentration of tartaric acid ($C_4H_6O_6$). As the grapes

ripen, this compound is converted to glucose ($C_6H_{12}O_6$). Is the tartaric acid oxidized or reduced?

35. Vitamin C (ascorbic acid) is thought to protect our stomachs from the carcinogenic effect of nitrite ions (NO_2^-) by converting the ions to nitric oxide (NO). Is the nitrite ion oxidized or reduced? Is ascorbic acid an oxidizing agent or a reducing agent?

36. In the reaction in Problem 35, ascorbic acid ($C_6H_8O_6$) is converted to dehydroascorbic acid ($C_6H_6O_6$). Is ascorbic acid oxidized or reduced in this reaction?

Combination with Oxygen

37. Write formula(s) for the product(s) formed when each of the following substances reacts with oxygen (O_2).
   a. S
   b. CH_3OH
   c. C_3H_6O

38. Write formula(s) for the product(s) formed when each of the following substances reacts with oxygen (O_2). (There may be more than one correct answer.)
   a. N_2
   b. CS_2
   c. C_5H_{12}

Additional Problems

39. The dye indigo (used to color blue jeans) is formed by exposure of indoxyl to air.

$$2\ C_8H_7ON + O_2 \longrightarrow C_{16}H_{10}N_2O_2 + 2\ H_2O$$
   Indoxyl   Indigo

What substance is oxidized? What is the oxidizing agent?

40. Why do some mechanics lightly coat their tools with grease or oil before storing them?

41. When an aluminum wire is placed in a blue solution of copper(II) chloride, the blue solution turns colorless and reddish-brown copper metal comes out of solution. Write an equation for the reaction. (Chloride ion is not involved in the reaction.)

42. Researchers led by Elisabeth Bouwman, a chemist at Leiden University in the Netherlands, discovered a copper-based catalyst that can convert CO_2 from the air to oxalate ion ($C_2O_4^{2-}$). Write the equation for the half-reaction. Is the CO_2 oxidized or reduced?

43. When exposed to air containing hydrogen sulfide, lead-based paints turn black because the Pb^{2+} ions react with the H_2S to form black lead sulfide (PbS). This has caused the darkening of old oil-based paintings. Hydrogen peroxide lightens the paints by oxidizing the black sulfide (S^{2-}) to white sulfates (SO_4^{2-}). **(a)** Write the equation for the darkening reaction. **(b)** Write the equation for this reaction that lightens the paints.

44. The oxidizing agent our bodies use to obtain energy from food is oxygen (from the air). If you breathe 15 times a minute (at rest), taking in and exhaling 0.5 L of air with each breath, what volume of air do you breathe each day? Air is 21% oxygen by volume. What volume of oxygen do you breathe each day?

45. To oxidize 1.0 kg of fat, our bodies require about 2000 L of oxygen. A healthy diet contains not more than about 80 g of fat per day. What volume (at STP) of oxygen is required to oxidize that fat?

46. The photosynthesis reaction (page 223) can be expressed as the net result of two processes, one of which requires light and is called the *light reaction*. This reaction may be written as

$$12\ H_2O \xrightarrow{\text{light}} 6\ O_2 + 24\ H^+ + 24\ e^-$$

   a. Is the light reaction an oxidation or reduction?
   b. Write the equation for the other half-reaction, called the *dark reaction*, for photosynthesis.

47. Indicate whether the first-named substance in each change undergoes an oxidation, a reduction, or neither. Explain your reasoning.
   a. A violet solution of vanadium(II) ions, V^{2+}(aq), is converted to a green solution of V^{3+}(aq).
   b. Nitrogen dioxide converts to dinitrogen tetroxide when cooled.
   c. Carbon monoxide reacts with hydrogen to form methanol.

48. As a rule, metallic elements act as reducing agents, not as oxidizing agents. Explain. (*Hint:* Consider the charges on metal ions.) Do nonmetals act only as oxidizing agents and not as reducing agents? Explain your answer.

49. If a stream of hydrogen gas is ignited in air, the flame can be immersed in a jar of chlorine gas and it will still burn. Write the balanced equation for the reaction that occurs in the jar. What is the oxidizing agent in the reaction?

50. Consider the following reaction of calcium hydride (CaH_2) with molten sodium metal. Identify the species being oxidized and the species being reduced according to **(a)** the second definition shown in Figure 8.2 and **(b)** the third definition in Figure 8.2. What difficulty arises?

$$CaH_2(s) + 2\ Na(l) \longrightarrow 2\ NaH(s) + Ca(l)$$

51. Aluminum metal can react with water, but the oxide coating normally found on the metal prevents that reaction. In 2007, a Purdue University researcher found that adding gallium to aluminum prevented the formation of the oxide coating, allowing the aluminum to react with water to form hydrogen gas. This process might lead to a compact source of hydrogen gas for fuel. Write a balanced equation for the reaction of aluminum with water (aluminum hydroxide is the other product), and identify the oxidizing and reducing agents in the reaction.

52. Refer to Problem 51. Aluminum has a density of 2.70 g/cm^3. What volume in cubic centimeters of aluminum metal would be needed to produce 2.0×10^4 L of hydrogen gas at STP? How many times smaller is this volume of aluminum than is the volume of hydrogen gas? (Recall that at STP, 1 mol of gas occupies 22.4 L.)

53. Consider the oxidation of ethanol (CH_3CH_2OH) to acetaldehyde (CH_3CHO) by NAD^+ (page 204). **(a)** Write half-reactions for the process. **(b)** NADH is a biochemical reducing agent, in the reverse of the oxidation reaction. Write half-reactions for the reduction of pyruvic acid ($CH_3COCOOH$) to lactic acid ($CH_3CHOHCOOH$) by NADH, and then combine these two half-reactions to get the equation for the overall reaction.

54. Following are some organic chemistry processes. Classify each as an oxidation or a reduction. R represents a hydrocarbon group, and does not change in the process.
    a. RCH_3 (alkane) → RCH_2OH (alcohol)
    b. RCHO (aldehyde) → RCH_2OH (alcohol)
    c. RCHO (aldehyde) → RCOOH (carboxylic acid)
    d. RCOOH (carboxylic acid) → RCHO (aldehyde)
    e. RCH_2OH (alcohol) → RCHO (aldehyde)

55. Which of the following describe industrial chemicals, and which describe specialty chemicals?
    a. made on a large scale
    b. complex molecules
    c. high-value chemicals
    d. building blocks for other chemicals

56. A green catalyst is one that
    a. contains earth-abundant elements
    b. makes reagents react more efficiently
    c. decreases the cost of producing a chemical
    d. does all of the above

57. Give one reason why it can be difficult to design a long-lived oxidation catalyst.

58. Identify the oxidizing agent and the substance that is oxidized in the following reaction.

$$3 C_2H_6O + Cr_2O_7^{2-} + 8 H^+ \longrightarrow 3 C_2H_4O + 2 Cr^{3+} + 7 H_2O$$

COLLABORATIVE GROUP PROJECTS

Prepare a PowerPoint, poster, or other presentation (as directed by your instructor) to share with the class.

1. Prepare a brief report on one of the following types of electrochemical cells or batteries. If possible, give the half-reactions, the overall reaction, and typical uses.
   a. lithium–SO_2 cell   b. lithium–iodine cell
   c. lithium–FeS_2 battery   d. Ni–Cad cell
   e. silver oxide cell   f. nickel–metal hydride cell

2. Prepare a brief report on one of the following methods of protecting steel from corrosion. Identify the chemical reactions involved in the process, and tell how the process is related to oxidation and reduction.
   a. galvanization   b. coating with tin
   c. cathodic protection

3. Batteries contain toxic substances and should be recycled rather than thrown in the trash. Prepare a brief report on battery recycling. Are there facilities in your area for recycling batteries?

4. Military personnel, outdoor recreation enthusiasts such as wilderness campers and trekkers, and others often have to drink water from untreated streams or lakes. People who temporarily lack safe drinking water after a natural disaster also need a way to purify water. A variety of water purification tablets are available to treat contaminated water. Research several such tablets, and list their ingredients.

5. Visit one or more Web sites about fuel cells. Write the reactions that occur in the different types of fuel cells in development. Prepare a brief report on one of the following topics:
   a. a cost–benefit analysis of using fuel cells in automobiles versus using gasoline, electricity from batteries, or natural gas
   b. safety considerations about the hydrogen–oxygen fuel cell
   c. political–economic factors that may be hindering or promoting fuel cell research

Organic Chemistry

Have You Ever Wondered?

1. **Does organic food have anything to do with organic chemistry?**

2. **What is the "petroleum distillate" that I see listed on some product labels?**

3. **If a compound has *benzene* in its name, is the compound a carcinogen?**

4. **Why do some mouthwashes taste "medicine-y"?**

5. **Why does fresh fruit smell so good and rotting fruit so bad?**

6. **Why do dead animals smell so bad?**

The Infinite Variety of Carbon Compounds

The definition of organic chemistry has changed over the years. The changes exemplify the dynamic character of science and exemplify how scientific concepts change in response to experimental evidence. Until the nineteenth century, chemists believed that *organic* chemicals originated only in tissues of living *organisms* and required a "vital force" for their production. All chemicals not manufactured by living tissue were regarded

The compound capsaicin, a molecular model of which is shown here, is the principal compound responsible for the "hotness" of chili peppers. Capsaicin is organic in the original sense because it is obtained from a plant. It is also organic in the modern sense in that it is a compound containing carbon. Numerous organic chemicals are obtained from plants and animals, but many of the millions of organic compounds known today are synthetic. See Problem 51, page 264.

Learning Objectives

> Define *hydrocarbon*, and recognize structural features of alkanes, alkenes, and alkynes. (9.1)

> Identify hydrocarbon molecules as alkanes, alkenes, or alkynes, and name them. (9.1)

> Define *aromatic compound*, and recognize the structural feature such compounds share. (9.2)

> Name simple aromatic hydrocarbons. (9.2)

> Name a halogenated hydrocarbon given its formula, and write the formula for such a compound given its name. (9.3)

> Classify an organic compound according to its functional group(s), and explain why the concept of a functional group is useful in the study of organic chemistry. (9.4)

> Recognize and write the formulas of simple alkyl groups. (9.4)

> Recognize the general structure for an alcohol, a phenol, and an ether. (9.5)

> Name simple alcohols, phenols, and ethers. (9.5)

> Name simple aldehydes and ketones, and list their important properties. (9.6)

> Name simple carboxylic acids and esters, and list their important properties. (9.7)

> Name and write the formulas of simple amines and amides. (9.8)

> Recognize a structure as that of a heterocyclic compound. (9.8)

> Identify greener solvents that can replace those from nonrenewable fossil fuels, methods for incorporating renewable resources into organic synthesis, and efficient energy sources for enhancing chemical reactions.

The word *organic* has several different meanings. Organic fertilizer is organic in the original sense; it is derived from living organisms. Organic foods are those grown without synthetic pesticides or fertilizers. Organic chemistry is simply the chemistry of carbon-containing compounds.

In addition to carbon, almost all organic compounds also contain hydrogen, many contain oxygen and/or nitrogen, and quite a few contain sulfur or halogens. Nearly all the common elements are found in at least a few organic compounds.

as *inorganic*. Some chemists even believed that organic and inorganic chemicals followed different laws. This all changed in 1828, when Friedrich Wöhler synthesized the organic compound urea (found in urine) from ammonium cyanate, an inorganic compound. This important event led other chemists to attempt synthesis of organic chemicals from inorganic ones and changed the very definition of organic chemicals.

Organic chemistry is now defined as the chemistry of carbon-containing compounds. Most of these compounds do come from living things or from things that were once living, but some do not. Perhaps the most remarkable thing about organic compounds is their sheer number. Of the tens of millions of known chemical compounds, more than 95% are compounds of carbon.

One reason for the huge number of organic compounds is the carbon atom itself. Carbon is unique in that its atoms bond readily to each other and form long chains. (Silicon and a few other elements can form chains, but only short ones.) Carbon chains can also have branches or form rings of various sizes. When we consider that carbon atoms also bond strongly to other elements, particularly nonmetals such as hydrogen, oxygen, and nitrogen, and that these atoms can be arranged in many different ways, it soon becomes obvious why there are so many organic compounds.

In addition to the millions of carbon compounds already known, new ones are being discovered every day. Carbon can form an almost infinite number of molecules of various shapes, sizes, and compositions. We use thousands of carbon compounds every day without even realizing it because they are silently carrying out important chemical reactions within our bodies. Many of these carbon compounds are so vital that we cannot live without them.

9.1 Aliphatic Hydrocarbons

Learning Objectives ❯ Define *hydrocarbon*, and recognize structural features of alkanes, alkenes, and alkynes. ❯ Identify hydrocarbon molecules as alkanes, alkenes, or alkynes, and name them.

The simplest organic compounds are hydrocarbons. A **hydrocarbon** contains only hydrogen and carbon. There are several kinds of hydrocarbons, classified according to the type of bonding between carbon atoms. We divide hydrocarbons into two main classes. Those discussed in this section are **aliphatic compounds** (the Greek word *aleiphar* means "fat" or "oil"), usually defined as nonaromatic. The other category, benzene-like *aromatic compounds*, is discussed in Section 9.2.

Alkanes

Each carbon atom forms four bonds, and each hydrogen atom forms only one bond, so the simplest hydrocarbon molecule possible is methane, CH_4. Methane is the main component of natural gas. It has the structure

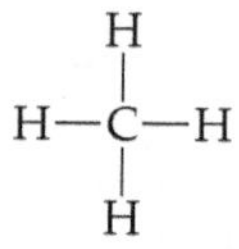

$$H-\overset{\displaystyle H}{\underset{\displaystyle H}{C}}-H$$

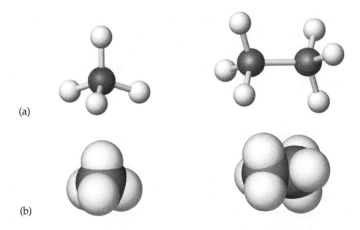

Figure 9.1 Ball-and-stick (a) and space-filling (b) models of methane (left) and ethane (right).

(a)

(b)

Methane is the first member of a group of related compounds called **alkanes**, hydrocarbons that contain only single bonds. Alkanes can have from one to several hundred or more carbon atoms. The next member of the series is ethane,

$$\begin{array}{c} \text{H}\quad\text{H} \\ | \quad\ | \\ \text{H}-\text{C}-\text{C}-\text{H} \\ | \quad\ | \\ \text{H}\quad\text{H} \end{array}$$

Ethane is a minor constituent of natural gas. It is seldom encountered as a pure compound in everyday life, but many common compounds are derived from it.

We saw in Chapter 4 that the methane molecule is tetrahedral, in accord with the VSEPR theory. In fact, the tetrahedral shape results whenever a carbon atom is connected to four other atoms, whether they are hydrogen, carbon, or other elements. Figure 9.1 shows models of methane and ethane. The ball-and-stick models show the bond angles best, but the space-filling models more accurately reflect the shapes of the molecules. Ordinarily, we use simple structural formulas such as the one shown previously for ethane because they are much easier to draw. A **structural formula** shows which atoms are bonded to each other, but it does not attempt to show the actual shape of the molecule.

Alkanes are often called **saturated hydrocarbons** because each carbon atom is *saturated* with hydrogen atoms; that is, each carbon is bonded to the maximum number of hydrogen atoms. In constructing a formula, we connect the carbon atoms to each other through single bonds; then we add enough hydrogen atoms to give each carbon atom four bonds. All alkanes have two more than twice as many hydrogen atoms as carbon atoms. That is, alkanes can be represented by a general formula C_nH_{2n+2}, in which n is the number of carbon atoms.

The three-carbon alkane is propane. Models of propane are shown in Figure 9.2. To draw its structural formula, we place three carbon atoms in a row.

$$\text{C}-\text{C}-\text{C}$$

Then we add enough hydrogen atoms (eight in this case) to give each carbon atom a total of four bonds. Therefore, the structural formula of propane is

$$\begin{array}{c} \text{H}\quad\text{H}\quad\text{H} \\ | \quad\ | \quad\ | \\ \text{H}-\text{C}-\text{C}-\text{C}-\text{H} \\ | \quad\ | \quad\ | \\ \text{H}\quad\text{H}\quad\text{H} \end{array}$$

Condensed Structural Formulas

The complete structural formulas that we have used so far show all the carbon and hydrogen atoms and how they are attached to one another. But these formulas take up a lot of space, and they can be a bit of trouble to draw. For these reasons, chemists usually prefer to use **condensed structural formulas**. These formulas show how

(a)

(b)

Figure 9.2 Ball-and-stick (a) and space-filling (b) models of propane.

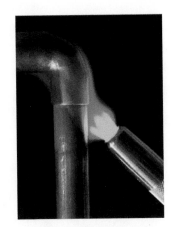

A propane torch. Propane burns in air with a hot flame.

Table 9.1 Stems for Organic Molecule Names

Stem	Number of Carbon Atoms
Meth-	1
Eth-	2
Prop-	3
But-	4
Pent-	5
Hex-	6
Hept-	7
Oct-	8
Non-	9
Dec-	10

many hydrogen atoms are attached to each carbon atom without showing the bond to each hydrogen atom. For example, the condensed structural formulas for ethane and propane are written $CH_3—CH_3$ and $CH_3—CH_2—CH_3$, respectively. These formulas can be simplified even further by omitting some (or all) of the remaining bond lines, resulting in CH_3CH_3 and $CH_3CH_2CH_3$.

Homologous Series

Note that methane, ethane, and propane form a pattern. We can build alkanes of any length simply by joining carbon atoms together in long chains and adding enough hydrogen atoms to give each carbon atom four bonds. Even the naming of these compounds follows a pattern (Table 9.1), with a stem name indicating the number of carbon atoms. For compounds of five carbon atoms or more, each stem is derived from the Greek or Latin name for the number. The compound names end in *-ane*, signifying that the compounds are *alkanes*. Table 9.2 gives condensed structural formulas and names for the continuous-chain (straight-chain, or unbranched) alkanes with up to ten carbon atoms.

Notice that the molecular formula for each alkane in Table 9.2 differs from the one preceding it by precisely one carbon atom and two hydrogen atoms—that is, by a CH_2 unit. Such a series of compounds has properties that vary in a regular and predictable manner. This principle, called *homology*, gives order to organic chemistry in much the same way that the periodic table gives organization to the chemistry of the elements. Instead of studying the chemistry of a bewildering array of individual carbon compounds, organic chemists study a few members—called *homologs*—of a **homologous series**, from which they can deduce the properties of other compounds in the series.

We need not stop at ten carbon atoms as Table 9.2 does. Hundreds, thousands, even millions of carbon atoms can be linked together. We can make an infinite number of alkanes simply by lengthening the chain. But lengthening the chain is not the only option. Beginning with alkanes having four carbon atoms, chain branching is also possible.

Isomerism

When we extend the carbon chain to four atoms and add enough hydrogen atoms to give each carbon atom four bonds, we get $CH_3CH_2CH_2CH_3$. This formula represents butane, a compound that boils at about 0 °C. A second compound, which has a boiling point of −12 °C, has the same molecular formula, C_4H_{10}, as butane. The structure of this compound, however, is not the same as that of butane. Instead of having four carbon atoms connected in a continuous chain, this compound has a continuous chain of only three carbon atoms. The fourth carbon is branched off the

Table 9.2 The First Ten Continuous-Chain Alkanes

Name	Molecular Formula	Condensed Structural Formula	Number of Possible Isomers
Methane	CH_4	CH_4	—
Ethane	C_2H_6	CH_3CH_3	—
Propane	C_3H_8	$CH_3CH_2CH_3$	—
Butane	C_4H_{10}	$CH_3CH_2CH_2CH_3$	2
Pentane	C_5H_{12}	$CH_3CH_2CH_2CH_2CH_3$	3
Hexane	C_6H_{14}	$CH_3CH_2CH_2CH_2CH_2CH_3$	5
Heptane	C_7H_{16}	$CH_3CH_2CH_2CH_2CH_2CH_2CH_3$	9
Octane	C_8H_{18}	$CH_3CH_2CH_2CH_2CH_2CH_2CH_2CH_3$	18
Nonane	C_9H_{20}	$CH_3CH_2CH_2CH_2CH_2CH_2CH_2CH_2CH_3$	35
Decane	$C_{10}H_{22}$	$CH_3CH_2CH_2CH_2CH_2CH_2CH_2CH_2CH_2CH_3$	75

middle carbon of the three-carbon chain. To show the two structures more clearly, let's use complete structural formulas, showing all the bonds to hydrogen atoms.

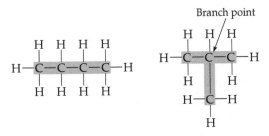

Branch point

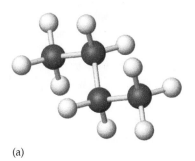

(a)

Compounds that have the same molecular formula but different structural formulas are called **isomers**. Because it is an isomer of butane, the branched four-carbon alkane is sometimes called *isobutane*. Condensed structural formulas for the two isomeric butanes are written as follows.

$$CH_3CH_2CH_2CH_3 \qquad CH_3CHCH_3$$
$$\qquad\qquad\qquad\qquad | $$
$$\qquad\qquad\qquad\qquad CH_3$$

Butane   Isobutane

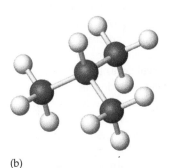

(b)

▲ **Figure 9.3** Ball-and-stick models of (a) butane and (b) isobutane.

Figure 9.3 shows ball-and-stick models of the two compounds.

The number of isomers increases rapidly with the number of carbon atoms (Table 9.2). There are three pentanes, five hexanes, nine heptanes, and so on. Isomerism is common in carbon compounds and provides another reason for the existence of millions of organic compounds.

Propane and the butanes are familiar fuels. Although they are gases at ordinary temperatures and under normal atmospheric pressure, they are liquefied under pressure and are usually supplied in tanks as liquefied petroleum gas (LPG). Gasoline is a mixture of hydrocarbons, mostly alkanes, with 5–12 carbon atoms.

Not all the possible isomers of the larger molecules have been isolated. Indeed, the task rapidly becomes more and more prohibitive going up the series. There are, for example, 4,111,846,763 possible isomers with the molecular formula $C_{30}H_{62}$.

▲ Gasoline is a mixture containing dozens of hydrocarbons, many of which are alkanes.

Example 9.1 Hydrocarbon Formulas

Without referring to Table 9.2, write the molecular formula, the complete structural formula, and the condensed structural formula for heptane.

Solution
The stem *hept-* means seven carbon atoms, and the ending *-ane* indicates an alkane. For the complete structural formula, we write a string of seven carbon atoms.

$$C-C-C-C-C-C-C$$

Then we attach enough hydrogen atoms to the carbon atoms to give each carbon four bonds. This requires three hydrogens on each end carbon and two hydrogens on each of the other carbons.

$$H-C-C-C-C-C-C-C-H$$

For the condensed form, we simply write each set of hydrogen atoms following the carbon atom to which they are bonded.

$$CH_3CH_2CH_2CH_2CH_2CH_2CH_3$$

For the molecular formula, we can simply count the carbon and hydrogen atoms to arrive at C_7H_{16}. Alternatively, we could use the general formula C_nH_{2n+2}, with $n = 7$, to get C_7H_{16}.

2. What is the "petroleum distillate" that I see listed on some product labels? Petroleum distillates are various components of crude oil, most of which are hydrocarbons. Paint thinner, lighter fluid, paraffin wax, petroleum jelly, and asphalt are all petroleum distillates.

Recall that water has a density of 1.00 g/mL at room temperature. All the alkanes listed in Table 9.3 have densities less than that.

■ EXERCISE 9.1

Write the molecular, complete structural, and condensed structural formulas for **(a)** hexane and **(b)** octane.

Properties of Alkanes

Note in Table 9.3 that after the first few members of the alkane series, the rest show an increase in boiling point of about 30° with each added CH_2 group. Note also that at room temperature alkanes that have 1 to 4 carbon atoms per molecule are gases, those with 5 to about 16 carbon atoms per molecule are liquids, and those with more than 16 carbon atoms per molecule are solids. The densities of liquid and solid alkanes are less than that of water. Alkanes are nonpolar molecules and are insoluble in water; thus, they float on top of water. They dissolve many organic substances of low polarity—such as fats, oils, and waxes.

Alkanes undergo few chemical reactions, but one important chemical property is that they burn, producing a lot of heat. Alkanes have many uses, but they mainly serve as fuels.

The effects of alkanes on the human body vary. Methane appears to be physiologically inert. We probably could breathe a mixture of 80% methane and 20% oxygen without ill effect. This mixture would be flammable, however, and no fire or spark of any kind could be permitted in such an atmosphere. Breathing an atmosphere of pure methane (the "gas" of a gas-operated stove) can lead to death—not because of the presence of methane but because of the absence of oxygen, a condition called *asphyxia*.

Light liquid alkanes such as those in gasoline will dissolve and wash away body oils when spilled on the skin. Repeated contact may cause dermatitis. (Other components of gasoline are less innocuous.) If swallowed, most alkanes do little harm in the stomach; in fact, mineral oil is a mixture of long-chain liquid alkanes that has been used for many years as a laxative.

Heavier liquid alkanes act as emollients (skin softeners). Petroleum jelly (Vaseline™ is one brand) is a semisolid mixture of hydrocarbons that can be applied as an emollient or simply as a protective film. (Skin lotions and creams are discussed in Chapter 21.) However, in the lungs, alkanes cause chemical pneumonia by dissolving fatlike molecules from the cell membranes in the alveoli, allowing the lungs to fill with fluid.

⚠ SAFETY ALERT

Hydrocarbons and most other organic compounds are flammable or combustible. Volatile ones may form explosive mixtures with air. Hydrocarbons are the main ingredients in gasoline, motor oils, fuel gases (natural gas and bottled gas), and fuel oils. They are also ingredients, identified on labels as "petroleum distillates" and "mineral spirits," of products such as floor cleaners, furniture polishes, paint thinners, wood stains and varnishes, and car waxes and polishes. Some products also contain flammable alcohols, esters, and ketones. Products containing flammable substances can be dangerous but may be used safely with proper precautions. Use only as directed and keep all such products away from open flames.

Table 9.3 Physical Properties, Uses and Occurrences of Selected Alkanes

Name	Molecular Formula	Melting Point (°C)	Boiling Point (°C)	Density[a] at 20 °C (g/mL)	Use/Occurrence
Methane	CH_4	−183	−162	(Gas)	Natural gas (main component); fuel
Ethane	C_2H_6	−172	−89	(Gas)	Natural gas (minor component); plastics
Propane	C_3H_8	−188	−42	(Gas)	LPG (bottled gas); plastics
Butane	C_4H_{10}	−138	0	(Gas)	LPG; lighter fuel
Pentane	C_5H_{12}	−130	36	0.626	Gasoline component
Hexane	C_6H_{14}	−95	69	0.659	Gasoline component; extraction solvent for food oils
Heptane	C_7H_{16}	−91	98	0.684	Gasoline component
Octane	C_8H_{18}	−57	126	0.703	Gasoline component
Decane	$C_{10}H_{22}$	−30	174	0.730	Gasoline component
Dodecane	$C_{12}H_{26}$	−10	216	0.749	Gasoline component
Tetradecane	$C_{14}H_{30}$	6	254	0.763	Diesel fuel component
Hexadecane	$C_{16}H_{34}$	18	280	0.775	Diesel fuel component
Octadecane	$C_{18}H_{38}$	28	316	(Solid)	Paraffin wax component
Eicosane	$C_{20}H_{42}$	37	343	(Solid)	Paraffin wax and asphalt component

[a]Densities of the gaseous alkanes vary with pressure. Densities of the solids are not available.

Cyclic Hydrocarbons: Rings and Things

The hydrocarbons we have encountered so far (alkanes) have open-ended chains of carbon atoms. Carbon atoms can also connect to form closed rings. The simplest possible ring-containing hydrocarbon, or **cyclic hydrocarbon**, has the molecular formula C_3H_6 and is called *cyclopropane* (Figure 9.4).

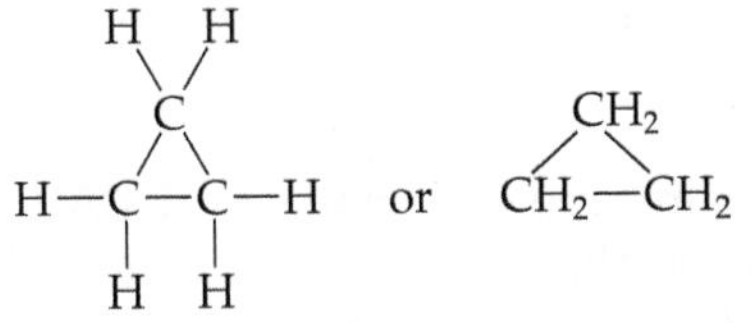

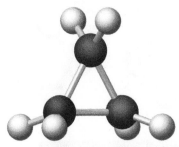

▲ **Figure 9.4** Ball-and-stick model of cyclopropane. Cyclopropane is a potent, quick-acting anesthetic with few undesirable side effects. It is no longer used in surgery, however, because it forms an explosive mixture with air at nearly all concentrations.

Names of *cycloalkanes* (cyclic hydrocarbons containing only single bonds) are formed by adding the prefix *cyclo-* to the name of the open-chain compound with the same number of carbon atoms as are in the cycloalkane's ring.

Chemists often use geometric shapes to represent cyclic compounds (Figure 9.5). For example, a triangle is used to represent the cyclopropane ring, and a hexagon represents cyclohexane. Each corner of such a shape represents a carbon atom with its associated hydrogen atoms.

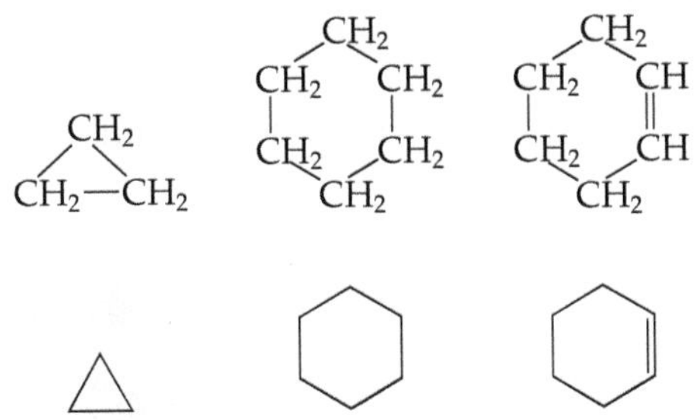

Cyclopropane   Cyclohexane   Cyclohexene

◀ **Figure 9.5** Structural formulas and symbolic representations of some cyclic hydrocarbons.

Example 9.2   Structural Formulas of Cyclic Hydrocarbons

Write the structural formula for cyclobutane. What geometric figure is used to represent cyclobutane?

Solution
Cyclobutane has four carbon atoms arranged in a ring.

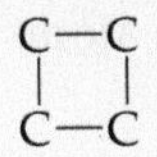

Each carbon atom needs two hydrogen atoms to complete its set of four bonds.

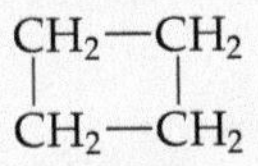

Cyclobutane can also be represented by a square.

▪ EXERCISE 9.2A
Write the structural formula for cyclopentane and the geometric shape used to represent it.

▪ EXERCISE 9.2B
What is the general formula for a cycloalkane?

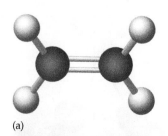

(a)

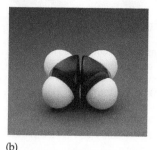

(b)

▲ **Figure 9.6** Ball-and-stick (a) and space-filling (b) models of ethylene.

▶ **Figure 9.7** Ball-and-stick (a) and space-filling (b) models of acetylene.

Unsaturated Hydrocarbons: Alkenes and Alkynes

Two carbon atoms can share more than one pair of electrons. In ethylene (C_2H_4), the two carbon atoms share two pairs of electrons and are therefore joined by a double bond (Figure 9.6).

$$H_2C::CH_2 \quad \text{or} \quad \begin{array}{c} H \\ \end{array}C=C\begin{array}{c} H \\ H \end{array} \quad \text{or} \quad CH_2{=}CH_2$$

(Ethylene is the common name; the systematic, or IUPAC, name is *ethene*.) Ethylene is the simplest member of the alkene family. An **alkene** is a hydrocarbon that contains one or more carbon-to-carbon double bonds. Alkenes with one double bond have the general formula C_nH_{2n}, where n is the number of carbon atoms.

Ethylene is the most important organic chemical commercially. Annual U.S. production is over 20 billion kg. More than half goes into the manufacture of polyethylene, one of the most familiar plastics. Another 15% or so is converted to ethylene glycol, the major component of many formulations of antifreeze used in automobile radiators.

In acetylene (C_2H_2), the two carbon atoms share three pairs of electrons. The carbon atoms are joined by a triple bond (Figure 9.7).

$$H{:}C{:::}C{:}H \quad \text{or} \quad H{-}C{\equiv}C{-}H$$

Acetylene (IUPAC name, ethyne) is the simplest member of the alkyne family. An **alkyne** is a hydrocarbon that contains one or more carbon-to-carbon triple bonds. Alkynes with one triple bond have the general formula C_nH_{2n-2}, where n is the number of carbon atoms.

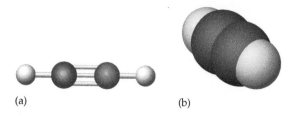

(a)   (b)

Acetylene is used in oxyacetylene torches for cutting and welding metals. Such torches can produce very high temperatures. Acetylene is also converted to a variety of other chemical products.

Collectively, alkenes and alkynes are called *unsaturated hydrocarbons*. Recall that a *saturated hydrocarbon* (alkane) has the maximum number of hydrogen atoms attached to each carbon atom; it has no double or triple bonds. An **unsaturated hydrocarbon** can have more hydrogen atoms added to it.

Unsaturated		Saturated

$$\begin{array}{c} H \\ \end{array}C=C\begin{array}{c} H \\ H \end{array} \; + \; H{-}H \; \longrightarrow \; H{-}\underset{H}{\overset{H}{C}}{-}\underset{H}{\overset{H}{C}}{-}H$$

Ethylene   Ethane

Unsaturated		Saturated

$$H{-}C{\equiv}C{-}H \; + \; 2\,H{-}H \; \longrightarrow \; H{-}\underset{H}{\overset{H}{C}}{-}\underset{H}{\overset{H}{C}}{-}H$$

Acetylene   Ethane

Example 9.3 Molecular Formulas of Unsaturated Hydrocarbons

What is the molecular formula for 1-hexene? (The "1-" is a part of a systematic name that indicates the location of the double bond, which in this case connects the first carbon atom of the chain to the second.)

Solution

The stem *hex-* indicates six carbon atoms, the ending *-ene* tells us that the compound is an alkene. Using the general formula C_nH_{2n} for an alkene, with $n = 6$, we see that an alkene with six carbon atoms has the molecular formula C_6H_{14}.

■ EXERCISE 9.3

What are the molecular formulas for (a) 2-hexene and (b) 3-heptyne?

Properties of Alkenes and Alkynes

The physical properties of alkenes and alkynes are much like those of the corresponding alkanes. Unsaturated hydrocarbons with 2 to 4 carbon atoms per molecule are gases at room temperature, those with 5 to 18 carbon atoms are liquids, and most of those with more than 18 carbon atoms are solids. Like alkanes, alkenes and alkynes are insoluble in, and float on, water.

Like alkanes, both alkenes and alkynes burn. However, these unsaturated hydrocarbons undergo many more chemical reactions than alkanes do. An alkene or alkyne can undergo an **addition reaction** to the double or triple bond, in which all the atoms of the reactants are incorporated into a single product. In the preceding reactions, ethylene (C_2H_4) adds hydrogen (H_2) to form ethane (C_2H_6), and acetylene (C_2H_2) adds two moles of hydrogen ($2\,H_2$) to form ethane. Chlorine, bromine, water, and many other kinds of small molecules also add to double and triple bonds.

One of the most unusual features of alkene (and alkyne) molecules is that they can add *to each other* to form large molecules called *polymers*. These interesting molecules are discussed in Chapter 10.

▲ It DOES Matter!

Fats are probably the best-known examples of compounds that can be saturated or unsaturated. In saturated fats, all the carbon-carbon bonds are single bonds. These fats are found mostly in milk, meats, and eggs, and their consumption tends to increase low-density lipoproteins ("bad" cholesterol) in the human bloodstream. Most plant oils are unsaturated fats, with one or more carbon-carbon double bonds. Consumption of unsaturated fats tends to increase high-density lipoproteins ("good" cholesterol) in the blood.

Self-Assessment Questions

1. Which of the following is *not* a reason for the great number of carbon compounds?
   a. Carbon atoms can form chains.
   b. Carbon compounds are easily oxidized.
   c. Carbon atoms can form rings.
   d. The same carbon atoms can be arranged different ways.

2. A saturated hydrocarbon is one that
   a. contains only carbon-carbon single bonds
   b. has the maximum number of carbon atoms
   c. has a vapor pressure equal to atmospheric pressure
   d. is solid at room temperature

3. Successive members of the alkane series differ from the preceding member by one additional
   a. C atom and one H atom
   b. C atom and two H atoms
   c. C atom and three H atoms
   d. H atom and two C atoms

4. Isomers are compounds whose molecules have the same
   a. numbers of C atoms but different numbers of H atoms
   b. numbers of H atoms but different numbers of C atoms
   c. numbers and kinds of atoms but different structures
   d. kinds of atoms but different numbers of these atoms

5. As the molecular mass of the members of the alkane series increases, their boiling points
   a. decrease   b. increase   c. remain the same   d. vary randomly

6. A cyclic compound with 6 C atoms and 12 H atoms is
   a. cyclobutane   b. cycloheptane   c. cyclohexane   d. cyclosexane

An unsaturated hydrocarbon tends to burn with a smoky flame, especially if the oxygen supply is limited. Saturated hydrocarbons usually burn with a clean yellow flame. Burning of natural gas, propane, and butane is almost soot-free, but paint thinner, gasoline, and kerosene (all containing unsaturated hydrocarbons) burn with sooty flames.

7. The family of hydrocarbons whose molecules have a triple bond between carbon atoms is the
   a. alkanes   **b.** alkenes   **c.** alkynes   **d.** aromatic hydrocarbons

8. Addition reactions occur with alkenes but not with alkanes because alkenes have
   a. double bonds   **b.** a greater molecular mass
   c. more C atoms per molecule   **d.** a tetrahedral arrangement of bonds

9. The following equation is an example of what kind of reaction?
$$C_2H_4 + H_2 \longrightarrow C_2H_6$$
   a. addition   **b.** neutralization   **c.** oxidation   **d.** ionization

9.2 Aromatic Compounds: Benzene and its Relatives

Learning Objectives ❯ Define *aromatic* compound, and recognize the structural feature such compounds share. ❯ Name simple aromatic hydrocarbons.

An important and interesting hydrocarbon is benzene. Discovered by Michael Faraday in 1825, benzene has the molecular formula C_6H_6. The structure of benzene puzzled chemists for decades. The formula seems to indicate an unsaturated compound, but benzene does not react as if it contains any double or triple bonds. It does not readily undergo addition reactions the way unsaturated compounds usually do.

Finally, in 1865, August Kekulé proposed a structure with a ring of six carbon atoms, each attached to one hydrogen atom.

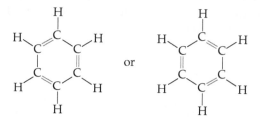

The two structures shown appear to contain double bonds, but in fact they do not. Both structures represent the same molecule, and the actual structure of this molecule is a *hybrid* of these two structures. The benzene molecule actually has six identical carbon-to-carbon bonds that are neither single bonds nor double bonds but something in between. In other words, the three pairs of electrons that would form the three double bonds are not tied down in one location but are spread around the ring (Figure 9.8). Today, we usually represent the benzene ring with a circle inside a hexagon.

The hexagon represents the ring of six carbon atoms, and the inscribed circle represents the six unassigned electrons. Because its ring of electrons resists being disrupted, the benzene molecule is exceptionally stable.

Benzene and similar compounds are called *aromatic hydrocarbons*, because quite a few of the first benzene-like substances to be discovered had strong aromas. Even though many compounds derived from benzene have turned out to be odorless, the name has stuck. Today, an **aromatic compound** is any compound that contains a benzene ring or has certain properties like those of benzene. All other compounds are said to be aliphatic (Section 9.1).

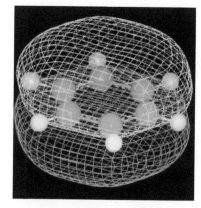

▲ **Figure 9.8** A computer-generated model of the benzene molecule. The six unassigned electrons occupy the yellow and blue areas above and below the plane of the ring of carbon atoms.

A circle inside a ring indicates that a compound is aromatic. It does not always mean six electrons. The structural formula for naphthalene (Figure 9.9), for example, has a circle in each ring, indicating that it is an aromatic hydrocarbon. The total number of unassigned electrons, however, is only ten. Some chemists still prefer to represent naphthalene (and other aromatic compounds) with alternating double and single bonds.

Structures of some common aromatic hydrocarbons are shown in Figure 9.9. Benzene, toluene, and the xylenes are all liquids that float on water. They are used mainly as solvents and fuels but are also used to make other benzene derivatives. Their vapors can act as narcotics when inhaled. Because benzene may cause leukemia after long exposure, its use has been restricted. Naphthalene is a volatile, white, crystalline solid used as an insecticide, especially as a moth repellant.

Monosubstituted benzenes—in which one hydrogen is replaced by another atom or group, called a **substituent**—are often represented in by condensed formulas—for example, toluene is $C_6H_5CH_3$ and ethylbenzene is $C_6H_5CH_2CH_3$. Similar designations are sometimes used for disubstituted aromatic rings, indicating the relative positions of substituents with numbers, as in $1,4\text{-}C_6H_4(CH_3)_2$ for 1,4-dimethylbenzene.

3. If a compound has *benzene* in its name, is the compound a carcinogen? No. Aromatic compounds are often named as derivatives of benzene simply because their structures contain a benzene ring. In fact, many compounds that are useful or even necessary to life contain benzene rings, including penicillin, aspirin, and the amino acids phenylalanine and tryptophan.

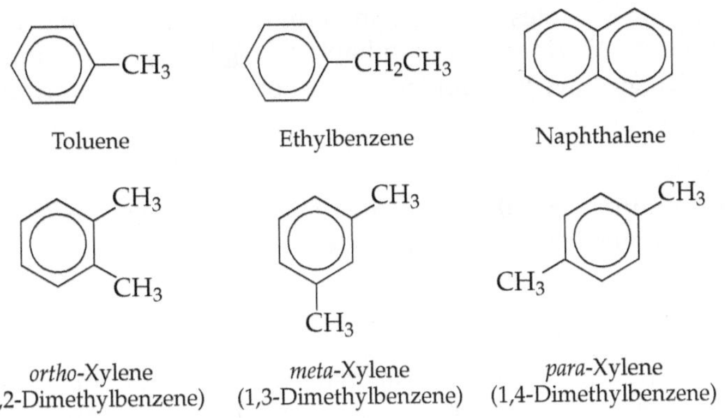

Toluene   Ethylbenzene   Naphthalene

ortho-Xylene
(1,2-Dimethylbenzene)

meta-Xylene
(1,3-Dimethylbenzene)

para-Xylene
(1,4-Dimethylbenzene)

◄ **Figure 9.9** Some aromatic hydrocarbons. Like benzene, toluene and the three xylenes are components of gasoline and also serve as solvents. All these compounds are intermediates in the synthesis of polymers (Chapter 10) and other organic chemicals.

Self-Assessment Questions

1. The molecular formula of benzene is
   a. C_4H_4 b. C_4H_{10} c. C_6H_6 d. C_6H_{10}

2. Which compound is an aromatic hydrocarbon?
   a. acetylene   b. butadiene   c. chlorobenzene   d. cyclohexene

3. Which organic molecule is represented as a hybrid of two structures?
   a. benzene   b. butadiene   c. 1-butene   d. propyne

4. Naphthalene is an
   a. alkane   b. alkene   c. alkyne   d. aromatic hydrocarbon

5. The reactivity of the benzene ring reflects
   a. its aromatic odor
   b. the presence of carbon-carbon double bonds
   c. its saturated structure
   d. the spreading of six electrons over all six carbon atoms

Answers: 1, c; 2, c; 3, a; 4, d; 5, d

9.3 Chlorinated Hydrocarbons: Many Uses, Some Hazards

Learning Objective ❯ Name a chlorinated hydrocarbon given its formula, and write the formula for such a compound given its name.

Many other organic compounds are derived from hydrocarbons by replacing one or more hydrogen atoms by another atom or group of atoms. For example, replacement of hydrogen atoms by chlorine atoms gives chlorinated hydrocarbons. When chlorine gas (Cl_2) is mixed with methane gas (CH_4) in the presence of ultraviolet (UV) light, a reaction takes place at a very rapid, even explosive, rate. The result is a mixture of products, some of which may be familiar to you (see Example 9.4 and Exercise 9.4). Several billion kilograms of chlorinated methanes are produced each year for use as solvents and as starting materials for other commercially valuable compounds. We can write an equation for the reaction in which one hydrogen atom of methane is replaced by a chlorine atom to give methyl chloride (chloromethane).

$$CH_4(g) + Cl_2(g) \longrightarrow CH_3Cl(g) + HCl(g)$$

Example 9.4 Formulas of Chlorinated Hydrocarbons

What is the formula for dichloromethane (also known as methylene chloride)?

Solution

The prefix *dichloro-* indicates two chlorine atoms. The rest of the name indicates that the compound is derived from methane (CH_4). We conclude that two hydrogen atoms of methane have been replaced by chlorine atoms; the formula for dichloromethane is therefore CH_2Cl_2.

▪ **EXERCISE 9.4**

What are the formulas for **(a)** trichloromethane (also known as chloroform) and **(b)** tetrachloromethane (carbon tetrachloride)?

Methyl chloride is used mainly in making silicone polymers (Chapter 10). Methylene chloride (dichloromethane) is a solvent used, for example, as a paint remover. Chloroform (trichloromethane), also a solvent, was once used as an anesthetic, but such use is now considered dangerous. The dosage required for effective anesthesia is too close to a lethal dose. Carbon tetrachloride (tetrachloromethane) has been used as a dry-cleaning solvent and in fire extinguishers, but it is no longer recommended for either use. Exposure to carbon tetrachloride or most other chlorinated hydrocarbons can cause severe damage to the liver. The use of a carbon tetrachloride fire extinguisher in conjunction with water to put out a fire can be deadly. Carbon tetrachloride reacts with water at elevated temperatures to form phosgene ($COCl_2$), an extremely poisonous gas that was used against troops during World War I.

A number of chlorinated hydrocarbons are of considerable interest. Vinyl chloride ($CH_2{=}CHCl$) is the starting material for manufacture of polyvinylchloride (Chapter 10).

Many chlorinated hydrocarbons have similar properties. Most are only slightly polar and do not dissolve in (highly polar) water. Instead, they dissolve (and dissolve in) fats, oils, greases, and other substances of low polarity. This is why certain chlorinated hydrocarbons make good degreasing and dry-cleaning solvents; they remove grease and oily stains from fabrics. This is also why DDT and PCBs cause problems for fish and birds and perhaps for people; these toxic substances are concentrated in fatty animal tissues rather than being easily excreted in (aqueous) urine. DDT (dichlorodiphenyltrichloroethane) and other chlorinated hydrocarbon insecticides are discussed in Chapter 20. In Chapter 10, we will discuss polychlorinated biphenyls (PCBs).

Chlorofluorocarbons and Fluorocarbons

Compounds containing carbon and both fluorine and chlorine are called *chlorofluorocarbons (CFCs)*. CFCs have been used as the dispersing gases in aerosol cans, for making foamed plastics, and as refrigerants. Three common CFCs are best known by their industrial code designations:

$$CFCl_3 \qquad CF_2Cl_2 \qquad CF_2ClCF_2Cl$$
CFC 11 CFC 12 CFC 114

At room temperature, CFCs are gases or liquids with low boiling points. They are insoluble in water and inert toward most other substances. These properties make them ideal propellants in aerosol cans for deodorant, hair spray, and food products. CFCs are being phased out because their inertness allows them to persist in the environment and diffuse into the stratosphere, where they participate in chemical reactions that lead to depletion of the ozone layer that protects Earth from harmful UV radiation. We will look at this problem and some attempts to solve it in Chapter 13.

Fluorinated compounds have found some interesting uses. Some have been used as blood extenders. Oxygen is quite soluble in certain *perfluorocarbons*. (The prefix *per-* means that all hydrogen atoms have been replaced, in this case, by fluorine atoms.) These compounds can therefore serve as temporary substitutes for hemoglobin, the oxygen-carrying protein in blood. Perfluoro compounds have been used to treat premature babies, whose lungs are often underdeveloped.

Polytetrafluoroethylene (PTFE, or Teflon®, discussed in Chapter 10) is a perfluorinated polymer. It has many interesting applications because of its resistance to corrosive chemicals and to high temperatures. It is especially noted for its unusual nonstick properties.

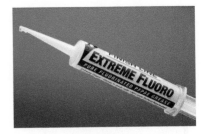

▲ Perfluorinated lubricants are used where highly corrosive or reactive conditions would cause most hydrocarbon greases to burst into flame.

Self-Assessment Questions

1. The compound CH_3Cl is named
   a. chloroform
   b. methyl chloride
   c. methylene chloride
   d. methyl formate

2. The compound CF_2Cl_2 is
   a. a chlorofluorocarbon
   b. chloroform
   c. methyl chloride
   d. methylene chloride

3. Which of the following is an isomer of 2-chloropropane ($CH_3CHClCH_3$)?
   a. butane
   b. 2-chlorobutane
   c. 1-chloropropane
   d. propane

Answers: 1, b; 2, a; 3, c

9.4 The Functional Group

Learning Objectives ❯ Classify an organic compound according to its functional group(s), and explain why the concept of a functional group is useful in the study of organic chemistry. ❯ Recognize and write the formulas of simple alkyl groups.

Many organic compounds contain oxygen as well as carbon and hydrogen. This section introduces several important families of oxygen-containing organic compounds. First, however, we need to cover a fundamental concept of organic chemistry.

Double and triple carbon–carbon bonds and halogen substituents are examples of **functional groups**, atoms or groups of atoms that give a family of organic compounds its characteristic chemical and physical properties. Table 9.4 lists a number of common functional groups found in organic molecules. Each of these groups is the basis for its own homologous series.

In many simple molecules, a functional group is attached as a substituent to a hydrocarbon stem called an *alkyl group*. An **alkyl group** is derived from an alkane by removing a hydrogen atom. The methyl group (CH_3—), for example,

Table 9.4	Selected Organic Functional Groups	
Name of Class	**Functional Group[a]**	**General Formula of Class**
Alkane	None	$R-H$
Alkene	$-C=C-$	$R_2C=CR_2$
Alkyne	$-C\equiv C-$	$RC\equiv CR$
Alcohol	$-\overset{\mid}{\underset{\mid}{C}}-OH$	$R-OH$
Ether	$-\overset{\mid}{\underset{\mid}{C}}-O-\overset{\mid}{\underset{\mid}{C}}-$	$R-O-R'$
Aldehyde	$-\overset{O}{\overset{\|}{C}}-H$	$R-\overset{O}{\overset{\|}{C}}-H$
Ketone	$-\overset{O}{\overset{\|}{C}}-$	$R-\overset{O}{\overset{\|}{C}}-R'$
Carboxylic acid	$-\overset{O}{\overset{\|}{C}}-OH$	$R-\overset{O}{\overset{\|}{C}}-O-H$
Ester	$-\overset{O}{\overset{\|}{C}}-O-\overset{\mid}{\underset{\mid}{C}}-$	$R-\overset{O}{\overset{\|}{C}}-O-R'$
Amine	$-\overset{\mid}{\underset{\mid}{C}}-\overset{\mid}{N}-$	$R-\overset{H}{\underset{\mid}{N}}-H$ $R-\overset{H}{\underset{\mid}{N}}-R'$ $R-\overset{R'}{\underset{\mid}{N}}-R''$
Amide	$-\overset{O}{\overset{\|}{C}}-\overset{}{\underset{\mid}{N}}-$	$R-\overset{O}{\overset{\|}{C}}-\overset{}{\underset{\mid}{N}}-H$ with H below; $R-\overset{O}{\overset{\|}{C}}-\overset{}{\underset{\mid}{N}}-R'$ with H below; $R-\overset{O}{\overset{\|}{C}}-\overset{}{\underset{\mid}{N}}-R'$ with R'' below

[a] Neutral functional groups are shown in green, acidic groups in red, and basic groups in blue.

is derived from methane (CH_4), and the ethyl group (CH_3CH_2-) from ethane (CH_3CH_3). Propane yields two different alkyl groups, depending on whether the hydrogen atom is removed from an end or from the middle carbon atom; see Table 9.5. Table 9.5 also lists the four alkyl groups derived from the two butanes.

Often the letter R is used to stand for an alkyl group in general. Thus, ROH is a general formula for an alcohol, and RCl represents any alkyl chloride.

Table 9.5 Common Alkyl Groups

	Name	Structural Formula	Condensed Structural Formula
Derived from Propane	Propyl	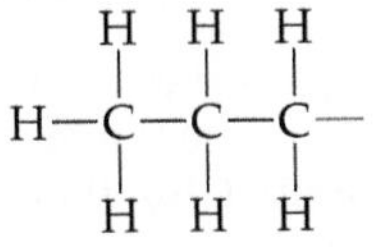	$CH_3CH_2CH_2-$
	Isopropyl	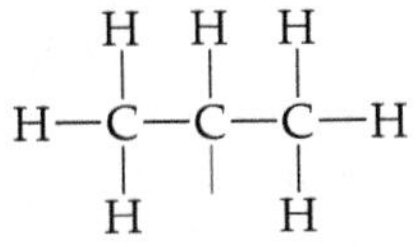	CH_3CHCH_3
Derived from Butane	Butyl	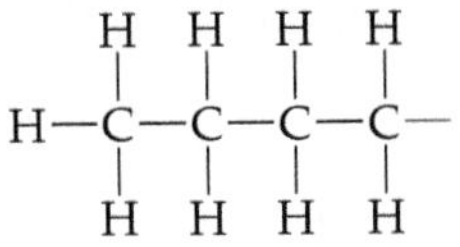	$CH_3CH_2CH_2CH_2-$
	Secondary butyl (*sec*-butyl)	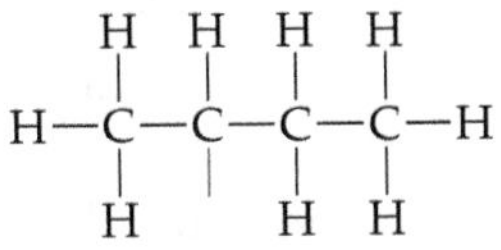	$CH_3CHCH_2CH_3$
Derived from Isobutane	Isobutyl	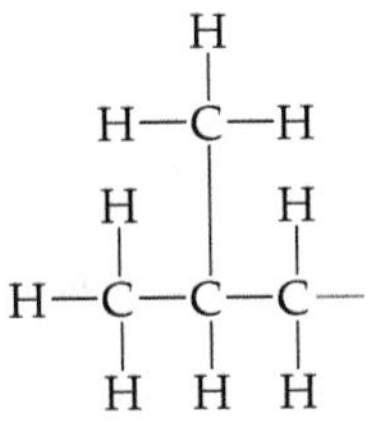	CH_3 CH_3CHCH_2-
	Tertiary butyl (*tert*-butyl)	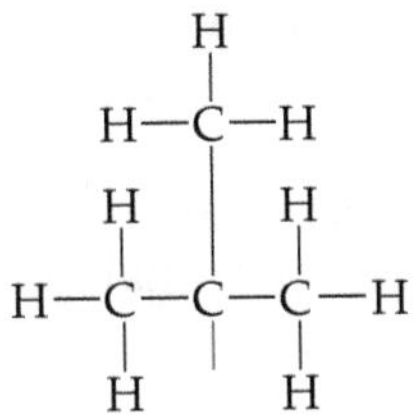	CH_3 CH_3-C-CH_3

Self-Assessment Questions

1. A specific arrangement of atoms that gives characteristic properties to an organic molecule is called a(n)
   a. alkyl group
   b. carbonyl group
   c. functional group
   d. hydroxyl group

2. The formula $CH_3CH_2CH_2-$ represents
   a. an alkyl group
   b. a functional group
   c. propane
   d. propylene

3. How many carbon atoms are there in a butyl group?
   a. 2   b. 3   c. 4   d. 6

4. The formula $CH_3CH_2CH_2CH_2-$ represents a(n)
   a. butyl group
   b. isobutyl group
   c. isopropyl group
   d. propyl group

Answers: 1, c; 2, a; 3, c; 4, a

9.5 Alcohols, Phenols, and Ethers

Learning Objectives ❯ Recognize the general structure for an alcohol, a phenol, and an ether. ❯ Name simple alcohols, phenols, and ethers.

When a hydroxyl group (—OH) is substituted for any hydrogen atom in an alkane (R—H), the molecule becomes an **alcohol** (ROH). Like many organic compounds, alcohols can be called by their common names or by the systematic names of IUPAC. The IUPAC names for alcohols are based on those of alkanes, with the ending changed from *-e* to *-ol*. Methanol, ethanol, and 1-propanol are the first three members of the homologous series of straight-chain alcohols.

A number designates the carbon to which the —OH group is attached when more than one location is possible. For example, the 1 in 1-propanol indicates that —OH is attached to an end carbon atom of the three-carbon chain; the isomeric compound, 2-propanol, has the —OH group on the second (middle) carbon atom of the chain.

CH_3—OH CH_3CH_2—OH $CH_3CH_2CH_2$—OH $\begin{array}{c} CH_3CHCH_3 \\ | \\ OH \end{array}$

Methanol   Ethanol   1–Propanol   2–Propanol

Common names for these alcohols are methyl alcohol, ethyl alcohol, and propyl alcohol. The IUPAC names are the ones used in most scientific literature.

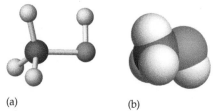

(a)   (b)

▲ **Figure 9.10** Ball-and-stick (a) and space-filling (b) models of methanol.

Methyl Alcohol (Methanol)

The simplest alcohol is *methanol*, or *methyl alcohol* (Figure 9.10). Methanol is sometimes called *wood alcohol* because it was once made from wood. The modern industrial process makes methanol from carbon monoxide and hydrogen at high temperature and pressure in the presence of a catalyst.

$$CO(g) + 2\,H_2(g) \longrightarrow CH_3OH(l)$$

Methanol is important as a solvent and as a chemical intermediate. It is also a gasoline additive and a potential replacement for gasoline in automobiles.

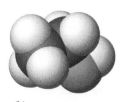

(a)   (b)

▲ **Figure 9.11** Ball-and-stick (a) and space-filling (b) models of ethanol.

Is it poisonous? That seems to be a simple question, but it is a difficult one to answer. Toxicity depends on the nature of the substance, the amount, and the route by which it is taken into the body. Toxicity is discussed in detail in Chapter 22.

Ethyl Alcohol (Ethanol)

The next member of the homologous series of alcohols is *ethyl alcohol* (CH_3CH_2OH), also called ethanol or *grain alcohol* (Figure 9.11). Ethanol is made by fermentation of grain (or other starchy or sugary materials). If the sugar is glucose, the reaction is

$$C_6H_{12}O_6(aq) \xrightarrow{\text{yeast}} 2\,CH_3CH_2OH(aq) + 2\,CO_2(g)$$

Ethanol for beverages and for automotive fuel is made in this way. Ethanol for industrial use is made by reacting ethylene with water.

$$CH_2{=}CH_2(g) + H_2O(l) \xrightarrow{H^+} CH_3CH_2OH(l)$$

This industrial alcohol is identical to that made by fermentation and is generally cheaper, but by law, it cannot be used in alcoholic beverages. Because it carries no excise tax, the law requires that noxious substances be added to this alcohol to prevent people from drinking it. The resulting *denatured alcohol* is not fit to drink. This is the kind of alcohol commonly found on the shelves in chemical laboratories.

Table 9.6 Approximate Relationship among Drinks Consumed, Blood-Alcohol Level, and Behavior[a]

Number of Drinks[b]	Blood-Alcohol Level (percent by volume)	Behavior[c]
2	0.05	Mild sedation; tranquility
4	0.10	Lack of coordination
6	0.15	Obvious intoxication
10	0.30	Unconsciousness
20	0.50	Possible death

[a]Data are for a 70-kg (154-lb) moderate drinker.

[b]Rapidly consumed 30-mL (1-oz) shots of 90-proof whiskey, 360-mL (12-oz) bottles of beer, or 150-mL (5-oz) glasses of wine.

[c]An inexperienced drinker would be affected more strongly, or more quickly, than someone who is ordinarily a moderate drinker. Conversely, an experienced heavy drinker would be affected less.

Gasoline in many parts of the United States contains up to 10% ethanol that is produced by fermentation. Because the United States has a large corn (maize) surplus, there is a generous government subsidy for gasoline producers who use ethanol made this way. As a result, many factories now make ethanol by fermentation of corn.

Toxicity of Alcohols

Although ethanol is an ingredient in wine, beer, and other alcoholic beverages, alcohols in general are rather toxic. Methanol, for example, is oxidized in the body to formaldehyde (HCHO). Drinking as little as 1 oz (about 30 mL or 2 tablespoonfuls) can cause blindness and even death. Several poisonings each year result when people mistake methanol for the less toxic ethanol.

Ethanol is not as poisonous as methanol, but it is still toxic. About 50,000 cases of ethanol poisoning are reported each year in the United States, and dozens of people die of acute ethanol poisoning.

Generally, ethanol acts as a mild depressant; it slows down both physical and mental activity. Table 9.6 lists the effects of various doses. Although ethanol generally is a depressant, small amounts of it seem to act as a stimulant, perhaps by relaxing tensions and relieving inhibitions.

Ingesting too much ethanol over a long period of time can alter brain-cell function, cause nerve damage, and shorten life span by contributing to diseases of the liver, cardiovascular system, and practically every other organ of the body. In addition, about half of fatal automobile accidents involve at least one drinking driver. Babies born to alcoholic mothers often are small, deformed, and mentally retarded. Some investigators believe that this *fetal alcohol syndrome* can occur even if mothers drink only moderately. Ethanol, by far the most abused drug in the United States, is discussed more fully in Chapter 18.

Rubbing alcohol is a 70% solution of isopropyl alcohol. Because isopropyl alcohol is also more toxic than ethanol, it is not surprising that people become ill, and sometimes die, after drinking rubbing alcohol.

Multifunctional Alcohols

Several alcohols have more than one hydroxyl group. Examples are ethylene glycol, propylene glycol, and glycerol.

The *proof* of an alcoholic beverage is twice the percentage of alcohol by volume. The term originated in a seventeenth-century English method for testing whiskey to ensure that a dealer was not increasing profits by adding water to the booze. A qualitative test was to pour some of the whiskey on gunpowder and ignite it. Ignition of the gunpowder after the alcohol had burned away was considered "proof" that the whiskey did not contain too much water.

▲ Warning labels on alcoholic beverages alert consumers to the hazards of consumption.

Ethylene glycol

Propylene glycol

Glycerol

Ethylene glycol is the main ingredient in many permanent antifreeze mixtures. Its high boiling point keeps it from boiling away in automobile radiators. Ethylene glycol is a syrupy liquid with a sweet taste, but it is quite toxic. It is oxidized in the liver to oxalic acid.

Oxalic acid forms crystals of its calcium salt, calcium oxalate (CaC_2O_4), which can damage the kidneys, leading to kidney failure and death. Propylene glycol, a high-boiling substance that is not poisonous, is now marketed as a safer permanent anti-freeze.

Glycerol (or glycerin) is a sweet, syrupy liquid that is a by-product from fats during soap manufacture (Chapter 21). It is used in lotions to keep the skin soft and as a food additive to keep cakes moist. Its reaction with nitric acid makes nitroglyc-erin, the explosive material in dynamite. Nitroglycerin is also important as a vaso-dilator, a medication taken by heart patients to relieve angina pain.

▲ It DOES Matter!
Antifreeze containing ethylene glycol should always be drained into a container and disposed of properly. Pets have been known to die from licking the sweet, but toxic, ethylene glycol mixture from a driveway or open container.

Example 9.5 Structural Formulas of Alcohols

Write the structural formula for *tert*-butyl alcohol, sometimes used as an octane booster in gasoline.

Solution
An alcohol consists of an alkyl group joined to a hydroxyl group. From Table 9.5, we see that the *tert*-butyl group is

Connecting this group to an OH group gives *tert*-butyl alcohol.

■ EXERCISE 9.5
Write the structural formulas for **(a)** butyl alcohol and **(b)** *sec*-butyl alcohol.

4. Why do some mouthwashes taste "medicine-y"? Some mouthwashes and sore-throat remedies contain certain phenols, which often have what might be termed a "hospital" odor and a medicinal taste.

Phenols

When a hydroxyl group is attached to a benzene ring, the compound is called a **phenol**. Although a phenol may appear to be an alcohol, it is not. The benzene ring greatly alters the properties of the hydroxyl group. Unlike alcohols, phenol is a weak acid (sometimes called *carbolic acid*), and it is quite poisonous compared to most simple alcohols.

Phenol

Phenol was the first antiseptic used in an operating room—by Joseph Lister in 1867. Up until that time, surgery was not antiseptic, and many patients died from infections following surgical operations. Although phenol has a strong germicidal action, it is far from an ideal antiseptic because it causes severe skin burns and kills healthy cells along with harmful microorganisms.

Phenol is still sometimes employed as a disinfectant for floors and furniture, but other phenolic compounds are now used as antiseptics. Hexylresorcinol, for example, is a more powerful germicide than phenol, and it is less damaging to the skin and has fewer other side effects.

Ethers

Compounds with two alkyl or aromatic groups attached to the same oxygen atom are called **ethers**. The general formula is ROR (or ROR' because the alkyl groups need not be alike). The best-known ether is *diethyl ether* ($CH_3CH_2OCH_2CH_3$), often called simply *ether*.

Diethyl ether was once used as an anesthetic but is now used mainly as a solvent. It dissolves many organic substances that are insoluble in water. It boils at 36 °C, which means that it evaporates readily, making it easy to recover dissolved materials. Although diethyl ether has little chemical reactivity, it is highly flammable. Great care must be taken to avoid sparks or flames when it is in use.

Another problem with ethers is that they can react slowly with oxygen to form unstable peroxides, which may decompose explosively. Beware of previously opened containers of ether, especially old ones.

The ether produced in the largest amount commercially is a cyclic compound called *ethylene oxide*. Its two carbon atoms and one oxygen atom form a three-membered ring. Ethylene oxide is a toxic gas, used mainly to make ethylene glycol.

$$H_2C\!-\!CH_2 \ + \ H_2O \ \xrightarrow{H^+} \ \overset{\displaystyle CH_2\!-\!CH_2}{\underset{\displaystyle OH \quad\ OH}{}}$$

Ethylene oxide   Water   Ethylene glycol

Ethylene oxide is also used to sterilize medical instruments and as an intermediate in the synthesis of some detergents (Chapter 21). Most of the ethylene glycol produced is used in making polyester fibers (Chapter 10) and antifreeze.

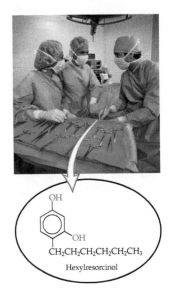

▲ Phenolic compounds help to ensure antiseptic conditions in hospital operating rooms.

Diethyl ether was introduced in 1842 as a general anesthetic for surgery and was once the most widely used anesthetic. It is rarely used for humans today because it has undesirable side effects, such as postanesthetic nausea and vomiting. We will discuss modern anesthesia in Chapter 18.

Like cyclic hydrocarbons, cyclic ethers can be represented by geometric shapes. Each corner of such a shape (except the O) stands for a C atom with enough H atoms attached to give the carbon four bonds. For example, ethylene oxide is represented as

---

CONCEPTUAL Example 9.6 | Identifying Functional Groups

Classify each of the following as an alcohol, an ether, or a phenol.

$$HO-\!\!\bigcirc\!\!-Cl \qquad CH_3CH_2OCH_3 \qquad \overset{\displaystyle CH_3CHCH_2CH_3}{\underset{\displaystyle OH}{|}}$$

(a)   (b)   (c)

$$\bigcirc\!\!-CH_2OH \qquad\qquad$$

(d)   (e)

Solution

a. The OH functional group, is attached directly to the benzene ring; the compound is a phenol.

b. The O atom is between two alkyl groups; the compound is an ether.

c. The OH group is attached to an alkyl group; the compound is an alcohol.
d. The compound is an alcohol; the OH is not attached directly to the benzene ring.
e. The compound is an ether; the O atom is between two C atoms.

■ EXERCISE 9.6
Classify each of the following as an alcohol, an ether, or a phenol.

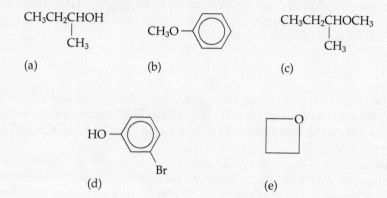

Example 9.7   Formulas for Ethers

What is the formula for isopropyl methyl ether?

Solution
Isopropyl methyl ether has an oxygen atom joined to an isopropyl group (three carbons joined to oxygen by the middle carbon) and a methyl group. The formula is

$$CH_3CHOCH_3 \quad \text{Methyl group}$$
$$\text{Isopropyl group} \quad | \quad CH_3$$

■ EXERCISE 9.7
Write formulas for **(a)** methyl propyl ether and **(b)** ethyl *tert*-butyl ether.

Self-Assessment Questions

1. Which of the following formulas represents an alcohol?
   a. $CH_3CHOHCH_2CH_3$ **b.** CH_3COCH_3
   c. CdOH   **d.** CH_3CHO

2. Which of the following alcohols has molecules with more than one hydroxyl group?
   a. 2-butanol   **b.** glycerol   **c.** 4-octanol   **d.** 3-pentanol

3. The formula for ethylene glycol is
   a. CH_3CH_2OH **b.** $CH_3CH(OH)_2$
   c. $C_3H_5(OH)_3$ **d.** $HOCH_2CH_2OH$

4. A structural formula that has a hydroxyl (OH) group attached to a benzene ring represents a(n)
   a. alcohol   **b.** ether   **c.** hexanol   **d.** phenol

5. An important use of phenols is as
   a. anesthetics   **b.** antiseptics   **c.** flavors   **d.** solvents

6. The general formula R—O—R′ represents a(n)
   a. ester   **b.** ether   **c.** ketone   **d.** phenol

7. The formula $CH_3CH_2OCH_2CH_3$ represents
   a. 2-butanol   **b.** 2-butanone   **c.** butyraldehyde   **d.** diethyl ether

8. The formula for butyl ethyl ether is
   a. $CH_3CH_2OCH_2CH_3$ **b.** $CH_3OCH_2CH_2CH_3$
   c. $CH_3CH_2CH_2OCH_2CH_3$ **d.** $CH_3CH_2OCH_2CH_2CH_2CH_3$

9. The compound $CH_3CHOHCH_2CH_3$ is an isomer of
   a. $CH_3COCH_2CH_2CH_3$
   b. $CH_3CH_2OCH_2CH_3$
   c. $CH_3COOCH_2CH_3$
   d. $CH_3CH_2CH_2COOH$

9.6 Aldehydes and Ketones

Learning Objective ❯ Name simple aldehydes and ketones, and list their important properties.

Two families of organic compounds that share the same functional group are **aldehydes** and **ketones**. Both types of compounds contain the **carbonyl group** (C=O), but aldehydes have at least one hydrogen atom attached to the carbonyl carbon, whereas ketones have two other carbon atoms joined to the carbonyl carbon.

$$\begin{array}{ccc} \overset{O}{\underset{|}{\overset{||}{-C-}}} & R-\overset{O}{\overset{||}{C}}-H & R-\overset{O}{\overset{||}{C}}-R' \\ \text{A carbonyl group} & \text{An aldehyde} & \text{A ketone} \end{array}$$

To simplify typing, these structures are often written on one line with the C=O bond omitted.

$$\begin{array}{ccc} -C(=O)- \text{ or } -CO- & R-CH(=O) \text{ or } R-CHO & R-C(=O)-R' \text{ or } R-CO-R' \\ \text{A carbonyl group} & \text{An aldehyde} & \text{A ketone} \end{array}$$

Models of three familiar carbonyl compounds are shown in Figure 9.12.

Some Common Aldehydes

The simplest aldehyde is *formaldehyde* (HCHO). It is a gas at room temperature but is readily soluble in water. As a 40% solution called *formalin*, it is used as a preservative for biological specimens and in embalming fluid. Systematic names for aldehydes are based on those of alkanes, with the ending changed from *-e* to *-al*. Thus, by the IUPAC system, formaldehyde is named methanal. IUPAC names are seldom used for simple aldehydes because of possible confusion with the corresponding alcohols. For example, "methanal" is easily confused with "methanol," when spoken or (especially) when handwritten.

◀ **Figure 9.12** Ball-and-stick (a) and space-filling (b) models of formaldehyde (left), acetaldehyde (center), and acetone (right).

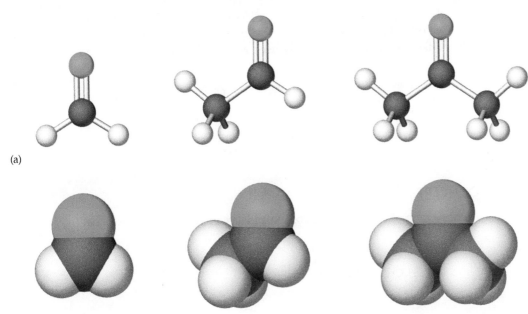

(a)

(b)

Formaldehyde is used in making certain plastics (Chapter 10). It also is used to disinfect homes, ships, and warehouses. Commercially, formaldehyde is made by the oxidation of methanol. The same net reaction occurs in the human body when methanol is ingested and accounts for the high toxicity of that alcohol.

$$CH_3OH \xrightarrow{\text{oxidation}} H-\overset{\displaystyle O}{\overset{\|}{C}}-H$$

Methanol   Formaldehyde

The next member of the homologous series of aldehydes is acetaldehyde (ethanal), formed by the oxidation of ethanol.

$$CH_3CH_2OH \xrightarrow{\text{oxidation}} CH_3-\overset{\displaystyle O}{\overset{\|}{C}}-H$$

Ethanol   Acetaldehyde

The next two members of the aldehyde series are propionaldehyde (propanal) and butyraldehyde (butanal). Both have strong, unpleasant odors. Benzaldehyde has an aldehyde group attached to a benzene ring. Also called (synthetic) oil of almond, benzaldehyde is used in perfumery, and is the flavor ingredient in mara-schino cherries.

$$CH_3CH_2-\overset{\displaystyle O}{\overset{\|}{C}}-H \qquad CH_3CH_2CH_2-\overset{\displaystyle O}{\overset{\|}{C}}-H$$

Propionaldehyde   Butyraldehyde   Benzaldehyde

Some Common Ketones

The simplest ketone is *acetone*, made by the oxidation of isopropyl alcohol.

$$CH_3-\overset{\displaystyle OH}{\overset{|}{C}H}-CH_3 \xrightarrow{\text{oxidation}} CH_3-\overset{\displaystyle O}{\overset{\|}{C}}-CH_3$$

Isopropyl alcohol   Acetone

Acetone is a common solvent for such organic materials as fats, rubbers, plastics, and varnishes. It is also used in paint and varnish removers and is a major ingredient in some fingernail polish removers. By the IUPAC system, acetone is named propanone. The systematic names for ketones are based on those of alkanes, with the ending changed from -*e* to -*one*. When necessary, a number is used to indicate the location of the carbonyl group. For example, $CH_3CH_2COCH_2CH_2CH_3$ is 3-hexanone.

Two other familiar ketones are ethyl methyl ketone and isobutyl methyl ketone, which, like acetone, are frequently used as solvents.

$$CH_3CH_2-\overset{\displaystyle O}{\overset{\|}{C}}-CH_3 \qquad CH_3\overset{\displaystyle }{\underset{\underset{\displaystyle CH_3}{|}}{C}}HCH_2-\overset{\displaystyle O}{\overset{\|}{C}}-CH_3$$

Ethyl methyl ketone   Isobutyl methyl ketone

CONCEPTUAL Example 9.8   Aldehyde or Ketone?

Identify each of the following compounds as an aldehyde or a ketone.

$$CH_3CH_2CH_2CH_2-\overset{\displaystyle O}{\overset{\|}{C}}-H$$

(a)   (b)   (c)

Solution

a. A hydrogen atom is attached to the carbonyl carbon atom; the compound is an aldehyde.

b. The carbonyl group is between two other (ring) carbon atoms; the compound is a ketone.

c. The compound is a ketone. (Remember that the corner of the hexagon stands for a carbon atom.)

▪ EXERCISE 9.8

Identify each of the following compounds as an aldehyde or a ketone.

$$\underset{(a)}{\underset{\displaystyle CH_3CH_2CH_2CCH_3}{\overset{\displaystyle \overset{O}{\|}}{}}}$$

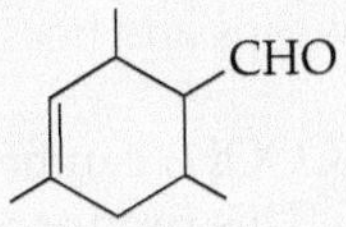

(b)

$$H_3C \!-\!\!\!\bigcirc\!\!\!-\! CHO$$

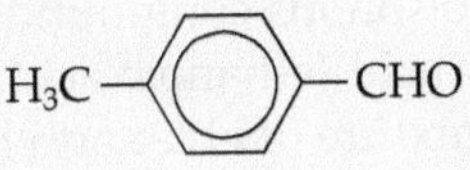

(c)

Self-Assessment Questions

1. The aldehyde functional group has a carbonyl group attached to
   a. an H atom b. an N atom c. an OH group d. two other C atoms

2. The ketone functional group has a carbonyl group attached to
   a. an OH group b. an OR group
   c. two other C atoms d. two OR groups

3. The general formula R—CO—R′ represents a(n)
   a. ester b. ether c. ketone d. phenol

4. A name for $CH_3COCH_2CH_3$ is
   a. 2-butanal b. ethyl methyl ether
   c. ethyl methyl ketone d. 2-propanone

5. A name for $CH_3CH_2CH_2CHO$ is
   a. 1-butanone b. butyraldehyde c. propanone d. propylaldehyde

6. Which alcohol is oxidized to produce formaldehyde?
   a. CH_3OH b. CH_3CH_2OH
   c. $CH_3CH_2CH_2OH$ d. $CH_3CHOHCH_3$

7. Which alcohol is oxidized to produce acetone?
   a. CH_3OH b. CH_3CH_2OH
   c. $CH_3CH_2CH_2OH$ d. $CH_3CHOHCH_3$

Answers: 1, a; 2, c; 3, c; 4, c; 5, b; 6, a; 7, d

9.7 Carboxylic Acids and Esters

Learning Objective ❯ Name simple carboxylic acids and esters, and list their important properties.

Carboxylic Acids

The functional group of organic acids is called the **carboxyl group**, and the acids are called **carboxylic acids**.

$$\underset{\text{A carboxyl group}}{\underset{\displaystyle -\overset{\displaystyle \overset{O}{\|}}{C}-OH}{}} \qquad \underset{\text{A carboxylic acid}}{\underset{\displaystyle R-\overset{\displaystyle \overset{O}{\|}}{C}-OH}{}}$$

As with aldehydes and ketones, these formulas are often written on one line:

$$—C(=O)OH \text{ or } —COOH \qquad R—C(=O)OH \text{ or } R—COOH$$

A carboxyl group   A carboxylic acid

The simplest carboxylic acid is formic acid (HCOOH). The systematic (IUPAC) names for carboxylic acids are based on those of alkanes, with the ending changed from -*e* to -*oic acid*. For example, the IUPAC name for formic acid is methanoic acid, and $CH_3CH_2CH_2CH_2COOH$ is pentanoic acid.

Formic acid was first obtained by the destructive distillation of ants (the Latin word *formica* means "ant"). It smarts when an ant bites because the ant injects formic acid into the skin. The stings of wasps and bees also contain formic acid (as well as other poisonous compounds).

Acetic acid (ethanoic acid, CH_3COOH) can be made by the aerobic fermentation of a mixture of cider and honey. This produces a solution (vinegar) containing about 4–10% acetic acid plus a number of other compounds that add flavor. Acetic acid is probably the most familiar weak acid used in academic and industrial chemistry laboratories.

The third member of the homologous series of acids, propionic acid (propanoic acid, CH_3CH_2COOH), is seldom encountered in everyday life. The fourth member is more familiar, at least by its odor. If you've ever smelled rancid butter, you know the odor of butyric acid (butanoic acid, $CH_3CH_2CH_2COOH$). It is one of the most foul-smelling substances imaginable. Butyric acid can be isolated from butterfat or synthesized in the laboratory. It is one of the ingredients of body odor, and extremely small quantities of this acid and other chemicals enable bloodhounds to track lost people and fugitives.

The acid with a carboxyl group attached directly to a benzene ring is called *benzoic acid*.

▲ Acetic acid is a familiar weak acid in chemistry laboratories. It is also the principal active ingredient in vinegar.

Benzoic acid

Carboxylic acid salts—calcium propionate, sodium benzoate, and others—are widely used as food additives to prevent mold (Chapter 17).

Example 9.9   Structural Formulas of Oxygen-Containing Organic Compounds

Write the structural formula for each of the following compounds.

a. propionaldehyde   **b.** ethanoic acid   **c.** ethyl methyl ketone

Solution

a. Propionaldehyde has three carbon atoms with an aldehyde function.

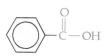

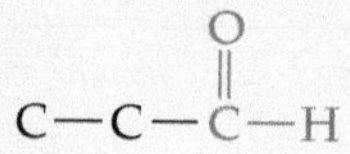

Adding the proper number of hydrogen atoms to the other two carbon atoms gives the structure

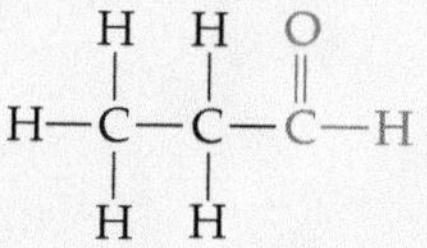

$$H—\underset{\underset{H}{|}}{\overset{\overset{H}{|}}{C}}—\underset{\underset{H}{|}}{\overset{\overset{H}{|}}{C}}—\overset{\overset{O}{\|}}{C}—H \text{ or } CH_3CH_2CHO$$

b. Ethanoic acid has two carbon atoms with a carboxylic acid function.

$$\begin{array}{c} H \quad O \\ | \quad \parallel \\ H-C-C-OH \\ | \\ H \end{array} \quad \text{or} \quad CH_3COOH$$

c. Ethyl methyl ketone has a ketone function between an ethyl and a methyl group.

$$\begin{array}{c} H \quad H \quad O \quad H \\ | \quad | \quad \parallel \quad | \\ H-C-C-C-C-H \\ | \quad | \qquad | \\ H \quad H \qquad H \end{array} \quad \text{or} \quad CH_3CH_2COCH_3$$

▪ **EXERCISE 9.9**

Write the structural formula for each of the following compounds.

a. butyric acid   **b.** acetaldehyde   **c.** diethyl ketone

d. 3-octanone   **e.** heptanal   **f.** hexanoic acid

Esters: The Sweet Smell of RCOOR′

Esters are derived from carboxylic acids and alcohols or phenols. The general reaction involves splitting out a molecule of water.

$$\underset{\text{An acid}}{R-\overset{\overset{\displaystyle O}{\parallel}}{C}-OH} + \underset{\text{An alcohol}}{R'OH} \xrightarrow{\;H^+\;} \underset{\text{An ester}}{R-\overset{\overset{\displaystyle O}{\parallel}}{C}-OR'} + HOH$$

The name of an ester ends in *-ate* and is formed by naming the part from the alcohol first and the part from the carboxylic acid last. For example, the ester derived from butyric acid and methyl alcohol is methyl butyrate.

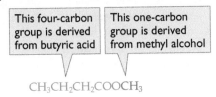

| This four-carbon group is derived from butyric acid | This one-carbon group is derived from methyl alcohol |

$$CH_3CH_2CH_2COOCH_3$$

Although carboxylic acids often have strongly unpleasant odors, the esters derived from them are usually quite fragrant, especially when dilute. Many esters have fruity odors and tastes. Some examples are given in Table 9.7. Esters are widely used as flavorings in cakes, candies, and other foods and as ingredients in perfumes.

5. Why does fresh fruit smell so good and rotting fruit so bad? Esters are often the main components of fruity flavors. When fruit is broken down by bacteria, the esters are often broken down into their corresponding alcohols and (unpleasant!) carboxylic acids.

Table 9.7   Ester Flavors and Fragrances

Ester	Formula	Flavor/Fragrance
Methyl butyrate	$CH_3CH_2CH_2COOCH_3$	Apple
Ethyl butyrate	$CH_3CH_2CH_2COOCH_2CH_3$	Pineapple
Propyl acetate	$CH_3COOCH_2CH_2CH_3$	Pear
Pentyl acetate	$CH_3COOCH_2CH_2CH_2CH_2CH_3$	Banana
Pentyl butyrate	$CH_3CH_2CH_2COOCH_2CH_2CH_2CH_2CH_3$	Apricot
Octyl acetate	$CH_3COOCH_2CH_2CH_2CH_2CH_2CH_2CH_2CH_3$	Orange
Methyl benzoate	$C_6H_5COOCH_3$	Ripe kiwifruit
Ethyl formate	$HCOOCH_2CH_3$	Rum
Methyl salicylate	$o\text{-}HOC_6H_4COOCH_3$	Wintergreen
Benzyl acetate	$CH_3COOCH_2C_6H_5$	Jasmine

GREEN CHEMISTRY

Thomas E. Goodwin, *Hendrix College*

The Art of Organic Synthesis: Green Chemists Find a Better Way

At one time or another, most of us have taken medicines purchased over the counter or obtained by prescription. Many of these are synthetic drugs prepared by an organic chemist at a pharmaceutical company or in a research lab at a college or university, not compounds that occur in nature. These drugs are synthesized via chemical transformations that make more complicated organic compounds from simpler ones. (You will learn more about drugs in Chapter 18.)

Chemical reactions generally proceed faster when collision probabilities for reacting molecules are high, as they are in heated, homogeneous solutions. In the past, many reactions were carried out in nonrenewable, petroleum-based solvents such as hydrocarbons, chlorinated hydrocarbons, esters, ketones, and ethers (Sections 9.1, 9.3, and 9.5–9.7). These solvents are often flammable, toxic, or both and present serious disposal problems. Using the Twelve Principles of Green Chemistry (inside front cover), chemists are now replacing these solvents with greener alternatives—or using no solvent at all. They also are seeking to improve the efficiency of reactions by reducing energy, time, and chemical quantities.

An increasing number of chemical reactions are run successfully in the absence of a solvent but more often in solvents from renewable resources in place of petrochemicals (Principle 5). Aqueous media have become popular because water is an ideal green solvent: cheap, abundant, and safe.

Unfortunately, many organic compounds have little solubility in water. Solutions normally form readily when intermolecular forces in the solvent and solute are of similar strength (Section 6.4). Most organic compounds have relatively weak dispersion and dipole–dipole intermolecular forces, whereas water molecules are held together by a strong network of hydrogen bonds. Therefore, water molecules tend to stay associated with one another rather than exchanging some of their hydrogen bonds for weaker attractions to the nonpolar organic solutes.

Homogeneity is not always required, however. K. B. Sharpless (2001 Nobel Laureate) and his colleagues developed procedures in which the reactants are simply floated on water. In these "on water" reactions, rapid stirring produces suspensions of reactants with large surface contact areas that enhance reaction rates. Green benefits include reduced use of organic solvents, faster reaction times, and simplified isolation of hydrophobic products.

Green organic chemistry is also demonstrated in the Pfizer pharmaceutical company's improved route to the antidepressant sertraline (Zoloft®) (Section 18.7). Four solvents (toluene, tetrahydrofuran, dichloromethane, and hexane) were replaced with ethanol (Section 9.5). In addition, overall solvent use was reduced from 60,000 gallons to 6,000 gallons per ton of sertra-

line. Pfizer received a Presidential Green Chemistry Challenge Award in 2002 for its improvements.

Another green organic synthesis was developed by Dow Chemical Company to prepare the high-volume commercial chemical epichlorohydrin. Although the compound itself is hazardous, its value in the production of epoxies, paints, and resins has led to a green chemistry focus on improving its synthesis. The traditional synthesis used a petrochemical reactant and only incorporated one-fourth of the Cl atoms used. The Dow process utilizes glycerol, a by-product from the production of biodiesel (see green chemistry essay, Chapter 7), to produce epichlorohydrin under solventless reaction conditions. This process prevents the generation of waste and turns a waste material into a valuable product.

Green chemistry can also use microwaves to speed up reactions and reduce energy consumption. Microwaves are a form of electromagnetic radiation (Section 3.2) and are more energetic than radio waves but less energetic than X-rays (essay Section 11.1). In kitchen microwave ovens, the targets for microwave energy are the water, sugar, and fat molecules in food. Although home microwave ovens must not be used to carry out chemical reactions due to potential dangers, specially designed microwave ovens are available for laboratory use.

Organic chemists today are actively designing ways to use greener solvents, renewable starting materials, and more energy-efficient techniques. These green chemistry innovations will provide sustainable solutions for us and for future generations.

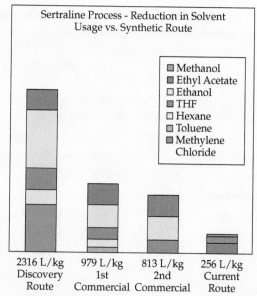

Sertraline Process - Reduction in Solvent Usage vs. Synthetic Route

Legend:
- Methanol
- Ethyl Acetate
- Ethanol
- THF
- Hexane
- Toluene
- Methylene Chloride

2316 L/kg Discovery Route | 979 L/kg 1st Commercial | 813 L/kg 2nd Commercial | 256 L/kg Current Route

▲ Proper application of green chemistry principles in the synthesis of Sertraline reduced the amount of solvents used by almost 90 percent!

Salicylates: Pain Relievers Based on Salicylic Acid

Salicylic acid is both a carboxylic acid and a phenol. We can use it to illustrate some of the reactions of these two families of compounds.

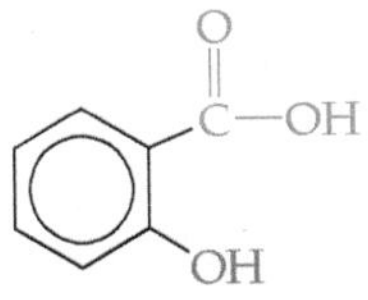

Salicylic acid

Since ancient times, various peoples around the world have used willow bark to treat fevers. Edward Stone, an English clergyman, reported to the Royal Society in 1763 that an extract of willow bark was useful in reducing fever.

Salicylic acid was first isolated from willow bark in 1838. It was first prepared synthetically in 1860 and soon was used in medicine as an *antipyretic* (fever reducer) and as an *analgesic* (pain reliever). However, it is sour and irritating when taken orally. Chemists sought to use chemical reactions to modify its structure so that these undesirable properties would be reduced while retaining or even enhancing its desirable properties. These reactions are summarized in Figure 9.13. The first such modification was simply to neutralize the acid (Reaction 1 in Figure 9.13). The resulting salt, sodium salicylate, was first used

in 1875. It was less unpleasant to swallow than the acid but was still highly irritating to the stomach.

By 1886, chemists had produced another derivative (Reaction 2), the phenyl ester of salicylic acid, called *phenyl salicylate*, or *salol*. Salol was less unpleasant to swallow, and it passed largely unchanged through the stomach. In the small intestine, salol was converted to the desired salicylic acid, but phenol was formed as a by-product. A large dose could produce phenol poisoning.

Acetylsalicylic acid, an ester formed when the phenol group of salicylic acid reacts with acetic acid, was first produced in 1853. It is usually made by reacting salicylic acid with acetic anhydride, the acid anhydride of acetic acid (Reaction 3). The German Bayer Company introduced acetylsalicylic acid as a medicine in 1899 under the trade name Aspirin. It soon became the best-selling drug in the world.

Another derivative, methyl salicylate, is made by reacting the carboxyl group of salicylic acid with methanol, producing a different ester (Reaction 4). Methyl salicylate, called *oil of wintergreen*, is used as a flavoring agent and in rub-on analgesics. When applied to the skin, it causes a mild warming sensation, providing some relief for sore muscles.

Aspirin and its use as a drug are discussed in more detail in Chapter 18.

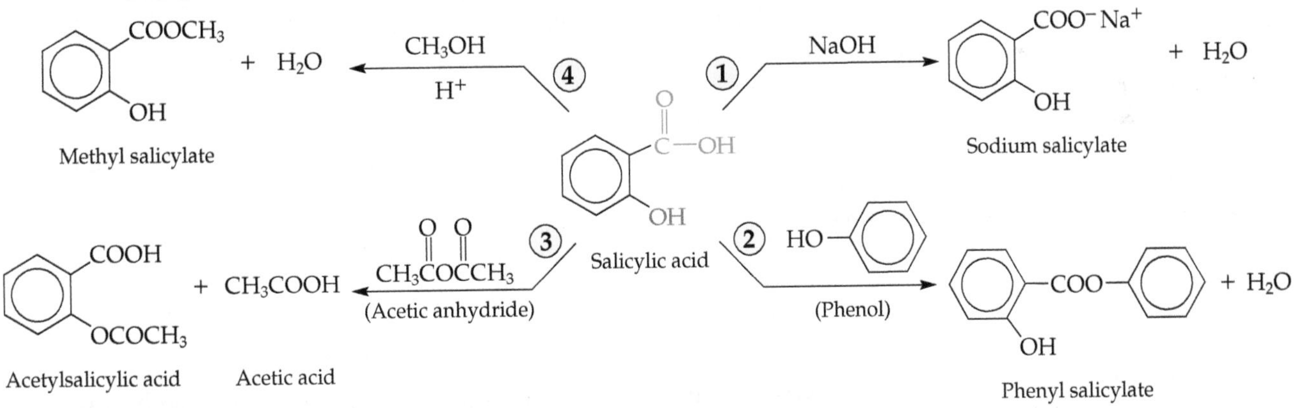

▲ **Figure 9.13** Some reactions of salicylic acid. In Reactions 1, 2, and 4, salicylic acid reacts as a carboxylic acid; the reactions occur at the carboxyl group. In Reaction 3, salicylic acid reacts as a phenol; the reaction takes place at the hydroxyl group.

Q: Can you identify and name the functional groups present in (a) salicylic acid, (b) methyl salicylate, (c) acetylsalicylic acid, and (d) phenyl salicylate?

Self-Assessment Questions

1. Which of the following formulas represents a carboxylic acid?
   a. $CH_3CH_2CH_2OH$
   b. CH_3CH_2COOH
   c. CH_3COOCH_3
   d. $CH_3CH_2CH_2CHO$

2. Which of the following is the formula for butanoic acid?
   a. CH_3CH_2COOH
   b. $CH_3CH_2CH_2CH_2OH$
   c. $CH_3CH_2CH_2CHO$
   d. $CH_3CH_2CH_2COOH$

3. The carboxylic acid that has a —COOH group attached to a benzene ring is
   a. benzoic acid
   b. benzylic acid
   c. phenol
   d. phenolic acid

4. Alcohols can be oxidized with hot copper oxide to form carboxylic acids. If the alcohol is ethanol, the carboxylic acid will be
   a. CH_3COOH
   b. CH_3CH_2OH
   c. $CH_3CH_2CH_2OH$
   d. CH_3CH_2COOH

5. The general formula for an ester is
   a. ROR'
   b. RCOR'
   c. RCOOR'
   d. RCONHR'

6. A name for the compound with the formula $CH_3CH_2CH_2COOCH_2CH_3$ is
   a. ethyl propanoate
   b. ethyl butanoate
   c. methyl pentanoate
   d. propyl propanoate

7. A name for the compound with the formula $CH_3CH_2COOCH_3$ is
   a. ethyl acetate
   b. ethyl propanoate
   c. methyl pentanoate
   d. methyl propanoate

Answers: 1, b; 2, d; 3, a; 4, d; 5, c; 6, b; 7, d

9.8 Nitrogen-Containing Compounds: Amines and Amides

Learning Objectives ❯ Name and write formulas for simple amines and amides.
❯ Recognize a structure as that of a heterocyclic compound.

Many organic substances of interest to us in the chapters that follow contain nitrogen, which is the fourth most common element in organic compounds after carbon, hydrogen, and oxygen. The two nitrogen-containing functional groups that we consider in this section, amines and amides, provide a vital background for the material ahead.

Amines

Amines contain the elements carbon, hydrogen, and nitrogen. An **amine** is derived from ammonia by replacing one, two, or three of the hydrogen atoms by one, two, or three alkyl or aromatic groups:

$$H-N-H \qquad R-N-H \qquad R-N-H \qquad R-N-R''$$
$$\quad\ \ |\qquad\qquad\ \ |\qquad\qquad\ \ |\qquad\qquad\ \ |$$
$$\quad\ \ H\qquad\qquad\ \ H\qquad\qquad\ \ R'\qquad\qquad R'$$

Ammonia   Amines

The simplest amine is methylamine (CH_3NH_2). Amines with two or more carbon atoms can be isomers: Both ethylamine ($CH_3CH_2NH_2$) and dimethylamine (CH_3NHCH_3) have the molecular formula C_2H_7N. With three carbon atoms, there are several possibilities, including trimethylamine [$(CH_3)_3N$].

CONCEPTUAL Example 9.10 | Amine Isomers: Structures and Names

Write structural formulas and names for the other three-carbon amines.

Solution

Three carbon atoms can be in one alkyl group, and there are two such propyl groups.

$$CH_3CH_2CH_2NH_2 \qquad\qquad CH_3CHCH_3$$
$$\qquad\qquad\qquad\qquad\qquad\qquad |$$
$$\qquad\qquad\qquad\qquad\qquad\ NH_2$$

Propylamine   Isopropylamine

Three carbon atoms can also be split into one methyl group and one ethyl group.

$$CH_3CH_2NHCH_3$$

Ethylmethylamine

▪ **EXERCISE 9.10**

Write structural formulas for the following amines.

a. butylamine
b. diethylamine
c. methylpropylamine
d. isopropylmethylamine

The amine with an $-NH_2$ group (called an **amino group**) attached directly to a benzene ring has the special name *aniline*. Like many other aromatic amines, aniline is used in making dyes. Aromatic amines tend to be toxic, and some are strongly carcinogenic.

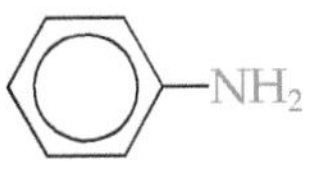

Simple amines are similar to ammonia in odor, basicity, and other properties. The larger and aromatic amines are more interesting. Figure 9.14 shows a variety of these.

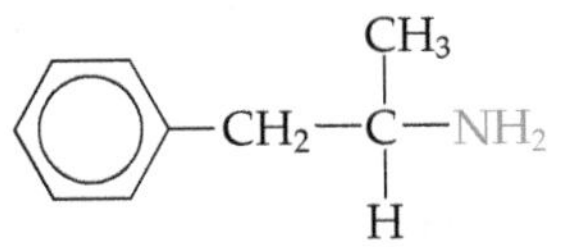

Amphetamine

1,6-Hexanediamine

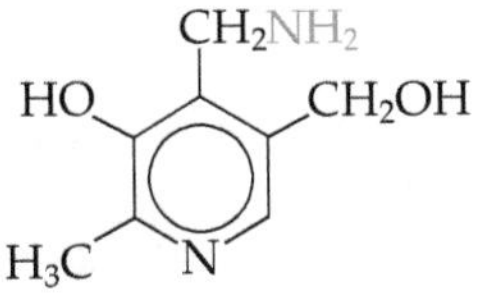

Cadaverine

Pyridoxamine

Among the most important kinds of organic molecules are *amino acids*. As the name implies, these compounds have both amine and carboxylic acid functional groups. Amino acids are the building blocks of proteins. The simplest amino acid, H_2NCH_2COOH, is glycine. Amino acids and proteins are considered in detail in Chapter 15.

Amides

Another important nitrogen-containing functional group is the **amide group**, which contains a nitrogen atom attached directly to a carbonyl group.

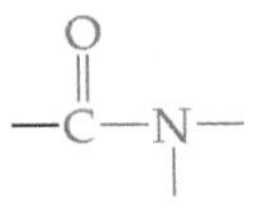

Amide group

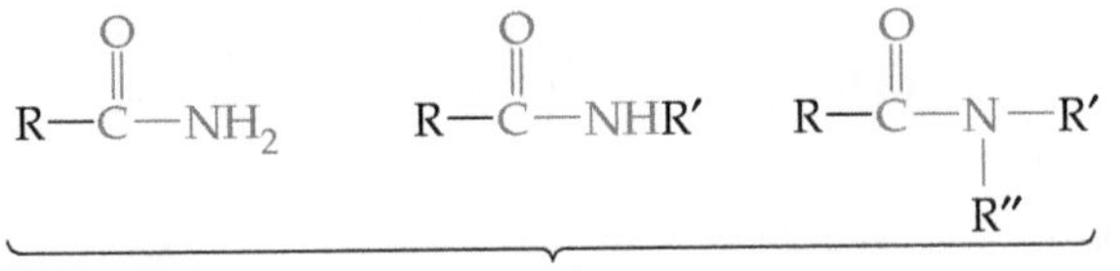

Amides

Like those of other compounds that have $C{=}O$ groups, the formulas of amides are often written on one line.

$$RCONH_2 \quad RCONHR' \quad RCONR'R''$$

Note that urea (H_2NCONH_2), the compound that helped change the understanding of organic chemistry (page 230), is an amide.

Complex amides are of much greater interest than the simple ones considered here. Your body contains many kinds of proteins, all held together by amide linkages (Chapter 15). Nylon, silk, and wool molecules also contain hundreds of amide functional groups.

6. Why do dead animals smell so bad? Most amines have unpleasant odors, and many of the compounds formed when animal matter breaks down—such as putrescine and cadaverine—are amines.

Aniline

◄ **Figure 9.14** Some amines of interest. Amphetamine is a stimulant drug (Chapter 18). Cadaverine has the odor of decaying flesh. 1,6-Hexanediamine is used in the synthesis of nylon (Chapter 10). Pyridoxamine is a B vitamin (Chapter 17).

Q: *1,6-Hexanediamine is the IUPAC name for a compound also known by the common name hexamethylenediamine. Cadaverine is a common name. What is the IUPAC name for cadaverine?*

Names for simple amides are derived from those of the corresponding carboxylic acids. For example, $HCONH_2$ is formamide (IUPAC name, methanamide), and CH_3CONH_2 is acetamide (IUPAC name, ethanamide). Alternatively, we can also view amide names as based on those of alkanes, with the ending changed from -e to -amide. For example, $CH_3CH_2CH_2CH_2CONH_2$ is pentanamide.

CONCEPTUAL Example 9.11 Amine or Amide?

Which of the following compounds are amides and which are amines? Identify the functional groups.

a. $CH_3CH_2CH_2NH_2$ **b.** CH_3CONH_2
c. $CH_3CH_2NHCH_3$ **d.** $CH_3COCH_2CH_2NH_2$

Solution

a. An amine: NH_2 is an amine group; there is no C=O group.
b. An amide: $CONH_2$ is the amide functional group.
c. An amine: NH is an amine functional group.
d. An amine: NH_2 is an amine functional group; there is a C=O group, but the NH_2 is not attached to it.

■ **EXERCISE 9.11**

Which of the following compounds are amides and which are amines? Identify the functional groups.

a. CH_3NHCH_3 **b.** $CH_3CONHCH_3$
c. $CH_3CH_2N(CH_3)_2$ **d.** $CH_3NHCH_2CONH_2$

Heterocyclic Compounds: Alkaloids and Others

Cyclic hydrocarbons feature rings of carbon atoms. Now let's look at some compounds that have atoms other than carbon within the ring. These **heterocyclic compounds** usually have one or more nitrogen, oxygen, or sulfur atoms.

CONCEPTUAL Example 9.12 Heterocyclic Compounds

Which of the following structures represent heterocyclic compounds?

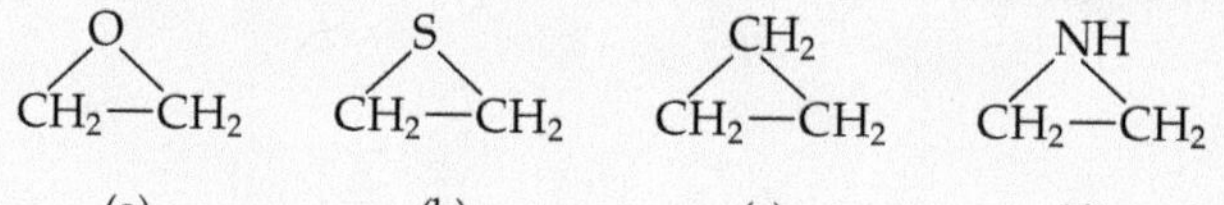

(a)   (b)   (c)   (d)

Solution

Compounds a, b, and d have an oxygen, a sulfur, and a nitrogen atom, respectively, in a ring structure; these are heterocyclic compounds.

■ **EXERCISE 9.12**

Which of the following structures represent heterocyclic compounds?

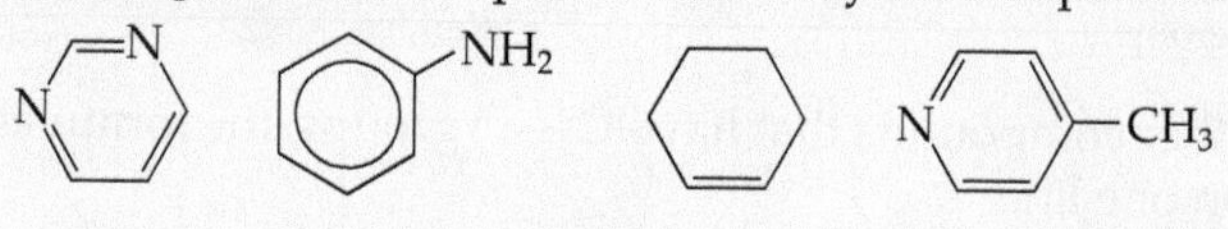

(a)   (b)   (c)   (d)

Many amines, particularly heterocyclic ones, occur naturally in plants. Like other amines, these compounds are basic. They are called **alkaloids**, which means "like alkalis." Among the familiar alkaloids are morphine, caffeine, nicotine, and cocaine. The actions of these compounds as drugs are considered in Chapter 18.

Other important heterocyclic amines are pyrimidine, which has two nitrogen atoms in a six-membered ring, and purine, which has four nitrogen atoms in two rings that share a common side. Compounds related to pyrimidine and purine are constituents of nucleic acids (Chapter 16).

Pyrimidine   Purine

Self-Assessment Questions

1. A name for $CH_3CH_2CH_2CH_2NH_2$ is
   a. butanamide   **b.** butylamine   **c.** propanamide   **d.** propylamide

2. A name for $CH_3CH_2NHCH_3$ is
   a. butylamine   **b.** ethylmethylamine **c.** propanamide   **d.** propylamine

3. A name for CH_3CONH_2 is
   a. acetamide   **b.** ethylamine   **c.** propanamide   **d.** propylamine

4. The amide functional group has a carbonyl group attached to
   a. an H atom.   **b.** an N atom   **c.** an OH group   **d.** two other C atoms

5. A cyclic organic compound that contains at least one atom that is not a carbon atom is called a(n)
   a. aromatic compound   **b.** cyclic amide
   c. heterocyclic compound   **d.** saturated compound

6. A basic organic heterocyclic compound that contains at least one nitrogen atom and is found in plants is called a(n)
   a. alkaloid   **b.** amide   **c.** cyclic ester   **d.** phenol

Answers: 1, b; 2, b; 3, a; 4, b; 5, c; 6, a

CRITICAL THINKING EXERCISES

Apply knowledge that you have gained in this chapter and one or more of the FLaReS principles (Chapter 1) to evaluate the following statements or claims.

9.1 A television advertisement claims that gasoline with added ethanol burns more cleanly than gasoline without added ethanol.

9.2 A news feature states that scientists have found that the odor of a certain ester improves workplace performance.

9.3 An environmental activist states that all toxic chemicals should be banned from the home.

9.4 An advertisement claims that calcium carbonate from oyster shells is superior to other forms of calcium carbonate because it contains a life force.

9.5 A Web page claims that acetylsalicylic acid (aspirin), polyester plastics, and polystyrene plastics are all carcinogens (cancer-causing agents). The reason given is that all three contain benzene rings in their structures, and benzene is a carcinogen.

9.6 A television program suggests that life on a distant planet could be based on silicon instead of carbon, because silicon (like carbon) tends to form four bonds. The narrator of the program proposes that long protein molecules and DNA molecules could be based on silicon chains.

SUMMARY

Section 9.1—**Organic chemistry** is the chemistry of carbon-containing compounds. More than 95% of all known compounds contain carbon. Carbon is unique in its ability to form long chains, rings, and branches. **Hydrocarbons** contain only carbon and hydrogen. One main class of hydrocarbons is **aliphatic compounds**. **Alkanes** are hydrocarbons that contain only single bonds; they have names ending in *-ane*. Alkanes are **saturated hydrocarbons** because each of their carbon atoms is bonded to the maximum number of hydrogen atoms. A **structural formula** shows which

atoms are bonded to one another. A **condensed structural formula** omits the C—H bond lines and is easier to write. A larger straight-chain alkane can be generated by inserting a CH_2 unit into a given straight-chain alkane. A **homologous series** of such compounds has properties that vary in a regular and predictable manner. A member of a homologous series is called a *homolog*.

Alkanes with more than three carbon atoms have **isomers**, compounds with the same molecular formula but different structures. Alkanes are nonpolar and insoluble in water. They undergo few chemical reactions and are used mainly as fuels.

Cyclic hydrocarbons have one or more closed rings. Geometric figures often are used to represent such cyclic compounds: for example, a triangle for cyclopropane and a hexagon for cyclohexane.

An alkene is a hydrocarbon with at least one carbon-carbon double bond. Ethylene (CH_2═CH_2) is the simplest alkene and the most important one commercially. It is used to make polyethylene plastic and ethylene glycol. An alkyne is a hydrocarbon with at least one carbon-to-carbon triple bond. Acetylene (HC≡CH), the simplest alkyne, is used in welding torches and as a starting material for other chemical products. Alkenes and alkynes are unsaturated hydrocarbons, to which more hydrogen atoms can be added. They undergo addition reactions in which hydrogen or another small molecule adds to the double or triple bond. They can also add to one another to form polymers.

Section 9.2—Benzene (C_6H_6) can be drawn as though it has three double bonds, but its ring of carbon atoms has six pairs of bonding electrons between the carbon atoms, plus six unassigned electrons spread over the ring. Benzene and similar compounds with this type of stable ring structure are called aromatic compounds. Substituted benzenes have one or more H atoms replaced by another atom or group called a substituent. Aromatic hydrocarbons are used as solvents and fuels and to make other aromatic compounds.

Section 9.3—Chlorinated hydrocarbons are derived from hydrocarbons by replacing one or more hydrogen atoms with chlorine atom(s). Chlorofluorocarbons (CFCs) contain both chlorine and fluorine. They are used as aerosol propellants and as refrigerants, but their use has been restricted because of their role in the depletion of the ozone layer. Perfluorinated compounds, in which all hydrogens have been replaced with fluorine, have important uses in plastics manufacture and in medicine.

Section 9.4—A functional group is an atom or group of atoms that confers characteristic properties to a family of organic compounds. Compounds with the same functional group undergo similar reactions and have similar properties. A functional group is often attached to an alkyl group (R—), an alkane with a hydrogen atom removed.

Section 9.5—A hydroxyl group (—OH) joined to an alkyl group produces an alcohol (ROH). Methanol (CH_3OH), ethanol (CH_3CH_2OH), and 2-propanol [$(CH_3)_2CHOH$] are well-known and widely used alcohols. Alcohols with more than one —OH group include ethylene glycol, used in antifreeze, and glycerol, used in skin lotions and as a food addi-

tive. A phenol is a compound with an —OH group attached to a benzene ring. Phenols are slightly acidic, and some are used as antiseptics.

An ether has two alkyl or aromatic groups attached to the same oxygen atom (ROR′). Ethers are used as solvents, and they can react slowly with oxygen to form explosive peroxides. Diethyl ether ($CH_3CH_2OCH_2CH_3$) is a commonly used solvent. Ethylene oxide is a cyclic ether used to make ethylene glycol and to sterilize instruments.

Section 9.6—An aldehyde contains a carbonyl group (C═O) with a hydrogen atom attached to the carbonyl carbon. A ketone has two carbon atoms attached to the carbonyl carbon. Formaldehyde is used in making plastics and as a preservative and a disinfectant. Benzaldehyde is a flavoring ingredient. Acetone, the simplest ketone, is a widely used solvent.

Section 9.7—A carboxylic acid has a carboxyl group (—COOH) as its functional group. Formic acid (HCOOH) is the acid in ant, bee, and wasp stings. Acetic acid (CH_3COOH) is the acid in vinegar. Butyric acid is the substance that gives rancid butter its odor. Carboxylic acid salts are used as food additives to prevent mold.

The structure of an ester (RCOOR′) is similar to that of a carboxylic acid, with an alkyl group replacing the hydrogen atom of the carboxyl group. Esters are made by reaction of a carboxylic acid with an alcohol or phenol. They often have fruity or flowery odors and are used as flavorings and in perfumes.

Section 9.8—An amine is an organic derivative of ammonia in which one or more hydrogen atoms are replaced by alkyl or aromatic groups. Many amines consist of an alkyl group joined to an amino group (—NH₂). Like ammonia, amines are basic and often have strong odors. Amino acids, the building blocks of proteins, contain both amine and carboxylic acid functional groups. An amide group consists of a carbonyl group whose carbon atom is attached to a nitrogen atom. Proteins, nylon, silk, and wool contain amide groups.

A heterocyclic compound has one or more rings containing one or more nitrogen, sulfur, or oxygen atoms. Alkaloids are (usually heterocyclic) amines that occur naturally in plants and include morphine, caffeine, nicotine, and cocaine. Heterocyclic structures are constituents of DNA and RNA.

Green chemistry Organic chemistry plays an important role in enhancing the quality of human life, such as in the preparation of new life-saving drugs. Organic chemists are designing ways to use greener solvents, renewable starting materials, and more energy-efficient techniques.

Learning Objectives

> Define *hydrocarbon*, and recognize structural features of alkanes, alkenes, and alkynes. Problems 17, 18, 20, 21, 53, 54

> Identify hydrocarbon molecules as alkanes, alkenes, or alkynes, and name them. Problems 2, 17–26, 45, 46

> Define *aromatic compound*, and recognize the structural feature such compounds share. Problems 5, 6

> Name simple aromatic hydrocarbons. Problem 22

> Name a halogenated hydrocarbon given its formula, and write the formula for such a compound given its name. Problem 52

> Classify an organic compound according to its functional group(s), and explain why the concept of a functional group is useful in the study of organic chemistry. Problems 47–51, 62

> ❯ Recognize and write the formulas of simple alkyl groups.
> ❯ Recognize the general structure for an alcohol, a phenol, and an ether.
> ❯ Name simple alcohols, phenols, and ethers.
> ❯ Name simple aldehydes and ketones, and list their important properties.
> ❯ Name simple carboxylic acids and esters, and list their important properties.
> ❯ Name and write the formulas of simple amines and amides.
> ❯ Recognize a structure as that of a heterocyclic compound.
> ❯ Identify greener solvents that can replace those from nonrenewable fossil fuels, methods for incorporating renewable resources into organic synthesis, and efficient energy sources for enhancing chemical reactions.

REVIEW QUESTIONS

1. List three characteristics of the carbon atom that make possible the existence of millions of organic compounds.

2. Define or give an example for each of the following terms.
   a. hydrocarbon   b. alkyne
   c. alkane   d. alkene

3. What are isomers? How can you tell whether or not two compounds are isomers?

4. What is an unsaturated hydrocarbon? Give examples of two types of unsaturated hydrocarbons.

5. What is the meaning of the circle inside the hexagon in the modern representation of the structure of benzene?

6. What is an aromatic hydrocarbon? How can you recognize an aromatic compound from its structure?

7. Which alkanes are gases at room temperature? Which are liquids? Which are solids? State your answers in terms of the number of carbon atoms per molecule.

8. Compare the densities of liquid alkanes with that of water. If you added hexane to water in a beaker, what would you expect to observe?

9. What are the systematic names for the alcohols known by the following familiar names?
   a. grain alcohol   b. rubbing alcohol
   c. wood alcohol

10. What are some of the long-term effects of excessive ethanol consumption?

11. State an important historical use of diethyl ether. What is its main use today?

12. How do carboxylic acids and esters differ in odor? In chemical structure?

13. For what family is each of the following the general formula?
    a. ROH   b. RCOR′   c. RCOOR′
    d. ROR′   e. RCOOH   f. RCHO

14. What is an alkaloid? Name three common alkaloids.

PROBLEMS

Organic and Inorganic Compounds

15. Which of the following compounds are organic?
    a. $CH_3CH_2SCH_2CH_3$ b. $F_3CCH_2CH_3$
    c. $HONH_2$ d. H_2SiCl_2

16. Which of the following compounds are organic?
    a. $C_8H_{18}O$ b. H_2CS
    c. OsO_4 d. $Co(NH_3)_6Cl_2$

Names and Formulas of Hydrocarbons

17. How many carbon atoms are there in a molecule of each of the following?
    a. hexane   b. decane
    c. cyclopentane   d. 2-pentene

18. How many carbon atoms are there in a molecule of each of the following?
    a. ethane   b. 1-butyne
    c. propene   d. cyclooctane

19. The general formula for an alkane is given on page 231. Give the molecular formulas for the alkanes with **(a)** 9 carbon atoms and **(b)** 13 carbon atoms.

20. A particular alkyne has one triple bond and five carbon atoms. How many hydrogen atoms does it have?

21. Name the following hydrocarbons.
    a. $CH_3CH_2CH_2CH_3$ b. $H_2C{=}CH_2$
    c. $HC{\equiv}CH$

22. Name the following hydrocarbons.

    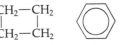

        a.   b.   c.

23. Write the molecular formulas and condensed structural formulas for **(a)** pentane and **(b)** nonane.

24. Write the structural formulas for the four-carbon alkanes (C_4H_{10}). Identify butane and isobutane.

25. Name the following alkyl groups.
    a. CH_3-
    b. CH_3CH_2CH-
       $\overset{\displaystyle |}{CH_3}$

26. Name the following alkyl groups.
    a. CH_3-CH-
       $\overset{\displaystyle |}{CH_3}$
    b. $CH_3-\overset{\displaystyle \overset{CH_3}{|}}{\underset{\displaystyle \underset{CH_3}{|}}{C}}-$

Names and Formulas: Alcohols and Phenols

27. Give a structure to match the name or a name to match the structure for each of the following compounds.
    a. CH_3OH
    b. $CH_3CH_2CH_2OH$
    c. ethanol
    d. 1-heptanol

28. Give a structure to match the name or a name to match the structure for each of the following compounds.
    a. $CH_3CH_2CHCH_3$
       $\overset{\displaystyle |}{OH}$
    b. $CH_3CH_2CH_2CH_2CH_2CH_2OH$
    c. *sec*-butyl alcohol
    d. isobutyl alcohol

29. Phenols and other aromatic compounds are often named by numbering the carbon atoms of the benzene ring, starting with the carbon atom bounded to the major functional group. (In a phenol, this group is the $-OH$ group.) To illustrate, the structure in Exercise 9.6d (page 248) is named 3-bromophenol. With this information, write the structures for (a) 2-methylphenol and (b) 4-iodophenol.

30. How do phenols differ from alcohols? How are they similar?

Names and Formulas: Ethers

31. Write the structure for each of the following.
    a. dipropyl ether
    b. butyl ethyl ether

32. Write the structure for (a) methyl propyl ether, an anesthetic known as Neothyl, and (b) dimethyl ether, used as a compressed gas to "freeze" warts from the skin. What alcohol is an isomer of dimethyl ether?

Names and Formulas: Aldehydes and Ketones

33. Give a structure to match the name or a name to match the formula of each of the following compounds.
    a. acetone
    b. formaldehyde
    c. $CH_3CH_2CH_2\overset{\displaystyle \overset{O}{\|}}{C}-H$
    d. $CH_3CH_2-\overset{\displaystyle \overset{O}{\|}}{C}-CH_2CH_2CH_2CH_3$

34. Give a structure to match the name or a name to match the formula of each of the following compounds.
    a. ethyl methyl ketone
    b. propionaldehyde
    c. $CH_3CH_2-\overset{\displaystyle \overset{O}{\|}}{C}-CH_2CH_3$
    d. $\langle\!\bigcirc\!\rangle-\overset{\displaystyle \overset{O}{\|}}{C}-H$

Names and Formulas: Carboxylic Acids

35. Give a structure to match the name or a name to match the structure for each of the following compounds:
    a. CH_3COOH
    b. $CH_3CH_2CH_2CH_2COOH$
    c. formic acid
    d. octanoic acid

36. Give a structure to match the name or a name to match the structure for each of the following compounds.
    a. CH_3CH_2COOH
    b. $CH_3CH_2CH_2CH_2CH_2COOH$
    c. butanoic acid
    d. chloroacetic acid [*Hint*: To what atom must the chlorine atom (chloro group) be attached?]

Names and Formulas: Esters

37. Give a structure to match the name or a name to match the structure for each of the following.
    a. ethyl acetate
    b. methyl butyrate
    c. $CH_3CH_2\overset{\displaystyle \overset{O}{\|}}{C}OCH_2CH_3$

38. Give a structure to match the name or a name to match the structure for each of the following.
    a. ethyl butyrate
    b. methyl acetate
    c. $H-\overset{\displaystyle \overset{O}{\|}}{C}-OCH_2CH_2CH_2CH_3$

Names and Formulas: Nitrogen-Containing Compounds

39. Give a structural formula to match the name or a name to match the structure for each of the following.
    a. methylamine
    b. ethylmethylamine
    c. $CH_3CH_2CH_2NH_2$
    d. $CH_3CH_2NHCH_3$

40. Give a structural formula to match the name or a name to match the structure for each of the following.
    a. ethylamine
    b. isopropylamine
    c. $CH_3CH_2NHCH_2CH_3$
    d. $\langle\!\bigcirc\!\rangle-NH_2$

Isomers and Homologs

41. Indicate whether the structures in each pair represent the same compound or isomers.

a. CH$_3$CH$_3$ and $\underset{\displaystyle CH_3}{\overset{\displaystyle CH_3}{|}}$

b. CH$_3$CH$_2$ and CH$_3$CH$_2$CH$_3$
$\quad\quad\ |$
$\quad\quad CH_3$

c. CH$_3$CHCH$_2$CH$_2$CH$_3$ and CH$_3$CH$_2$CHCH$_2$CH$_3$
$\quad\quad\ |$ $\quad\quad\quad\quad\quad\quad\quad\quad\quad\ |$
$\quad\quad CH_3$ $\quad\quad\quad\quad\quad\quad\quad\quad\quad CH_3$

42. Indicate whether the structures in each pair represent the same compound or isomers.

a. CH$_3$CHCH$_2$OH and CH$_3$CHCH$_2$CH$_3$
$\quad\ |$ $\quad\quad\quad\quad\quad\quad\quad\quad |$
$\quad CH_3$ $\quad\quad\quad\quad\quad\quad\quad OH$

b. CH$_3$CHCH$_2$CH$_3$ and CH$_3$CH$_2$CHNH$_2$
$\quad\ |$ $\quad\quad\quad\quad\quad\quad\quad\quad\quad\quad |$
$\quad NH_2$ $\quad\quad\quad\quad\quad\quad\quad\quad\quad CH_3$

43. Classify the following pairs as homologs, the same compound, isomers, or none of these.
a. CH$_3$CH$_2$CH$_3$ and CH$_3$CH$_2$CH$_2$CH$_3$
b. CH$_2$–CH$_2$ and CH$_3$CH$_2$CH$_2$CH$_2$CH$_3$
$\quad\quad /\quad\quad\ \backslash$
$\quad CH_2\quad\quad CH_2$
$\quad\quad\ \backslash\quad\quad /$
$\quad\quad\quad CH_2$

44. Classify the following pairs as homologs, the same compound, isomers, or none of these.

a. CH$_3$CHCH$_2$CH$_2$CH$_3$ and CH$_3$CH$_2$CH$_2$CHCH$_3$
$\quad\quad\ |$ $\quad\quad\quad\quad\quad\quad\quad\quad\quad\quad\quad\quad\ |$
$\quad\quad CH_3$ $\quad\quad\quad\quad\quad\quad\quad\quad\quad\quad\quad CH_3$

b. CH$_3$CHCH=CH$_2$ $\quad$ CH$_2$—CH—CH$_3$
$\quad\quad\ |$ $\quad\quad\quad\quad\quad\quad\quad |\quad\quad\ |$
$\quad\quad CH_3$ $\quad\quad$ and $\quad$ CH$_2$—CH$_2$

Classification of Hydrocarbons

45. Indicate whether each of the following compounds is saturated or unsaturated. Classify each as an alkane, alkene, or alkyne.

a. CH$_3$C=CH$_2$ $\quad\quad$ **b.** CH$_3$—$\underset{\displaystyle CH_3}{\overset{\displaystyle CH_3}{\underset{|}{\overset{|}{C}}}}$—CH$_3$
$\quad\quad |$
$\quad\ CH_3$

46. Indicate whether each of the following compounds is saturated or unsaturated. Classify each as an alkane, alkene, or alkyne.

a. CH$_3$—C≡C—CH$_3$ $\quad$ **b.**

Functional Groups

47. Classify each of the following as an alcohol, amine, amide, ketone, aldehyde, ester, carboxylic acid, or ether. Identify the functional group in each.

a. CH$_3$CH$_2\overset{\displaystyle O}{\overset{\displaystyle ||}{C}}OCH_3$

b. CH$_3$CH$_2\overset{\displaystyle O}{\overset{\displaystyle ||}{C}}$H

c. CH$_3$CH$_2$CH$_2$NH$_2$

d. CH$_3$CH$_2$OCH$_3$

e. CH$_3$CH$_2\overset{\displaystyle O}{\overset{\displaystyle ||}{C}}CH_2CH_3$

f. CH$_3$CH$_2\overset{\displaystyle O}{\overset{\displaystyle ||}{C}}$OH

48. Classify each of the following as an alcohol, amine, amide, ketone, aldehyde, ester, carboxylic acid, or ether. Identify the functional group in each.
a. HCOOH
b. CH$_3$CH$_2$COOCH$_3$
c. CH$_3$CH$_2$CH$_2$CH$_2$OH
d. CH$_3$CH$_2$CONHCH$_2$CH$_2$CH$_3$
e. CH$_3$CH$_2$CH$_2$COOH
f. HCOOCH$_2$CH$_2$CH$_3$

49. Which of the following represents a heterocyclic compound? Classify each compound as an amine, ether, or cycloalkane.

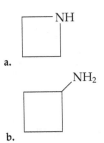

50. Which of the following represents a heterocyclic compound? Classify each compound as an amine, ether, or cycloalkane.

ADDITIONAL PROBLEMS

51. A molecular model of capsaicin, the compound primarily responsible for the "hotness" of jalapenos and other hot peppers, is shown on page 229. The color code for the atoms is carbon (black), hydrogen (white), nitrogen (blue), and oxygen (red). What is the molecular formula of capsaicin? Name three functional groups of capsaicin.

52. Noting the following color code for atoms—carbon (black), hydrogen (white), oxygen (red), nitrogen (blue), and chlorine (green)—write the structural and molecular formulas for the compounds whose models are shown here.

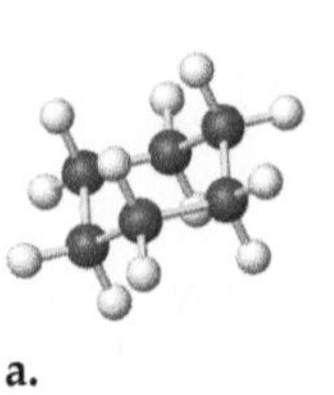

a.

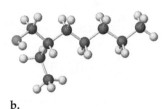

b.

c.

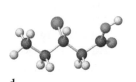

d.

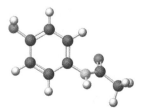

e.

53. As noted on page 236, alkenes and alkynes can add hydrogen to form alkanes. These addition reactions, called *hydrogenations*, are carried out using H_2 gas and a catalyst such as nickel or platinum. Write equations, using condensed structural formulas, for the complete hydrogenation of each of the following.

a. $CH_3CH_2C\equiv CCH_3$

b.
$$CH_3CH=CCH_2CH_2CH_2CH_3$$
$$\qquad\qquad |$$
$$\qquad\qquad CH_3$$

54. As exemplified by the reaction of ethylene on page 244, alkenes can add water to form alcohols. These addition reactions, called *hydrations*, are carried out using H_2O and an acid (H^+) as catalyst. Write an equation, using structural formulas, for the hydration of each of the following.

a. 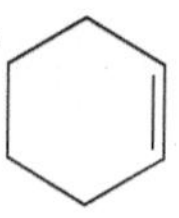 (hexagon structure)

b. $CH_3CH=CHCH_3$

55. As shown on page 250, alcohols can be oxidized to aldehydes and ketones. Write the structure of the alcohol that can be oxidized to each of the following.
a. $CH_3CH_2CH_2CHO$ b. $CH_3CH_2COCH_2CH_3$
c. $CH_3COCH(CH_3)_2$ d. C_6H_5CHO

56. Consider the following set of compounds. What concept does the set illustrate?

CH_3OH CH_3CH_2OH

$CH_3CH_2CH_2OH$ $CH_3CH_2CH_2CH_2OH$

57. Consider the following set of compounds. What concept does the set illustrate?

$CH_3CH_2CH_2CH_2OH$ $CH_3CH_2OCH_2CH_3$

CH_3CHCH_2OH CH_3CHOCH_3
$\qquad |$ $\qquad |$
$\qquad CH_3$ $\qquad CH_3$

58. Methanol is a possible replacement for gasoline. The complete combustion of methanol forms carbon dioxide and water.

$$CH_3OH + O_2 \longrightarrow CO_2 + H_2O$$

Balance the equation. What mass of carbon dioxide is formed by the complete combustion of 775 g of methanol?

59. Water adds to ethylene to form ethyl alcohol.

$$CH_2=CH_2 + H_2O \xrightarrow{H^+} CH_3CH_2OH$$

Balance the equation. What mass of ethyl alcohol is formed by the addition reaction of water and 445 g of ethylene?

60. Referring to Table 9.7, give the name and condensed structural formula of **(a)** the alcohol and the carboxylic acid that would be needed to make pineapple flavoring and **(b)** the alcohol and the carboxylic acid that would be needed to make apricot flavoring.

61. Refer back to Section 6.3. Describe the type of intermolecular forces that exist **(a)** between dimethyl ether molecules and **(b)** between ethanol molecules. Use this information to explain why ethanol is a liquid at room temperature but dimethyl ether is a gas.

62. Diacetyl ($CH_3COCOCH_3$) is an additive used to impart buttery flavor to popcorn. Popcorn-factory workers exposed to high levels of diacetyl may develop a characteristic lung disease. What functional group is present in diacetyl?

63. Hydroquinone ($HO-C_6H_4-OH$), a phenol with two hydroxyl groups in the 1 and 4 (or *para*) positions on the ring, is commonly used as a developer in black and white photography. **(a)** Write the structural formula for hydroquinone. (*Hint*: See Figure 9.9.) **(b)** In the developing process, hydroquinone is oxidized to *para*-benzoquinone ($C_6H_4O_2$), a compound that is not aromatic and has two ketone functions. Write the structural formula for *para*-benzoquinone.

64. Using data from Table 9.3, a printed reference such as the *CRC Handbook* or the *Merck Index*, or an online source such as the Web site of the National Institutes for Standards and

Technology (NIST), state which of each pair of isomers boils at a lower temperature.

a. hexane or 2,3-dimethylbutane
b. pentane or neopentane (2,2-dimethylpropane)
c. heptane or 2,4-dimethylpentane
d. octane or 2,2,4-trimethylpentane

Use this information to form a generalization about the boiling points of branched-chain versus straight-chain alkanes.

65. Use the ideal gas law to determine the densities in grams per milliliter of the first four alkanes in Table 9.3 at 1.00 atm and 20.0 °C. (*Hint*: Begin with one mole of each gas.) Suggest a more appropriate unit for expressing these densities.

66. Give three reasons why water is often considered to be a green solvent for organic synthesis.

67. Which of the following is a potential drawback to using water as a solvent for organic synthesis?
a. Water is derived from fossil fuels.
b. Many organic molecules have limited solubility in water.
c. The intermolecular forces in water are similar to those in most organic solvents.
d. Reaction rates are always slower in water.

68. In an "on water" reaction:
a. Reactants are floated on water.
b. Rapid stirring leads to large surface contact areas.
c. Reactions often occur faster than if the reactants were dissolved in an organic solvent.
d. Insoluble products can be separated easily.
e. All of the above are true.

69. Identify two aspects of the new synthesis of sertraline that make it greener than the traditional process.

70. Give two examples of ways in which the improved synthesis of epichlorohydrin is more environmentally benign.

71. What advantage does microwave heating provide in carrying out chemical reactions? Why does it have this advantage?

COLLABORATIVE GROUP PROJECTS

Prepare a PowerPoint, poster, or other presentation (as directed by your instructor) to share with the class.

1. The theory that organic chemistry was the chemistry of living organisms, which was overturned by Wöhler's discovery in 1828, was known as *vitalism*. Search the Internet for information about this theory. What was the effect of this philosophy on areas outside chemistry?

2. Many organic molecules contain more than one functional group. Look up the structural formula for each of the following in this text (use the index), by searching online, or in a reference work such as the *Merck Index*. Identify and name the functional groups in each.
a. butesin   b. estrone   c. tyrosine
d. morphine   e. eugenol   f. methyl anthranilate

3. Prepare a brief report on one of the alcohols with three or more carbon atoms per molecule. List sources and commercial uses.

4. Prepare a brief report on one of the carboxylic acids with three or more carbon atoms per molecule. List sources and commercial uses.

5. Consider the series of compounds methane (CH_4), chloromethane (CH_3Cl), dichloromethane (CH_2Cl_2), trichloromethane ($CHCl_3$), and tetrachloromethane (CCl_4). Repeat parts (a) through (e) of Problem 49 (Chapter 6) for these compounds. Boiling points may be found in a printed reference such as the *CRC Handbook* or the *Merck Index* or on a Web site such as that of the National Institutes for Standards and Technology (NIST). Use intermolecular forces to explain any deviation in the relationship between molar mass and boiling point.

6. Referring to the graph from Problem 49 (Chapter 6), use the molar mass to estimate boiling points for (a) acetic acid (CH_3COOH), (b) acetone (CH_3COCH_3), (c) ethanol (CH_3CH_2OH), (d) hexane ($CH_3CH_2CH_2CH_2CH_2CH_3$), and (e) methyl acetate (CH_3COOCH_3). Compare the values obtained from the graph with the actual boiling points. Is molar mass alone a good predictor of boiling point? Explain.

10

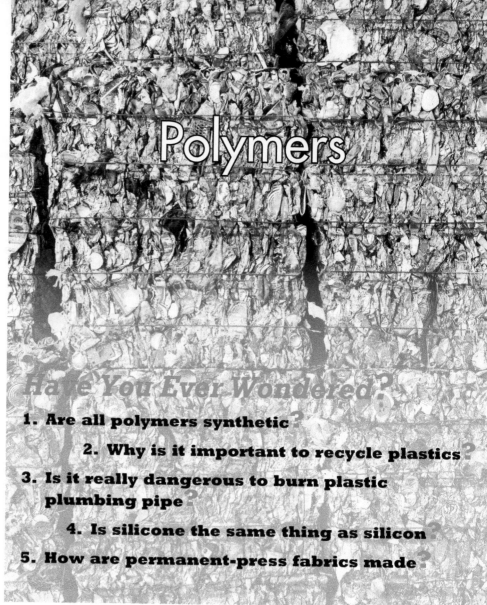

Polymers

Learning Objectives

> Define *polymer* and *monomer*. (10.1)

> List several natural polymers including a chemically modified one. (10.1)

> Describe the structure and properties of the two main types of polyethylene. (10.2)

> Use the terms *thermoplastic* and *thermosetting* to explain how polymer structure determines properties. (10.2)

> Identify the monomer(s) of an addition polymer, and write the structural formula for a polymer from its monomer structure(s). (10.3)

> Define *cross-linking*, and explain how it changes the properties of a polymer. (10.4)

> Differentiate between addition and condensation polymerization. (10.5)

> Write the structures of the monomers that form polyesters and polyamides. (10.5)

> Understand the concept of the glass transition temperature. (10.6)

> Explain how crystallinity affects the physical properties of polymers. (10.6)

> Describe the environmental problems associated with plastics and plasticizers. (10.7)

> Name two types of sustainable, non-petroleum-derived polymers and give their sources. (10.7)

> Describe plastic recycling, biodegradation, and production from renewable resources.

Have You Ever Wondered?

1. **Are all polymers synthetic**

2. **Why is it important to recycle plastics**

3. **Is it really dangerous to burn plastic plumbing pipe**

4. **Is silicone the same thing as silicon**

5. **How are permanent-press fabrics made**

Giants Among Molecules

Look around you. Polymers are everywhere. Carpets, curtains, upholstery, towels, sheets, floor tile, books, furniture, most toys and containers (not to mention such things as telephones, toothbrushes, and piano keys), and even your clothes are made of polymers. Your car's dashboard, seats, tires, steering wheel, floor mats, and many parts that you cannot see are made of polymers. Much of the food you eat contains polymers, and many vital molecules in your body are polymers. You couldn't live without them. Some of the polymers that permeate our lives come from nature, but many are synthetic, made in chemical plants in an attempt to improve on nature in some way.

Plastics—synthetic polymers—are used in most consumer items, including bottles, telephones, calculators, computers, cooking utensils, wire insulation, sunglasses, pens, and most types of packaging. The source of most of these polymers is crude oil, of which there is a limited supply. This means that it is important to recycle these polymers when possible. The bales of plastics shown above are ready to go to the recycling center, where they may be used directly to make toys, pipes, or building materials. Or the recycled material may be converted to shreds or beads of plastic (left) that can be used by molding machines. In this chapter, we examine how polymers are made, review their useful properties, and explain why they have those properties.

10.1 Polymerization: Making Big Ones Out of Little Ones

Learning Objectives ❯ Define *polymer* and *monomer*. ❯ List several natural polymers including a chemically modified one.

Polymers are composed of *macromolecules* (from the Greek *makros*, meaning "large" or "long"). Macromolecules are not actually very large (in fact, most such "giant" molecules are invisible to the human eye), but compared to other molecules, they are enormous.

A **polymer** (from the Greek *poly*, meaning "many," and *meros*, meaning "part") is made from much smaller molecules called *monomers* (from the Greek *monos*, meaning "one"). Hundreds, even thousands, of monomer units combine to make one polymer molecule. A **monomer** is a small-molecule building block from which a polymer is made. The process by which monomers are converted to polymers is called *polymerization*. A polymer is as different from its monomer as a long strand of spaghetti is from tiny specks of flour. For example, polyethylene, the familiar waxy material used to make plastic bags, is made from the monomer ethylene, a gas.

▲ Cotton is nearly pure cellulose, a natural polymer of the simple sugar glucose.

Natural Polymers

Polymers have served humanity for centuries in the starches and proteins in our food, in the wood we use for shelter, and in the wool, cotton, and silk we make into clothing. Starch is a polymer made up of glucose ($C_6H_{12}O_6$, a simple sugar) units. Cotton is made of cellulose, also a glucose polymer; and wood is largely cellulose as well. Proteins are polymers made up of amino acid monomers. Wool and silk are two of the thousands of different kinds of proteins found in nature.

Living things could not exist without polymers. Each plant and animal requires many different specific types of polymers. Probably the most amazing natural polymers are nucleic acids, which carry the coded genetic information that makes each individual unique. The polymers found in nature are discussed in Chapter 15. In this chapter, we focus mainly on macromolecules made in the laboratory.

Celluloid: Billiard Balls and Collars

The oldest attempt to improve on natural polymers involved chemical modification of a common macromolecule. The semisynthetic material **celluloid**, as its name implies, was derived from natural cellulose (from cotton and wood, for example). When cellulose is treated with nitric acid, a derivative called *cellulose nitrate* is formed.

In response to a contest to find a substitute for ivory to use in billiard balls, American inventor John Wesley Hyatt (1837–1920) found a way to soften cellulose nitrate by treating it with ethyl alcohol and camphor. The softened material could be molded into smooth, hard balls. Thus, Hyatt brought the game of billiards within the economic reach of more people—and saved a number of elephants.

Celluloid was also used in movie film and for stiff shirt collars (which didn't require laundering and repeated starching). Because of its dangerous flammability (cellulose nitrate is also used as smokeless gunpowder), celluloid was removed from the market when safer substitutes became available. Today, movie film is made mainly from polyethylene terephthalate, a polyester (Section 10.5). And high, stiff collars on men's shirts are out of fashion.

It didn't take long for the chemical industry to recognize the potential of synthetics. Scientists found ways to make macromolecules from small molecules rather than simply modifying large ones. The first such truly synthetic polymers were phenol–formaldehyde resins (such as Bakelite), first made in 1909. These complex polymers are discussed in Section 10.5. We'll look at some simpler ones next.

1. Are all polymers synthetic? The total weight of natural polymers on Earth's surface far exceeds the weight of synthetic polymers. Starches, proteins, cellulose, latex, DNA, and RNA all are natural polymers.

A century ago, celluloid was widely used as a substitute for more expensive substances such as ivory, amber, and tortoiseshell. The movie industry was once known as the "celluloid industry." The 1988 Oscar-winning Italian movie *Cinema Paradiso* shows the evolution of film technology and includes a tragic scene in which the heat from a bulb in the movie projector ignites a fire in a film that failed to wind properly through the machine.

Self-Assessment Questions

1. A long-chain protein molecule is an example of a(n)
   a. fat   b. isomer   c. monomer   d. polymer

2. Which is *not* a polymer?
   a. cellulose   b. glucose   c. silk   d. wool

3. The first semisynthetic polymer was actually made from a natural polymer. It was
   a. Bakelite, based on bacon grease
   b. celluloid, based on cellulose from cotton
   c. polypropylene, based on isopropyl alcohol
   d. polypantene, based on human hair

4. The first truly synthetic polymer was
   a. Bakelite, made from phenol and formaldehyde
   b. cellulose, made from glucose
   c. polyethylene, made from ethanol
   d. rubber, made from isoprene

Answers: 1, d; 2, b; 3, b; 4, a

10.2 Polyethylene: From the Battle of Britain to Bread Bags

Learning Objectives ❯ Describe the structure and properties of the two main types of polyethylene. ❯ Use the terms *thermoplastic* and *thermosetting* to explain how polymer structure determines properties.

The prevalent plastic *polyethylene* is the simplest and least expensive synthetic polymer. It is familiar to us in the form of plastic bags used for packaging fruit and vegetables, garment bags for dry-cleaned clothing, garbage-can liners, and many other items. Polyethylene is made from ethylene ($CH_2{=}CH_2$), an unsaturated hydrocarbon (Chapter 9). Ethylene is produced in large quantities from the cracking of petroleum, a process by which large hydrocarbon molecules are broken down into simpler hydrocarbons.

The ellipses (⋯) and tildes (∼) serve as *et ceteras*; they indicate, respectively, that the number of monomers is greater than the four shown and that the polymer structure extends for many more units in each direction.

With pressure and heat and in the presence of a catalyst, ethylene monomers join together in long chains.

$$\cdots + \underset{\underset{H}{|}}{\overset{\overset{H}{|}}{C}}{=}\underset{\underset{H}{|}}{\overset{\overset{H}{|}}{C} + \underset{\underset{H}{|}}{\overset{\overset{H}{|}}{C}}{=}\underset{\underset{H}{|}}{\overset{\overset{H}{|}}{C} + \underset{\underset{H}{|}}{\overset{\overset{H}{|}}{C}}{=}\underset{\underset{H}{|}}{\overset{\overset{H}{|}}{C} + \underset{\underset{H}{|}}{\overset{\overset{H}{|}}{C}}{=}\underset{\underset{H}{|}}{\overset{\overset{H}{|}}{C} + \cdots \longrightarrow \sim C{-}C{-}C{-}C{-}C{-}C{-}C{-}C\sim$$

Using condensed formulas, this becomes

$$\cdots + CH_2{=}CH_2 + CH_2{=}CH_2 + CH_2{=}CH_2 + CH_2{=}CH_2 + \cdots \longrightarrow \sim CH_2CH_2CH_2CH_2CH_2CH_2CH_2CH_2\sim$$

Such equations can be tedious to draw, so we often use abbreviated forms like these:

$$n\, \underset{\underset{H}{|}}{\overset{\overset{H}{|}}{C}}{=}\underset{\underset{H}{|}}{\overset{\overset{H}{|}}{C} \longrightarrow \left[\underset{\underset{H}{|}}{\overset{\overset{H}{|}}{C}}{-}\underset{\underset{H}{|}}{\overset{\overset{H}{|}}{C}\right]_n \quad \text{or} \quad n\, CH_2{=}CH_2 \longrightarrow {+}CH_2CH_2{+}_n$$

The molecular fragment within square brackets is called the *repeat unit* of the polymer. In the formula for the polymeric product, the repeat unit is placed within brackets with bonds extending to both sides. The subscript n indicates that this unit is repeated many times (n in the equation above) in the full polymer structure.

10.2 Polyethylene: From the Battle of Britain to Bread Bags ▪ **269**

The simplicity of the abbreviated formulas facilitates certain comparisons between the monomer and the polymer. Note that the monomer ethylene contains a double bond and polyethylene does not. The double bond of the reactant consists of two shared pairs of electrons. One of these pairs is used to connect one monomer unit to the next in the polymer (indicated by the lines sticking out to the sides in the repeat unit). This leaves only a single pair of electrons—a single bond—between the two carbon atoms of the repeat unit. Note also that each repeat unit in the polymer has the same composition (C_2H_4) as the monomer.

Molecular models provide three-dimensional representations. Figure 10.1 presents models of a tiny part of a very long polyethylene molecule, whose number of carbon atoms can vary from a few hundred to several thousand.

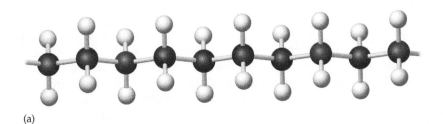

(a)

(b)

◀ **Figure 10.1** Ball-and-stick (a) and space-filling (b) models of a short segment of a polyethylene molecule.

2. Why is it important to recycle plastics? Polyethylene and most other polymers are made of petroleum. Since our supply of petroleum is limited, we can make the best use of that resource by reusing those polymers. Most plastic items are imprinted with a code number so that they can be sorted for recycling.

Polyethylene was invented shortly before the start of World War II. It proved to be tough and flexible, excellent as an electric insulator, and able to withstand both high and low temperatures. Before long, it was used for insulating cables in radar equipment, a top-secret invention that helped British pilots detect enemy aircraft before the aircraft could be spotted visually. Without polyethylene, the British could not have had effective radar, and without radar, the Battle of Britain might have been lost. The invention of this simple plastic helped change the course of history.

Types of Polyethylene

Today, there are three main kinds of polyethylene. *High-density polyethylene* (*HDPE*) has mostly linear molecules that pack closely together and can assume a fairly well-ordered, crystalline structure. HDPEs therefore are rather rigid and have good tensile strength. As the name implies, the densities of HDPEs (0.94–0.96 g/cm^3) are high compared to those of other polyethylenes. HDPEs are used for such items as threaded bottle caps, toys, bottles, and milk jugs.

Low-density polyethylene (*LDPE*), on the other hand, has many side chains branching off the polymer molecules. The branches prevent the molecules from packing closely together and assuming a crystalline structure. LDPEs are waxy,

The Many Forms of Carbon

In many of the smaller molecules that we studied in Chapter 9 and the macromolecules that we encounter here, carbon atoms are bonded to other atoms, especially hydrogen. Carbon atoms alone can form a variety of interesting structures, however, some of which have been known since ancient times. Diamond is pure crystalline carbon, in which each atom is bonded to four other atoms. In graphite, the black material of pencil lead, each carbon atom is bonded to three others. But the most intriguing forms of carbon were discovered only in the last few decades.

Andre Geim and Konstantin Novoselov of the University of Manchester, United Kingdom, used adhesive tape to lift one-atom-thick planar sheets of carbon atoms from graphite. The material, called *graphene*, is like molecular-scale chicken wire made of carbon atoms. Graphene has properties that make it suitable for applications in electronics, sensing devices, and touch screens and for fundamental studies of electron flow in two-dimensional materials. Geim and Novoselov were awarded the 2010 Nobel Prize in Physics for their work on graphene.

Graphite is composed of many stacked graphene layers. A stack of three million graphene sheets would be only a millimeter thick. Graphene can also be thought of as an extremely large aromatic molecule, a system of fused benzene rings.

Many other structures are formed exclusively of carbon atoms. The tube-shaped carbon molecule called a *nanotube* can be visualized as a sheet of graphene rolled into a hollow cylinder. Nanotubes have unusual mechanical and electrical properties. They are good conductors of heat, and they are among the strongest and stiffest materials known.

Yet another structure consisting only of carbon is a roughly spherical collection of hexagons and pentagons like the pattern on a soccer ball. This carbon molecule has the formula C_{60}. Because it resembles the geodesic-dome structures pioneered by architect R. Buckminster Fuller, the molecule is called *buckminsterfullerene*. The general name *fullerenes* is used for C_{60} and similar molecules with formulas such as C_{70}, C_{74}, and C_{82}, which are often colloquially referred to as "buckyballs." These materials have enormous potential in basic studies as well as in applied research.

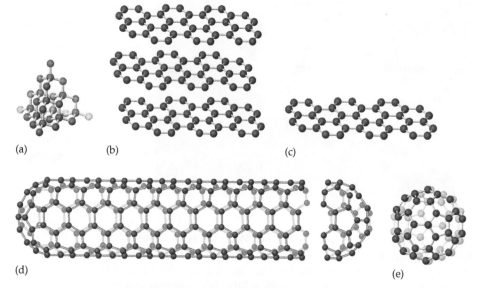

(a)   (b)   (c)

(d)   (e)

▲ Different forms of carbon have dramatically different properties. (a) Diamond is hard and transparent. (b) Graphite is soft, gray, and conducts electricity. (c) Graphene is a single layer of graphite. (d) Rolling a sheet of graphene into a cylinder makes a carbon nanotube, the strongest material known. (e) Buckminsterfullerene, a C_{60} molecule, resembles a soccer ball.

Scientists estimate that plastic bags and other plastic trash thrown into the ocean kill as many as a million sea creatures each year.

bendable plastics that have lower densities (0.91–0.94 g/cm^3) and are lower melting than high-density polyethylenes. Objects made of HDPE hold their shape in boiling water, whereas those made of LDPE are severely deformed (Figure 10.2). LDPEs are used to make plastic bags, plastic film, squeeze bottles, electric wire insulation, and many common household products for which flexibility is important.

The third type of polyethylene, called *linear low-density polyethylene* (LLDPE), is actually a **copolymer**, a polymer formed from two (or more) different monomers. LLDPEs are made by polymerizing ethylene with a branched-chain alkene such as 4-methyl-1-pentene.

$$n\ CH_2{=}CH_2 + m\ CH_2{=}CH \longrightarrow \left[CH_2{-}CH_2\right]_n \left[\begin{array}{c} CH_2{-}CH{-} \\ | \\ CH_2 \\ | \\ CH_3{-}CH{-}CH_3 \end{array}\right]_m$$

Ethylene   4-Methyl-1-pentene   An LLDPE

LLDPEs are used to make such things as plastic films for use as landfill liners, trash cans, tubing, and automotive parts.

Thermoplastic and Thermosetting Polymers

Polyethylene is one of a variety of thermoplastic polymers. Because its molecules can slide past one another when heat and pressure are applied, a **thermoplastic polymer** can be softened and then reshaped. It can be repeatedly melted down and remolded. Total annual production of thermoplastic polymers in the United States is about 40 billion kg, of which 17 billion kg is polyethylene.

Not all polymers can be readily melted. About 12% of U.S. production of polymers consists of *thermosetting polymers*, which harden permanently when formed. They cannot be softened by heat and remolded. Instead, strong heating causes them to discolor and decompose. The permanent hardness of thermosetting plastics is due to cross-linking (side-to-side connection) of the polymer chains, which we'll discuss later in this chapter.

Self-Assessment Questions

1. When addition polymers form, the monomer units are joined by
   a. delocalized electrons that flow along the polymer chain
   b. dispersion forces
   c. double bonds
   d. new bonds formed by electrons from the double bonds in the monomers

2. Compared to HDPE, LDPE has a lower melting point because it
   a. is made from less polar monomers
   b. is composed of molecules with a much lower molecular mass
   c. has fewer cross-links
   d. has more branches in its molecules, preventing them from packing closely

3. Which of the following is *not* made of polyethylene?
   a. electric wire insulation
   b. foamed coffee cups
   c. plastic grocery bags
   d. squeeze bottles

4. A copolymer is made
   a. by blending two simple polymers
   b. from cobalt and an alkene
   c. from two identical monomers
   d. from two different monomers

5. A polymer that cannot be melted and reshaped is said to be
   a. highly crystalline
   b. rubbery
   c. thermoplastic
   d. thermosetting

▲ **It DOES Matter!**
Polyethylene with a molecular mass from two to six million, called *ultra-high-molecular-weight polyethylene (UHMWPE)*, is used to make fibers 10 times stronger than steel and around 40% stronger than Kevlar (see Problem 30 on page 292) for use in body armor. Most modern skis are coated with UHMWPE on the bottom surface.

About 180 billion kg of various plastics and 22 billion kg of rubber are manufactured globally each year.

▲ **Figure 10.2** Two bottles, both made of polyethylene, were heated in the same oven for the same length of time.

Q: *Which of these bottles is made of HDPE and which of LDPE? Explain.*

10.3 Addition Polymerization: One + One + One + ··· Gives One!

Learning Objectives ❯ Identify the monomer(s) of an addition polymer, and write the structural formula for a polymer from its monomer structure(s).

There are two general types of polymerization reactions: addition polymerization and condensation polymerization. In **addition polymerization** (also called *chain-reaction polymerization*), the monomer molecules add to one another in such a way that the polymeric product contains all the atoms of the starting monomers. The polymerization of ethylene to form polyethylene is an example. In polyethylene, as we noted in Section 10.2, the two carbon atoms and the four hydrogen atoms of each monomer molecule are incorporated into the polymer structure. In *condensation polymerization* (Section 10.5), some part of each monomer molecule is not incorporated in the final polymer.

Polypropylene

Most of the many familiar addition polymers are made from derivatives of ethylene in which one or more of the hydrogen atoms are replaced by another atom or group. Replacing one of the hydrogen atoms with a methyl group gives the monomer propylene (propene). Polypropylene molecules look much like polyethylene's molecules, except that there is a methyl group ($-CH_3$) attached to every other carbon atom.

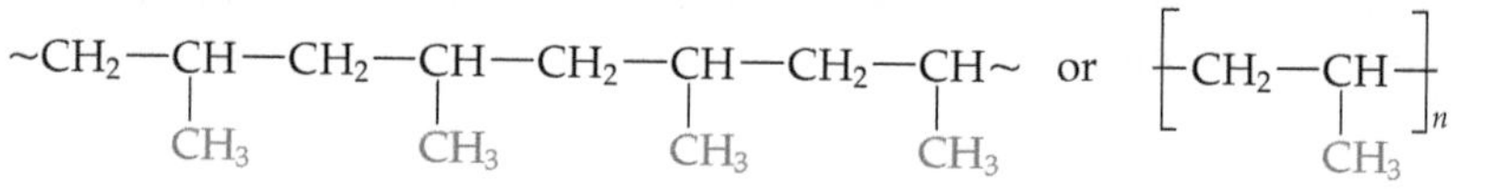

$$\sim CH_2-\underset{\underset{CH_3}{|}}{CH}-CH_2-\underset{\underset{CH_3}{|}}{CH}-CH_2-\underset{\underset{CH_3}{|}}{CH}-CH_2-\underset{\underset{CH_3}{|}}{CH}\sim \quad or \quad \left[CH_2-\underset{\underset{CH_3}{|}}{CH} \right]_n$$

Polypropylene

The chain of carbon atoms is called the polymer *backbone*. Groups attached to the backbone, such as the CH_3 groups of polypropylene, are called *pendant groups*.

Polypropylene is a tough plastic material that resists moisture, oils, and solvents. It is molded into hard-shell luggage, battery cases, and various kinds of appliance parts. It is also used to make packaging material, fibers for textiles such as upholstery fabrics and carpets, and ropes that float. Because of polypropylene's high melting point (121 °C), objects made of it can be sterilized with steam.

Polystyrene

Replacing one of the hydrogen atoms in ethylene with a benzene ring gives a monomer called *styrene*, which has the formula $C_6H_5CH=CH_2$, where C_6H_5 represents the benzene ring. Polymerization of styrene produces polystyrene, which has benzene rings as pendant groups.

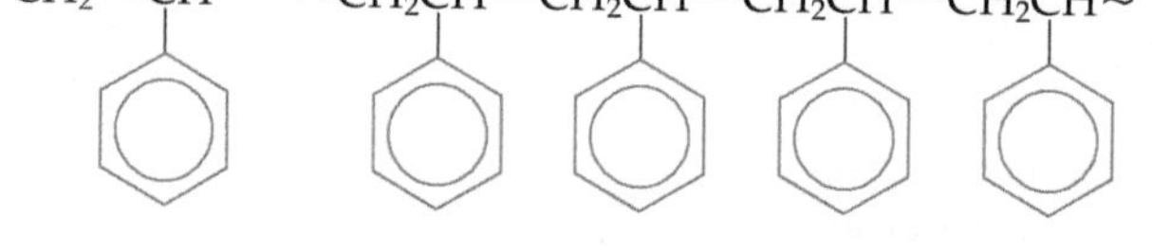

$$CH_2=CH \qquad \sim CH_2CH-CH_2CH-CH_2CH-CH_2CH\sim$$

Styrene

Polystyrene

Americans throw away about 25 billion coffee cups made of polystyrene foam each year.

Polystyrene is the plastic used to make transparent disposable drinking cups. With color and filler added, it is the material of thousands of inexpensive toys and household items. When a gas is blown into polystyrene liquid, it foams and hardens into the familiar material (called Styrofoam®) of ice chests and disposable coffee cups. The polymer can easily be formed into shapes as packing material for shipping instruments and appliances, and it is widely used for home insulation.

Vinyl Polymers

Would you like a tough synthetic material that looks like leather at a fraction of the cost? Perhaps a clear, rigid material from which unbreakable bottles could be made? Do you need an attractive, long-lasting floor covering? Or lightweight, rust-proof, easy-to-connect plumbing? Polyvinyl chloride (PVC) has all these properties—and more.

Replacing one of the hydrogen atoms of ethylene with a chlorine atom gives vinyl chloride ($CH_2{=}CHCl$), a compound that is a gas at room temperature. Polymerization of vinyl chloride yields the tough thermoplastic material PVC. A segment of the PVC molecule is shown below.

$$\sim CH_2CH{-}CH_2CH{-}CH_2CH{-}CH_2CH\sim$$
$$||||$$
$$ClClClCl$$

Polyvinyl chloride (PVC)

▲ Styrofoam insulation saves energy by reducing the transfer of heat from the warm interior of a house to the outside in winter and from the hot outside to the cooled interior in summer.

PVC is readily formed into various shapes. The clear, transparent polymer is used in plastic wrap and clear plastic bottles. Adding color and other ingredients to a vinyl plastic yields artificial leather. Most floor tile and shower curtains are made from vinyl plastics, which are also widely used to simulate wood in home siding panels and window frames. About 40% of the PVC produced is molded into pipes.

◀ Some furniture, window sashes, house trim, and waterproof clothing are made from PVC. PVC can also be coated onto copper wire for insulation, made into colorful resilient flooring, or formed into many other familiar consumer products.

3. Is it really dangerous to burn plastic plumbing pipe? Most plastic plumbing pipe is made of PVC. When PVC is burned, its carcinogenic monomer, vinyl chloride, can be released. PVC may be safely burned in specially constructed incinerators that reach temperatures that decompose the monomer.

Vinyl chloride, the monomer from which vinyl plastics are made, is a carcinogen. Several people who worked closely with this gas later developed a kind of cancer called *angiosarcoma*. (Carcinogens are discussed in Chapter 22.)

PTFE: The Nonstick Coating

In 1938, young Roy Plunkett, a chemist at DuPont, was working with the gas tetrafluoroethylene ($CF_2{=}CF_2$). He opened the valve on a tank of the gas—and nothing came out. Rather than discarding the tank, he decided to investigate. The tank was found to be filled with a waxy, white solid. He attempted to analyze the solid but ran into a problem: It simply wouldn't dissolve, even in hot concentrated acids. Plunkett had discovered polytetrafluoroethylene (PTFE), the polymer of tetrafluoroethylene, best known by its trade name, Teflon®.

$$\sim CF_2{-}CF_2{-}CF_2{-}CF_2{-}CF_2{-}CF_2{-}CF_2{-}CF_2\sim$$

Teflon

▲ Frying pans, baking pans, and other cookware often take advantage of the inert, non-stick nature of PTFE.

Because its C—F bonds are exceptionally strong and resistant to heat and chemicals, PTFE is a tough, unreactive, nonflammable material. It is used to make electric insulation, bearings, and gaskets, as well as to coat surfaces of cookware to eliminate sticking of food.

CONCEPTUAL Example 10.1 | Repeat Units in Polymers

What is the repeat unit in polyvinylidene chloride? A segment of the polymer is represented as

$$\sim\underset{\underset{H}{|}}{\overset{\overset{H}{|}}{C}}-\underset{\underset{Cl}{|}}{\overset{\overset{Cl}{|}}{C}}-\underset{\underset{H}{|}}{\overset{\overset{H}{|}}{C}}-\underset{\underset{Cl}{|}}{\overset{\overset{Cl}{|}}{C}}-\underset{\underset{H}{|}}{\overset{\overset{H}{|}}{C}}-\underset{\underset{Cl}{|}}{\overset{\overset{Cl}{|}}{C}}\sim$$

Solution

Inspection of the segment above reveals that it consists of three repeat units, each with two carbon atoms, two hydrogen atoms, and two chlorine atoms. Placing a double bond between the carbon atoms of one unit, we get

$$\underset{\underset{H}{|}}{\overset{\overset{H}{|}}{C}}=\underset{\underset{Cl}{|}}{\overset{\overset{Cl}{|}}{C}}$$

Joining hundreds of these units would yield a molecule of the polymer.

■ EXERCISE 10.1

What is the repeat unit in polyacrylonitrile? A segment of the polymer is represented as

$$\sim CH_2\underset{\underset{CN}{|}}{CH}CH_2\underset{\underset{CN}{|}}{CH}CH_2\underset{\underset{CN}{|}}{CH}CH_2\underset{\underset{CN}{|}}{CH}CH_2\underset{\underset{CN}{|}}{CH}CH_2\underset{\underset{CN}{|}}{CH}\sim$$

▲ Granular polymeric resins are the basic stock for many molded plastic goods.

Example 10.2 | Structure of Polymers

Write the structure of the polymer made from vinyl fluoride ($CH_2{=}CHF$). Show at least four repeat units.

Solution

The carbon atoms bond to form a chain with only single bonds between carbon atoms. The fluorine atom is a pendant group on the chain. (Two of the electrons in the double bond of the monomer form the bond joining units.) The polymer is

$$\sim CH_2\underset{\underset{F}{|}}{CH}CH_2\underset{\underset{F}{|}}{CH}CH_2\underset{\underset{F}{|}}{CH}CH_2\underset{\underset{F}{|}}{CH}\sim$$

■ EXERCISE 10.2

Write the structures of the polymers made from **(a)** methyl vinyl ketone ($CH_2{=}CHCOCH_3$) and **(b)** vinyl acetate ($CH_2{=}CHOCOCH_3$). Show at least four repeat units of each polymer.

▲ Large plastic items with thin walls, such as the polyethylene terephthalate containers shown here, are often blow-molded. Blow molding is very similar to blowing a soap bubble, except that the bubble is blown inside a mold.

Processing Polymers

In everyday life, many polymers are called plastics. In chemistry, a *plastic* material is one that can be made to flow under heat and pressure. The material can then be shaped in a mold or in other ways. Plastic products are often made from granular polymeric material. In *compression molding*, heat and pressure are applied directly to such grains in the mold cavity. In *transfer molding*, the polymer is softened by heating before being poured into molds to harden.

There also are several methods of molding molten polymers. In *injection molding*, the plastic is melted in a heating chamber and then forced by a plunger into cold molds to set. In *extrusion molding*, the melted polymer is extruded through a die in continuous form to be cut into lengths or coiled. Bottles and similar hollow objects often are *blow-molded*; a "bubble" of molten polymer is blown up like a balloon inside a hollow mold.

Table 10.1 lists some of the more important addition polymers, along with a few of their uses.

Table 10.1 Some Addition Polymers

Monomer	Polymer	Polymer Name	Some Uses
$CH_2{=}CH_2$	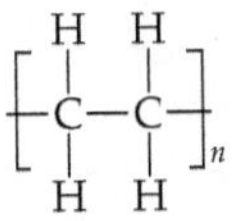	Polyethylene	Bags, bottles, toys, electrical insulation
$CH_2{=}CH{-}CH_3$	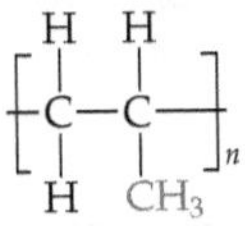	Polypropylene	Carpeting, bottles, luggage
$CH_2{=}CH{-}$⬡ 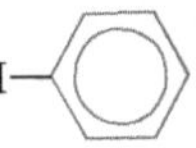	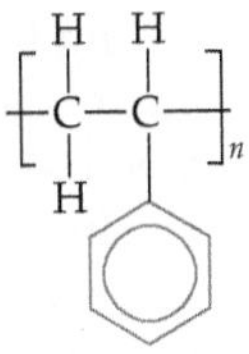	Polystyrene	Simulated wood furniture, insulation, cups, toys, packing materials
$CH_2{=}CH{-}Cl$	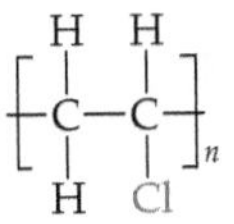	Polyvinyl chloride (PVC)	Food wrap, simulated leather, plumbing, garden hoses, floor tile
$CH_2{=}CCl_2$	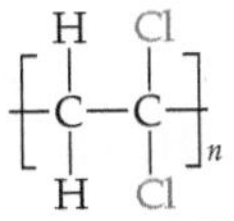	Polyvinylidene chloride (Saran®)	Food wrap, seat covers
$CF_2{=}CF_2$	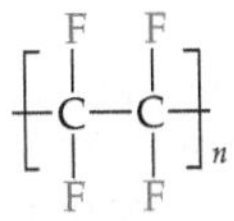	Polytetrafluoroethylene (Teflon)	Nonstick coating for cooking utensils, electrical insulation
$CH_2{=}CH{-}C{\equiv}N$	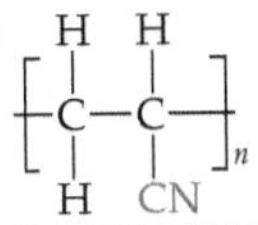	Polyacrylonitrile (Acrilan, Creslan, Dynel)	Yarns, wigs, paints
$CH_2{=}CH{-}OCOCH_3$	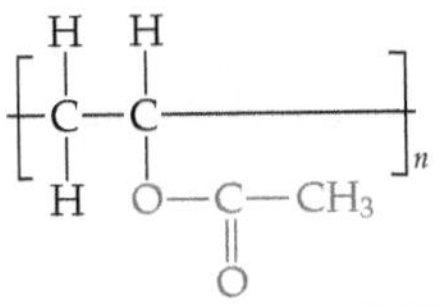	Polyvinyl acetate	Adhesives, textile coatings, chewing gum resin, paints
$CH_2{=}C(CH_3)COOCH_3$	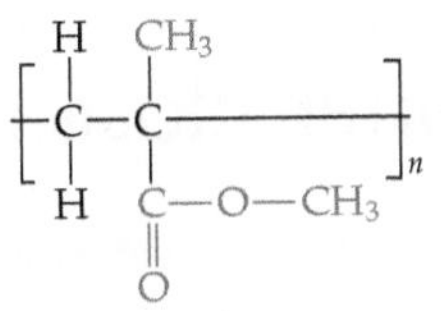	Polymethyl methacrylate (Lucite, Plexiglas)	Glass substitute, bowling balls

Conducting Polymers: Polyacetylene

Acetylene ($H—C\equiv C—H$) has a triple bond rather than a double bond, but it can still undergo addition polymerization, forming polyacetylene (Figure 10.3). Notice that, unlike polyethylene, which has a carbon chain containing only single bonds, every other carbon to carbon bond in polyacetylene is a double bond.

$$\sim CH{=}CH—CH{=}CH—CH{=}CH—CH{=}CH—CH{=}CH—CH{=}CH\sim$$

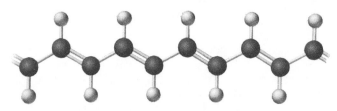

Figure 10.3 A ball-and-stick model of polyacetylene.

Q: *Write an equation for the formation of polyacetylene similar to that for polyethylene on page 268, in which the repeat polymer unit is placed within brackets.*

The alternating double and single bonds form a *conjugated* system. Such a system makes it easy for electrons to travel along the chain, so polyacetylene is able to conduct electricity. Most other plastics are electrical insulators. Polyacetylene and similar conjugated polymers can be used as lightweight substitutes for metal. In fact, the plastic even has a silvery luster like metal.

Polyacetylene, the first conducting polymer, was discovered in 1970. Since then, a number of other polymers that conduct electricity have been made.

▲ Conducting polymers have conjugated systems, as seen in Figure 10.3, and they are used to make electronic sensors, such as the ones shown here. The conductivity of the polymer is affected by impurities on the surface. The change in conductivity varies with the concentration of that impurity.

Self-Assessment Questions

1. Starting materials for many polymers are
   a. alkanes   **b.** alkenes   **c.** carboxylic acids   **d.** esters   **e.** ethers

2. The monomer styrene ($C_6H_5CH{=}CH_2$, where C_6H_5 represents a benzene ring) forms a polymer that has chains with repeating
   a. eight-carbon units in the backbone
   b. six-carbon units in the backbone and two-carbon groups as pendants
   c. CH_2CH units in the backbone and C_6H_5 groups as pendants
   d. $CH_2{=}CH$ units in the backbone and C_6H_5 groups as pendants

3. Which of the following could *not* serve as the monomer to make an addition polymer?
   a. $C_2H_2F_2$ **b.** C_2F_4 **c.** C_2H_5Cl **d.** $C_2H_3C_6H_5$

4. A buckyball is a
   a. large carbon molecule (C_{60})
   b. carbon nanotube wound up like a ball of string
   c. long polymer molecule wound up like a ball of string
   d. circular ring of carbon atoms

Answers: 1, b; 2, c; 3, c; 4, a

10.4 Rubber and Other Elastomers

Learning Objectives ❯ Define *cross-linking*, and explain how it changes the properties of a polymer.

Although rubber is a natural polymer, it was the basis for much of the development of the synthetic polymer industry. During World War II, Japanese occupation of Southeast Asia cut off most of the Allies' supply of natural rubber. The search for synthetic substitutes resulted in much more than just a replacement for natural rubber. The plastics industry, to a large extent, developed out of the search for synthetic rubber.

Natural rubber can be broken down into a simple hydrocarbon called *isoprene*. Isoprene is a volatile liquid, whereas rubber is a semisolid, elastic material. Chemists can make polyisoprene, a substance identical to natural rubber, except that the isoprene comes from petroleum refineries rather than from the cells of rubber trees.

$$n \; CH_2{=}C{-}CH{=}CH_2 \longrightarrow \big(\!\!- CH_2{-}C{=}CH{-}CH_2 \!-\!\big)_n$$
$$\qquad\qquad \underset{CH_3}{|} \qquad\qquad\qquad\quad \underset{CH_3}{|}$$

Isoprene   Polyisoprene (rubber)

Chemists have also developed several synthetic rubbers and devised ways to modify these polymers to change their properties.

Vulcanization: Cross-Linking

The long-chain molecules that make up rubber are coiled and twisted and intertwined with one another. When rubber is stretched, its coiled molecules are straightened. Natural rubber is soft and tacky when hot. It can be made harder by reaction with sulfur. In this process, called **vulcanization**, sulfur atoms *cross-link* the hydrocarbon chains side-to-side (Figure 10.4). Charles Goodyear discovered vulcanization and was issued U.S. Patent 3633 in 1844 for the process.

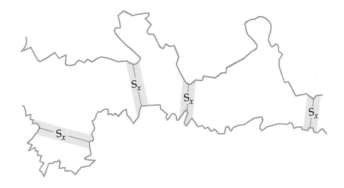

◀ **Figure 10.4** Vulcanized rubber has long hydrocarbon chains (represented here by red lines) cross-linked by short chains of sulfur atoms. The subscript x indicates a small, indefinite number of S atoms, usually not more than four.

Its cross-linked structure makes vulcanized rubber a harder, stronger substance that is suitable for automobile tires. Surprisingly, cross-linking also improves the elasticity of rubber. With just the right degree of cross-linking, the individual chains are still free to uncoil and stretch somewhat. When stretched vulcanized rubber is released, the cross-links pull the chains back to their original arrangement (Figure 10.5). Rubber bands owe their snap to this sort of molecular structure. Materials that can be extended and will return to their original size are called **elastomers**.

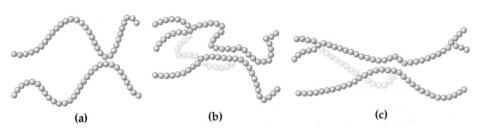

(a)   (b)   (c)

◦ = Carbon

◦ = Sulfur

▲ **Figure 10.5** Vulcanization of rubber cross-links the hydrocarbon chains. (a) In unvulcanized rubber, the chains slip past one another when the rubber is stretched. (b) Vulcanization involves the addition of sulfur cross-links between the chains. (c) When vulcanized rubber is stretched, the sulfur cross-links prevent the chains from slipping past one another. Vulcanized rubber is stronger than unvulcanized rubber.

Synthetic Rubber

Natural rubber is a polymer of isoprene, and some synthetic elastomers are closely related to natural rubber. For example, polybutadiene is made from the monomer butadiene (CH_2=CH—CH=CH_2), which differs from isoprene only in that it lacks a methyl group on the second carbon atom. Polybutadiene is made rather easily from this monomer.

$$n\, CH_2\!\!=\!\!CH\!-\!CH\!\!=\!\!CH_2 \longrightarrow \{CH_2\!-\!CH\!\!=\!\!CH\!-\!CH_2\}_n$$

However, this polymer has only fair tensile strength and poor resistance to gasoline and oils. These properties limit its value for automobile tires, the main use of elastomers.

Another synthetic elastomer, polychloroprene (Neoprene), is made from a monomer similar to isoprene, but with a chlorine in place of the methyl group on isoprene.

$$n\, CH_2\!\!=\!\!\underset{Cl}{C}\!-\!CH\!\!=\!\!CH_2 \longrightarrow \{CH_2\!-\!\underset{Cl}{C}\!\!=\!\!CH\!-\!CH_2\}_n$$

Neoprene is more resistant to oil and gasoline than other elastomers are. It is used to make gasoline pump hoses and similar items used at automobile service stations.

Styrene–butadiene rubber (SBR) is a copolymer of styrene (about 25%) and butadiene (about 75%). A segment of an SBR molecule might look something like this.

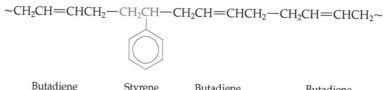

| Butadiene unit | Styrene unit | Butadiene unit | Butadiene unit |

SBR is more resistant to oxidation and abrasion than natural rubber, but its mechanical properties are less satisfactory.

Like those of natural rubber, SBR molecules contain double bonds and can be cross-linked by vulcanization. SBR accounts for about a third of the total U.S. production of elastomers and is used mainly for making tires.

Polymers in Paints

A surprising use for elastomers is in paints and other coatings. The substance in a paint that hardens to form a continuous surface coating, often called the *binder*, or resin, is a polymer, usually an elastomer. Paint made with elastomers is resistant to cracking. Various kinds of polymers can be used as binders, depending on the specific qualities desired in the paint. Latex paints, which have polymer particles dispersed in water, and thus avoiding the use of organic solvents, are most common. Brushes and rollers are easily cleaned in soap and water. This replacement of the hazardous organic solvents historically used in paints with water is a good example of green chemistry.

▲ It DOES Matter!
A polymer related to SBR is poly(styrene-butadiene-styrene), or SBS. Called a *block copolymer*, SBS has molecules made up of three segments: one end is a chain of polystyrene repeat units; the middle is a long chain of polybutadiene repeat units; and the other end is another chain of polystyrene repeat units. SBS is a hard rubber used in items where durability is important, such as shoe soles and tire treads.

▲ Synthetic polymers serve as binders in paints. Pigments provide color and opacity to the paint. Titanium dioxide (TiO_2), a white solid, is the most widely used pigment.

Self-Assessment Questions

1. Natural rubber is a polymer of
   a. butadiene   **b.** isobutylene   **c.** isoprene   **d.** propylene

2. Which of the following is the structure of isoprene?
   a. CH_2=CH—C≡N
   b. CH_2=$C(CH_3)$—CH_3
   c. CH_2=CCl—CH—CH_2
   d. CH_2=$C(CH_3)$—CH=CH_2

3. Vulcanization of natural rubber
   a. cross-links the rubber, making it harder and tougher
   b. makes the rubber more crystalline and thus more glassy
   c. makes the rubber totally amorphous
   d. makes the rubber tacky, forming rubber cement

4. Charles Goodyear discovered that natural rubber could be cross-linked by heating it with
   a. a binder   **b.** carbon   **c.** isoprene   **d.** sulfur

5. Styrene–butadiene rubber is an example of a
   a. copolymer
   c. natural cross-linked polymer
   b. natural elastomer
   d. polyamide
6. Polymers, usually elastomers, are used in paints as the
   a. binder   **b.** initiator   **c.** pigment   **d.** solvent

10.5 Condensation Polymers

Learning Objectives ❯ Differentiate between addition and condensation polymerization. ❯ Write the structures of the monomers that form polyesters and polyamides.

The polymers considered so far are all addition polymers. All the atoms of the monomer molecules are incorporated into the polymer molecules. In a *condensation polymer*, part of the monomer molecule is not incorporated in the final polymer. During **condensation polymerization**, also called *step-reaction polymerization*, a small molecule, usually water but sometimes methanol, ammonia or HCl, is formed as a by-product.

Nylon and Other Polyamides

As an example, let's consider the formation of nylon. The monomer in one type of nylon, called *nylon 6*, is a six-carbon carboxylic acid with an amino group on the sixth carbon atom: 6-aminohexanoic acid ($HOOCCH_2CH_2CH_2CH_2CH_2NH_2$). (There are several different nylons, each prepared from a different monomer or set of monomers, but all share certain common structural features.)

In the polymerization reaction, a carboxyl group of one monomer molecule forms an amide bond with the amine group of another.

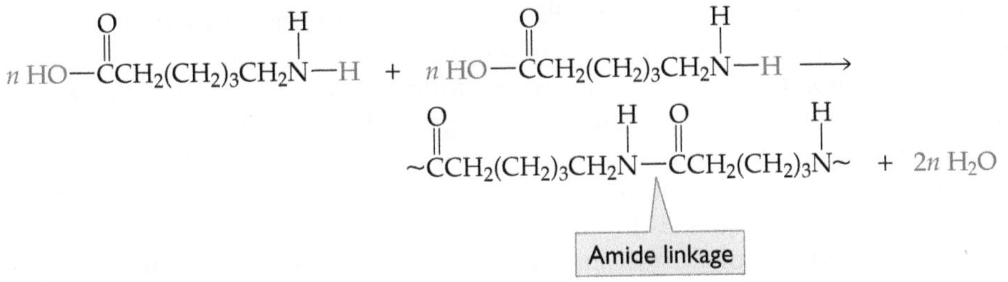

$$n \; HO-\overset{\overset{O}{\|}}{C}CH_2(CH_2)_3CH_2\overset{\overset{H}{|}}{N}-H \;+\; n \; HO-\overset{\overset{O}{\|}}{C}CH_2(CH_2)_3CH_2\overset{\overset{H}{|}}{N}-H \longrightarrow$$

$$\sim\overset{\overset{O}{\|}}{C}CH_2(CH_2)_3CH_2\overset{\overset{H}{|}}{N}-\overset{\overset{O}{\|}}{C}CH_2(CH_2)_3\overset{\overset{H}{|}}{N}\sim \;+\; 2n \; H_2O$$

Amide linkage

Water molecules are formed as a by-product. This formation of a nonpolymeric by-product distinguishes condensation polymerization from addition polymerization. Note that the formula of a repeat unit of a condensation polymer is not the same as that of the monomer.

Because the linkages holding the polymer together are amide bonds, nylon 6 is a **polyamide**. Another nylon is made by the condensation of two different monomers: 1,6-hexanediamine ($H_2NCH_2CH_2CH_2CH_2CH_2CH_2NH_2$) and adipic acid ($HOOCCH_2CH_2CH_2CH_2COOH$). Each monomer has six carbon atoms; the polymer is called *nylon 66*.

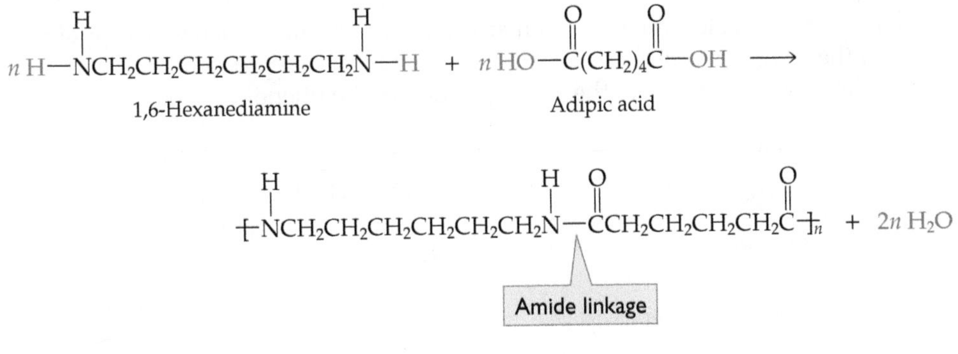

$$n \; H-\overset{\overset{H}{|}}{N}CH_2CH_2CH_2CH_2CH_2CH_2\overset{\overset{H}{|}}{N}-H \;+\; n \; HO-\overset{\overset{O}{\|}}{C}(CH_2)_4\overset{\overset{O}{\|}}{C}-OH \longrightarrow$$

1,6-Hexanediamine   Adipic acid

$$\overset{}{+}\overset{\overset{H}{|}}{N}CH_2CH_2CH_2CH_2CH_2CH_2\overset{\overset{H}{|}}{N}-\overset{\overset{O}{\|}}{C}CH_2CH_2CH_2CH_2\overset{\overset{O}{\|}}{C}\overset{}{+}_n \;+\; 2n \; H_2O$$

Amide linkage

This was the original nylon polymer discovered in 1937 by DuPont chemist Wallace Carothers. Note that one monomer has two amino groups and the other has two carboxyl groups, but the product is still a polyamide, quite similar to nylon 6. Silk and wool, which are protein fibers, are natural polyamides.

Although nylon can be molded into various shapes, most nylon is made into fibers. Some is spun into fine thread to be woven into silklike fabrics, and some is made into yarn that is much like wool. Carpeting, which was once made primarily from wool, is now made largely from nylon.

Polyethylene Terephthalate and Other Polyesters

A **polyester** is a condensation polymer made from molecules with alcohol and carboxylic acid functional groups. The most common polyester is made from ethylene glycol and terephthalic acid. It is called *polyethylene terephthalate (PET)*.

Polyethylene terephthalate

The hydroxyl groups in ethylene glycol react with the carboxylic acid groups in terephthalic acid to produce long chains held together by many ester linkages.

PET can be molded into bottles for beverages and other liquids. It can also be formed into a film, which is used to laminate documents and to make tough packaging tape. Polyester finishes are used on premium wood products such as guitars, pianos, and the interiors of vehicles and boats. Polyester fibers are strong, quick-drying, and resistant to mildew, wrinkling, stretching, and shrinking. They are used in home furnishings such as carpets, curtains, sheets and pillow cases, and upholstery. Because polyester fibers do not absorb water, they are ideal for outdoor clothing to be worn in wet and damp environments and for insulation in boots and sleeping bags. For other clothing, they are often blended with cotton for a more natural feel. A familiar use of polyester film (Mylar®) is in the shiny balloons that are filled with helium to celebrate special occasions.

Phenol–Formaldehyde and Related Resins

Let's go back to Bakelite, the original synthetic polymer. Bakelite, a phenol–formaldehyde resin, was first synthesized by Leo Baekeland, who received U.S. Patent 942,699 for the process in 1909. Phenolic resins are no longer important as industrial polymers, but they are used as a substitute for porcelain and in board and tabletop game pieces such as billiard balls, dominoes, and checkers.

Phenol–formaldehyde resins are formed in a condensation reaction that also yields water molecules, the hydrogen atoms coming from the benzene ring of phenol and the oxygen atoms from the aldehyde. The reaction proceeds stepwise, with formaldehyde first adding to the 2 or 4 position of the phenol molecule.

The substituted phenol molecules then link up as water molecules are formed. (Remember that there are hydrogen atoms at all the unsubstituted corners of a benzene ring.) The hookup of molecules continues until an extensive network is achieved.

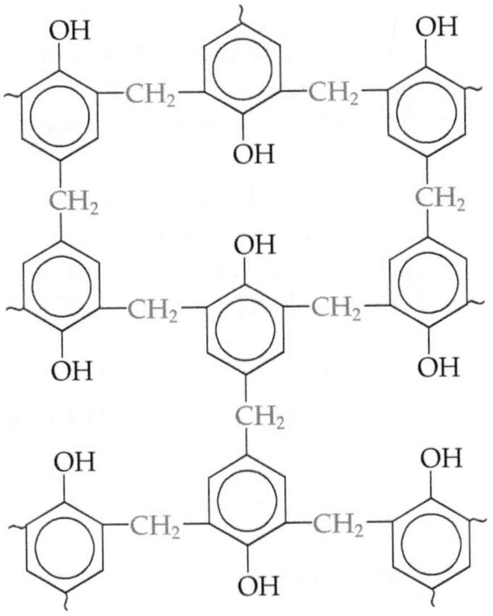

Phenol–formaldehyde resin

Water is driven off by heat as the polymer sets. The structure of the polymer is extremely complex, a three-dimensional network somewhat like the framework of a giant building. Note that the phenolic rings are joined together by CH_2 units from the formaldehyde. These network polymers are **thermosetting resins**; they cannot be melted and remolded. Instead, they decompose when heated to high temperatures.

Formaldehyde is also condensed with urea [$H_2N(C{=}O)NH_2$] to make urea–formaldehyde resins and with melamine to form melamine–formaldehyde resins. (Melamine is formed by condensation of three molecules of urea.)

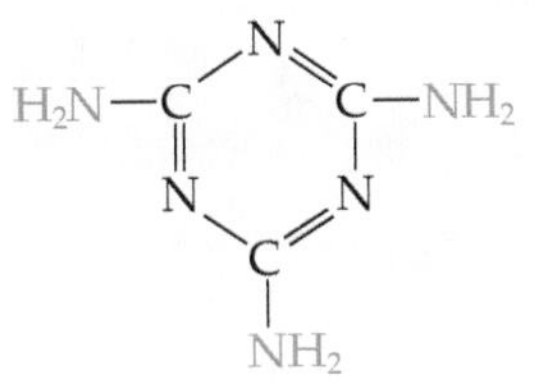

These resins, like phenolic resins, are thermosetting. The polymers are complex three-dimensional networks formed by the condensation reaction of formaldehyde ($H_2C{=}O$) molecules and amino ($-NH_2$) groups. Urea–formaldehyde resins are used to bind wood chips together in panels of particle board. Melamine–formaldehyde resins are used in plastic (Melmac) dinnerware and laminate countertops.

Melamine

Other Condensation Polymers

There are many other kinds of condensation polymers, but we will look at only a few.

Polycarbonates are "clear as glass" polymers tough enough to be used in bulletproof windows. They are also used in protective helmets, safety glasses, clear plastic water bottles, baby bottles, and even dental crowns. One polycarbonate is made from bisphenol-A (BPA) and phosgene ($COCl_2$).

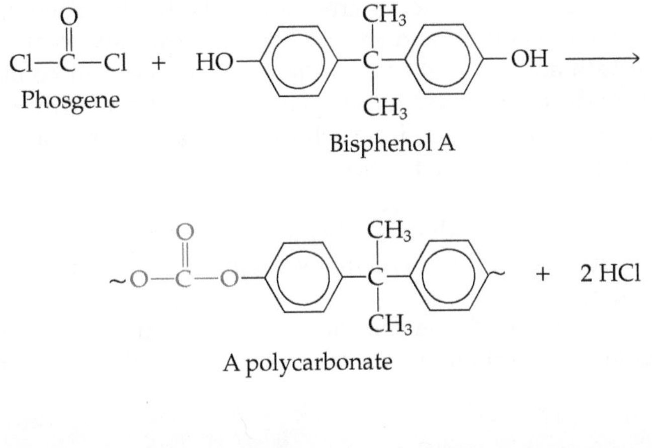

Phosgene   Bisphenol A

A polycarbonate

▲ It DOES Matter!

Bisphenol-A (BPA) is an endocrine disruptor in laboratory animals; that is, it can act like a hormone. A tiny amount of BPA leaches out of poly-carbonate bottles, especially when they are heated. Concern over long-term, low-dose exposure to BPA led Canada to ban BPA in baby bottles in 2008. Threats of legislation in the United States and elsewhere caused manufacturers of polycarbonate bottles to switch to BPA-free bottles.

▲ Composite construction using carbon fiber and epoxies makes bicycle frames incredibly strong and light (about 1 kg!). The direction of the carbon fiber allows the maker to tailor the material for maximum strength where needed.

Silicon is in the same group (4A) as carbon and, like carbon, is tet-ravalent and able to form chains. However, carbon can form chains consisting only of car-bon atoms (as in polyethylene), whereas the chains of silicone polymers have alternating silicon and oxygen atoms.

4. Is silicon the same thing as silicone? Although the names are very similar, the materi-als are quite different. *Silicon* is a hard, brittle element. A *silicone* is a polymer that contains silicon as well as carbon, hydrogen, and oxygen. Most silicones are flexible.

Polyurethanes are similar to nylon polymers in structure. The repeat unit in one common polyurethane is

$$\sim \overset{\overset{\displaystyle O}{\|}}{C}-NH-CH_2CH_2CH_2CH_2CH_2CH_2-NH-\overset{\overset{\displaystyle O}{\|}}{C}-O-CH_2CH_2CH_2CH_2-O\sim$$

Polyurethanes may be elastomeric or tough and rigid, depending on the monomers used. They are common in foamed padding (foam rubber) in cushions, mattresses, and padded furniture. They are also used for skate wheels, in running shoes, and in protective gear for sports activities.

Epoxies make excellent surface paints and coatings. They are used to protect steel pipes and fittings from corrosion. The insides of metal cans are often coated with an epoxy to prevent rusting, especially in cans for acidic foods like tomatoes. A common epoxy is made from epichlorohydrin and BPA.

$$\sim O-\underset{}{\bigcirc}-\underset{\underset{CH_3}{|}}{\overset{\overset{CH_3}{|}}{C}}-\underset{}{\bigcirc}-O-CH_2\underset{\underset{OH}{|}}{CH}CH_2\sim$$

An epoxy

Epoxies also make powerful adhesives. These adhesives usually have two compo-nents that are mixed just before use. The polymer chains become cross-linked, and the bonding is extremely strong.

Composite Materials

Composite materials are made up of high-strength fibers (of glass, graphite, syn-thetic polymers, or ceramics) held together by a polymeric matrix, usually a ther-mosetting condensation polymer. The fiber reinforcement provides the support, and the surrounding plastic keeps the fibers from breaking.

Among the most commonly used composite materials are polyester resins rein-forced with glass fibers. These are widely used in boat hulls, molded chairs, auto-mobile panels, and sports gear such as tennis rackets. Some composite materials have the strength and rigidity of steel but with a fraction of the weight of steel.

Silicones

Not all polymers are based on chains of carbon atoms. A good example of a differ-ent type of polymer is **silicone** (polysiloxane), whose chains have a series of alter-nating silicon and oxygen atoms.

$$\sim \underset{\underset{R}{|}}{\overset{\overset{R}{|}}{Si}}-O-\underset{\underset{R}{|}}{\overset{\overset{R}{|}}{Si}}-O-\underset{\underset{R}{|}}{\overset{\overset{R}{|}}{Si}}-O-\underset{\underset{R}{|}}{\overset{\overset{R}{|}}{Si}}-O-\underset{\underset{R}{|}}{\overset{\overset{R}{|}}{Si}}-O-\underset{\underset{R}{|}}{\overset{\overset{R}{|}}{Si}}-O-\underset{\underset{R}{|}}{\overset{\overset{R}{|}}{Si}}\sim$$

(In simple silicones, R represents a hydrocarbon group, such as methyl, ethyl, or butyl.)

Silicones can be linear, cyclic, or cross-linked networks. They are heat-stable and resistant to most chemicals and are excellent waterproofing materials. Depend-ing on chain length and amount of cross-linking, silicones can be oils or greases, rubbery compounds, or solid resins. Silicone oils are used as hydraulic fluids and lubricants; other silicones are used in such products as sealants, auto polish, shoe polish, and waterproof sheeting. Fabrics for raincoats and umbrellas are frequently treated with silicone.

An interesting silicone product is Silly Putty. It can be molded like clay or rolled up and bounced like a ball. But it is actually a liquid (see page 153) and flows very slowly on standing.

Perhaps the most remarkable silicones are the ones used for synthetic human body parts, ranging from finger joints to eye sockets. Artificial ears and noses are also made from silicone polymers. These can even be specially colored to match the surrounding skin.

Example 10.3 Condensed Structural Formulas for Polymers

Write the condensed structural formula for the polymer formed from dimethylsilanol, $(CH_3)_2Si(OH)_2$.

Solution

Let's start by writing the structural formula of the monomer.

$$\begin{array}{c} CH_3 \\ | \\ HO-Si-OH \\ | \\ CH_3 \end{array}$$

Because there are no double bonds in this molecule, we do not expect it to undergo addition polymerization. Rather, we expect a condensation reaction, in which an OH group of one molecule and an H atom of another combine to form a molecule of water. Moreover, because there are two OH groups per molecule, each monomer can form bonds with two others, on both sides. This is a key requirement for polymerization. We can represent the reaction as follows.

$$\underset{\underset{CH_3}{|}}{\overset{\overset{CH_3}{|}}{HO-Si-OH}} + \underset{\underset{CH_3}{|}}{\overset{\overset{CH_3}{|}}{HO-Si-OH}} + \underset{\underset{CH_3}{|}}{\overset{\overset{CH_3}{|}}{HO-Si-OH}} + \cdots \longrightarrow \left[\underset{\underset{CH_3}{|}}{\overset{\overset{CH_3}{|}}{-Si-O-}}\right]_n + n\,H_2O$$

▪ **EXERCISE 10.3**

a. Write the structural formula for the polymer formed from glycolic acid (hydroxyacetic acid, $HOCH_2COOH$), showing at least four repeat units.

b. Write a condensed structural formula in which the repeat unit in part (a) is shown in brackets.

▲ Cookware made of silicone is colorful, flexible, and nonstick.

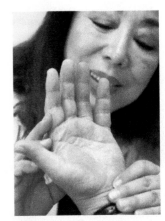

▲ Silicone is an excellent material for some replacement body parts. It is very flexible and chemically inert; the body does not often reject silicone.

Self-Assessment Questions

1. In a condensation polymerization, the two products formed are a polymer and (usually)
   a. an acid
   b. a base
   c. carbon dioxide
   d. water

2. Which of the following pairs of molecules can form a polyester?
   a. $HOCH_2CH_2OH$ and $HOCH_2CH_2CH_2CH_2OH$
   b. $H_2NCH_2CH_2CH_2CH_2CH_2NH_2$ and $HOOCCH_2CH_2CH_2CH_2COOH$
   c. $H_2NCH_2CH_2CH_2CH_2CH_2NH_2$ and $HOCH_2CH_2CH_2CH_2CH_2OH$
   d. $HOOCCH_2CH_2CH_2CH_2COOH$ and $HOCH_2CH_2CH_2CH_2OH$

3. Which of the following molecules can serve as the sole monomer for a polyamide?
   a. $H_2NCH_2CH_2CH_2CH_2OH$
   b. $H_2NCH_2CH_2CH_2CH_2NH_2$
   c. $HOOCCH_2CH_2CH_2CH_2CH_2NH_2$
   d. $HOOCCH_2CH_2CH_2CONH_2$

4. Thermosetting polymers
   a. are easily recycled
   b. are always addition polymers
   c. cannot be melted and remolded
   d. usually melt at a lower temperature than do thermoplastic polymers

5. The backbone of a silicone polymer chain is composed of the repeating unit
   a. ~OCH_2CH_2OSi~
   b. ~OCH_2CH_2Si~
   c. ~SiO~
   d. ~$OSiSi$~

Answers: 1, d; 2, d; 3, c; 4, c; 5, c

10.6 Properties of Polymers

Learning Objectives ❯ Understand the concept of the glass transition temperature.
❯ Explain how crystallinity affects the physical properties of polymers.

Polymers differ from substances consisting of small molecules in three main ways. First, the long chains can be entangled with one another, much like the strands in a dish of spaghetti. It is difficult to untangle the polymer molecules, especially at low temperatures. This property lends strength to many plastics, elastomers, and other materials.

Second, although intermolecular forces affect polymers just as they do small molecules, these forces are greatly multiplied for large molecules. The larger the molecules are, the greater the intermolecular forces between them. Even when ordinarily weak dispersion forces are the only intermolecular forces present, they can strongly bind polymer chains. This property, too, provides strength in polymeric materials. For example, polyethylene is nonpolar, with only dispersion forces between its molecules. As noted on page 271, though, ultra-high-molecular-weight polyethylene forms fibers so strong they can be used in bullet-proof vests.

Third, large polymer molecules move more slowly than small molecules do. A group of small molecules (monomers) can move around more rapidly and more randomly when independent than they can when joined together in a long chain (polymer). The slower molecular speed makes a polymeric material different from one made of small molecules. For example, a polymer dissolved in a solvent will form a solution that is a lot more viscous than the pure solvent.

Crystalline and Amorphous Polymers

Some polymers are highly crystalline; their molecules line up neatly to form long fibers of great strength. Other polymers are largely amorphous, composed of randomly oriented molecules that get tangled up with one another (Figure 10.6). Crystalline polymers tend to make good synthetic fibers, while amorphous polymers are often elastomers.

❯ **Figure 10.6** Organization of polymer molecules. (a) Crystalline arrangement. (b) Amorphous arrangement.

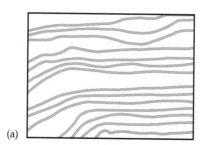
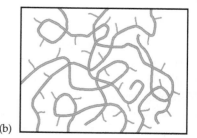

(a)   (b)

Sometimes, the same polymer is crystalline in one region and amorphous in another. For example, scientists designed spandex fibers (used in stretch fabrics [Lycra] in ski pants, exercise clothing, and swimsuits) to combine the tensile strength of crystalline fibers with the elasticity of amorphous rubber. Two molecular structures are combined in one polymer chain, with crystalline blocks alternating with amorphous blocks. The amorphous blocks are soft and rubbery, while the crystalline parts are quite rigid. The resulting polymer exhibits both sets of properties—flexibility and rigidity.

The Glass Transition Temperature

We can apply the glass transition temperature in everyday life. For example, we can remove chewing gum from clothing by applying ice to lower the temperature of the polyvinyl acetate resin that gives the gum its "chewiness" below its T_g. The cold, brittle resin then crumbles readily and can be removed.

An important property of most thermoplastic polymers is the **glass transition temperature** (T_g). Above this temperature, the polymer is rubbery and tough. Below it, the polymer is like glass: hard, stiff, and brittle. Each polymer has a characteristic T_g.

We want automobile tires to be tough and elastic, so we make them from polymers with low T_g values. On the other hand, we want plastic substitutes for glass to be glassy. Therefore, these polymers have T_g values well above room temperature.

Fiber Formation

Not all synthetic polymers can be formed into useful fibers, but those that can often yield fibers with properties superior to those of natural fibers. More than half of the 60 billion kg of textile fibers produced each year in the United States are synthetic.

Silk fabrics are beautiful and have a luxurious "feel," but nylon fabrics are also attractive and feel much like silk. Moreover, nylon fabrics wear longer, are easier to care for, and are less expensive than silk.

Polyesters such as PET can substitute for either cotton or silk, but they outperform the natural fibers in many ways. Polyesters are not subject to mildew as cotton is, and many polyester fabrics do not need ironing. Fabrics in which polyester fibers are blended with 35–50% cotton combine the comfort of cotton with the no-iron easy care of polyester.

Acrylic fibers, made from polyacrylonitrile, can be spun into yarns that look like wool. Acrylic sweaters have the beauty and warmth of wool, but they do not shrink in hot water, are not attacked by moths, and do not cause the allergic skin reaction wool causes in some people.

Exceedingly fine fibers—called *microfibers* because they measure less than 10 μm in diameter, half as thick as a silk fibers—can be made from almost any fiber-forming polymer, but most are made of polyesters or polyamides or a combination of the two. Varying the size, shape, and composition of the fibers results in products that are water repellent (for apparel) or absorbent (for a mop). Microfibers can be shaped for efficient trapping of dust or for wicking away liquids. These fibers already have many uses and are likely to have many more.

5. How are permanent-press fabrics made? Cotton is largely cellulose, which can engage in hydrogen bonding among its molecules. Moisture causes random hydrogen bonding in cotton fabric, which causes wrinkles. The earliest permanent-press fabrics were designed to allow less hydrogen bonding than in cotton. Newer permanent-press clothing takes advantage of the fabric's low T_g to minimize wrinkles after drying.

▲ Formation of fibers by extrusion through a spinneret. A melted polymer is forced through the tiny holes to make fibers that solidify as they cool.

Self-Assessment Questions

1. The glass transition temperature of a polymer is the temperature
   a. above which the polymer becomes highly crystalline
   b. at which the polymer changes to a thermosetting material
   c. at which the polymer melts to a clear liquid
   d. below which the polymer becomes glassy and brittle

2. Crystalline polymers are
   a. elastic   b. flexible   c. highly cross-linked   d. used in fibers

Answers: 1, d; 2, d

10.7 Plastics and the Environment

Learning Objectives ❯ Describe the environmental problems associated with plastics and plasticizers. ❯ Name two types of sustainable, non-petroleum-derived polymers and give their sources.

An advantage of many plastics is that they are durable and resistant to environmental conditions. Perhaps some of them are too resistant: They last almost forever. Once plastic objects are dumped, they do not go away. You see them littering our parks, our sidewalks, and our highways, and if you should go out into the middle of the ocean, you would see them there, too. Many small fish have been found dead with their digestive tracts clogged by bits of plastic foam ingested with their food.

Plastics make up about 12% by mass of solid waste in the United States, but about 25% by volume. Their bulk creates a problem because 55% of all solid waste

Americans use about 60 million plastic bottles each day, with only about 12% being recycled. Recycling one plastic bottle conserves enough energy to burn a 60-W lightbulb for six hours. Recycling plastics reduces our dependency on oil and decreases CO_2 emissions due to the use of fossil fuels.

▲ Recycled plastic can be used for many things. The Adirondack chair and the cafe chair are colorful and strong and made from recycled milk jugs.

goes into landfills, and it is increasingly difficult to find suitable landfill space. (Solid wastes are discussed in more detail in Chapter 12.)

Another way to dispose of discarded plastics is to burn them. Most plastics have a high fuel value. For example, a pound of polyethylene has about the same energy content as a pound of fuel oil. Some communities generate electricity with the heat from garbage incinerators. Some utility companies burn powdered coal mixed with a small proportion of ground-up rubber tires, thereby not only obtaining extra energy from the tires but also helping to solve the problem of tire disposal.

On the other hand, the burning of plastics and rubber can create new problems. For example, PVC produces toxic hydrogen chloride and vinyl chloride gases when it burns, and burning automobile tires give off soot and a stinking smoke. Incinerators are corroded by acidic fumes and clogged by materials that are not readily burned.

Degradable Plastics

About half of the waste plastic generated in the United States is from packaging. One approach to the problem of disposal of plastics is to make plastic packages that are biodegradable or photodegradable (broken down in the presence of bacteria or light). Of course, such packages must remain intact and not start to decompose while still being used. And many people still seem reluctant to pay extra for garbage bags that are designed to fall apart. Recently, though, there has been an increase in degradable, more environmentally friendly plastic items, including plastic tableware, cups, bottles, and delicatessen food containers.

Recycling

Recycling is perhaps the best way to handle waste plastics. The plastics must be collected, sorted, chopped, melted, and then remolded. Collection works well when there is strong community cooperation. The separation step is simplified by code numbers stamped on plastic containers. Once the plastics have been separated, they can be chopped into flakes, melted, and remolded or spun into fibers.

Only two kinds of plastics are recycled on a large scale, PET (28% recycled) and HDPE (29%). PET bottles can be made into fibers, mainly for carpets, and HDPE containers can be remolded into detergent bottles. Recycling is green because it keeps plastics out of landfills, and it increases sustainability by lessening the use of petroleum-derived monomers or hazardous chemicals. We have a long way to go: in 2009, only about 7% of the 27 billion kg per year of plastic wastes in the United States are recycled.

Plastics and Fire Hazards

The accidental ignition of fabrics, synthetic or other, has caused untold human misery. The U.S. Department of Health and Human Services estimates that fires involving flammable fabrics kill several thousand people annually and injure between 150,000 and 200,000.

Research has led to a variety of flame-retardant fabrics. Many incorporate chlorine and bromine atoms within the polymeric fibers. In particular, federal regulations require that children's sleepwear be made of such flame-retardant materials.

Another synthetic fabric, meta-aramid, or Nomex (from DuPont), has such high heat resistance that it is used for protective clothing for firefighters and race-car drivers. The fibers don't ignite or melt when exposed to flames or high heat. Nomex is also used in electric insulation and for machine parts exposed to high heat.

Burning plastics often produce toxic gases. Hydrogen cyanide is formed in large quantities when polyacrylonitrile and other nitrogen-containing polymers burn. Lethal amounts of cyanide found in the bodies of victims of plane crashes have been traced to burned plastics. Firefighters often refuse to enter burning buildings without gas masks for fear of being overcome by fumes from burning plastics. Smoldering fires also produce lethal quantities of carbon monoxide. To make plastics safer, green chemists are making new kinds of polymers that don't burn or that don't generate toxic chemicals when burned.

Jennifer L. Young, *ACS Green Chemistry Institute*®

Greener Polymers

Many products that we use today are made of plastic. Therefore, it is important to apply the twelve principles of green chemistry to plastics and polymers. You might ask, how can plastics be made sustainably using green chemistry? Two areas where greener processes have had large impacts are the recycling and biodegradation of plastics (Section 10.7, Principle 10) and the production of plastics from renewable resources (Principle 7).

You probably use polyethylene bags (Section 10.2), polystyrene cups (Section 10.3), polyethylene terephthalate (PET) soft drink bottles (Section 10.5), nylon clothing and carpeting (Section 10.5), and styrene–butadiene rubber tires (Section 10.4). These polymers and most others on the market are made from nonrenewable resources and do not biodegrade. After use, the polymers often are discarded into the environment or buried in landfills.

There are other, greener options for plastic materials. Many polymers that you use every day are recyclable. Recycling decreases the amount of plastic that ends up in landfills and also reduces the amount of new plastic that must be made from fossil fuels.

To make recycling easier, most plastic objects are stamped with a triangular recycle symbol and a number code. These numbers, called *resin identification codes*, identify types of plastics as follows: #1, polyethylene terephthalate (PET or PETE); #2, high-density polyethylene (HDPE); #3, polyvinyl chloride (PVC or V); #4, low-density polyethylene (LDPE); #5, polypropylene (PP); #6, polystyrene (PS); and #7, all other kinds of polymers.

PET (#1) and HDPE (#2) are the most commonly recycled plastics. Other types may also be accepted for recycling in some locales. In the recycling process, the plastics are separated by resin identification code. The plastic is then chopped up, softened by raising the temperature above the polymer's glass transition temperature (Section 10.6), molded into a new shape, and cooled back to room temperature to harden. Because the process uses heat to recycle the polymer, only thermoplastics (not thermosetting polymers; Section 10.2) can be recycled in this way.

Typically, recycled plastic is used to make different objects than the things recycled because the polymer's properties are changed. For example, park benches and plastic outdoor decking material are made from recycled plastic bottles. Just because

▲ Although they may appear to be like any other pens at first glance, these pens from Micro Roller are made from corn and straw. The pens are over 70% degradable within a relatively short period of time.

a polymer falls into the "other" category (#7) does not mean that the polymer cannot be recycled. For instance, nylon-based carpet is commonly recycled.

Some polymers, including PET, can be depolymerized. Chemical reactions can reverse the polymerization and break the polymer into the original monomer units. The monomer can then be polymerized again to make polymer that is as pure as the original material. Since the new polymer has the same properties as the original polymer, it can be used to make the same objects. Some companies that make these types of plastics will accept their plastic products for recycling, then depolymerize and reuse the monomers.

Some types of plastics can be degraded into carbon dioxide and water. Over some period of time, these polymers will biodegrade under the right conditions of temperature and moisture or in the presence of microorganisms. This means biodegradable plastics generally do not degrade readily when thrown at the side of the road or when dumped into trash that ends up in a landfill. Official bodies apply different definitions for biodegradability. For instance, the USA ASTM D6400 Standard requires 60% conversion into carbon dioxide in 180 days, and the European Standard EN13432 requires 90% conversion over the same span of time.

New kinds of polymers are being made from renewable resources, such as corn, soy, grass, and other types of biomass. One example is polylactic acid (PLA), made from corn. PLA is used to make plastic bottles, salad containers, coffee mugs, and even fibers for clothing. PLA can be depolymerized to monomers and can also degrade by composting. Cargill Dow LLC (now NatureWorks LLC) received a Presidential Green Chemistry Challenge Award for developing PLA from renewable resources. Polyhydroxyalkanoates (PHAs) are made from plant sugars and oils, are biodegradable, and can even be made using bacteria. Metabolix, Inc. was awarded a Presidential Green Chemistry Challenge Award for producing PHAs with microorganisms. For many plastics, the most sustainable approach is using renewable resources—especially nonfood crops—as the source of the monomer.

Plasticizers and Pollution

Chemicals used in plastics manufacture can also present problems. Plasticizers are an important example. Some plastics, particularly vinyl polymers, are hard and brittle and thus difficult to process. A **plasticizer** can make such a plastic more flexible and less brittle by lowering its glass transition temperature. Unplasticized PVC is rigid and is used for water pipes. Thin sheets of pure PVC crack and break easily, but plasticizers make them soft and pliable. Plastic raincoats, garden hoses, and seat covers for automobiles can be made from plasticized PVC. Plasticizers are liquids of low volatility, but they are generally lost by diffusion and evaporation as a plastic article ages. The plastic becomes brittle and then cracks and breaks.

Once used widely as plasticizers but now banned, polychlorinated biphenyls (PCBs) are derived from biphenyl ($C_{12}H_{10}$), a hydrocarbon that has two benzene rings joined at a corner. In PCBs, some of the hydrogen atoms of biphenyl are replaced with chlorine atoms (Figure 10.7). Note that PCBs are structurally similar to the insecticide DDT.

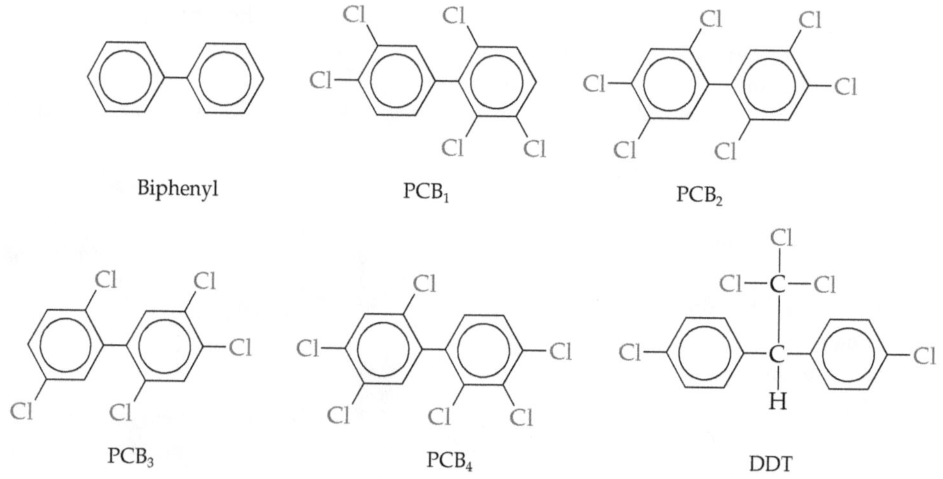

▶ **Figure 10.7** Biphenyl and some of the PCBs derived from it (only a few of the hundreds of possible PCBs). DDT is also shown for comparison.

Biphenyl   PCB$_1$ PCB$_2$

PCB$_3$ PCB$_4$ DDT

PCBs were also widely used as insulating materials in electric transformers because their stability and low polarity gave them high electrical resistance and the ability to absorb heat. The same properties that made PCBs so desirable as industrial chemicals cause them to be an environmental hazard. They degrade slowly in nature, and their solubility in nonpolar media—animal fat as well as vinyl plastics—leads to their becoming concentrated in the food chain, PCB residues have been found in fish, birds, water, and sediments. The physiological effect of PCBs is similar to that of DDT. Monsanto Corporation, the only company in the United States that produced PCBs, discontinued production in 1977, but the compounds still remain in the environment.

Today, the most widely used plasticizers for vinyl plastics are phthalate esters, a group of diesters derived from phthalic acid (1,2-benzenedicarboxylic acid). Phthalate plasticizers (Figure 10.8) have low acute toxicity and, although some studies have suggested possible harm to young children, the FDA has recognized these plasticizers as being generally safe. They pose little threat to the environment because they degrade fairly rapidly. Another approach of green chemists is to make plastics that have the right amount of flexibility and thus do not require any plasticizers when they are manufactured.

Plastics and the Future

Widely used today, synthetic polymers are the materials of the future. New kinds and new uses will be discovered. We already have polymers that conduct electricity, amazing adhesives, and synthetic materials that are stronger than steel but much lighter in weight. Plastics present problems, but they have become such an important part of our daily lives that we would find it difficult to live without them.

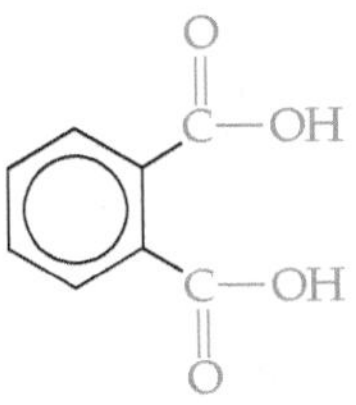

◀ **Figure 10.8** Phthalic acid and some esters derived from it. Dioctyl phthalate is also called di-2-ethylhexyl phthalate.

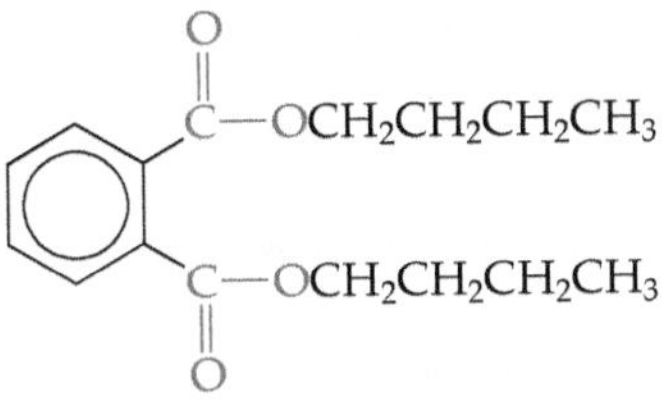

Phthalic acid

Dibutyl phthalate (DBP)

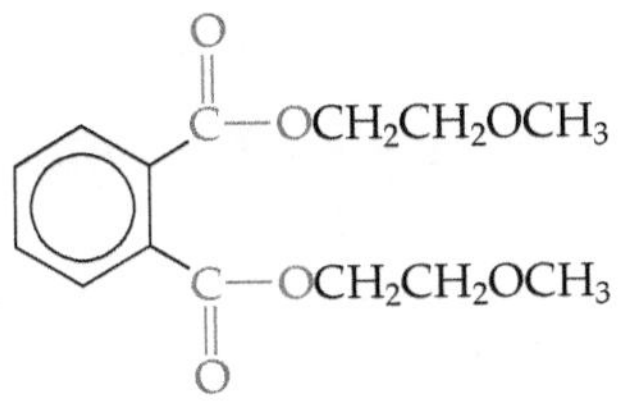

Dimethoxyethyl phthalate (DMEP)

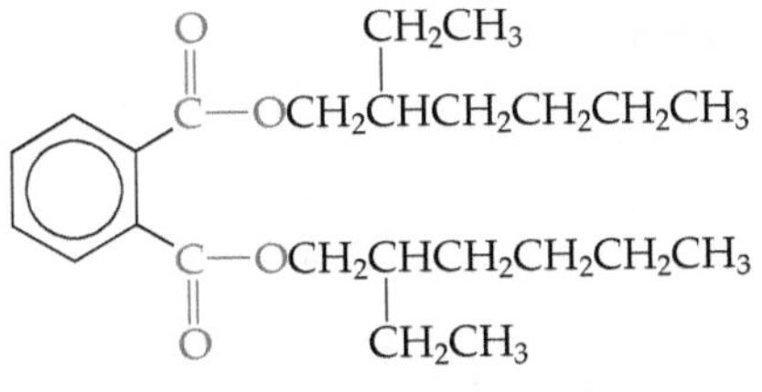

Dioctyl phthalate (DOP)

In medicine, body replacement parts made from polymers have become common. There are about 200,000 total hip replacements in the United States each year. Artificial lungs and artificial hearts are available, but they are enormously expensive and used for the most part only during recovery from injury or illness or until donor organs are available for transplantation. The cost of these replacements is likely to drop, and their efficacy will probably improve, in the future.

PVC water pipes, siding, and window frames, plastic foam insulation, and polymeric surface coatings are used in home construction today. Some homes also contain lumber and wall panels of artificial wood, made from recycled plastics.

Synthetic polymers are used extensively in airplane interiors, and the bodies and wings of some planes are made of lightweight composite materials. Many automobiles have bodies made from plastic composites. Electrically conducting polymers will aid in making lightweight batteries for electric automobiles. The electronics industry will use increasing amounts of electrically conducting thermoplastics in miniaturized circuits.

But here is something to think about: Most synthetic polymers are made from petroleum or natural gas. Both of these natural resources are nonrenewable, and our supplies are limited. We are likely to run out of petroleum during this century. You might suppose that we would be actively conserving this valuable resource, but unfortunately this is not the case. We are taking petroleum out of the ground at a rapid rate, converting most of it to gasoline and other fuels, and then simply burning it. There are other sources of energy, but is there anything that can replace petroleum as the raw material for making plastics? Yes! Several new types of plastics, such as polylactic acid and polyhydroxybutyrates, are made from renewable resources such as corn, soybeans, and sugarcane. Polymers are an active area of green chemistry research.

Self-Assessment Questions

1. In general, the best way to dispose of plastics is
   a. composting
   b. incineration
   c. in landfills
   d. recycling

2. Many plastics are fire hazards because they burn and produce
   a. CFCs
   b. nitrogen oxides
   c. solid wastes
   d. toxic gases

3. A plasticizer acts by
   a. initiating addition polymerization
   b. lowering the glass transition temperature
   c. participating in condensation polymerization
   d. wetting polymer powders

4. Many flame-retardant fabrics incorporate
   a. Br and Cl atoms
   c. PCBs
   b. CFCs
   d. phthalate plasticizers

5. Most synthetic polymers are made from
   a. coal
   c. petroleum and natural gas
   b. cotton
   d. sustainable sources

6. A polymer made from a renewable resource is
   a. LDPE
   c. polylactic acid
   b. polyacrylonitrile
   d. styrene–butadiene rubber

CRITICAL THINKING EXERCISES

Apply knowledge that you have gained in this chapter and one or more of the FLaReS principles (Chapter 1) to evaluate the following statements or claims.

10.1 An environmental activist states that all synthetic plastics should be banned and replaced by those derived from natural materials.

10.2 A news report states that incinerators that burn plastics are a major source of chlorine-containing toxic compounds called *dioxins* (Chapter 20).

10.3 Vinyl chloride is a carcinogen. Some people warn that children will get cancer from playing with toys made of PVC.

10.4 The Plastics Division of the American Chemistry Council says that, in comparison to paper bags, "plastic bags are . . . an environmentally responsible choice."

SUMMARY

Section 10.1—A **polymer** is a giant molecule made from smaller molecules. The small molecules that are the building blocks used to make polymers are called **monomers**. There are many natural polymers, including starch, cellulose, nucleic acids, and proteins.

Celluloid was the first semisynthetic polymer, made from natural cellulose treated with nitric acid.

Section 10.2—The simplest, least expensive, and highest-volume synthetic polymer is polyethylene, made from the monomer ethylene. High-density polyethylene molecules can pack closely together to yield a rigid, strong structure. Low-density polyethylene molecules have many side chains, resulting in more flexible plastics. Linear low-density polyethylene is a **copolymer**, formed from two (or more) different monomers.

Polyethylene is one of many **thermoplastic polymers** that can be softened and reshaped with heat and pressure. *Thermosetting* polymers decompose, rather than soften, when heated. They cannot be reshaped.

Section 10.3—In **addition polymerization**, the monomer molecules add to one another; the polymer contains all the atoms of the monomers. Addition polymers, such as polyethylene, polypropylene, polystyrene, and PVC, are made from monomers containing carbon-to-carbon double bonds. Polypropylene is tough and resists moisture, oils, and solvents. Polystyrene is used mainly to make Styrofoam. PVC or polyvinyl chloride is used for plumbing, artificial leather,

and flexible tubing. PTFE, or Teflon, is chemically inert and nonflammable; it is widely used in nonstick coatings. Thermoplastic polymers can be molded in many different ways.

Section 10.4—Natural rubber is an **elastomer**, a material that returns to its original shape after being stretched. The monomer of natural rubber, isoprene, can be made artificially and polymerized. Polyisoprene is soft and tacky when hot. In a process called **vulcanization**, polyisoprene is reacted with sulfur. The sulfur atoms cross-link the hydrocarbon chains, making the rubber harder, stronger, and more elastic.

Other elastomers that are similar in structure to polyisoprene include polybutadiene, polychloroprene, and styrene–butadiene rubber (SBR). All of these have molecules that can coil and uncoil. Elastomers are used as binders in paints.

Section 10.5—In **condensation polymerization**, parts of the monomer molecules are not incorporated in the product. Small molecules such as water are formed as by-products. Nylon is a condensation polymer that is a **polyamide**, with amide [—(CO)NH—] linkages joining the monomers.

A **polyester** is a condensation polymer made from monomers with alcohol and carboxylic acid functional groups. Polyethylene terephthalate (PET) is the most common polyester.

Various **thermosetting resins** can be prepared by condensing formaldehyde with urea, melamine, or phenol. Other condensation polymers include polycarbonates (bulletproof windows), polyurethanes (foam rubber), and epoxies (coatings and adhesives). Combining a polymer with high-strength fibers gives a composite material that exploits the best properties of both materials. Silicones, which have chains consisting of silicon and oxygen atoms instead of carbon atoms, have varied structures and many uses.

Section 10.6—Properties of polymers differ greatly from those of their monomers. A polymer's strength arises partly because the molecules entangle with one another and partly because the large molecules have strong dispersion forces. Polymers may be crystalline or amorphous. Above the glass transition temperature (T_g) a polymer is rubbery and tough; below it, the polymer is brittle. Strong synthetic fibers are made from crystalline polymers because their long molecules align neatly with one another.

Section 10.7—The durability of plastics means that they make up a large fraction of the content of landfills. Proper incineration is one way of disposing of discarded plastics, but it can produce toxic gases. Some polymers are engineered to be degradable. Recycling of plastics requires that they be collected and sorted according to the code numbers. Recycled plastics are being used more and more. Flame-retardant fabrics for clothing are made of polymers that often incorporate chlorine or bromine atoms.

The chemicals used in manufacturing plastics, especially plasticizers, can present problems. A plasticizer makes a polymer more flexible. Polychlorinated biphenyls (PCBs) were once used as plasticizers but are now banned. Phthalate esters are the most widely used plasticizers today.

Synthetic polymers will be used even more in the future. However, most synthetic polymers come from petroleum, a limited and nonrenewable resource. This is another important reason for recycling plastics.

Green chemistry Many products we use today are made of plastic. Green chemistry applies to the recycling and biodegradation of plastics and to the production of plastics from renewable resources.

Learning Objectives

❯ Define *polymer* and *monomer*.	Problems 3, 5, 7
❯ List several natural polymers including a chemically modified one.	Problems 9, 43, 55
❯ Describe the structure and properties of the two main types of polyethylene.	Problems 13, 14
❯ Use the terms *thermoplastic* and *thermosetting* to explain how polymer structure determines properties.	Problem 8
❯ Identify the monomer(s) of an addition polymer, and write the structural formula for a polymer from its monomer structure(s).	Problems 15–20 , 21, 37–39, 41–45, 52, 53
❯ Define *cross-linking*, and explain how it changes the properties of a polymer.	Problem 22
❯ Differentiate between addition and condensation polymerization.	Problems 3, 35, 36
❯ Write the structures of the monomers that form polyesters and polyamides.	Problem 46
❯ Understand the concept of the glass transition temperature.	Problems 33, 40
❯ Explain how crystallinity affects the physical properties of polymers.	Problems 13, 14, 33, 34
❯ Describe the environmental problems associated with plastics and plasticizers.	Problems 11, 12
❯ Name two types of sustainable, non-petroleum-derived polymers and give their sources.	Problems 54, 55, 57
❯ Describe plastic recycling, biodegradation, and production from renewable resources.	Problems 55–58

REVIEW QUESTIONS

1. How does the structure of PVC differ from that of polyethylene? List several uses of PVC.

2. Define the following terms.
   a. macromolecule **b.** elastomer
   c. copolymer **d.** plasticizer

3. What is addition polymerization? What structural feature usually characterizes molecules used as monomers in addition polymerization?

4. What is Teflon? What special property does it have? What are some of its uses?

5. From what monomer are disposable foamed plastic coffee cups made?

6. What plastic is used to make **(a)** gallon milk jugs and **(b)** 2-L soft drink bottles?

7. What is Bakelite? From what monomers is it made?

8. What is a thermosetting polymer? Give an example.

9. Which type of fibers, natural or synthetic, is used most in the United States? Why?

10. What are PCBs? Why are they no longer used as plasticizers?

11. What steps must be taken to recycle plastics?

12. What problems arise when plastics are **(a)** discarded into the environment, **(b)** disposed of in landfills, and **(c)** disposed of by incineration?

PROBLEMS

Polyethylene

13. Describe the structure of low-density polyethylene (LDPE). How does this structure explain the properties of this polymer?

14. Describe the structure of high-density polyethylene (HDPE). How does this structure explain the properties of this polymer?

Addition Polymerization

15. Write the structure of the monomer from which each of the following polymers is made.
   a. polyethylene
   b. polyacrylonitrile

16. Write the structure of the monomer from which each of the following polymers is made.
   a. polypropylene
   b. polytetrafluoroethylene

17. Write the structure of a chain segment that is at least eight carbon atoms long for the polymer made from each of the following.
   a. polyvinyl chloride
   b. vinylidene fluoride (H_2C=CF_2)

18. Write the structure of a chain segment that is at least four repeat units long for the polymer formed from each of the following monomers.
   a. styrene
   b. methyl methacrylate

$$\begin{array}{c} CH_3 \\ | \\ CH_2\!=\!CCOOCH_3 \end{array}$$

19. Write the structure of the polymer made from each of the following. Show at least four repeat units.
   a. 1-pentene (CH_2=$CHCH_2CH_2CH_3$)
   b. methyl cyanoacrylate

$$\begin{array}{c} C\!\equiv\!N \\ | \\ CH_2\!=\!CCOOCH_3 \end{array}$$

20. Write the structure of the polymer made from each of the following. Show at least four repeat units.
   a. vinyl acetate [H_2C=CH—$O(C$=$O)CH_3$]
   b. methyl acrylate [H_2C=CH—$(C$=$O)OCH_3$]

Rubber and Other Elastomers

21. Draw the structure of the monomer from which polybutadiene is made.

22. Describe the process of vulcanization. How does vulcanization change the properties of rubber?

23. Explain why rubber is elastic, while many other polymers are rigid.

24. How does polybutadiene differ from natural rubber in properties? In structure?

25. How is SBR made? From what monomer(s) is it made?

26. Name three synthetic elastomers and the monomer(s) from which they are made.

Condensation Polymers

27. Nylon 88 is made from the monomers $H_2N(CH_2)_8NH_2$ and $HOOC(CH_2)_6COOH$. Draw the structure of nylon 88, showing at least two repeat units from each monomer.

28. Kodel is a polyester fiber. The monomers used to make it are terephthalic acid (page 280) and 1,4-cyclohexanedi-methanol (shown below). Write a condensed structural formula for the repeat unit of Kodel molecule.

$$HOCH_2\!-\!\langle\ \rangle\!-\!CH_2OH$$

1,4-Cyclohexanedimethanol

29. Draw the structure of a polymer made from glycolic acid (hydroxyacetic acid, $HOCH_2COOH$). Show at least four repeat units. (*Hint:* Compare with nylon 6 in Section 10.5.)

30. Kevlar, a polyamide used to make bulletproof vests, is made from terephthalic acid (page 280) and *para*-phenylenediamine (shown below). Write a condensed structural formula for the repeat unit of the Kevlar molecule.

$$H_2N\!-\!\langle\bigcirc\rangle\!-\!NH_2$$

para-Phenylenediamine

Properties of Polymers

31. What three factors give polymers properties that are different from those of materials made up of small molecules?

32. What does the word *plastic* mean (a) in everyday life and (b) in chemistry?

33. What is the glass transition temperature (T_g) of a polymer? For what uses do we want polymers with a low T_g? With a high T_g?

34. How do plasticizers make polymers less brittle?

Additional Problems

35. In the following equation, identify the parts labeled a, b, and c as monomer, polymer, and repeat unit. What type of polymerization (addition or condensation) is represented?

$$n\ \overbrace{CH_2\!=\!CHF}^{a}\ \longrightarrow$$

$$\sim\!CH_2\!-\!CHF\!-\!\overbrace{CH_2\!-\!CHF}^{b}\!-\!CH_2\!-\!CHF\!-\!\underbrace{CH_2\!-\!CHF}_{c}\!\sim$$

36. Is nylon 88 (Problem 27) an addition polymer or a condensation polymer? Explain.

37. One type of Saran has the structure shown below. Write the structures of the two monomers from which it is made.

$$\sim\!CH_2CCl_2\!-\!CH_2CHCl\!-\!CH_2CCl_2\!-\!CH_2CHCl\!\sim$$

38. From what monomers could the following copolymer, called poly(styrene-co-acrylonitrile) (SAN), be made?

$$\sim CH_2CH - CH_2CH - CH_2CH \sim$$

(with $C \equiv N$, phenyl ring, $C \equiv N$ substituents)

39. Cyanoacrylates, such as those made from methyl cyanoacrylate (Problem 19b), are used in instant-setting "superglues." However, poly(methyl cyanoacrylate) can irritate tissues. Cyanoacrylates with longer alkyl ester groups are less harsh and can be used in surgery in place of sutures. A good example is poly(octyl cyanoacrylate). Write a polymerization reaction for the formation of poly(octyl cyanoacrylate) from octyl cyanoacrylate, using a condensed structural formula to show the repeat unit of the polymer.

40. Polyethylene terephthalate has a high T_g. How can its T_g be lowered so that a manufacturer can permanently crease a pair of polyethylene terephthalate slacks?

41. Isobutylene [$CH_2{=}C(CH_3)_2$] polymerizes to form polyisobutylene, a sticky polymer used as an adhesive. Draw the structure of polyisobutylene. Show at least four repeat units.

42. Copolymerization of isoprene and isobutylene (Problem 41) forms butyl rubber. Write the structure of butyl rubber. Show at least three isobutylene repeat units and one isoprene repeat unit.

43. The bacteria *Alcaligenes eutrophus* produce a polymer called polyhydroxybutyrate whose structure is shown below. Write the structure of the hydroxy acid from which this polymer is made.

$$\left[O - CH - CH_2 - C \right]_n$$
(with CH_3 and O substituents)

44. DSM Engineering Plastics makes two specialty polymers: Stanyl® nylon 46 and polytetramethylene terephthalamide (PA$_4$T). (A methylene group is CH_2; tetramethylene consists of four methylene groups: $CH_2CH_2CH_2CH_2$.) Both polymers are made using 1,4-diaminobutane as the diamine. **(a)** What diacid is used for each? Write a condensed structural formula showing the repeat unit of **(b)** Stanyl® nylon 46 and **(c)** PA$_4$T.

45. A student writes the formula for polypropylene as shown below. Identify the error(s) in the formula.

$$\left[CH_2 - CH - CH_3 \right]_n$$

46. Based on the condensed structural formula of the repeat unit of poly(ethylene naphthalate) (PEN) shown below, **(a)** write the structure(s) of the monomer(s) and **(b)** state whether the polymer is a polyester or a polyamide.

(structure of PEN repeat unit showing naphthalene ring with two ester linkages $-O-C(=O)-$ ... $-C(=O)-O-CH_2-CH_2-$)

47. A rubber ball dropped from 100 cm will bounce back up to about 60 cm. Balls made from polybutadiene, called SuperBalls, bounce back up to about 85 cm. Golf balls, made from cross-linked polybutadiene, bounce back up to 89 cm. What type of polymer are all three balls made of? Which kind of ball exhibits the property of this type of polymer to the greatest degree?

48. Draw a structure of a likely product if 1,3-propanediol ($HOCH_2CH_2CH_2OH$) is substituted for ethylene glycol in the reaction with terephthalic acid (page 280).

49. A student is asked to synthesize a polyester from terephthalic acid (page 280) and 1,4-butanediol ($HOCH_2CH_2CH_2CH_2OH$). By mistake, the student uses 1-butanol rather than 1,4-butanediol. What is the likely result of this substitution?

50. A student is asked to synthesize a polyester from terephthalic acid and 1,4-butanediol ($HOCH_2CH_2CH_2CH_2OH$). By mistake, the student uses isophthalic acid (shown below) rather than terephthalic acid (page 280). What is the likely result of this substitution?

(benzene ring with two COOH groups in meta position)

51. Draw the structure of the silicone polymer formed from the compound shown below, showing four repeating units.

$$(CH_3)_2CH - \underset{\underset{OH}{|}}{\overset{\overset{OH}{|}}{Si}} - CH_2CH_3$$

52. The two alkenes shown below are different compounds, but when each undergoes addition polymerization, the same polymer is formed. Explain.

$$CH_3 - \underset{Cl}{\overset{|}{C}}{=}\underset{Br}{\overset{|}{C}} - CH_2CH_3 \qquad CH_3 - \underset{Cl}{\overset{|}{C}}{=}\underset{CH_2CH_3}{\overset{|}{C}} - Br$$

53. The structures of epoxies contain heterocyclic rings, similar to those shown in Example 9.12. Some heterocyclic rings are polymerized by breaking one of the bonds between a carbon atom and the oxygen, nitrogen, or sulfur atom and then undergoing an addition reaction. Draw the structures of the polymers that could result from polymerization of the molecules in parts (a) and (b) of Example 9.12. Show four repeat units for each polymer.

54. Each *amino acid* shown in Table 15.3 (page 417) has an amino group ($-NH_3^+$) and a carboxylic acid group ($-COO^-$). (In each case, a proton has been donated from the carboxylic group to the amino group.) Proteins are polymers of amino acids. Draw the structure of the protein formed by polymerization of glycine, showing four repeat units.

55. Which polymer can be made from renewable resources such as corn?
  a. polystyrene (PS)
  b. polylactic acid (PLA)
  c. polyethylene terephthalate (PET)
  d. polyvinyl chloride (PVC)

56. Will a biodegradable polymer degrade in a landfill?

57. Which two polymers are most commonly recycled?
  a. polystyrene (PS) and polyvinyl chloride (PVC)
  b. low-density polyethylene (LDPE) and polypropylene (PP)
  c. polyethylene terephthalate (PET) and high-density polyethylene (HDPE)
  d. polylactic acid (PLA) and polyhydroxyalkanoate (PHA)

58. Which type of polymer can be recycled using heat?

COLLABORATIVE GROUP PROJECTS

Prepare a PowerPoint, poster, or other presentation (as directed by your instructor) to share with the class.

1. Prepare a brief report on possible sources of plastics when Earth's supplies of coal and petroleum become scarce.

2. Prepare a brief report on biobased polymers such as bioHDPE, nylon 11 (polyundecylamide), biobased PET, and biobased polytrimethylene terephthalate (PTT). Identify the natural source from which each is derived, and describe intermediate steps from source to final product.

3. Evaluate fully the competition between Pepsi and Coca-Cola as to which company is doing more to reduce its environmental impact by using biobased plastic bottles.

4. Do a risk–benefit analysis (Section 1.4) of the use of synthetic polymers for one or more of the following.
   a. grocery bags
   b. building materials
   c. clothing
   d. carpets
   e. food packaging
   f. picnic coolers
   g. automobile tires
   h. artificial hip sockets

5. To what extent is plastic litter a problem in your community? Survey one city block (or other area as directed by your instructor), and inventory the litter found. (You might as well pick it up while you are at it.) What proportion of the litter is plastics? What proportion of it is fast-food containers? To what extent are plastics recycled in your community? What factors limit further recycling?

6. Prepare a brief report on one of the following polymers. List sources and commercial uses.
   a. polybutadiene
   b. ethylene–propylene rubber
   c. polyurethanes
   d. epoxy resins

7. Do some research on Kevlar, which is used in body armor. Report on its other uses, and explain why it is so strong. Describe the Kevlar Survivors' Club, jointly sponsored by the International Chiefs of Police and DuPont.

8. Compare the treatment of the topic of the environmental impact of plastics and other polymers at several Web sites, such as those of the American Plastics Council, an industry group, and an environmental group such as Greenpeace or the Sierra Club.

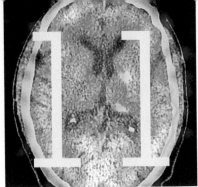

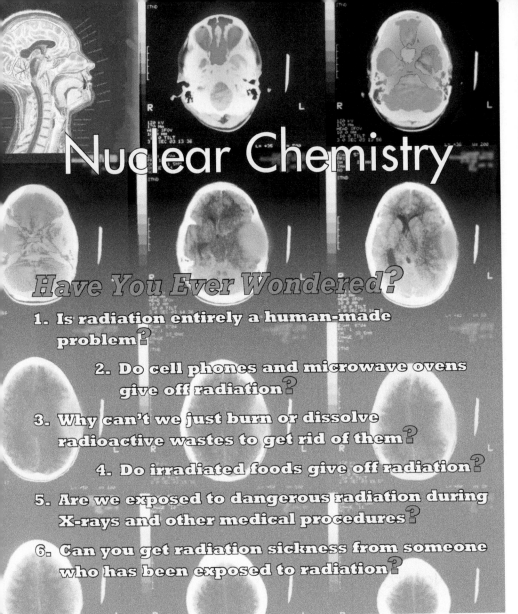

Nuclear Chemistry

Have You Ever Wondered?

1. **Is radiation entirely a human-made problem?**

2. **Do cell phones and microwave ovens give off radiation?**

3. **Why can't we just burn or dissolve radioactive wastes to get rid of them?**

4. **Do irradiated foods give off radiation?**

5. **Are we exposed to dangerous radiation during X-rays and other medical procedures?**

6. **Can you get radiation sickness from someone who has been exposed to radiation?**

Learning Objectives

> Identify the sources of the natural radiation to which we are exposed. (11.1)

> List the sources and dangers of ionizing radiation. (11.1)

> Balance nuclear equations. (11.2)

> Identify the products formed by various decay processes. (11.2)

> Solve simple half-life problems. (11.3)

> Use the concept of half-life to solve simple radioisotopic dating problems. (11.3)

> Write a nuclear equation for a transmutation, and identify the product element formed. (11.4)

> List some applications of radioisotopes. (11.5)

> Describe the nature of materials needed to block alpha, beta, and gamma radiation (11.6)

> Explain where nuclear energy comes from. (11.7)

> Describe the difference between fission and fusion. (11.7)

> Describe how uranium and plutonium bombs are made. (11.8)

> Identify the most hazardous fallout isotopes, and explain why they are particularly dangerous. (11.8)

> List some uses of nuclear energy. (11.9)

> Identify green chemistry principles that can help solve existing problems in nuclear chemistry.

> Explain how molecules used in nuclear waste processing can be designed to be safer, and give examples of such molecules.

The heart of matter

Many people associate the term *nuclear energy* with fearsome images of a mighty force: giant mushroom clouds from nuclear explosions that devastated cities, and nuclear power plant accidents at Three Mile Island, Pennsylvania, in 1979, Chernobyl, Ukraine, in 1986, and Fukushima, Japan, in 2011 (discussed in Chapter 15). But some amazing stories can also be told about life-giving applications of nuclear energy.

The discussion of atomic structure in Chapter 3 focused mainly on the electrons, because the electrons are the particles that determine an element's chemistry. In this chapter, we take a closer look at that tiny speck in the center of the atom—the atomic nucleus.

The photos show images from MRI (magnetic resonance imaging), PET (positron emission tomography), and x-rays for examining bones and internal organs. All of these diagnostic techniques use radiation or a radioactive isotope. With these techniques, we can examine tissues and diagnose diseases that were previously possible only by biopsy or exploratory surgery. The nuclear age has produced both serious problems and tremendous advantages, which will be examined in this chapter.

An atom is incomprehensibly small, but the infinitesimal size of the atomic nucleus is almost beyond our imagination. The diameter of an atom is roughly 100,000 times greater than the diameter of its nucleus. If an atom could be magnified until it was as large as your classroom, the nucleus would be about as big as the period at the end of this sentence. Yet this tiny nucleus contains almost all the atom's mass. How dense the atomic nucleus must be! A cubic centimeter of water weighs 1 g, and a cubic centimeter of gold about 19 g. A cubic centimeter of pure atomic nuclei would weigh more than 100 million metric tons!

Even more amazing than the density of the nucleus is the enormous amount of energy contained within it. Some atomic nuclei undergo reactions that can fuel the most powerful bombs ever built or provide electricity for millions of people. Our sun is one huge nuclear power plant, supplying the energy that warms our planet and the light necessary for plant growth. The twinkling light from every star we see in the night sky is produced by powerful nuclear reactions. Radioactive isotopes are used in medicine to save lives every day, through diagnosis and treatment of diseases. Many applications of nuclear chemistry in science and industry have improved the human condition significantly. Nuclear reactions allow us to date archaeological and geological finds, to assess the quality of industrial materials, and to be alerted to deadly fires. In this chapter, you will learn about the destructive and the healing power of that infinitesimally small and wonderfully dense heart of every atom—the nucleus.

11.1 Natural Radioactivity

Learning Objectives ❯ Identify the sources of the natural radiation to which we are exposed. ❯ List the sources and dangers of ionizing radiation.

Recall from Chapter 3 that most elements occur in nature in several isotopic forms, whose nuclei differ in their number of neutrons. Many of these nuclei are unstable and undergo **radioactive decay**. The nuclei that undergo such decay are called **radioisotopes**, and the process produces one or more types of radiation.

Background Radiation

Humans have always been exposed to radiation. Even as you read this sentence, you are being bombarded by *cosmic rays*, which originate from the sun and outer space. Other radiation reaches us from natural radioactive isotopes in air, water, soil, and rocks. We cannot escape radiation, because it is part of many natural processes, including those in our bodies. A naturally occurring radioactive isotope of potassium, ^{40}K, exists in all our cells and in many foods. The average person absorbs about 4000 particles of radiation each second from ^{40}K and another 1200 particles per second from ^{14}C. (This may sound like a lot, but recall how small atoms are and how many there are in even a tiny sample of matter.)

This ever-present natural radiation is called **background radiation**. Figure 11.1 shows that over three-fourths of the average radiation exposure comes from background radiation. Most of the remainder comes from medical irradiation such as X-rays. Other sources, such as fallout from testing of nuclear bombs, releases from nuclear industry power plants, and occupational exposure, account for only a minute fraction of the total average exposure.

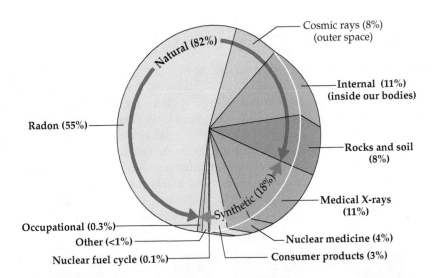

Q: *What natural source of ionizing radiation contributes most to our exposure? What source provides the largest proportion of our exposure due to human activities?*

Harmful effects arise from the interaction of radiation with living tissue. Radiation with enough energy to knock electrons from atoms and molecules, converting them into ions (electrically charged atoms or groups of atoms), is called **ionizing radiation**. Nuclear radiation and X-rays are examples. Because radiation is invisible and because it has such great potential for harm, we are very much concerned with our exposure to it. However, it is worth noting that the total amount of background radiation the average person is exposed to is less than 0.5% of the amount that can cause symptoms of radiation sickness.

Radiation Damage to Cells

Radiation-caused chemical changes in living cells can be highly disruptive. Ionizing radiation can devastate living cells by interfering with their normal chemical processes. Molecules can be splintered into reactive fragments called *free radicals* (Section 4.10), which can disrupt vital cellular processes. White blood cells, the body's first line of defense against bacterial infection, are particularly vulnerable. High levels of radiation also affect bone marrow, causing a drop in the production of red blood cells, which results in anemia. Radiation has also been shown to induce leukemia, a disease of the blood-forming organs.

Ionizing radiation also can cause changes in the molecules of heredity (DNA) in reproductive cells. Such changes can show up as mutations in the offspring of exposed parents. Little is known of the effects of such exposure on humans. However, many of the mutations that occurred during the evolution of present species may have been caused by background radiation.

Because of these potentially devastating effects on living things, knowledge of radiation, radioactive decay, and nuclear chemistry in general is crucial. Next, we will see how to write balanced nuclear equations and how to identify the various types of radiation that are emitted.

1. Is radiation entirely a human-made problem?
Figure 11.1 shows that the majority of the ionizing radiation to which we are exposed is from natural sources.

In 1993, a Ukrainian Academy of Science study group led by Vladimir Chernousenko investigated the aftereffects of the Chernobyl nuclear accident. Chernousenko claimed that 15,000 of those who helped clean up the accident site have died and that another 250,000 have become invalids. He also said that 200,000 children have experienced radiation-induced illnesses and that half of the children in Ukraine and Belarus have symptoms.

Self-Assessment Questions

1. What percentage of background radiation comes from natural sources?
   a. 5%   **b.** 18%   **c.** 45%   **d.** 82%

2. The largest artificial source of background radiation is
   a. accidents at nuclear power plants   **b.** consumer products
   c. fallout from tests of nuclear bombs   **d.** medical X-rays

3. The largest source of natural background radiation is
   a. cosmic rays   **b.** isotopes in the body
   c. radon   **d.** isotopes in rocks and soil

Answers: 1, d; 2, d; 3, c

Cell Phones and Microwaves and Power Lines, Oh My!

There are many types of radiation. *Ionizing* radiation that comes from decaying atomic nuclei is highly energetic and can damage tissue, as discussed above. *Electromagnetic* radiation has many forms—visible light, radio waves, television broadcast waves, microwaves, ultraviolet light, military ULF (ultra-low-frequency), and others. A few types of electromagnetic radiation—X-rays and gamma rays—have enough energy to ionize tissue, and ultraviolet light has been strongly implicated in *melanoma* (skin cancer). But what about microwaves and radio waves, which don't have nearly as much energy? Although very large amounts of microwaves can cause burns (by heating), there is no conclusive evidence that low levels of microwaves pose significant threat to human health. A 2006 study involving almost half a million Danish citizens failed to show a relationship between cell phone use and cancer, though some scientists consider this study inconclusive. However, higher levels of radio frequencies over long periods of time *may* be a different matter. In May 2011, the World Health Organization (WHO) classified heavy cell phone use—30 minutes of talking daily for ten years—as possible posing an increased risk of *glioma*, a type of brain cancer. The WHO's press release was very cautious, stating that "there could be some risk ... therefore we need to keep a close watch for a link between cell phones and cancer risk." For low levels of exposure to non-ionizing electromagnetic radiation, the hazard appears to be difficult to measure, let alone assess.

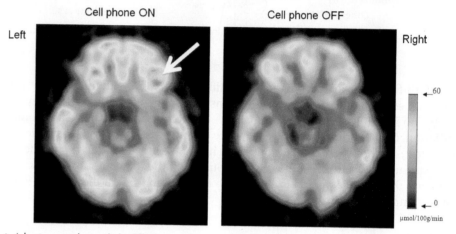

Cell phone ON   Cell phone OFF

Left   Right

60

0

μmol/100g/min

▲ A brain scan shows slight differences when a cell phone held to the ear is on (left) and off (right).

2. Do cell phones and microwave ovens give off radiation? Cell phones and microwave ovens *do* give off radiation, but it is not ionizing radiation and thus does not cause cell damage.

11.2 Nuclear Equations

Learning Objectives ❯ Balance nuclear equations. ❯ Identify the products formed by various decay processes.

Writing balanced equations for nuclear processes is relatively simple. Nuclear equations differ in two ways from the chemical equations discussed in Chapter 5. First, while chemical equations must have the same elements on both sides of the arrow, nuclear equations rarely do. Second, while we balance atoms in ordinary chemical equations, we balance the *nucleons* (protons and neutrons) in nuclear equations. What this really means is that we must balance the atomic numbers (number of protons) and nucleon numbers (number of nucleons) of the starting materials and products. For this reason, we must always specify the *isotope* of each element appearing in a nuclear equation. We use nuclear symbols (Section 3.5) when writing nuclear equations because they make the equations easier to balance.

In one example of a nuclear reaction, radon-222 atoms break down spontaneously in a process called **alpha decay**, giving off alpha (α) particles, as shown in Figure 11.2(a). Because alpha particles are identical to helium nuclei, this reaction can be summarized by the equation

Mass number of starting material = 222   Mass numbers of products = 4 + 218 = 222

$$^{222}_{86}\text{Rn} \longrightarrow {}^{4}_{2}\text{He} + {}^{218}_{84}\text{Po}$$

Atomic number of starting material = 86   Atomic numbers of products = 2 + 84 = 86

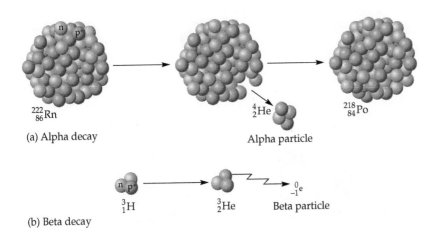

◀ **Figure 11.2** Nuclear emission of (a) an alpha particle and (b) a beta particle.

Q: *What changes occur in a nucleus when it emits an alpha particle? A beta particle?*

(a) Alpha decay

Alpha particle

(b) Beta decay

We use the symbol $_2^4\text{He}$ (rather than α) for the alpha particle because it allows us to check the balancing of mass and atomic numbers more readily. The atomic number, $Z = 84$, identifies the element produced as polonium (Po). In nuclear chemistry, the mass number, A, equates with the number of nucleons in the starting material. The number of nucleons in the starting material must equal the total number of the nucleons in the products. The same is true for the atomic numbers.

The heaviest isotope of hydrogen, hydrogen-3, often called *tritium*, decomposes by a process called **beta decay** (Figure 11.2b). Because a beta (β) particle is identical to an electron, this process can be written as

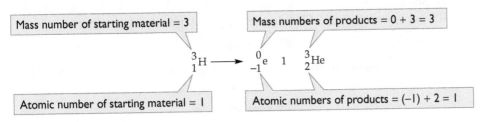

The atomic number, $Z = 2$, identifies the product isotope as helium.

Beta decay is a little more complicated than indicated by the preceding reaction. In beta decay, a neutron within the nucleus is converted into a proton (which remains in the nucleus) and an electron (which is ejected).

$$_0^1\text{n} \longrightarrow {}_1^1\text{p} + {}_{-1}^{0}\text{e}$$

With beta decay, the atomic number increases, but the number of nucleons remains the same.

A third kind of radiation may be emitted in a nuclear reaction: gamma (γ) rays. **Gamma decay** is different from alpha and beta decay in that gamma radiation has no charge and no mass. Neither the nucleon number nor the atomic number of the emitting atom is changed; the nucleus simply become less energetic. Table 11.1 compares the properties of alpha, beta, and gamma radiation. Note that the penetrating power of gamma rays is extremely high. While a few millimeters of aluminum will stop most β particles, several centimeters of lead are needed to stop γ rays.

Table 11.1	Common Types of Radiation in Nuclear Reactions				
Radiation	Mass (u)	Charge	Identity	Velocity[a]	Penetrating Power
Alpha (α)	4	2+	He^{2+}	$0.1c$	Very low
Beta (β)	0.00055	1−	e^-	$<0.9c$	Moderate
Gamma (γ)	0	0	High-energy photon	c	Extremely high

[a]c is the speed of light.

▶ **Figure 11.3** Nuclear change accompanying (a) positron emission and (b) electron capture.

Q: *What changes occur in a nucleus when it emits a positron? When it undergoes electron capture?*

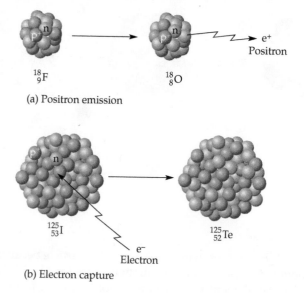

(a) Positron emission

(b) Electron capture

Two other types of radioactive decay are *positron emission* and *electron capture.* These two processes have the same effect on the atomic nucleus, but they occur by different pathways. Both result in a decrease of one in atomic number with no change in nucleon number (Figure 11.3).

The **positron** (β^+) is a particle equal in mass but opposite in charge to the electron. It is represented as $_{+1}^{0}e$. Fluorine-18 decays by positron emission.

$$_{9}^{18}\text{F} \longrightarrow \;_{+1}^{0}e + \;_{8}^{18}\text{O}$$

We can envision positron emission as the change of a proton in the nucleus into a neutron and a positron.

$$_{1}^{1}\text{p} \longrightarrow \;_{0}^{1}\text{n} + \;_{+1}^{0}e$$

After the positron is emitted, the original nucleus has one less proton and one more neutron than it had before. The nucleon number of the product nucleus is the same, but its atomic number has been reduced by one. The emitted positron quickly encounters an electron (there are many electrons in all kinds of matter), and both particles are changing into energy—in this case, two gamma rays.

$$_{+1}^{0}e + \;_{-1}^{0}e \longrightarrow 2\,_{0}^{0}\gamma$$

Electron capture (EC) is a process in which a nucleus absorbs an electron from an inner electron shell, usually the first or second. When an electron from a higher shell drops to the level vacated by the captured electron, an X-ray is released. Once inside the nucleus, the captured electron combines with a proton to form a neutron.

$$_{1}^{1}\text{p} + \;_{-1}^{0}e \longrightarrow \;_{0}^{1}\text{n}$$

Iodine-125, used in medicine to diagnose pancreatic function and intestinal fat absorption, decays by electron capture.

$$_{53}^{125}\text{I} + \;_{-1}^{0}e \longrightarrow \;_{52}^{125}\text{Te}$$

Note that, unlike alpha, beta, gamma, or positron emission, electron capture has the electron as a reactant (on the left side) and not a product. Conversion of a proton to a neutron (by the absorbed electron) yields a nucleus with the atomic number lowered by 1 but unchanged in atomic mass. Emission of a positron and absorption of an electron have the same effect on an atomic nucleus (lowering the atomic number by 1), except that positron emission is accompanied by gamma radiation and electron capture by X-radiation. Positron-emitting isotopes and those that undergo electron capture have important medical applications (Section 11.5).

The five types of radioactive decay are summarized in Table 11.2.

Table 11.2 Radioactive Decay and Nuclear Change

Type of Decay	Decay Particle	Particle Mass (u)	Particle Charge	Change in Nucleon Number	Change in Atomic Number
Alpha decay	α	4	2+	Decreases by 4	Decreases by 2
Beta decay	β	0	1−	No change	Increases by 1
Gamma radiation	γ	0	0	No change	No change
Positron emission	β^+	0	1+	No change	Decreases by 1
Electron capture (EC)	e^- absorbed	0	1−	No change	Decreases by 1

Example 11.1 Balancing Nuclear Equations

Write balanced nuclear equations for the following processes. In each case, identify the product element formed.

a. Plutonium-239 emits an alpha particle when it decays.

b. Protactinium-234 undergoes beta decay.

c. Carbon-11 emits a positron when it decays.

d. Carbon-11 undergoes electron capture.

Solution

a. We start by writing the symbol for plutonium-239 and a partial equation showing that one of the products is an alpha particle (helium nucleus).

$$^{239}_{94}\text{Pu} \longrightarrow {}^{4}_{2}\text{He} + ?$$

For this equation to balance, the other product must have $A = 239 - 4 = 235$ and $Z = 94 - 2 = 92$. The atomic number 92 identifies the element as uranium (U).

$$^{239}_{94}\text{Pu} \longrightarrow {}^{4}_{2}\text{He} + {}^{235}_{92}\text{U}$$

b. We write the symbol for protactinium-234 and a partial equation showing that one of the products is a beta particle (electron).

$$^{234}_{91}\text{Pa} \longrightarrow {}^{0}_{-1}\text{e} + ?$$

The other product must have a nucleon number of 234 and $Z = 92$ to balance the equation. The atomic number identifies this product as another isotope of uranium.

$$^{234}_{91}\text{Pa} \longrightarrow {}^{0}_{-1}\text{e} + {}^{234}_{92}\text{U}$$

c. We write the symbol for carbon-11 and a partial equation showing that one of the products is a positron.

$$^{11}_{6}\text{C} \longrightarrow {}^{0}_{+1}\text{e} + ?$$

To balance the equation, a particle with $A = 11 - 0 = 11$ and $Z = 6 - 1 = 5$ (boron) is required.

$$^{11}_{6}\text{C} \longrightarrow {}^{0}_{+1}\text{e} + {}^{11}_{5}\text{B}$$

d. We write the symbol for carbon-11 and a partial equation showing it capturing an electron.

$$^{11}_{6}\text{C} + {}^{0}_{-1}\text{e} \longrightarrow ?$$

To balance the equation, the product must have $A = 11 + 0 = 11$ and $Z = 6 + (-1) = 5$ (boron).

$$^{11}_{6}\text{C} + {}^{0}_{-1}\text{e} \longrightarrow {}^{11}_{5}\text{B}$$

As we noted previously, positron emission and electron capture result in identical changes in atomic number and, therefore, affect a given nucleus in the same way, as parts (c) and (d) illustrate for carbon-11. Also note that carbon-11 (and certain other nuclei) can undergo more than one type of radioactive decay.

▪ **EXERCISE 11.1**
Write balanced nuclear equations for the following processes. In each case, identify the product element formed.
  a. Uranium-235 decays by alpha emission.
  b. Lead-210 undergoes beta decay.
  c. Fluorine-18 decays by positron emission.
  d. Oxygen-13 undergoes electron capture.

We noted earlier that nuclear *equations* differ in two ways from ordinary chemical equations. Nuclear *reactions* also exhibit many differences from chemical reactions. Some important ones are summarized in Table 11.3. Some nuclear reactions also involve processes other than the five simple ones we have discussed here. Regardless, all nuclear equations must be balanced according to nucleon (mass) numbers and atomic numbers. When an unknown particle has an atomic number that does not correspond to an atom, that particle may be a subatomic particle. A list of nuclear symbols for subatomic particles is given in Table 11.4.

Table 11.3	Some Differences Between Chemical Reactions and Nuclear Reactions
Chemical Reactions	**Nuclear Reactions**
Atoms retain their identity.	Atoms usually change their identity—from one element to another.
Reactions involve only electrons and usually only outermost electrons.	Reactions involve mainly protons and neutrons. It does not matter what the valence electrons do.
Reaction rates can be increased by raising the temperature.	Reaction rates are unaffected by changes in temperature.
The energy absorbed or given off in reactions is comparatively small.	Reactions sometimes involve enormous changes in energy.
Mass is conserved. The mass of products equals the mass of starting materials.	Huge changes in energy are accompanied by measurable changes in mass ($E = mc^2$).

Table 11.4	Symbols for Subatomic Particles	
Particle	**Symbol**	**Nuclear Symbol**
Proton	p	^1_1p or ^1_1H
Neutron	n	^1_0n
Electron	e^- or β	$^0_{-1}e$ or $^0_{-1}\beta$
Positron	e^+ or β^+	$^0_{+1}e$ or $^0_{+1}\beta$
Alpha particle	α	^4_2He or $^4_2\alpha$
Beta particle	β or β^-	$^0_{-1}e$ or $^0_{-1}\beta$
Gamma ray	γ	$^0_0\gamma$

Self-Assessment Questions

Identify items 1–4 as one of the following.
  a. alpha particle   **b.** beta particle   **c.** nucleon number   **d.** radioactivity

  1. an electron
  2. atomic mass of 4 u
  3. emission of particles and energy from a nucleus
  4. number of protons and neutrons in an atom

5. What are the mass and the charge, respectively, of gamma radiation?
   a. 0, – 1   **b.** 0, 0   **c.** 0, +1   **d.** 4, +2
6. What particle is needed to complete the following nuclear equation?

$$^{9}_{4}Be + ? \longrightarrow {}^{12}_{6}C + {}^{1}_{0}n$$

   a. alpha particle   **b.** beta particle   **c.** neutron   **d.** proton

Answers: 1, b; 2, a; 3, d; 4, c; 5, b; 6, a

11.3 Half-Life and Radioisotopic Dating

Learning Objectives ❭ Solve simple half-life problems. ❭ Use the concept of half-life to solve simple radioisotope dating problems.

Thus far, we have discussed radioactivity as applied to single atoms. In the laboratory, we generally deal with great numbers of atoms—numbers far larger than the number of all the people on Earth. If we could see the nucleus of an individual atom, we could tell whether or not it would undergo radioactive decay by noting its composition. Certain combinations of protons and neutrons are unstable. However, we could not determine *when* the atom would undergo a change. Radioactivity is a random process, generally independent of outside influences.

Half-Life

With large numbers of atoms, the process of radioactive decay becomes more predictable. We can measure the *half-life*, a property characteristic of each radioisotope. The **half-life** of a radioactive isotope is the time it takes for one-half of the original number of atoms to undergo radioactive decay.

Suppose, for example, we had 16.00 mg of the radioactive isotope iodine-131. The half-life of iodine-131 is 8.0 days. This means that in 8.0 days, half the iodine-131, or 8.00 mg, will have decayed, and there will be 8.00 mg left. In another 8.0 days, half of the remaining 8.00 mg will have decayed. After two half-lives, or 16.0 days, then, one-quarter of the original iodine-131, or 4.00 mg, will remain. Note that two half-lives, do not make a whole. The concept of half-life is illustrated by the graph in Figure 11.4. Half-lives of radio isotopes can differ enormously. The half-life of tellurium-128 is 8×10^{24} y, while that of beryllium-13 is 2.7×10^{-21} s.

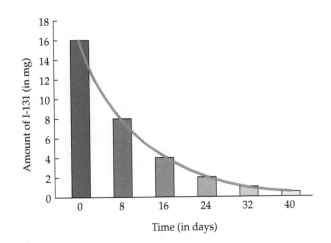

Time (in days)

◀ **Figure 11.4** The radioactive decay of iodine-131, which has a half-life of 8 days.

Q: *How much of a 32-mg sample of iodine-131 remains after five half-lives have passed?*

The rate of decay is inversely related to half-life. An isotope with a long half-life decays slowly; an isotope with a short half-life decays at a high rate. We measure the rate of decay, also referred to as the isotope's **activity**, in disintegrations per second, a unit called a **becquerel (Bq)**.

We cannot say when *all* the atoms of a radioisotope will have decayed. For most samples, we can assume that the activity is essentially gone after about ten half-lives (when the activity is $\frac{1}{2^{10}} = \frac{1}{1024}$ of the original value). That is, about a thousandth of the original activity remains.

3. Why can't we just burn or dissolve radioactive wastes to get rid of them?

The half-life of a radioisotope is a nuclear property that isn't changed by chemical reactions. For example, if we burn radioactive carbon, we get radioactive carbon dioxide as the product. Dissolving radioactive plutonium in nitric acid produces radioactive plutonium nitrate. An isotope will be radioactive for a length of time determined by its half-life—and we can't change the half-life.

We can calculate the fraction of the original isotope that remains after a given number of half-lives from the relationship

$$\text{Fraction remaining} = \frac{1}{2^n}$$

where n is the number of half-lives.

Example 11.2 Half-Lives

A 4.00-mg sample of cobalt-60, half-life 5.271 y, is to be used for radiation treatment. How much cobalt-60 remains after 15.813 years (three half-lives)?

Solution

The fraction remaining after three half-lives is

$$\frac{1}{2^n} = \frac{1}{2^3} = \frac{1}{2 \times 2 \times 2} = \frac{1}{8}$$

The amount of cobalt-60 remaining is $\frac{1}{8} \times 4.00$ mg $= 0.50$ mg.

■ EXERCISE 11.2A

The half-life of phosphorus-32 is 14.3 days. What percentage of a sample of phosphorus-32 remains after four half-lives?

■ EXERCISE 11.2B

On April 4, 2011, a small fish caught about 50 mi south of the Fukushima nuclear complex had an activity of 4000 Bq of iodine-131 per kilogram. The half-life of iodine-131 is 8.0 d. What was the activity of the isotope **(a)** on April 28, 2011 (three half-lives later)? **(b)** On June 23, 2011 (ten half-lives later)?

CONCEPTUAL Example 11.3 Time and Radioactive Decay

We cannot determine how long it will take for *all* of a radioactive isotope to decay. For many isotopes, it is assumed that the activity is near zero after about ten half-lives. What mass of a 0.0260-mg sample of mercury-190, half-life 20 min, remains after ten half-lives?

Solution

The fraction remaining after ten half-lives is found in the usual manner.

$$\frac{1}{2^n} = \frac{1}{2^{10}} = \frac{1}{2 \times 2 \times 2 \times 2 \times 2 \times 2 \times 2 \times 2 \times 2 \times 2} = \frac{1}{1024}$$

The amount of mercury-190 remaining is $\frac{1}{1024} \times 0.0260$ mg $= 0.000025$ mg.

■ EXERCISE 11.3

The disposal of some radioactive materials is scheduled according to the rule stated in Conceptual Example 11.3. Would the rule work **(a)** for a 1.00-g sample of rubidium-87 with an initial decay rate of 3200 Bq? **(b)** For a 1.00-g sample of cobalt-60, which has an initial activity of 4.1×10^{13} Bq? Explain.

Radioisotopic Dating

The half-lives of certain radioisotopes can be used to estimate the ages of rocks and archaeological artifacts. Uranium-238 decays with a half-life of 4.5 billion years. The initial products of this decay are also radioactive, and they and subsequent products continue to decay until lead-206 is formed. By measuring the relative amounts of uranium-238 and lead-206, chemists can estimate the age of a rock. Some of the older rocks on Earth have been found to be 3.0–4.5 billion years old. Moon rocks

Why Are Isotopes Stable—or Unstable?

Most isotopes are radioactive, but some are stable. What factors tend to make an atomic nucleus stable? Stable isotopes tend to have:

1. *Even* numbers of either protons or neutrons or (especially) both. Of the 264 stable isotopes, 157 have *even* numbers of both protons and neutrons, and only four have odd numbers of both protons and neutrons. Elements with even Z have more stable isotopes than do those with odd Z.

2. So-called *magic numbers* of either protons or neutrons. (Magic numbers are 2, 8, 20, 50, 82, and 126.)

3. An atomic number of 83 or less. All isotopes with Z > 83 are radioactive.

4. Fewer, or the same number of, protons as neutrons in the nucleus, and a ratio of neutrons to protons close to 1 if the atomic number is 20 or below. As atomic number gets larger, the stable n/p ratio also increases, up to about 1.5. There is a zone of stability within which the n/p ratio should lie for an atom with a given atomic number.

and meteorites have been dated at a maximum age of about 4.5 billion years. Thus, the age of Earth (and the solar system itself) is generally estimated to be about 4.5 billion years.

The dating of artifacts derived from plants or animals usually involves radioactive carbon-14. Of the carbon on Earth, about 99% is carbon-12 and 1% is carbon-13, and both of these isotopes are stable. However, in the upper atmosphere, carbon-14 is formed by the bombardment of ordinary nitrogen by neutrons from cosmic rays.

$$^{14}_{7}N + ^{1}_{0}n \longrightarrow ^{14}_{6}C + ^{1}_{1}H$$

This process results in a tiny but steady concentration of carbon-14 in the CO_2 molecules of Earth's atmosphere. Plants use CO_2, and animals consume plants and other animals; thus, living things constantly incorporate this isotope into their cells. When organisms die, the incorporation of carbon-14 ceases, and the isotope begins to decay—with a half-life of 5730 years—back to nitrogen-14. We can measure the carbon-14 activity remaining in an artifact of plant or animal origin to determine its age, using the technique called **carbon-14 dating**. For instance, a sample that has half the carbon-14 activity of new plant material is 5730 years old; it has been dead for one half-life. Similarly, an artifact with a fourth of the carbon-14 activity of new plant material is 11,460 years old; it has been dead for two half-lives.

We have assumed that the formation of the carbon-14 isotope has been constant over the years, but this is not quite the case. For the last 7000 years or so, carbon-14 dates do correlate with those obtained from the annual growth rings of trees and with documents of known age. Calibration curves have been constructed from which accurate dates can be determined. Generally, carbon-14 is reasonably accurate for dating objects from about 100 to 50,000 years old. Newer objects may not yet have seen measurable decay of carbon-14. Objects older than 50,000 years have too little of the isotope left for accurate measurement.

Charcoal from the fires of ancient peoples, dated by determining the carbon-14 activity, is used to estimate the age of other artifacts found at the same archaeological sites. For example, carbon dating was used to confirm that ancient Hebrew writing found on a stone tablet unearthed in Israel dates from the ninth century B.C.E.

Tritium, the radioactive isotope of hydrogen, can also be used for dating materials. Its half-life of 12.26 years makes it useful for dating items up to about 100 years old. An interesting application of tritium dating is the dating of brandies. These alcoholic beverages are quite expensive when aged from 10 to 50 years. Tritium dating can be used to check the veracity of advertising claims about the ages of the most expensive kinds.

Many other isotopes are useful for estimating the ages of objects and materials. Several of the more important ones are listed in Table 11.5.

The Shroud of Turin

The Shroud of Turin is a very old piece of linen cloth, about 4 m long, bearing a faint human likeness. From about C.E. 1350 onward, it had been alleged to be part of the burial shroud of Jesus. However, carbon-14 dating studies in 1988 by three different laboratories indicated that the flax used to make the cloth was not grown until sometime between C.E. 1260 and 1390; therefore, the cloth could not possibly have existed at the time of Jesus. Unlike the Dead Sea Scrolls, which were shown by carbon-14 dating to be authentic records from a civilization that existed about 2000 years ago, the Shroud of Turin has been shown to be less than 800 years old. It is generally thought to be a work of art produced around that time.

Table 11.5	Several Isotopes Used in Radioactive Dating		
Isotope	**Half-Life (years)**	**Useful Range**	**Dating Applications**
Carbon-14	5730	100 to 50,000 years	Charcoal, organic material
Hydrogen-3 (tritium)	12.26	1 to 100 years	Aged wines and brandies
Lead-210	22	1 to 75 years	Skeletal remains
Potassium-40	1.25×10^9	10,000 years to the oldest Earth samples	Rocks, Earth's crust, the moon's crust
Rhenium-187	4.3×10^{10}	4×10^7 years to the oldest samples in the universe	Meteorites
Uranium-238	4.51×10^9	10^7 years to the oldest Earth samples	Rocks, the Earth's crust

Example 11.4 Radioisotopic Dating

An old wooden implement shows carbon-14 activity that is one-eighth that of new wood. How old is the artifact? The half-life of carbon-14 is 5730 y.

Solution
Using the relationship

$$\text{Fraction remaining} = \frac{1}{2^n}$$

we see that one-eighth is $\frac{1}{2^n}$, where $n = 3$; that is, the fraction $\frac{1}{8}$ is $\frac{1}{2^3}$. The carbon-14 has gone through three half-lives. The wood is therefore about $3 \times 5730 = 17{,}190$ y old.

■ EXERCISE 11.4
Calculate the approximate age of each of the following. (a) Human remains have been preserved for centuries in the bogs of Northern Europe. How old is a bog body that has carbon-14 activity one-fourth that of living tissue? The half-life of carbon-14 is 5730 y. (b) How old is a bottle of brandy that has a tritium activity one-sixteenth that of new brandy? The half-life of tritium (hydrogen-3) is 12.26 years.

Self-Assessment Questions

1. A patient is given a 48-mg dose of technetium-99m (half-life 6.0 h) to treat a brain cancer. How much of it will remain in his body after 36 h?
   a. 0.75 mg   b. 1.5 mg   c. 3.0 mg   d. 12 mg

2. What is the half-life of silver-112 if a 10.0-g sample decays to 2.5 g in 12.4 h?
   a. 1.6 h   b. 3.1 h   c. 6.2 h   d. 12.4 h

3. Of a 64.0-g sample of strontium-90 (half-life 28.5 y) produced by a nuclear explosion, what mass in grams would remain unchanged after 285 y?
   a. 0.000 g   b. 0.000625 g   c. 0.00625 g   d. 0.0625 g

4. Lead-210 (half-life 22.26 y) can be used to date skeletal remains. About how old is a bone that has an activity of 2.0 Bq if new bone has an activity of 16 Bq?

   a. 7.4 y   **b.** 44.5 y   **c.** 67 y   **d.** 89 y

5. About how old is a piece of wood from an aboriginal burial site that has a carbon-14 (half-life 5730 y) activity of 3.9 counts/min per gram of carbon? Assume that the carbon-14 activity of the wood was 15.6 counts per minute per gram of carbon at the time of the burial.

   a. 2865 y   **b.** 11,460 y   **c.** 17,190 y   **d.** 22,920 y

Isotopic Signatures

For most chemical reactions, isotopes are unimportant. However, differences in isotopes can be quite important to some investigations. Isotopes' variance in mass affects their rates of reaction, with lighter isotopes generally moving a bit faster than heavier ones. This difference can lead to a measurable characteristic called an *isotopic signature* in an investigated material. For example, the ratio of carbon-13 to carbon-12 in materials formed by photosynthesis is less than that isotopic ratio in inorganic carbonates.

The ratio of oxygen-18 to oxygen-16 depends on the extent of evaporation that water has undergone because water molecules with oxygen-18 atoms are heavier and thus vaporize less readily than do water molecules with oxygen-16 atoms. This difference is less pronounced at higher temperatures. As oxygen is incorporated into the calcium carbonate shells of aquatic organisms, the isotopic ratio in the shells shifts. Fossilized shells thus provide a chronological record of the temperature of the water in which the organisms lived. The oxygen isotope ratio in the atmosphere varies with the season and with geographic location. This variation allows scientists to determine the location in which a material originated.

The ratio of nitrogen-14 to nitrogen-15 is different for herbivores and carnivores, because organisms higher in the food chain tend to concentrate the nitrogen-15 isotope in their tissues. Such variations enable scientists to determine much about the diet of people from ages past.

11.4 Artificial Transmutation

Learning Objective ❯ Write a nuclear equation for a transmutation, and identify the product element formed.

During the Middle Ages, alchemists tried to turn base metals, such as lead, into gold. However, they were trying to do it chemically and were therefore doomed to failure because chemical reactions involve only atoms' outer electrons. **Transmutation** (changing one element into another) requires altering the *nucleus*.

Thus far, we have considered only natural forms of radioactivity. Nuclear reactions can also be brought about by bombardment of stable nuclei with alpha particles, neutrons, or other subatomic particles. These particles, given sufficient energy, can penetrate a stable nucleus and result in some kind of radioactive emission. Just as in natural radioactive processes, one element is changed into another. Because the change would not have occurred naturally, the process is called *artificial transmutation*.

In 1919, a few years after his famous gold-foil experiment (Section 3.4), Ernest Rutherford reported on the bombardment of a variety of light elements with alpha particles. One such experiment, in which he bombarded nitrogen, resulted in the production of protons, as shown in this balanced nuclear equation.

$$^{14}_{7}\text{N} + ^{4}_{2}\text{He} \longrightarrow ^{17}_{8}\text{O} + ^{1}_{1}\text{H}$$

(The hydrogen nucleus is simply a proton, which can be represented by the symbol $^{1}_{1}\text{H}$.) This provided the first empirical verification of the existence of protons in atomic nuclei, which Rutherford had first postulated in 1914.

Recall that Eugen Goldstein had produced protons in his gas-discharge tube experiments in 1886 (Section 3-1). The significance of Rutherford's experiment lay in the fact that he obtained protons from the *nucleus* of an atom other than hydrogen, thus establishing that protons are constituents of nuclei. Rutherford's experiment was the first induced nuclear reaction and the first example of artificial transmutation. In producing protons, he also changed nitrogen into oxygen.

▲ Ernest Rutherford (1871–1937) carried out the first nuclear bombardment experiment. Element 104 was named rutherfordium (Rf) in his honor.

Example 11.5 Artificial Transmutation Equations

When potassium-39 is bombarded with neutrons, chlorine-36 is produced. What other particle is emitted?

$$^{39}_{19}\text{K} + ^{1}_{0}\text{n} \longrightarrow ^{36}_{17}\text{Cl} + ?$$

Solution

To determine the particle, we need a balanced nuclear equation. To balance the equation, the unknown particle must have $A = 4$ and $Z = 2$—it is an alpha particle.

$$^{39}_{19}\text{K} + ^{1}_{0}\text{n} \longrightarrow ^{36}_{17}\text{Cl} + ^{4}_{2}\text{He}$$

■ EXERCISE 11.5A

Technetium-97 is produced by bombarding molybdenum-96 with a deuteron (a hydrogen-2 nucleus). What other particle is emitted?

$$^{96}_{42}\text{Mo} + ^{2}_{1}\text{H} \longrightarrow ^{97}_{43}\text{Tc} + ?$$

■ EXERCISE 11.5B

A team of scientists wants to form uranium-235 by bombarding a nucleus of another element with an alpha particle. They expect a neutron to be produced along with the uranium-235 nucleus. What nucleus must be bombarded with the alpha particle?

Self-Assessment Questions

1. What isotope is formed in the following artificial transmutation?

$$^{14}_{7}\text{N} + ^{1}_{0}\text{n} \longrightarrow ^{1}_{1}\text{H} + ?$$

   a. carbon-12   **b.** carbon-14   **c.** nitrogen-15   **d.** oxygen-15

2. What isotope is formed in the following artificial transmutation?

$$^{9}_{4}\text{Be} + ^{1}_{1}\text{H} \longrightarrow ^{4}_{2}\text{He} + ?$$

   a. boron-9   **b.** boron-10   **c.** lithium-6   **d.** lithium-7

3. What isotope is formed in the following artificial transmutation?

$$^{239}_{94}\text{Pu} + ^{4}_{2}\text{He} \longrightarrow ^{1}_{0}\text{n} + ?$$

   a. americium-242   **b.** berkelium-242   **c.** curium-242   **d.** curium-243

Answers: 1, b; 2, c; 3, c

11.5 Uses of Radioisotopes

Learning Objective › List some applications of radioisotopes.

Most of the 3000 known radioisotopes are produced by artificial transmutation of stable isotopes. The value of both naturally occurring and artificial radioisotopes goes far beyond their contributions to our knowledge of chemistry.

Radioisotopes in Industry and Agriculture

Scientists in a wide variety of fields use radioisotopes as **tracers** in physical, chemical, and biological systems. Isotopes of a given element, whether radioactive or not, behave nearly identically in chemical and physical processes. Because radioactive isotopes are easily detected through their decay products, it is relatively easy to trace their movement, even through a complicated system. For example, tracing radioisotopes allows as to do the following:

■ **Detect leaks in underground pipes.** Suppose there is a leak in a pipe that is buried beneath a concrete floor. We could locate the leak by digging up extensive areas of the floor, or we could add a small amount of radioactive material to liquid poured into the drain and trace the flow of the liquid with a Geiger counter (an instrument that detects radioactivity). Once we located the leak, only a small area of the floor would have to be dug up to repair it. A compound containing a short-lived isotope (for example, $_{53}^{131}$I, half-life 8.04 days) is usually employed for this purpose.

- **Measure thickness of sheet metal during production.** Radiation from a beta emitter is allowed to pass through sheet metal on the production line. The amount of radiation that passes through a sheet is related to its thickness.
- **Determine frictional wear in piston rings.** The ring is subjected to neutron bombardment, which converts some of the carbon in the steel to carbon-14. Wear in the piston ring is assessed by the rate at which the carbon-14 appears in the engine oil.
- **Determine the uptake of phosphorus and its distribution in plants.** This can be done by incorporating phosphorus-32, a β^- emitter with a half-life of 14.3 d, into phosphate fertilizers fed to plants.

Radioisotopes are also used to study the effectiveness of weed killers, compare the nutritional value of various feeds, determine optimal methods for insect control, and monitor the fate and persistence of pesticides in soil and groundwater.

One of the most successful applications of radioisotopes in agriculture involves inducing heritable genetic alterations known as *mutations.* Exposing seeds or other parts of plants to neutrons or gamma rays increases the likelihood of genetic mutations. At first glance, this technique may not seem very promising. However, genetic variability is vital, not only to improve varieties but also to protect species from extinction. Some hybrid plants, such as seedless watermelons and bananas, are sterile. The lack of genetic variability among these plants may place the entire population at risk.

Radioisotopes are also used to irradiate foodstuffs as a method of preservation (Figure 11.5). The radiation destroys microorganisms and enzymes that cause foods to spoil. Irradiated food shows little change in taste or appearance. Some people are concerned about possible harmful effects of chemical substances produced by the radiation, but there has been no good evidence of harm to laboratory animals fed irradiated food or any known adverse effects in humans living in countries where food irradiation has been used for years. No residual radiation remains in a food after irradiation because gamma rays do not have nearly enough energy to change nuclei.

Radioisotopes in Medicine

Nuclear medicine involves two distinct uses of radioisotopes: therapeutic and diagnostic. In a therapeutic application, an attempt is made to treat or cure disease with radiation. The diagnostic use of radioisotopes is aimed at obtaining information about the state of a patient's health.

▲ Scientists can trace the uptake of phosphorus by a green plant by adding a compound containing some phosphorus-32 to the applied fertilizer. When the plant is later placed on photographic film, radiation from the phosphorus isotopes exposes the film, much as light does. This type of exposure, called a *radiograph,* shows the distribution of phosphorus in the plant.

4. Do irradiated foods give off radiation? Irradiated foods have absorbed energy in the form of gamma rays. But the foods are *not* radioactive.

◀ **Figure 11.5** Exposure to gamma radiation delays the decay of strawberries. Those on the right were irradiated; the ones on the left were not.

Q: *Are the strawberries on the right radioactive?*

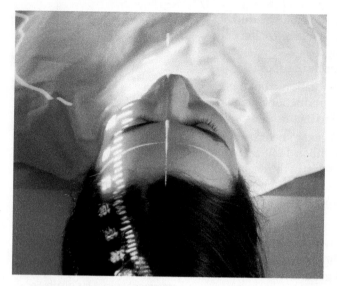

▲ It DOES Matter!

The difference between a radioactive isotope and the alpha, beta, gamma, or positron radiation that it produces is very important and often misunderstood. A radioisotope such as iodine-131 or radon-222, when absorbed by the human body, can cause great harm because the radiation continues to be released as the isotope decays. However, matter exposed to ionizing radiation simply absorbs that energy, causing a chemical change. A patient undergoing gamma-radiation treatment does *not* become radioactive.

5. Are we exposed to dangerous radiation during X-rays and other medical procedures? A number of medical procedures do use ionizing radiation or radioisotopes, but the amount of radiation is kept to a minimum. The hazard of the ionizing radiation is ordinarily much less than the risk due to a lack of diagnosis or treatment!

Table 11.6 lists some radioisotopes in common use in medicine. The list is necessarily incomplete, but it should give you an idea of their importance. The claim that nuclear medicine has saved many more lives than nuclear bombs have taken is not an idle one.

Cancer is not one disease but many. Some forms are particularly susceptible to radiation therapy. The aim of **radiation therapy** is to destroy cancerous cells before too much damage is done to healthy tissue. Radiation is most lethal to rapidly reproducing cells, and rapid reproduction is the characteristic of cancer cells that allows radiation therapy to be successful. Radiation is carefully aimed at cancerous tissue while minimizing the exposure of normal cells. If the cancer cells are killed by the destructive effects of the radiation, the malignancy is halted.

Patients undergoing radiation therapy often get sick from the treatment. Nausea and vomiting are the usual early symptoms of radiation sickness. Radiation therapy can also interfere with the replenishment of white blood cells and thus increase patients' susceptibility to infection.

Radioisotopes used for diagnostic purposes provide information about the functioning of some part of the body or about the type or extent of an illness. For example, radioactive iodine-131 is used to determine the size, shape, and activity of the thyroid gland, as well as to treat cancers in this gland and to control its hyperactivity. Small doses are used for diagnostic purposes, and large doses for treatment of thyroid cancer. After the patient drinks a solution of potassium iodide incorporating iodine-131, the iodide ions become concentrated in the thyroid. A detector showing the differential uptake of the isotope is used in diagnosis. The resulting

Table 11.6 Some Radioisotopes and Their Medical Applications

Isotope	Name	Half-Life[a]	Use
^{11}C	Carbon-11	20.39 min	Brain scans
^{51}Cr	Chromium-51	27.8 d	Blood volume determination
^{57}Co	Cobalt-57	270 d	Measuring vitamin B_{12} uptake
^{60}Co	Cobalt-60	5.271 y	Radiation cancer therapy
^{153}Gd	Gadolinium-153	242 d	Determining bone density
^{67}Ga	Gallium-67	78.1 h	Scan for lung tumors
^{131}I	Iodine-131	8.040 d	Thyroid diagnoses and therapy
^{192}Ir	Iridium-192	74 d	Breast cancer therapy
^{59}Fe	Iron-59	44.496 d	Detection of anemia
^{32}P	Phosphorus-32	14.3 d	Detection of skin cancer or eye tumors
^{238}Pu	Plutonium-238	86 y	Provision of power in pacemakers
^{226}Ra	Radium-226	1600 y	Radiation therapy for cancer
^{75}Se	Selenium-75	120 d	Pancreas scans
^{24}Na	Sodium-24	14.659 h	Locating obstructions in blood flow
^{99m}Tc	Technetium-99m	6.0 h	Imaging of brain, liver, bone marrow, kidney, lung, or heart
^{201}Tl	Thallium-201	73 h	Detecting heart problems during treadmill stress test
^{3}H	Tritium	12.26 y	Determining total body water
^{133}Xe	Xenon-133	5.27 d	Lung imaging

[a] Abbreviations: y, years; d, days; h, hours; min, minutes.

photoscan can pinpoint the location of tumors or other abnormalities in the thyroid. In cancer treatment, radiation from therapeutic (large) doses of iodine-131 kills the thyroid cells in which the radioisotope has concentrated.

The radioisotope gadolinium-153 is used to determine bone mineralization. Its widespread use is an indication of the large number of people, mostly women, who suffer from osteoporosis (reduction in the quantity of bone) as they grow older. Gadolinium-153 gives off two types of radiation: gamma rays and X-rays. A scanning device compares these types of radiation after they pass through bone. Bone density is then determined from the difference in absorption of the rays.

Technetium-99m is used in a variety of diagnostic tests (Figure 11.6). The *m* stands for *metastable*, which means that this isotope gives up some energy when it changes to a more stable version of technetium-99 (which has the same atomic number and same atomic mass). The energy it gives up is in the form of a gamma ray.

(a)

(b)

◀ **Figure 11.6** Gamma-ray imaging using technetium-99m. Directional slices through (a) a healthy human heart and (b) a diseased heart. The lighter regions of the images indicate regions receiving adequate blood flow.

$$^{99m}_{43}Tc \longrightarrow {}^{99}_{43}Tc + \gamma$$

Note that the decay of technetium-99m produces no alpha or beta particles that could cause unnecessary damage to the body. Technetium-99m also has a short half-life (6.0 h), which means that the radioactivity does not linger very long in the body after the scan has been completed. With so short a half-life, use of the isotope must be carefully planned. In fact, technetium-99m is not what is purchased by medical labs. Technetium-99m is formed by the decay of molybdenum-99.

$$^{99}_{42}Mo \longrightarrow {}^{99m}_{43}Tc + {}^{0}_{-1}e + \gamma$$

A container of this molybdenum isotope is obtained, and the decay product, technetium-99m, is "milked" from the container as needed.

Using modern computer technology, *positron emission tomography (PET)* can measure dynamic processes occurring in the body, such as blood flow or the rate at which oxygen or glucose is being metabolized. For example, PET scans have shown that the brain of a schizophrenic metabolizes only about one-fifth as much glucose as a normal brain. These scans can also reveal metabolic changes that occur in the brain during tactile learning (learning by the sense of touch). PET scans can also pinpoint the area of brain damage that triggers severe epileptic seizures.

Compounds incorporating a positron-emitting isotope, such as carbon-11 or oxygen-15, are inhaled or injected before the scan. Before the emitted positron can travel very far in the body, it encounters an electron (numerous in any ordinary matter), and two gamma rays are produced, exiting from the body in exactly opposite directions.

$$^{11}_{6}C \longrightarrow {}^{11}_{5}B + {}^{0}_{+1}e$$

$$^{0}_{+1}e + {}^{0}_{-1}e \longrightarrow 2\gamma$$

▶ **Figure 11.7** Modern computer technology used for medical diagnosis. (a) Patient undergoing positron emission tomography (PET), a technique that uses radioisotopes to scan internal organs. (b) Images created by PET scanning, showing parts of the brain involved in different functions.

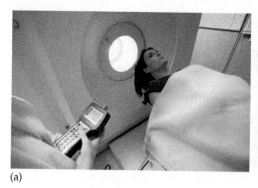
(a)

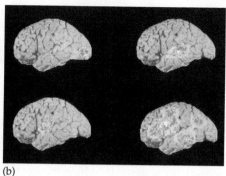
(b)

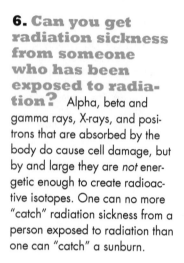

6. Can you get radiation sickness from someone who has been exposed to radiation? Alpha, beta and gamma rays, X-rays, and positrons that are absorbed by the body do cause cell damage, but by and large they are *not* energetic enough to create radioactive isotopes. One can no more "catch" radiation sickness from a person exposed to radiation than one can "catch" a sunburn.

Detectors, positioned on opposite sides of the patient, record the gamma rays. An image of an area in the body is formed using computerized calculations of the points at which annihilation of positrons and electrons occurs (Figure 11.7).

Example 11.6 Positron Emission Equations

One of the isotopes used to perform PET scans is oxygen-15, a positron emitter. What other isotope is formed when oxygen-15 decays?

Solution
First, we write the nuclear equation

$$^{15}_{8}O \longrightarrow {}^{0}_{+1}e + ?$$

The nucleon number, A, does not change, but the atomic number, Z, does: $8 - 1 = 7$. The product isotope is nitrogen-15.

$$^{15}_{8}O \longrightarrow {}^{0}_{+1}e + {}^{15}_{7}N$$

■ EXERCISE 11.6
Phosphorus-30 is a positron-emitting radioisotope suitable for doing PET scans. What other isotope is formed when phosphorus-30 decays?

Self-Assessment Questions

1. Iodine-131 is sometimes used for detecting leaks in underground pipes because
   a. it has a short half-life
   b. it is highly penetrating
   c. it is nontoxic
   d. its radiation is harmless

2. What is used to irradiate foodstuffs to extend shelf life?
   a. alpha particles   **b.** beta particles
   c. gamma rays   **d.** microwaves

For items 3–7, match each radioisotope with a major use.
3. cobalt-60   (a) bone density
4. gadolinium-153   (b) brain images
5. iodine-131   (c) heart problems
6. technetium-99m   (d) radiation therapy
7. thallium-201   (e) thyroid disorders
8. What form of radiation is detected in PET scans?
   a. beta   **b.** gamma   **c.** positron   **d.** X-rays

Answers: 1, a; 2, c; 3, d; 4, a; 5, e; 6, b; 7, c; 8, c

11.6 Penetrating Power of Radiation

Learning Objective ❯ Describe the nature of materials needed to block alpha, beta, and gamma radiation.

The danger of radiation to living organisms comes from its potential for damaging cells and tissues. The ability to inflict injury relates to the penetrating power of the radiation. The two aspects of nuclear medicine just discussed (therapeutic and diagnostic) are also dependent on the penetrating power of various types of radiation.

All other things being equal, the more massive the particle, the less its penetrating power. *Alpha particles*, which are helium nuclei with a mass of 4 u, are the least penetrating of the three main types of radiation. *Beta particles*, which are identical to the almost massless electrons, are somewhat more penetrating. *Gamma rays*, like X-rays, have no mass; they are considerably more penetrating than the other two types.

But all other things are not always equal. The faster a particle moves or the more energetic the radiation is, the more penetrating power it has.

It may seem contrary to common sense that the biggest particles make the least headway. But keep in mind that penetrating power reflects the ability of radiation to make its way through a sample of matter. It is as if you were trying to roll some rocks through a field of boulders. The alpha particle acts as if it were a boulder itself. Because of its size, it cannot get very far before it bumps into and is stopped by other boulders. The beta particle acts as if it were a small stone. It can sneak between and perhaps ricochet off boulders until it makes its way farther into the field. The gamma ray can be compared with a grain of sand that can get through the smallest openings.

The danger of a specific type of radiation to human tissue depends on the location of the radiation's source as well as on its penetrating power. If the radioactive substance is outside the body, alpha particles are the least dangerous; they have low penetrating power and are stopped by the outer layer of skin. Beta particles are also usually stopped before they reach vital organs. Gamma rays readily pass through tissues, and so an external gamma source can be quite dangerous. People working with radioactive materials can protect themselves through one or both of the following actions:

- Move away from the source. The intensity of radiation decreases with distance from the source.
- Use shielding. A sheet of paper can stop most alpha particles, and a block of wood or a thin sheet of aluminum can stop most beta particles, but it takes a meter of concrete or several centimeters of lead to stop most gamma rays (Figure 11.8).

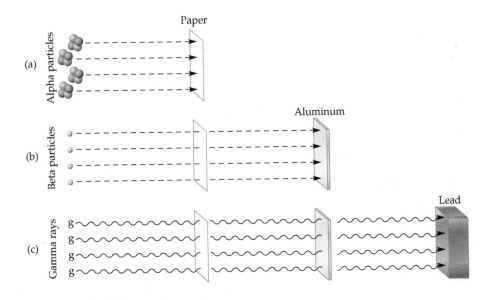

◀ **Figure 11.8** The relative penetrating power of alpha, beta, and gamma radiation. Alpha particles are stopped by a sheet of paper (a). Beta particles will not penetrate a sheet of aluminum (b). It takes several centimeters of lead to block gamma rays (c).

When the radioactive source is *inside* the body, as in the case of many medical applications, the situation is reversed. The nonpenetrating alpha particles can do great damage. All such particles are trapped within the body, which must then absorb all the energy the particles release. Alpha particles inflict all their damage in a tiny area because they do not travel far. Therefore, getting an alpha-emitting therapeutic radioisotope close to the targeted cells is vital.

Beta particles distribute their damage over a somewhat larger area because they travel farther. Tissue may recover from limited damage spread over a large area; it is less likely to survive concentrated damage.

Many diagnostic applications rely on the highly penetrating power of gamma rays. In most cases, the radiation created inside the body must be detected by instruments outside the body, so a minimum of absorption is desirable.

CONCEPTUAL Example 11.7 | Radiation Hazard

Most modern smoke detectors contain a tiny amount of americium-241, a solid element that is an alpha emitter. The americium is in a chamber that includes thin aluminum shielding, and the device is usually mounted on a ceiling. Rate the radiation hazard of this device in normal use as (a) high, (b) moderate, or (c) very low. Explain your choice.

Solution

Alpha particles have very little penetrating ability—they are stopped by a sheet of paper or a layer of skin. The emitted alpha particles cannot exit the detector's chamber, because even thin metal is more than sufficient to absorb them. Even if alpha particles could escape, they would likely be stopped by the air after a short distance or by the dead cells of your skin. Therefore, the radiation hazard is rated (c)—very low.

▪ EXERCISE 11.7

Radon-222 is a gas that can diffuse from the ground into homes. Like americium-241, it is an alpha emitter. Is the radiation hazard from radon-222 likely to be higher or lower than that from a smoke detector? Explain.

Self-Assessment Questions

1. Which of the following pairs represent the *most* and *least* (most/least) penetrating types of radiation?
   a. alpha/gamma
   b. beta/gamma
   c. gamma/alpha
   d. X-rays/beta

2. Which form of radiation could not readily penetrate a sheet of paper?
   a. alpha
   b. beta
   c. gamma
   d. all of these

3. A Geiger counter registered 50 Bq of activity from an unknown type of radiation. A piece of paper inserted between the source and the counter caused the reading to drop to about 2 Bq. The radiation was mostly
   a. alpha particles
   b. beta particles
   c. gamma rays
   d. X-rays

11.7 Energy from the Nucleus

Learning Objectives ❯ Explain where nuclear energy comes from. ❯ Describe the difference between fission and fusion.

We have seen that radioactivity—quiet and invisible—can be beneficial or danger-ous. A much more dramatic—and equally paradoxical—aspect of nuclear chemis-try is the release of nuclear energy by either *fission* (splitting of heavy nuclei into smaller nuclei) or *fusion* (combining of light nuclei to form heavier ones).

Einstein and the Equivalence of Mass and Energy

The potential power in the nucleus was established by Albert Einstein, a famous and most unusual scientist. Whereas most scientists work with glassware and instru-ments in laboratories, Einstein worked with a pencil and a notepad. By 1905, at the age of 26, he had already worked out his special theory of relativity and developed his famous **mass–energy equation**, in which mass (m) is multiplied by the square of the speed of light (c).

$$E = mc^2$$

The equation suggests that mass and energy are equivalent—just two different aspects of the same thing—and that a little bit of mass can yield enormous energy. The atomic bombs that destroyed Hiroshima and Nagasaki (Section 11.8) in World War II converted less than an ounce of matter into energy.

A chemical reaction that gives off heat must lose mass in the process, but the change in mass is far too small to measure. Reaction energy must be enormous—at the level of the energy given off by nuclear explosions—for the mass loss to be measurable. (If every atom in a 1-kg lump of coal became energy, it could produce 25 billion kWh of electricity—enough to keep a 100-W lightbulb going for 29 million years. Burning 1 kg of coal in a conventional power plant produces only enough energy to keep the bulb shining for 67 hours.)

Binding Energy

Nuclear fission releases the tremendous amounts of energy produced by atomic bombs and in nuclear power plants. Where does all this energy come from? It is locked inside the atomic nucleus. When protons and neutrons combine to form atomic nuclei, a small amount of mass is converted to energy. This is the **binding energy** that holds the nucleons together in the nucleus. For example, the helium nucleus contains two protons and two neutrons. The masses of these four par-ticles add up to $2 \times 1.0073\,u + 2 \times 1.0087\,u = 4.0320\,u$ (Figure 11.9). However, the actual mass of the helium nucleus is only $4.0015\,u$, and the missing mass—called the *mass defect*—amounts to $0.0305\,u$. Using Einstein's equation $E = mc^2$, we can calculate (see Problem 55) a value of 28.3 million electron volts (28 MeV; $1\,\text{MeV} = 1.6022 \times 10^{-13}\,J$) for the binding energy of the helium nucleus. This is the amount of energy it would take to separate one helium nucleus into two protons and two neutrons.

When the binding energy per nucleon is calculated for all the elements and plotted against nucleon number, a graph such as that in Figure 11.10 is obtained. The elements with the highest binding energies per nucleon have the most stable nuclei. They include iron and elements with nucleon members close to that of iron. When uranium atoms undergo nuclear fission, they split into atoms with higher binding energies. In other words, the fission reaction converts large atoms into smaller ones with greater nuclear stability.

We can also see from Figure 11.10 that even more energy can be obtained by combining small atoms, such as hydrogen or deuterium, to form larger atoms with more stable nuclei. This kind of reaction is called **nuclear fusion**. It is what happens when a hydrogen bomb explodes, and it is also the source of the sun's energy.

▲ Albert Einstein (1879–1955). Element 99 was named einsteinium (Es) in his honor.

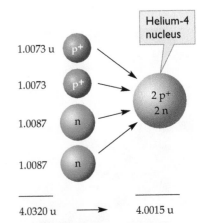

▲ **Figure 11.9** Nuclear bind-ing energy in $^4_2$He. The mass of a helium-4 nucleus is $4.0015\,u$, which is $0.0305\,u$ less than the masses of two protons and two neutrons. The missing mass is equivalent to the binding energy of the helium-4 nucleus.

▶ **Figure 11.10** Nuclear stability is greatest for iron and elements near iron in the periodic table. Fission of very large nuclei or fusion of very small ones results in greater nuclear stability.

Q: *Which process, fission of uranium nuclei or fusion of hydrogen nuclei, releases more energy?*

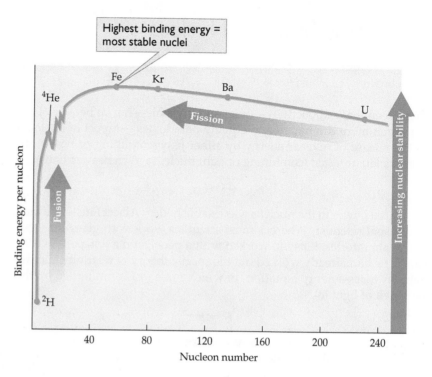

▲ Enrico Fermi (1901–1954). Element 100 was named fermium (Fm) in his honor.

▲ Lise Meitner (1878–1968). Element 109 was named meitnerium (Mt) in her honor.

Nuclear Fission

In 1934, the Italian scientists Enrico Fermi and Emilio Segrè (1905–1989) bombarded uranium atoms with neutrons. They were trying to make elements with higher atomic numbers than uranium, which then had the highest known atomic number. To their surprise, they found four radioactive species among the products. One was presumably element 93, formed by the initial conversion of uranium-238 to uranium-239, which then underwent beta decay.

$$^{238}_{92}U + ^{1}_{0}n \longrightarrow ^{239}_{92}U$$

$$^{239}_{92}U \longrightarrow ^{239}_{93}Np + ^{0}_{-1}e$$

They were unable to explain the remaining radioactivity.

When repeating the Fermi–Segrè experiment in 1938, German chemists Otto Hahn (1879–1968) and Fritz Strassman (1902–1980) were perplexed to find isotopes of barium among the many reaction products. Hahn wrote to Lise Meitner, his former longtime colleague, to ask what she thought about these strange results.

Lise Meitner was an Austrian physicist who had worked with Hahn in Berlin. Because she was Jewish, she fled to Sweden when the Nazis took over Austria in 1938. On hearing about Hahn's work, she noted that barium atoms were only about half the size of uranium atoms. Was it possible that the uranium nuclei might be splitting into fragments? She made some calculations that convinced her that the uranium nuclei had indeed been split apart. Her nephew, Otto Frisch (1904–1979), was visiting for the winter holidays, and they discussed this discovery with great excitement. It was Frisch who later coined the term **nuclear fission** (Figure 11.11).

Frisch was working with Niels Bohr at the University of Copenhagen, and when he returned to Denmark, he took the news of the fission reaction to Bohr, who happened to be going to the United States to attend a physics conference. The discussions in the corridors about this new reaction would be the most important talks to take place at that meeting.

Meanwhile, Enrico Fermi had just received the 1938 Nobel Prize in physics. Because Fermi's wife, Laura, was Jewish, and the fascist Italian dictator Mussolini was an ally of Hitler, Fermi accepted the award in Stockholm and then immediately fled with Laura and their children to the United States. Thus, by 1939, the United States had received news about the German discovery of nuclear fission and had also acquired from Italy one of the world's foremost nuclear scientists.

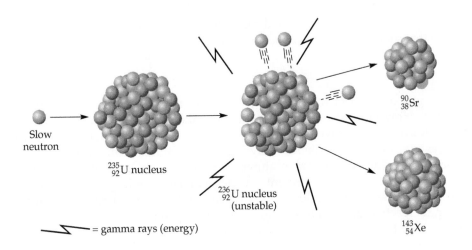

Q: *If each of the neutrons emitted by the ^{236}U nucleus caused another ^{235}U nucleus to split in the way shown here, how many more neutrons would be released?*

Nuclear Chain Reaction

Leo Szilard (1898–1964) was one of the first scientists to realize that nuclear fission could occur as a chain reaction. Szilard had been born in Hungary and educated in Germany, but he came to the United States in 1937 as one of the many Jewish refugees. He saw that neutrons released in the fission of one atom could trigger the fission of other uranium atoms, thus setting off a **chain reaction** (Figure 11.12). Because massive amounts of energy could be obtained from the fission of uranium, he saw that the chain reaction might be used in a bomb with tremendous explosive force.

Aware of the destructive forces that could be produced and concerned that Germany might develop such a bomb, Szilard prevailed on Einstein to sign a letter to

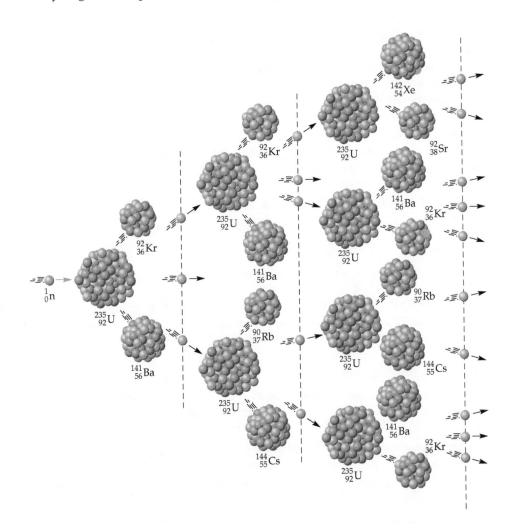

◀ **Figure 11.12** Schematic representation of a nuclear chain reaction. Neutrons released in the fission of one uranium-235 nucleus can strike other uranium-235 nuclei, causing them to split and release more neutrons as well as a variety of other nuclei. For simplicity, some fission fragments are not shown.

President Franklin D. Roosevelt indicating the importance of the discovery. It was critical that the U.S. government act quickly.

Thermonuclear Reactions

The chapter opening mentioned that the sun is a nuclear power plant vital to life on Earth. However, the nuclear reactions that take place in the sun are somewhat different from the ones we have discussed throughout this chapter. These **thermonuclear reactions** require enormously high temperatures (millions of degrees) to initiate them. The intense temperatures and pressures in the sun cause nuclei to fuse and release enormous amounts of energy. Instead of large nuclei being split into smaller fragments (fission), small nuclei are fused into larger ones (fusion). The main reaction in the sun is thought to be the fusion of four hydrogen nuclei to produce one helium nucleus and two positrons.

$$4\,^1_1H \longrightarrow\ ^4_2He + 2\,^0_{+1}e$$

Fusion of 1 g of hydrogen releases an amount of energy equivalent to the burning of nearly 20 tons of coal. Every second, the sun fuses 600 tons of hydrogen, producing millions of times more energy than has been produced on Earth in the entire history of humankind. Much current research is aimed at reproducing such a reaction in the laboratory, by using ultrapowerful magnets to contain the intense heat required for ignition. Fusion technology is discussed further in Chapter 14. To date, however, fusion reactions on Earth have been limited to the uncontrolled reactions in explosion tests of hydrogen (thermonuclear) bombs and to small amounts of energy produced by very expensive experimental fusion reactors.

Self-Assessment Questions

Look at the graph in Figure 11.10 to answer questions 1–3.

1. Helium has a particularly high binding energy per nucleon, which means that it
   a. is especially unstable compared to H and Li
   b. is more stable than H and Li
   c. will readily fuse into larger nuclei
   d. will readily split into hydrogen-2 atoms

2. The most stable nuclei are those of
   a. Ba   b. He   c. Fe   d. U

3. Nuclei with nuclear numbers greater than that of iron are
   a. all radioactive   b. increasingly stable
   c. less stable than iron   d. easily split into smaller nuclei

4. Which equation explains why the products of fission have less mass than the original substances?
   a. $E = h\nu/\lambda$ b. $E = h\nu$ c. $E = mc^2$ d. $PV = nRT$

5. Which subatomic particles are responsible for carrying on the chain reactions characteristic of nuclear fission?
   a. alpha particles   b. beta particles   c. neutrons   d. protons

6. When uranium-235 absorbs a neutron and undergoes fission, barium-142 and krypton-91 are two possible fission fragments. How many neutrons are released?
   $$^{235}_{92}U + ^1_0n \longrightarrow\ ^{142}_{56}Ba + ^{91}_{36}Kr + ?\ ^1_0n$$
   a. 0   b. 1   c. 2   d. 3

7. What process is represented by the equation $^2_1H + ^2_1H \longrightarrow\ ^4_2He$ + energy?
   a. alpha decay   b. artificial transmutation
   c. fission   d. fusion

8. Hydrogen-2 and hydrogen-3 fuse to form helium-4. The other product is a(n)
   a. electron   b. neutron   c. positron   d. proton

Answers: 1, b; 2, c; 3, c; 4, c; 5, c; 6, c; 7, d; 8, b

11.8 Nuclear Bombs

Learning Objectives ❯ Describe how uranium and plutonium bombs are made.
❯ Identify the most hazardous fallout isotopes, and explain why they are particularly dangerous.

In 1939, President Roosevelt launched a highly secret research project for the study of atomic energy. Called the *Manhattan Project*, it eventually became a massive research effort involving more scientific brainpower than ever was or has been devoted to a single project. Amazingly, it was conducted under such extreme secrecy that even Vice President Harry Truman did not know of its existence until after Roosevelt's death.

The Manhattan Project included four separate research teams trying to learn how to

- sustain the nuclear-fission chain reaction,
- enrich uranium so that it contained about 90% of the fissionable isotope ^{235}U,
- make plutonium-239 (another fissionable isotope), and
- construct a bomb based on nuclear fission.

Sustainable Chain Reaction

By that time, it had been established that neutron bombardment could initiate the fission reaction, but many attributes of this reaction were unknown. Enrico Fermi and his group, working in a lab under the bleachers at Stagg Field on the campus of the University of Chicago, worked on the fission reaction itself and how to sustain it. They found that the neutrons used to trigger the reaction had to be slowed down to increase the probability that they would hit a uranium nucleus. Because graphite slows down neutrons, a large "pile" of graphite was built to house the reaction. Then the amount of uranium "fuel" was gradually increased. The major goal was to determine the **critical mass**—the amount of uranium-235 needed to sustain the fission reaction. There had to be enough fissionable nuclei in the "fuel" for the neutrons released in one fission process to have a good chance of being captured by another fissionable nucleus before escaping from the pile.

On December 2, 1942, Fermi and his group achieved the first sustained nuclear fission reaction. The critical mass of uranium (enriched to about 94% ^{235}U) for this reactor turned out to be about 16 kg.

Isotopic Enrichment

Natural uranium is 99.27% uranium-238, which does not undergo fission. Uranium-235, the fissionable isotope, makes up only 0.72% of natural uranium. Because making a bomb required *enriching* the uranium to about 90% uranium-235, it was necessary to find a way to separate the uranium isotopes. This was the job of the Manhattan Project research team in Oak Ridge, Tennessee.

Chemical separation was almost impossible; ^{235}U and ^{238}U are chemically almost identical. The separation method eventually used involved converting uranium to gaseous uranium hexafluoride, UF_6. Molecules of UF_6 containing uranium-235 are slightly lighter and therefore move slightly faster than molecules containing uranium-238. Uranium hexafluoride was allowed to pass through a series of thousands of pinholes, and the molecules containing uranium-235 gradually outdistanced the others. Enough enriched uranium-235 was finally obtained to make a small explosive device.

Synthesis of Plutonium

While the tedious work of separating uranium isotopes was underway at Oak Ridge, another research team, led by Glenn T. Seaborg, approached the problem of obtaining fissionable material by another route. Although uranium-238 would

▲ Glenn T. Seaborg (1912–1999). Element 106 was named seaborgium (Sg) in his honor. Seaborg is the only person to have had an element named for him while still alive. He is shown here pointing to his namesake element on the periodic table of elements.

not fission when bombarded by neutrons, it was found that this more common isotope of uranium *would* decay to form a new element, named neptunium (Np). This product quickly decayed to another new element, plutonium (Pu).

$$^{238}_{92}U + ^{1}_{0}n \longrightarrow ^{239}_{92}U$$

$$^{239}_{92}U \longrightarrow ^{0}_{-1}e + ^{239}_{93}Np$$

$$^{239}_{93}Np \longrightarrow ^{239}_{94}Pu + ^{0}_{-1}e$$

Plutonium-239 was found to be fissionable and thus was suitable material for the making of a bomb. A group of large reactors was built near Hanford, Washington, to produce plutonium.

Bomb Construction

The actual building of the nuclear bombs was carried out at Los Alamos, New Mexico, under the direction of J. Robert Oppenheimer (1904–1967). In a top-secret laboratory at a remote site, a group of scientists planned and then constructed what would become known as atomic bombs. Two different models were developed, one based on ^{235}U and the other on ^{239}Pu.

The critical mass of uranium-235 could not be exceeded prematurely, so it was important that no single piece of fissionable material in the bomb be that large. The bomb was designed to contain pieces of uranium of subcritical mass, plus a neutron source to initiate the fission reaction. Then, at the chosen time, all the pieces would be forced together using an ordinary high explosive, thus triggering a runaway nuclear chain reaction.

The synthesis of plutonium turned out to be easier than the isotopic separation, and by July 1945, enough fissionable material had been made for three bombs to be assembled—two using plutonium, and one using uranium. The first atomic bomb (one of the plutonium devices) was tested in the desert near Alamogordo, New Mexico, on July 16, 1945. The heat from the explosion vaporized the 30-m steel tower on which the bomb was placed and melted the sand for several hectares around the site. The light produced was the brightest anyone had ever seen.

Some of the scientists were so awed by the force of the blast that they argued against using the bombs on Japan. A few, led by Leo Szilard, suggested a demonstration of the bombs' power at an uninhabited site. But fear of a well-publicized "dud" and the desire to avoid millions of casualties in an invasion of Japan led President Harry Truman to order the dropping of the bombs on Japanese cities. The lone uranium bomb, called "Little Boy" (Figure 11.13), was dropped on Hiroshima on August 6, 1945, and caused over 100,000 casualties. Three days later, the other plutonium bomb, called "Fat Man," was dropped on Nagasaki with comparable results (Figure 11.14). World War II ended with the surrender of Japan on August 14, 1945.

Radioactive Fallout

When a nuclear explosion occurs in the open atmosphere, radioactive materials can rain down on parts of Earth thousands of miles away, days and weeks later in what is called **radioactive fallout**. The uranium atom can split in several different ways.

▶ **Figure 11.13** An internal schematic of the atomic bomb "Little Boy" dropped on Hiroshima. Each of the cylinders of uranium-235 had less than the critical mass. The high explosive shot the cylindrical "bullet" down the gun barrel and onto the target spike. The result was about two critical masses of uranium-235, and a nuclear explosion occurred about a millisecond later.

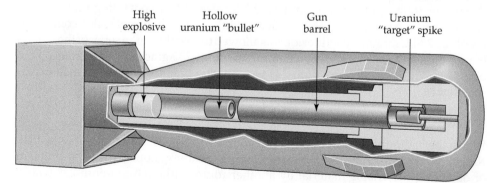

High explosive   Hollow uranium "bullet"   Gun barrel   Uranium "target" spike

$$^{235}_{92}U + ^{1}_{0}n \longrightarrow ^{90}_{38}Sr + ^{143}_{54}Xe + 3^{1}_{0}n$$

$$\longrightarrow ^{102}_{39}Y + ^{131}_{53}I + 3^{1}_{0}n$$

$$\longrightarrow ^{95}_{37}Rb + ^{137}_{55}Cs + 4^{1}_{0}n$$

▲ **Figure 11.14** The mushroom cloud over Nagasaki, following the detonation of "Fat Man" on August 9, 1945.

The primary (first) fission products are radioactive. These decay to daughter isotopes, many of which are also radioactive. In all, over 200 different fission products are produced, with half-lives that vary from less than a second to more than a billion years. Also, the neutrons produced in the explosion act on molecules in the atmosphere to produce carbon-14, tritium, and other radioisotopes. Fallout is therefore exceedingly complex. We consider three of the more worrisome isotopes here.

Of all the isotopes, strontium-90 (half-life 28.5 y) presents the greatest hazard to people. Strontium-90 reaches us primarily through dairy products and vegetables. Because of its similarity to calcium (both are group 2A elements), strontium-90 is incorporated into bone. There it remains an internal source of radiation for many years.

Iodine-131 may present a greater threat immediately after a nuclear explosion or reactor meltdown. Its half-life is only 8 days, but it is produced in relatively large amounts. Iodine-131 is readily transferred up the food chain. In the human body, it is concentrated in the thyroid gland, and it is precisely this characteristic that makes a trace of iodine-131 so useful for diagnostic scanning. However, for a healthy individual, larger amounts of radioactive iodine offer only damaging side effects. To minimize the absorption of radioactive iodine, many people in the areas of Chernobyl and Fukushima were given large amounts of potassium iodide, which effectively diluted the amount of radioactive iodine absorbed by their thyroid glands.

Cesium-137 (half-life 30.2 y) is, like strontium-90, capable of long-term effects. Because of its similarity to potassium (both are group 1A elements), it is taken up by living organisms as part of body fluids. It can be obtained from sources in the environment and reconcentrated in living organisms.

By the late 1950s, radioactive isotopes from atmospheric testing of nuclear weapons were detected in the environment. Concern over radiation damage from nuclear fallout led to a movement to ban atmospheric testing. Many scientists were leaders in the movement. Linus Pauling, who won the Nobel Prize in Chemistry in 1954 for his bonding theories and for his work in determining the structure of proteins, was a particularly articulate advocate of banning atmospheric tests. In 1963, a nuclear test ban treaty was signed by the major nations—with the exception of France and the People's Republic of China, which continued aboveground tests. Since the signing of the treaty, other countries have joined the nuclear club. Pauling, who had endured being called a communist and a traitor because of his outspoken position, was awarded the Nobel Peace Prize in 1962.

Self-Assessment Questions

1. The isotope used in uranium fission reactions is
   a. uranium-232
   b. uranium-234
   c. uranium-235
   d. uranium-238

2. What fraction of natural uranium is the fissionable isotope?
   a. <1%   **b.** 10%   **c.** 50%   **d.** >99%

3. Plutonium for fission reactions is
   a. made from uranium-238
   b. made from neptunium ores
   c. obtained from the dwarf planet Pluto
   d. obtained from plutonium ores

4. Strontium-90 substitutes for calcium in bones because Sr and Ca
   a. are in the same group of the periodic table
   b. are in the same period of the periodic table
   c. have identical electron configurations
   d. have identical half-lives

5. Which of the following radioisotopes in fallout is dangerous mainly because it becomes concentrated in the thyroid gland?
   a. cesium-137   **b.** iodine-131   **c.** strontium-90   **d.** radon-222

Answers: 1, c; 2, a; 3, a; 4, a; 5, b

11.9 Uses of Nuclear Energy

Learning Objective ❯ List some uses of nuclear energy.

A significant portion of the electricity we use today is generated by nuclear power plants. In the United States, one-fifth of all the electricity produced comes from nuclear power plants. Europeans rely even more on nuclear energy. France, for example, obtains 80% of its electric power from nuclear plants, while Belgium, Spain, Switzerland, and Sweden generate about one-third of their power from nuclear reactors.

Ironically, the same nuclear chain reaction that occurred in the detonation of the bomb dropped on Hiroshima is used extensively today under the familiar concrete containment tower of a nuclear power plant. The key difference is that the power plant employs a *slow, controlled* release of energy from the nuclear chain reaction, rather than an explosion. The slowness of the process is due to the use of uranium fuel that is much less enriched (2.5–3.5% ^{235}U rather than the 90% enrichment of weapons-grade uranium).

One of the main problems with the production of nuclear power arises from the products of the nuclear reactions. As in nuclear fallout, most of the daughter nuclei produced by the fission of uranium-235 are also radioactive, some with very long half-lives. We will discuss the problems associated with nuclear waste further in Chapter 15. Perhaps a more serious problem is the potential transformation of spent nuclear fuel into weapons-grade material (see the box titled "Nuclear Proliferation and Dirty Bombs" on page 324).

▶ The core of a nuclear reactor contains hollow rods filled with uranium pellets. The heat generated by the fission reaction is used to boil water, which drives turbines to generate electricity in the same way as in coal-fired or gas-fired generating plant. Because the pellets are only about 3% uranium-235, a nuclear explosion cannot occur, though loss of coolant may lead to a reactor meltdown.

GREEN CHEMISTRY

Principles 1, 4, 6, 10, 12

Bevin W. Parks-Lee, *Industrial organic chemist*

Green Remediation of Nuclear Waste

You learned that a large amount of ^{239}Pu was manufactured in Hanford, Washington, for the Manhattan Project (Section 11.8). The plutonium was produced from uranium in a nuclear reactor much like the ones used to produce electricity today. After the uranium rods reacted long enough to produce usable amounts of plutonium, they were transferred from the reactor and prepared for reprocessing. The goal was to maximize the plutonium production. The waste, still highly radioactive, was stored in many million-gallon tanks. Some of these tanks have been in service for 70 years, and leaks have been detected. Green chemistry principles can guide the development of methods to handle this legacy waste responsibly.

The Manhattan Project generated more than 91 million gallons of extremely acidic radioactive waste left over from the recovery of Pu and U. The solutions, referred to as high-level liquid waste (HLLW), are radioactive because small amounts of U and Pu remain with many other radioactive *nuclides* (nuclei having specific mass numbers and atomic numbers) that were produced during the fission reactions, including Np, Am, and Nd (Sections 11.3 and 11.7). If this small amount of radioactive material (1–2% of the 91 million gallons) could be removed, the impact would be tremendous.

Spent fuel rods are made up of different metals that can be separated and reclaimed through reprocessing. The aim is to remove any remaining radioactive nuclides, but many steps are necessary to achieve this. To access the separate atoms and free them from the solid matrix, the fuel rods are dissolved in concentrated nitric acid. An oxidation-reduction reaction occurs between the acid and the metals (Sections 8.1 and 8.6). The protons from the acid are reduced to form hydrogen gas, and the metals are oxidized to produce cations. The radioactive metal cations remain in the acidic water. At this point, it is possible to selectively remove metals by using special organic solutions that bind specific nuclides.

Processes that reduce the amount of HLLW align with Green Chemistry Principles 1, 6, and 12. How can these principles be put into action? One way is to design remediation processes that target the radioactive parts of the waste. Specifically, isolating only the radioactive compounds that require treatment avoids the need to store millions of gallons of acidic solution. Also, since the half-lives of these nuclides are so long (Section 11.3), encasing the waste in glass (vitrification) has been proposed as a good storage approach. Decreasing the volume of waste, though, would minimize the use of vitrification, which is energy-intensive and expensive.

In reprocessing, specific molecules can be used to bind to the radioactive cations and to manipulate the properties (e.g., solubility) of the resulting metal compounds. The molecules react with the metals to make compounds soluble in organic solvents. This enables the radioactive materials to be removed from water and transferred into a small volume of organic solvent. If the molecules are selective for one metal over another, they will bind to and carry only that metal into the organic solvent. This reprocessing method offers the opportunity to separate and reclaim individual types of metals.

One type of organic molecule that can extract the radioactive nuclides is an *amide* (Section 9.8). Amides are easy to synthesize, and they are stable in the highly acidic and radioactive environment. A way to further reduce the volume of radioactive waste would be to burn off the organic components—the molecules bound to the metals and the solvent carrying them—leaving only solid metal waste. Amides (composed of only C, H, N, and O) will burn completely, making them a good fit with Green Chemistry Principle 10—designing for degradation. The simple amides tested first did not bind the metal ions as well as other types of molecules, which were harder to synthesize, degraded in the waste solutions, could not be incinerated, and tended to be toxic. Further research uncovered that molecules containing two amide groups bound the metal ions very well. This example shows the application of Green Chemistry Principle 4 through the design of a safer chemical.

Overall, green chemistry principles can be used to dramatically reduce amounts of radioactive waste and to reprocess the waste in ways that are safer for human health and the environment.

▲ Construction of the storage tanks of HLLW that are buried on completion.

Nuclear Proliferation and Dirty Bombs

As power is generated in nuclear plants, important changes occur in the fuel. Neutron bombardment converts ^{235}U to radioactive daughter products. Eventually, the concentration of ^{235}U becomes too low to sustain the nuclear chain reaction. The fuel rods must be replaced about every three years. The rods then become high-level nuclear waste.

As ^{235}U undergo fission, the nonfissionable (and very concentrated) ^{238}U nuclei absorb neutrons and are converted to ^{239}Pu, a transmutation described in Section 11.8). In time, some ^{240}Pu is also formed. However, if the fuel rods are removed after only about three months, the fissionable plutonium-239 can be easily separated from the other fission products by chemical means. Plutonium bombs require less sophisticated technology to produce than is needed to make nuclear weapons from uranium. Plutonium is thus of greater concern with respect to weapons proliferation, because operation of a nuclear plant can produce materials suitable for use in a bomb. North Korea has nuclear power plants and a plutonium separation facility capable of producing enough ^{239}Pu for several weapons each year (Figure 11.15). Iran also has a facility for enriching uranium, which could lead to the production of nuclear bombs. The activities of these and other developing countries raise the fear of a dangerous proliferation of nuclear weapons.

Another security concern is a "dirty bomb," a device that uses a conventional explosive, such as dynamite, to disperse radioactive material that might be stolen from a hospital or other facility that uses radioactive isotopes. In most cases, the conventional bomb would do more immediate harm than the radioactive substances. At the levels most likely to be used, the dirty bomb would not contain enough radioactive material to kill people or cause severe illness.

▲ **Figure 11.15** Satellite photograph of the plutonium processing plant at Yongbyon, North Korea.

The Nuclear Age

The splitting of the atom made the Chinese curse "May you live in interesting times" seem quite appropriate. The goal of the alchemists, to change one element into another, has been achieved through the application of scientific principles. New elements have been formed, and the periodic table has been extended well beyond

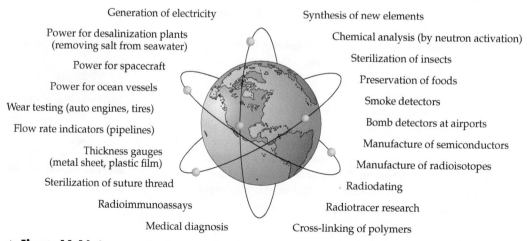

▲ **Figure 11.16** Some constructive uses of nuclear energy.

uranium (Z = 92). This modern alchemy produces plutonium by the ton; neptunium (Z = 93), americium (Z = 95), and curium (Z = 96) by the kilogram; and berkelium (Z = 97) and einsteinium (Z = 99) by the milligram.

As we have seen, radioactive isotopes have many uses, from killing tiny but deadly cancer cells and harmful microorganisms in food to serving as tracers in a variety of biological experiments and imaging technologies and generating fearsome weapons. Figure 11.16 displays a number of other constructive uses of nuclear energy. We live in an age in which the extraordinary forces present in the atom have been unleashed as a true double-edged sword. The threat of nuclear war—and nuclear terrorism—has been a constant specter for the last six decades, yet it is hard to believe that the world would be a better place if we had not discovered the secrets of the atomic nucleus.

CRITICAL THINKING EXERCISES

Apply knowledge that you have gained in this chapter and one or more of the FLaReS principles (Chapter 1) to evaluate the following statements or claims.

11.1 Brazil nuts are known to absorb and concentrate the element barium. A nationally known laboratory announces that Brazil nuts contain tiny traces of radium.

11.2 For more than 600 years, it was alleged that the Shroud of Turin was the burial shroud of Jesus. In 1988, several laboratories carried out carbon-14 analyses indicating that the flax from which the shroud was made was grown between C.E. 1260 and 1390. Recently there have been claims that the 1988 analyses are unreliable because the shroud is contaminated with pollen from plants grown in the fourteenth century, and it is the age of this pollen that was actually measured in 1988. At least one of the scientists has offered to repeat the analysis on a very carefully cleaned sample of the cloth, but further access to the shroud has been refused.

11.3 A scientist reports that he has found an artifact that has been shown to be 80,000 years old by carbon-14 dating.

11.4 The americium in a smoke detector (see Conceptual Example 11.7) is encased in a chamber with aluminum shielding, about as thick as the wall of a soft-drink can. A woman who purchases a smoke detector mounts it at the highest point on the ceiling. She claims that this minimizes her exposure to the radiation.

11.5 A young girl refuses to visit her grandmother after the woman has undergone radiation therapy for breast cancer. The teenager is afraid that she will catch radiation sickness from her grandmother.

SUMMARY

Section 11.1—Some isotopes of elements have unstable nuclei, which undergo changes in nucleon number, atomic number, or energy; this process is called radioactive decay. The nuclei that undergo such changes are called radioisotopes. We are constantly exposed to naturally occurring radiation, called background radiation. Radiation that causes harm by dislodging electrons from living tissue and forming ions is called ionizing radiation and includes nuclear radiation and X-rays. Radiation can disrupt normal chemical processes in cells and can damage DNA, sometimes causing mutations.

Section 11.2—Nuclear equations are used to represent nuclear processes. These equations are balanced when the sum of nucleon numbers on each side is the same and the sum of atomic numbers on each side is the same. Four types of radioactive decay are alpha $\left(_2^4\text{He}\right)$ decay, beta $\left(_{-1}^0\text{e}\right)$

decay, gamma $\left(_0^0\gamma\right)$ decay, and emission of a positron $\left(_{+1}^0\text{e}\right)$. Electron capture (EC) is a fifth type of decay, in which a nucleus absorbs one of the atom's electrons. There are a number of important differences between nuclear reactions and chemical reactions.

Section 11.3—The rate of radioactive decay is measured in becquerels (Bq).

$$1 \text{ becquerel (Bq)} = 1 \text{ disintegration/s}$$

The **half-life** of a radioactive isotope is the time it takes for half of a sample to undergo radioactive decay. The fraction of a radioisotope remaining after n half-lives is given by the expression

$$\text{Fraction remaining} = \frac{1}{2^n}$$

Half-lives of certain isotopes can be used to estimate the ages of various objects. Carbon-14 dating is the best-known of the radioisotopic dating techniques. Relying on carbon-14's half-life of 5730 years, this technique can be used to estimate the age of once-living items up to 50,000 years old. The decay of tritium can be used to date items up to 100 years old. Other isotopes can be used to date rocks, the Earth's crust, and meteorites.

Section 11.4—Transmutation, the conversion of one element into another, cannot be carried out by chemical means but can be accomplished by nuclear processes. Bombarding a stable nucleus with energetic particles can cause artificial transmutation. These processes can be represented with nuclear equations.

Section 11.5—Radioisotopes have many uses. A radioisotope and a stable isotope of an element behave nearly the same chemically, so radioisotopes can be used as tracers in physical and biological systems. A radioactive atom in a molecule labels it so that it can be followed by a radiation detector. Radioisotopes have many uses in agriculture, including the production of useful mutations. Radiation can be used to irradiate foodstuffs as a method of preservation. Radiation therapy to destroy cancer cells depends on the fact that radiation is more damaging to those rapidly reproducing cells than to healthy cells. Radioisotopes are used in the diagnosis of various disorders. Iodine-131 is used for thyroid diagnoses, gadolinium-153 for bone mineralization examinations, and technetium-99m for a variety of diagnostic tests. Positron emission tomography (PET) involves radioisotopes that emit positrons, which are then annihilated by electrons in the body, producing gamma rays that can be used to form an image.

Section 11.6—Different types of radiation have different penetrating abilities. Alpha particles (helium nuclei) are relatively slow and have low penetrating power. Beta particles (electrons) are much faster and more penetrating. Gamma rays (high-energy photons) travel at the speed of light and have great penetrating power. How hazardous radiation is depends on the location of the source; alpha particles from a source inside the body are highly damaging. Radiation hazard can be decreased by moving away from the source or by using shielding.

Section 11.7—Einstein's mass–energy equation, $E = mc^2$ shows that mass and energy are different aspects of the same thing. The total mass of the nucleons in a nucleus is greater than the actual mass of the nucleus. The missing mass, or the mass defect, is equivalent to the binding energy holding the nucleons together. Binding energy can be released either by breaking down heavy nuclei into smaller ones, a process called nuclear fission, or by

joining small nuclei to form larger ones, called nuclear fusion.

Fermi and Segrè bombarded uranium atoms with neutrons and found radioactive species among the products, while Hahn and Strassman found light nuclei among the reaction products. Meitner, aided by Frisch, hypothesized that the uranium nuclei were undergoing fission. Szilard saw that neutrons released in the fission of one nucleus could trigger the fission of other nuclei, setting off a chain reaction.

Thermonuclear reactions (fusion reactions) combine small nuclei to form larger ones. Nuclear fusion produces even more energy than nuclear fission. Fusion is the basis of the hydrogen bomb and the source of the sun's energy. Much research is aimed at producing controlled fusion commercially.

Section 11.8—The nuclear fission reaction became the center of the Manhattan Project during World War II. Its goals were (1) to achieve sustained nuclear fission and determine the critical mass, or minimum amount, of fissionable material required; (2) to enrich the amount of fissionable uranium-235 in ordinary uranium; (3) to synthesize plutonium-239, which is also fissionable; and (4) to construct a nuclear fission bomb before the Germans were able to do so. World War II ended shortly after the dropping of atomic bombs on Hiroshima and Nagasaki.

In addition to the devastation at the site of a nuclear explosion, much radioactive debris, or radioactive fallout, is, produced. Strontium-90 and iodine-131 are particularly hazardous components of fallout. Partly because of fallout, a nuclear test ban treaty was signed by most of the major nations; only underground testing is not banned.

Section 11.9—Nuclear power plants use the same nuclear chain reaction as in atomic bombs, but the reaction is much slower and can be controlled because of the low concentration of fissionable material. Disposal of the products of nuclear fission in power plants is an important problem facing us, as is the potential conversion of nuclear fuel into weapons. The forces within the nucleus truly constitute a double-edged sword for civilization.

Green chemistry Radioactive waste must be handled responsibly, and green chemistry principles can guide the development of new methods. A greener approach is to selectively isolate and treat the small amounts of radioactive isotopes instead of the large volumes of liquid waste. This can now be accomplished using safer chemicals, thereby reducing the amount of hazardous waste and the need for expensive and energy-intensive processing or storage methods.

Learning Objectives

› Identify the sources of the natural radiation to which we are exposed.	Problems 15, 54
› List the sources and dangers of ionizing radiation.	Problem 15
› Balance nuclear equations.	Problems 19–25, 43
› Identify the products formed by various decay processes.	Problems 26–30, 47
› Solve simple half-life problems.	Problems 31–38, 51
› Use the concept of half-life to solve simple radioisotopic dating problems.	Problems 39–42
› Write a nuclear equation for a transmutation, and identify the product element formed.	Problems 45, 46, 58

❭ List some applications of radioisotopes.   Problems 39–42, 50

❭ Describe the nature of materials needed to block alpha, beta, and gamma radiation.   Problem 13

❭ Explain where nuclear energy comes from.   Problems 52, 55

❭ Describe the difference between fission and fusion.   Problem 17

❭ Describe how uranium and plutonium bombs are made.   Problem 18

❭ Identify the most hazardous fallout isotopes, and explain why they are particularly dangerous. Problems 15, 52

❭ List some uses of nuclear energy.   Problems 31, 34, 39, 42, 44

❭ Identify green chemistry principles that can help solve existing problems in nuclear chemistry. Problems 59, 62

❭ Explain how molecules used in nuclear waste processing can be designed to be safer, and give examples of such molecules. Problems 60, 61

REVIEW QUESTIONS

1. Match each description with the type of change.
   (i) A new compound is formed.   a. nuclear
   (ii) A new element is formed.   b. chemical
   (iii) Size, shape, appearance,   c. physical
        or volume is changed without
        changing the composition.

2. Define or describe each of the following.
   a. half-life
   b. positron
   c. background radiation
   d. radioisotope

3. Write the nuclear symbols for protium, deuterium, and tritium (which are hydrogen-1, hydrogen-2, and hydrogen-3, respectively).

4. Why are isotopes important in nuclear reactions but not in most chemical reactions?

5. Write the nuclear symbols for the following isotopes. You may refer to the periodic table.
   a. cobalt-60
   b. iodine-127
   c. sodium-22
   d. calcium-42

6. Indicate the number of protons and the number of neutrons in atoms of the following isotopes.
   a. $^{65}_{30}Zn$ b. $^{236}_{93}Np$
   c. $^{101}_{43}Tc$ d. $^{81m}_{36}Kr$

7. Which of the following pairs represent isotopes? (X is a general symbol for an element.)
   a. $^{70}_{32}X$ and $^{70}_{32}X$
   b. $^{57}_{22}X$ and $^{52}_{22}X$
   c. $^{176}_{74}X$ and $^{167}_{74}X$
   d. $^{8}_{4}X$ and $^{16}_{8}X$

8. In which of the following atoms are there more protons than neutrons?
   a. ^{17}F b. ^{58}Ni c. ^{16}O d. ^{197}Au

9. The longest-lived isotope of einsteinium (Es) has a mass (nucleon) number of 254. How many neutrons are in the nucleus of an atom of this isotope?

10. The longest-lived isotope of polonium (Po) has 125 neutrons. What is a mass (nucleon) number of this isotope?

11. What changes occur in the nucleon number and the atomic number of a nucleus during emission of each of the following?
    a. alpha particle
    b. gamma ray
    c. proton

12. What changes occur in the nucleon number and atomic number of a nucleus during emission of each of the following?
    a. beta particle
    b. neutron
    c. positron

13. (a) From which type of radiation would a pair of gloves be sufficient to shield the hands: heavy alpha particles or massless gamma rays? (b) From which type of radiation would heavy lead shielding be necessary to protect a worker: alpha, beta, or gamma?

14. What are some of the characteristics that make technetium-99m such a useful radioisotope for diagnostic purposes?

15. Plutonium is especially hazardous when inhaled or ingested because it emits alpha particles. Why do alpha particles cause more damage to tissue than beta particles when their source is inside the body?

16. List two ways in which workers exposed to radioactive materials can protect themselves from radiation hazard.

17. Compare nuclear fission and nuclear fusion. Why is energy liberated in each case?

18. The compounds $^{235}UF_6$ and $^{238}UF_6$ are nearly chemically identical. How are they separated?

PROBLEMS

Nuclear Equations

19. Write a balanced equation for emission of **(a)** an alpha particle by californium-250, **(b)** a beta particle by bismuth-210, and **(c)** a positron by iodine-117.

20. Write a balanced equation for **(a)** alpha decay of gold-173, **(b)** beta decay of iodine-138, and **(c)** capture of an electron by cadmium-104.

21. Complete the following equations.

   a. $^{179}_{79}Au \longrightarrow ^{175}_{77}Ir + ?$

   b. $^{12}_{6}C + ^{2}_{1}H \longrightarrow ^{13}_{6}C + ?$

   c. $^{154}_{62}Sm + ^{1}_{0}n \longrightarrow ? + 2\,^{1}_{0}n$

22. Complete the following equations.

   a. $^{10}_{5}B + ^{1}_{0}n \longrightarrow ? + ^{4}_{2}He$

   b. $^{23}_{10}Ne \longrightarrow ^{23}_{11}Na + ?$

   c. $^{121}_{51}Sb + ? \longrightarrow ^{121}_{52}Te + ^{1}_{0}n$

23. Radiological laboratories often have a container of molybdenum-99, which decays to form technetium-99m. What other particle is formed? Complete the equation.

$$^{99}_{42}Mo \longrightarrow ^{99m}_{43}Tc + ?$$

24. Complete the equation for the decay of technetium-99m to technetium-99.

$$^{99m}_{43}Tc \longrightarrow ^{99}_{43}Tc + ?$$

25. When a magnesium-24 nucleus is bombarded with a neutron, a proton is ejected. What element is formed? (*Hint:* Write a balanced nuclear equation.)

26. A radioisotope decays to give an alpha particle and a protactinium-233 nucleus. What was the original nucleus?

27. A radioactive isotope decays to give an alpha particle and a bismuth-211 nucleus. What was the original nucleus?

28. When silver-107 is bombarded with a neutron, a different isotope of silver forms and then undergoes beta decay. What is the final product? (*Hint:* Write two separate nuclear equations.)

29. A nucleus of astatine-210 decays by beta emission, forming nucleus A. Nucleus A also decays by beta emission to nucleus B. Write the nuclear symbol for B.

30. A proposed method of making fissionable nuclear fuel is to bombard the relatively abundant isotope thorium-232 with a neutron. The product X of this bombardment decays quickly by beta emission to nucleus Y, and nucleus Y decays quickly to fissionable nucleus Z. Write the nuclear symbol for Z.

Half-Life

31. Gallium-67 is used in nuclear medicine (Table 11.6). After treatment, a patient's blood shows an activity of 20,000 counts per minute (counts/min). How long will it be before the activity decreases to about 5000 counts/min?

32. How long will it take for a 12.0-g sample of iodine-131 to decay to leave a total of 1.5 g of the isotope? The half-life of iodine-131 is 8.07 days.

33. A lab worker reports an activity of 80,000 counts/s for a sample of magnesium-21, whose half-life is 122 ms. Exactly 5.00 min later, another worker records an activity of 10 counts/min on the same sample. What best accounts for this difference? Magnesium-21

   a. gives off only neutrinos

   b. has a very short half-life, so almost every radioactive atom in the sample has decayed

   c. is an alpha emitter

   d. is a gamma emitter

34. A patient is injected with a radiopharmaceutical labeled with technetium-99m, half-life of 6.0 h, in preparation for a gamma ray scan to evaluate kidney function. If the original activity of the sample was 48 µCi, what activity (in µCi) remains **(a)** after 24 h and **(b)** after 48 h?

35. Krypton-81m is used for lung ventilation studies. Its half-life is 13 s. How long does it take the activity of this isotope to reach one-quarter of its original value?

36. Radium-223 has a half-life of 11.4 days. Approximately how long would it take for the activity of a sample of ^{223}Ra to decrease to 1% of its initial value?

37. In an experiment with dysprosium-197, half-life of 8.1 h, an activity of 500 counts/min was recorded at 4:00 p.m. on a Friday. What was the approximate activity of this sample at 8:30 a.m. the following Monday morning, when the experiment was resumed?

38. In determining the half-life of sulfur-35, students collected the following data, with the time in days and the activity in counts/s.

Time	Activity	Time	Activity
0	1000	80	525
20	851	100	446
40	725	120	380
60	616	140	323

Without doing detailed calculations, estimate a value for the half-life.

Radioisotopic Dating

39. Living matter has a carbon-14 activity of about 16 counts/min per gram of carbon. What is the age of an artifact for which the carbon-14 activity is 8 counts/min per gram of carbon?

40. A piece of wood from an Egyptian tomb has a carbon-14 activity of 980 counts/h. A piece of new wood of the same size shows 3920 counts/h. What is the age of the wood from the tomb?

41. The ratio of carbon-14 to carbon-12 in a piece of charcoal from an archaeological excavation is found to be one-half the ratio in a sample of modern wood. Approximately how old is the charcoal? How old would it be if the isotopic ratio were 25% of that in a sample of modern wood?

42. You are offered a great price on a case of brandy supposedly bottled during the lifetime of Napoleon (1769–1821). Before buying it, you insist on testing a sample of the brandy and find that its tritium content is 12.5% of that of newly produced brandy. How long ago was the brandy bottled? Is it likely to be authentic Napoleon-era brandy?

ADDITIONAL PROBLEMS

43. Write balanced nuclear equations for **(a)** the bombardment of $^{121}_{51}Sb$ by alpha particles to produce $^{124}_{53}I$, followed by **(b)** the radioactive decay of $^{124}_{53}I$ by positron emission.

44. A typical smoke detector contains about 0.25 mg of americium-241. The activity of 1 g of ^{241}Am is 1.26×10^{11} Bq. What is the activity of the americium-241 in the smoke detector?

45. In 2010, Russian and American scientists produced a few atoms of element 117 by shooting an intense beam of ions of the rare isotope calcium-48 at a target of berkelium-247. Two isotopes of element 117 were formed, one having 176 neutrons and the other 177 neutrons. Write two separate nuclear equations for the formation of the two isotopes. How many neutrons were released in each process?

46. Meitnerium undergoes alpha decay to form element 107, which in turn also emits an alpha particle. What are the atomic number and nucleon number of the isotope formed by these two steps? Write balanced nuclear equations for the two reactions.

47. Radium-223 nuclei usually decay by alpha emission. Once in every billion decays, a radium-223 nucleus emits a carbon-14 nucleus. Write a balanced nuclear equation for each type of emission.

48. A particular uranium alloy has a density of 18.75 g/cm^3. What volume is occupied by a critical mass of 49 kg of this alloy? The critical mass can be decreased to 16 kg if the alloy is surrounded by a layer of natural uranium (which acts as a neutron reflector). What is the volume of the smaller mass? Compare your answers to the approximate volumes of a baseball, a volleyball, and a basketball.

49. Plutonium has a density of 19.1 g/cm^3. What volume is occupied by a mass of 16.3 kg of plutonium? If a neutron-reflecting coating (made of beryllium) is used, the critical mass can be lowered to 2.5 kg. Compare the size of this mass to the volume of a baseball, a volleyball, and a basketball.

50. There are several technological applications for the transuranium elements ($Z > 92$). An important one is in smoke detectors, which can use the decay of a tiny amount of americium-241 to neptunium-237. What subatomic particle is emitted from that decay process?

51. The radioisotopic dating problems in this chapter are deceptively easy because they involve only integral numbers of half-lives. Calculations involving other than integral half-life values require a bit more complicated math. However, carbon-14 dating calculators that make the task quite easy can be accessed on the Web. Use one of those calculators to find **(a)** the age of a scrap of paper taken from the Dead Sea Scrolls that has a $^{14}C/^{12}C$ ratio that is 79.5% of that in living plants and **(b)** the age of a piece of charcoal from a Neanderthal site that has a $^{14}C/^{12}C$ ratio that is 17.5% of that in living plants.

52. In the first step of the chain reaction of a nuclear explosion, a ^{235}U nucleus absorbs a neutron. The resulting ^{236}U nucleus is unstable and can fission into ^{92}Kr and ^{141}Ba nuclei as shown in the figure. What are the other products of this reaction? After assessing this reaction, explain how the chain reaction can continue.

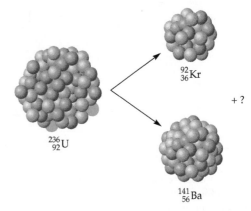

53. In 1932, James Chadwick discovered a new subatomic particle when he bombarded beryllium-9 with alpha particles. One of the products was carbon-12. What particle did Chadwick discover?

54. Several different radioisotopes can be used much like carbon-14 for determining the age of rocks and other matter. In the geosciences, the age of rocks may be determined using potassium-40, which decays to argon-40 with a half-life of 1.2 billion years. **(a)** Some rocks brought back from the moon were dated as being 3.6 billion years old. What percentage of the potassium-40 has decayed after that time? **(b)** Give a reason why uranium-238 (half-life of 4.6 billion years) is more useful for confirming this age than is carbon-14.

55. Einstein's mass–energy equation is $E = mc^2$, where mass is in kilograms and the speed of light is 3.00×10^8 m/s. The unit of energy is the joule (4.184 J = 1 cal; 1000 cal = 1 kcal).
  a. Calculate the energy released, in calories and kilocalories, when 1 g of matter is converted to energy.
  b. A bowl of cornflakes supplies 110 kcal (110 food calories). How many bowls of cornflakes would supply the same amount of energy as you calculated for 1 g of matter in part (a)?

56. Radioactive copper ($^{64}_{29}Cu$, half-life 12.7 h) is found in quantities exceeding the pollution standard in the sediments of a reservoir during a routine check on Monday, when 56 ppm/m^3 was measured. The standard allows up to 14 ppm/m^3. About when will the level of copper-64 return to 14 ppm/m^3?

57. An unidentified corpse was discovered on April 21 at 7:00 a.m. The pathologist discovered that there were 1.24×10^{17} atoms of $^{32}_{15}P$ remaining in the victim's bones and placed the time of death sometime on March 15. The half-life of $^{32}_{15}P$ is 14.28 days. How much $^{32}_{15}P$ was present in the bones at the time of death?

58. Scientists have tried to make element 120. Three different combinations of projectile and target were used to try to produce the nucleus $^{302}_{120}X$: **(a)** nickel-64 and uranium-238, **(b)** iron-58 and plutonium-244, and **(c)** chromium-54 and curium-248. However, after 120 days, no sign of element 120 was found. Write nuclear equations for the three expected reactions.

59. True or False? Green chemistry principles can be applied only as a process is being developed.

60. List four elements of which a compound that can be completely incinerated may be composed.

61. What is the benefit of having two amide groups on one molecule that binds radioactive metal ions?

62. Vitrification is an expensive and energy-intensive method involving encasing waste in glass. What portion of HLLW is radioactive, and why is that important with respect to vitrification?

COLLABORATIVE GROUP PROJECTS

Prepare a PowerPoint, poster, or other presentation (as directed by your instructor) to share with the class.

1. Write a brief report on the impact of nuclear science on one of the following.
   a. war and peace
   b. industrial progress
   c. medicine
   d. agriculture
   e. human, animal, and plant genetics

2. Write an essay on radioisotopic dating using one or more of the isotopes in Table 11.5 other than carbon-14 or tritium.

3. Write a brief biography of one of the following scientists.
   a. Otto Hahn   b. Enrico Fermi
   c. Glenn T. Seaborg   d. J. Robert Oppenheimer
   e. Lise Meitner   f. Albert Einstein

4. The positron is a particle of antimatter. Search the Web for information about antimatter, and the positron in particular.

5. Find a Web site that is strongly in favor of nuclear power plants and one that is strongly opposed. Note the sites' sponsors, and analyze their viewpoints. Try to find a Web site with a balanced viewpoint.

6. In July 1999, researchers at Lawrence Berkeley Laboratory reported the creation of the heaviest element to date, element 118. Two years later, that report was found to be fraudulent. Report on the scientific ethical questions raised by this episode.

7. Find the location of the nuclear power plant closest to where you live. Try to determine risks and benefits of the plant. To how many houses does it provide power? What are the environmental impacts of the plant under normal operating conditions?

8. Assemble two teams of two to four people each to debate the following resolution: The dropping of the atomic bombs on Hiroshima and Nagasaki was justified. Decide beforehand which team will take the affirmative and which the negative. Each team member is to give a three- to six-minute speech followed by a cross-examination by the opposing team members. Have the rest of the class judge the debate and give written or oral comments.

Energy

Have You Ever Wondered?

1. **Is energy a form of matter?**

2. **Do we really have an energy shortage?**

3. **Why don't we use more alternative fuels like ethanol?**

4. **Is solar power or wind power the answer to the energy crisis?**

5. **Is hydrogen really a nonpolluting fuel?**

A Fuel's Paradise

We were tempted to call this chapter "Fire" in order to have the titles of Chapters 12, 13, 14, and 15 be "Earth," "Air," "Water," and "Fire"—the four elements of the ancient Greeks.

Actually, "Fire" could be an appropriate title for this chapter. We obtain most of our energy by burning fuels, which certainly involves fire. Many sources of energy do not involve burning anything, however, and we will depend more heavily on these other sources as our reserves of fossil fuels are depleted.

Nearly all Earth's energy comes indirectly from the Sun, a nuclear fusion reactor about 150 million km away. The wind that drives windmills is a result of solar heating. Biofuels such as biodiesel and biomass come from plants, which use sunlight as their source of energy. Even fossil fuels are derived from the sun. An increasingly popular method of directly harnessing solar energy is the use of solar cells that convert sunlight to electricity. Today it is possible to buy enough solar cells to run an entire house, at fairly reasonable prices. In this chapter, we will look at the general nature and properties of energy and at various ways of generating energy or converting it from one form to another. Only tiny fractions of the energy we use come from Earth's internal heat, visible in geysers and tapped as geothermal energy, and from the Moon-powered tides.

Energy is the ability to do work (see Chapter 1). Everything we consume or use—our food and clothes, our homes and their contents, our cars and roads—requires energy to produce, package, distribute, operate, and discard. The United States, with less than 5% of the world's population, uses one-fifth of all the energy generated on the planet. Abundant energy provides people in the United States with a high standard of living. But much of this energy is wasted. Australia, Switzerland, France, and the Scandinavian countries achieve higher standards of living with lower per capita use of energy. Our high energy consumption has enormous costs: to our health, to the environment, and to our national security. It affects our foreign debt and the stability of other countries. It pollutes the air we breathe and the water we drink.

Industry uses about 30% of all energy produced in the United States. This energy is used to convert raw materials to the many products our society needs and wants. Transportation uses about 29%, to power automobiles, trucks, trains, airplanes, and buses. Private homes use about 22%, and commercial spaces use about 19%. Utilities use about 38% of the nation's energy production, mainly to generate electricity. (These figures add up to more than 100% because the electricity is used in industry, homes, and commercial spaces, and some of it is therefore counted twice.)

Energy lights our homes, heats and cools our living spaces, and makes us the most mobile society in the history of the human race. It powers the factories that provide us with abundant material goods. Indeed, energy is the basis of modern civilization.

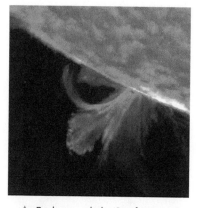

▲ Each second, the Sun fuses more than 600 million t of hydrogen into about 1 million t of helium and converts 4000 kg of hydrogen to energy in the form of gamma rays. Within the sun, the energy is absorbed and re-emitted at ever longer wavelengths, reaching the surface mainly as visible light. The Sun has enough hydrogen to last another 5 billion years. The solar flare shown here is over twenty times larger than Earth.

15.1 Energy: Starring Our Sun

Learning Objectives ❭ Perform power and energy calculations.

All living things on Earth— including us—depend on nuclear energy for survival. Most of the energy available to us on this planet comes from the giant nuclear reactor we call the Sun. Although the Sun is about 150 million km away, it has supplied Earth with most of its energy for billions of years, and is likely to continue to do so for billions more (Table 15.1).

The SI unit of energy is the joule (J). A *watt* (W), the SI unit of power, is 1 joule per second (J/s).

$$1\,W = 1\frac{J}{s}$$

A unit of more convenient size is the kilowatt: 1 kW = 1000 W. To express energy consumption, the watt is combined with a unit of time. For example, electricity usage is usually measured (and billed for) in terms of the *kilowatt hour (kWh)*, the quantity of energy used by a 1-kW device in 1 h. There are 3600 seconds in an hour, so 1 kWh = 3600 kJ. Power is the *rate* at which energy is used (just as speed is the *rate* at which distance is covered).

Recall (Chapter 11) that the Sun is a nuclear fusion reactor that steadily converts hydrogen to helium. The Sun has a power output of 4×10^{26} W. Earth receives only about 1 part in 50 *billion* of this energy. Even so, this tiny fraction is equivalent to over 100 million nuclear power plants. In three days, Earth receives energy from the Sun equivalent to all our fossil fuel reserves!

Table 15.1	Earth's Energy Ledger (Estimated)	
Item	**Energy (TW)ᵃ**	**Approximate Percent**
Energy in		
Solar radiation	174,000	99.97%
Internal heat	46	0.025%
Tides	3	0.002
Waste heatᵇ	13	0.007
Energy out		
Direct reflection	52,000	30
Direct heatingᶜ	81,000	47
Water cycleᶜ	40,000	23
Windsᶜ	370	0.2
Photosynthesisᶜ	40	0.02

ᵃTW (terawatt) = 10^{12} W.

ᵇFrom fossil fuel use.

ᶜThis energy is eventually returned to space by means of long-wave radiation (heat).

▲ **It DOES Matter!**

Consumers often have misconceptions about energy usage in the home. Appliances that generate or transfer heat usually consume a lot of energy. The two major energy "sinks" in most homes are the heating and cooling system and the water heater. Refrigerators, stoves, toasters, and similar appliances are also energy hogs. Lighting is often responsible for a surprisingly small fraction of the monthly energy bill. An ordinary toaster oven heating a slice of pizza for 10 minutes consumes as much energy as a 20-W fluorescent lightbulb uses in 10 hours.

Example 15.1 | Power and Energy Conversion

How much electrical energy, in joules, is consumed by a 75-W bulb burning for 1.0 h?

Solution

One watt is 1 J/s, so we know that 75 W = 75 J/s. The bulb burns for 1 h so

$$1 \text{ h} \times \frac{60 \text{ min}}{1 \text{ h}} \times \frac{60 \text{ s}}{1 \text{ min}} = 3600 \text{ s}$$

$$3600 \text{ s} \times \frac{75 \text{ J}}{1 \text{ s}} = 270,000 \text{ J}$$

■ EXERCISE 15.1A

How much electrical energy, in joules, does a 650-W microwave oven consume in heating a cup of coffee for 1.0 min?

■ EXERCISE 15.1B

In January 2011, the average cost of residential electricity in the United States was 10.99¢/kWh. A typical desktop computer uses about 150 W. How much does it cost to run such a computer for 3.75 h at that rate?

Kinetic and Potential Energy

Energy exists in two main forms. Energy due to position or arrangement is called **potential energy**. The water at the top of a dam has potential energy due to gravitational attraction. When the water is allowed to flow through a turbine to a lower level, the potential energy is converted to **kinetic energy** (energy of motion). As the water falls, it moves faster. Its kinetic energy increases as its potential energy decreases. The turbine can convert part of the kinetic energy of the water into electrical energy. The electricity thus produced can be carried by wires to homes and factories, where it can be converted to light energy, to heat, or to mechanical energy. Table 15.2 gives examples of kinetic and potential energy.

Table 15.2	Some Examples of Potential and Kinetic Energy	
Potential Energy	
Energy stored by position	Water at the top of a waterfall (hydroelectric power; Section 15.9)
	A hammer poised to drive a nail
	A rock teetering at the edge of a cliff
	A swimmer ready to dive
Energy stored in chemical bonds	Fuels (coal, gasoline, natural gas; Sections 15.5–15.7)
	Foods (carbohydrates, fats, proteins; Chapter 17)
	Explosives (nitroglycerin, TNT)
Energy stored in atomic nuclei	Nuclear energy (power plants, bombs; Section 15.8)
Kinetic Energy	
Energy of any moving object	A rolling freight train
	A spinning water turbine (hydroelectric power; Section 15.9)
	A rolling bowling ball
	A moving molecule
	A sailboat skimming across a lake
	A volleyball being spiked

Energy and the Life-Support System

The *biosphere* is the thin (about 15 km thick) film of air, water, and soil in which all life exists. Only a small fraction of the energy the biosphere receives is used to support life. About 30% of the incident solar radiation is immediately reflected back into space as ultraviolet and visible light. Nearly half is converted to heat, making our planet a warm and habitable place. About 23% of solar radiation powers the water cycle (Section 14.2), evaporating water from land and seas. The radiant energy of the Sun is converted to the potential energy of water vapor, water droplets, and ice crystals in the atmosphere. This potential energy is converted to the kinetic energy of falling rain and snow and of flowing rivers.

A tiny but most important fraction—less than 0.02%—of solar energy is absorbed by green plants, which use it to power **photosynthesis**. In the presence of chlorophyll and a series of enzymes, the energy converts carbon dioxide and water to glucose, a simple sugar rich in energy.

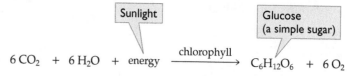

$$6\,CO_2 \;+\; 6\,H_2O \;+\; energy \xrightarrow{\text{chlorophyll}} C_6H_{12}O_6 \;+\; 6\,O_2$$

Photosynthesis also replenishes oxygen in the atmosphere. Glucose can be stored, or it can be converted to more complex foods and structural materials. All animals depend on the stored energy of green plants for survival.

Self-Assessment Questions

1. The ability or capacity to do work is
   a. force   **b.** energy   **c.** power   **d.** pressure

2. What sector of the U.S. economy uses the largest fraction of the nation's energy?
   a. residential   **b.** commercial   **c.** industrial   **d.** transportation

3. About how much of the world's energy is used by the United States?
   a. 3%   **b.** 5%   **c.** 10%   **d.** 20%

4. An apple hanging on a branch above Isaac Newton's head has
   a. force energy   **b.** kinetic energy   **c.** potential energy   **d.** rotational energy

5. The largest portion of Earth's incident solar radiation
   a. powers the water cycle   **b.** is converted to heat
   c. powers photosynthesis   **d.** is reflected back to space

6. About what percentage of Earth's incident solar radiation is used in photosynthesis?
   a. 0.02%   **b.** 2%   **c.** 5%   **d.** 10%

Answers: 1, b; 2, c; 3, d; 4, c; 5, d; 6, a

15.2 Energy and Chemical Reactions

Learning Objectives ❯ Classify chemical reactions and physical processes as exothermic or endothermic. ❯ List factors that affect the rates of chemical reactions.

A study of chemistry is incomplete without a discussion of energy. Two areas of chemistry that focus on energy are *kinetics* and *thermodynamics*. Chemical kinetics describes the rate at which a chemical reaction occurs. That rate depends on several factors, including temperature, concentrations of reactants, and presence of catalysts.

Reactions generally proceed faster at higher temperatures. For example, at room temperature, coal (carbon) reacts so slowly with oxygen (from the air) that the change is imperceptible. However, if coal is heated to several hundred degrees, it reacts rapidly. The heat evolved in the reaction keeps the coal burning smoothly. We use the kinetic–molecular theory (Section 6.5) to explain this phenomenon. At high temperatures, molecules move faster and collide more frequently, increasing the chance that they will react. The increase in temperature also supplies more energy to break chemical bonds—a condition necessary for most reactions.

The concentrations of reactants affect the rate of most reactions, because when we crowd more molecules into a given volume of space, the molecules collide more often. More collisions each second means more reactions each second. For example, if you light a wood splint and then blow out the flame, the splint continues to glow as the wood reacts slowly with oxygen in the air. If the glowing splint is placed in pure oxygen—five times more concentrated than O_2 in air—the splint bursts into flame because of the increase in reaction rate.

Catalysts also affect the rates of chemical reactions. A carefully selected catalyst can increase the rate of a reaction that otherwise would be so slow as to be impractical. For example, the platinum in your automobile's catalytic converter causes carbon monoxide (CO) to react more rapidly with atmospheric oxygen. This means that less unreacted CO is emitted into our atmosphere. Catalysts are of great importance in the chemical industry and in biology.

▲ **It DOES Matter!**
We use the effect of temperature on chemical reactions in our daily lives. For example, we refrigerate milk or freeze vegetables to retard the chemical reactions that lead to spoilage. When we want to stir-fry faster, we turn up the temperature.

▲ When liquid oxygen—much more concentrated than oxygen gas—is poured on a lit cigarette, the cigarette sparks, bursts into flame, and quickly disintegrates.

(a)   (b)

▲ The action of a catalyst is illustrated. Hydrogen peroxide decomposes slowly to water and oxygen (a). When platinum metal is inserted into a solution of hydrogen peroxide (b), the reaction proceeds rapidly. The heat released during the process produces steam, and the solution froths as oxygen gas is evolved.

Catalysts are vital in living organisms. Biological catalysts, called *enzymes*, mediate nearly all the chemical reactions that take place in living systems (Chapter 16).

Energy Changes and Chemical Reactions: Thermochemistry

The study of energy changes that occur during chemical reactions (and physical processes) is called **thermochemistry**. These energy changes are quantitatively related to the *amounts* of chemicals involved. For example, burning 1.00 mol (16.0 g) of methane to form carbon dioxide and water releases 803 kJ (192 kcal) of energy as heat. We can consider the amount of heat evolved as a *product* of the reaction.

$$CH_4(g) + 2 O_2(g) \longrightarrow CO_2(g) + 2 H_2O(g) + 803 \text{ kJ}$$

Burning 2.00 mol (32.0 g) of methane produces twice as much heat, 1606 kJ.

To convert between the SI unit of energy, the joule (J), and the commonly used unit, the calorie (cal), we can use the equality 1 cal = 4.184 J.

Example 15.2 | Energies of Chemical Reactions

Burning 1.00 mol of propane releases 2201 kJ of energy.

$$C_3H_8(g) + 5 O_2(g) \longrightarrow 3 CO_2(g) + 4 H_2O(g) + 2201 \text{ kJ}$$

How much energy in kilojoules is released when 15.0 mol of propane is burned?

Solution

We start with 15.0 mol C_3H_8 and use the balanced equation to form a conversion factor, just as we did with chemical conversions in Chapter 5.

$$15.0 \text{ mol } C_3H_8 \times \frac{2201 \text{ kJ}}{1 \text{ mol } C_3H_8} = 33,000 \text{ kJ}$$

▪ **EXERCISE 15.2A**

The reaction of nitrogen and oxygen to form nitrogen monoxide requires an input of energy.

$$N_2(g) + O_2(g) + 18.07 \text{ kJ} \longrightarrow 2 NO(g)$$

How much energy in kilojoules is absorbed when 10.1 mol N_2 reacts with O_2 to form NO?

▪ **EXERCISE 15.2B**

In photosynthesis, carbon dioxide and water are converted to glucose in a reaction that requires an input of 2700 kJ of energy to produce 1.00 mol of glucose. How much energy, in kilojoules, is required to make 1.00 kg of glucose?

We usually discuss energy changes in terms of an object or region losing energy and another object or region gaining it. When we warm our cold hands over a campfire, the burning wood gives off energy (as heat) and our hands gain energy, raising their temperature. In science, however, we need to describe the two "somethings" that exchange energy more precisely. We therefore define the **system** as the part of the universe under consideration. A real or imaginary boundary separates the system from the rest of the universe. The **surroundings** are everything else—the rest of the universe in theory, but we usually limit the surroundings to those parts of the universe that exchange energy or matter or both with the system. For example, if the system is a block of frozen spinach in a dish, the surroundings are the air around the block and dish, the counter on which it sits, and the rest of the kitchen.

Chemical reactions (or physical processes) that result in the release of heat from the system to the surroundings are **exothermic**. The burning of methane, gasoline, and coal (Figure 15.1) are all exothermic reactions. In each case, chemical energy is converted to heat energy, which is absorbed by the surroundings.

In other reactions, such as the decomposition of water, energy must be supplied to the reactants from the surroundings. We can write the amount of heat required for this process as a reactant in the chemical equation:

$$2 H_2O(g) + 573 \text{ kJ} \longrightarrow 2 H_2(g) + O_2(g)$$

◀ **Figure 15.1** Coal burns in a highly exothermic reaction. The heat released can convert water to steam that can turn a turbine to generate electricity.

▲ **Figure 15.2** A striking endothermic reaction occurs when barium hydroxide octahydrate reacts with ammonium thiocyanate to produce barium thiocyanate, ammonia gas, and water.

$$Heat + Ba(OH)_2 \cdot 8\,H_2O(s) +$$
$$2\,NH_4SCN(s) \longrightarrow Ba(SCN)_2(s) +$$
$$2\,NH_3(g) + 10\,H_2O(l)$$

Here the reaction is carried out in a flask placed on a wet block of wood. The temperature drops well below the freezing point of water, freezing the flask to the block.

In a reaction like this, which is **endothermic**, energy is absorbed as heat (Figure 15.2). It takes 573 kJ of energy to decompose 36.0 g (2.00 mol) of water into hydrogen and oxygen. Note that exactly the same amount of energy is released when enough hydrogen is burned to form 36.0 g of water.

$$2\,H_2(g) + O_2(g) \longrightarrow 2\,H_2O(g) + 573\,kJ$$

Physical processes can also be either exothermic or endothermic. Table 15.3 lists several examples of physical and chemical processes and classifies them as exothermic or endothermic.

An endothermic reaction you can do: Dissolve about 15 g of citric acid ($H_3C_6H_5O_7$) in enough water to make about 25 mL of solution. Measure the initial temperature. Stir in 15 g of sodium bicarbonate (baking soda). Note the change in temperature. The reaction mixture can be discarded in the sink. No toxic substances are involved.

Table 15.3   Some Exothermic and Endothermic Processes

Exothermic Processes	Endothermic Processes
Freezing of water	Melting of ice
Condensation of water vapor	Evaporation of water
Metabolism in animals	Photosynthesis in plants
Forming chemical bonds	Breaking chemical bonds
Discharging a battery	Charging a battery
Explosion of dynamite	Evaporation of a chlorofluorocarbon

Example 15.3   Energy Changes in Chemical Reactions

How much energy, in kilojoules, is released when 225 g of propane (see Example 15.2) is burned?

Solution

The formula mass of propane, with 3 C atoms and 8 H atoms, is

$$(3 \times 12.0\,u) + (8 \times 1.0) = 36.0\,u + 8.0\,u = 44.0\,u$$

The molar mass is therefore 44.0 g. Next, we use the molar mass to convert grams of propane to moles of propane.

$$225\,g\;C_3H_8 \times \frac{1\,mol\;C_3H_8}{44.0\,g\;C_3H_8} = 5.11\,mol\;C_3H_8$$

Now, proceeding as in Example 15.2,

$$5.11 \text{ mol } C_3H_8 \times \frac{2201 \text{ kJ}}{1 \text{ mol } C_3H_8} = 11{,}200 \text{ kJ}$$

■ **EXERCISE 15.3A**
How much energy, in kilojoules, is released when 44.2 g of methane is burned?

$$CH_4(g) + 2\,O_2(g) \longrightarrow CO_2(g) + 2\,H_2O(g) + 803 \text{ kJ}$$

■ **EXERCISE 15.3B**
How much energy, in kilocalories, is absorbed when 0.528 g N_2 is converted to NO (see Exercise 15.2A)?

Self-Assessment Questions

1. The rate of a chemical reaction usually decreases when
   a. a catalyst is added
   b. a chemist is watching
   c. the concentration of one of the reactants is decreased
   d. the temperature is increased

2. Which of the following physical changes is exothermic?
   a. $H_2O(s) \longrightarrow H_2O(l)$
   b. $H_2O(g) \longrightarrow H_2O(l)$
   c. $H_2O(s) \longrightarrow H_2O(g)$
   d. $H_2O(l) \longrightarrow H_2O(g)$

3. How much heat is absorbed in the complete reaction of 0.10 mol SiO_2 with excess carbon, according to the following equation?

   $$SiO_2(g) + 3\,C(s) + 624.7 \text{ kJ} \longrightarrow SiC(s) + 2\,CO(g)$$

   a. 20.8 kJ   b. 62.47 kJ   c. 208 kJ   d. 1870 kJ

4. When solid NaOH is dissolved in water, the water gets hotter, indicating that this dissolving is an
   a. endothermic process because it absorbs heat
   b. endothermic process because it releases heat
   c. exothermic process because it absorbs heat
   d. exothermic process because it releases heat

Answers: 1, c; 2, b; 3, b; 4, d

15.3 The Laws of Thermodynamics

Learning Objective ❯ State the first and second laws of thermodynamics, and discuss their implications for energy production and use.

We will take a look at our present energy sources and our future energy prospects shortly. To do so scientifically, we first examine some natural laws. Recall that natural laws merely summarize the results of many experiments. We won't recount all those experiments here. We will merely state the laws and some of their consequences.

Energy and the Laws of Thermodynamics

The **first law of thermodynamics** states that energy can be neither created nor destroyed. The first law of thermodynamics (*thermo* refers to heat; *dynamics* refers to motion) grew out of a variety of experiments conducted during the early nineteenth century. By 1840, it was clear that energy can be changed from one form to another, but it is neither created nor destroyed. This law (also called the **law of conservation**

of energy) has been restated in several ways, including "You can't get something for nothing" and "There is no such thing as a free lunch." Energy cannot be made from nothing, which means that a machine cannot be made that produces more energy than it takes in. Nor does energy just disappear, although it may change to a different form.

From the first law alone, we might conclude that we can't possibly run out of energy because energy is conserved. This is true enough, but it doesn't mean that we don't have problems. There is another long-armed law from which we cannot escape.

Energy and the Second Law: You CAN'T Break Even

Despite innumerable attempts (and even the granting of several patents), no one has ever built a successful perpetual-motion machine. You can't make a machine that runs indefinitely without consuming energy. Even if an engine isn't doing any work, it loses energy (as heat) because of the friction of its moving parts. In fact, in any real engine, it impossible to get as much useful energy out as you put in. In other words, you can't break even.

If energy is neither created nor destroyed, why do we always need more? Won't the energy we have now last forever? The answer lies in these facts:

■ Energy can be changed from one form to another.
■ Not all forms are equally useful.
■ More useful forms of energy are constantly being degraded into less useful forms.

Energy "flows downhill." Mechanical energy is eventually changed into heat energy. Heat always flows from a hot object to a cooler one (Figure 15.3). The reverse does not occur spontaneously. There is a tendency toward an even distribution of energy.

Observations of heat flow led to formulation of the **second law of thermodynamics**, which can be stated: The energy available for work in the universe is continually decreasing. The second law also can be stated: Energy does not flow spontaneously from a cold object to a hot one. (A *spontaneous* process is one that can proceed in a specified direction without being forced by an external source of energy.)

It is true that we can make energy flow from a cold region to a hot one—refrigerators and freezers do so—but we cannot do so without an input of energy and without producing changes elsewhere. We can reverse a spontaneous process

◀ **Figure 15.3** Energy always flows spontaneously from a hot object to a cold one, never the reverse. It flows from a hot fire to the cooler marshmallow. (A spontaneous event is one that occurs without outside influence.)

▲ **It DOES Matter!**

The tendency of energy to disperse helps to explain why it is relatively easy to pollute air or water and hard to clean up such pollution. For example, it would take little energy to dump a ton of a chlorofluorocarbon (CFC) into the air. The rapidly moving CFC molecules would quickly disperse among the nitrogen, oxygen, and other molecules in the air. Once the CFC molecules were scattered, the entire atmosphere would have to be processed to separate them from the air. Cleaning up pollution is good, but prevention of pollution is a far better alternative.

only at a price. The price, in the case of a refrigerator, is the consumption of electricity; that is, you must use energy to cause energy flow from a cold space to a warmer one.

When we change energy from one form to another, we can't concentrate all the energy in a particular source to do the job we want it to do. For example, we use the energy in a fuel to push a piston in a car engine, or we use water rushing down from the top of a dam to run dynamos to generate electricity. In either case—indeed in all cases—some of the energy is converted to heat and thus not available to do *useful* work.

Entropy

Yet another way to look at the second law is in terms of *entropy*. Scientists use **entropy** as a measure of the dispersal of energy in a system. The more the energy is spread out, the higher the entropy of the system and the less likely it is that this energy can be harnessed to do useful work. Spontaneous processes tend toward greater entropy or are exothermic, or both. The total entropy always increases for an isolated system.

As was noted in Chapter 6, molecules move about constantly. Their motion in solids is limited to rapid but tiny back-and-forth movements much like vibrations about a nearly fixed point. The molecules in liquids move more freely but still over only short distances. Those in gases move still more freely and over much greater distances.

In Chapter 3, we saw that the energy of light occurs in little packets called *photons*. Similarly, the energy of molecular motion is described using a concept called *microstates*. If you could take a snapshot capturing the positions of all molecules in a sample of matter at a given instant, you would have captured an image of a microstate. The number of microstates in which a given sample of matter can exist differs depending upon whether it is in the solid, liquid, or gaseous state. The number of possible energy microstates will be lowest for a solid because the molecules in a solid are limited mainly to vibrational motion. Because molecules in the liquid state can move more freely, the number of possible energy microstates is much larger for liquids than for solids. When converted to a gas, the molecules can move still more freely and for much greater distances, so even more microstates are available to molecules in the gaseous state.

As any form of matter is heated, the energy in it is spread out among more accessible microstates (see Figure 15.4). Technically, entropy is the dispersal of

▲ **Figure 15.4** The photograph depicts the vaporization of water; a sample of liquid water [$H_2O(l)$] at room temperature spontaneously changes to $H_2O(g)$ through the process of evaporation. At the macroscopic level, nothing appears to be taking place. However, in the molecular view, we see that the molecules are in motion and are much more widely spaced in the gaseous state than in the liquid state. Vaporization is spontaneous because the gas has greater *entropy* than the liquid. Molecules in the gas can be "arranged" in many more ways in their spread-out spacing than can molecules of the liquid. We can make liquid water from water vapor but only by compressing the gas and/or lowering its temperature.

energy among these microstates. In practice, entropy is often thought of as being analogous to "molecular disorder." Of course, we can often reverse the tendency toward greater entropy—but only through an input of energy.

Self-Assessment Questions

1. The first law of thermodynamics is also called the law of
   a. conservation of energy
   b. conservation of mass
   c. entropy
   d. perpetual motion

2. That energy always goes spontaneously from more useful forms to less useful forms is a statement of the
   a. first law of thermodynamics
   b. law of unintended consequences
   c. second law of thermodynamics
   d. standard law of energy conversion

3. According to the second law of thermodynamics, the
   a. entropy of a system always decreases
   b. entropy of a system always increases
   c. total entropy always decreases for an isolated system
   d. total entropy always increases for an isolated system

4. In the process represented by the equation $H_2O(l) \longrightarrow H_2O(g)$, the entropy
   a. decreases
   b. depends on the catalyst used
   c. increases
   d. remains the same

Answers: 1, a; 2, c; 3, d; 4, c

15.4 Power: People, Horses, and Fossils

Learning Objective ❭ List the common fossil fuels, and describe how modern society is based on their use.

Early people obtained their energy (food and fuel) by collecting wild plants and hunting wild animals. They expended this energy in hunting and gathering. Domestication of horses and oxen increased the availability of energy only slightly. The raw materials used by these work animals were natural, replaceable plant materials.

A **fuel** is a substance that burns readily with the release of significant amounts of energy. Plant materials were also the first fuels. These combustible materials kept early fires burning. As late as 1760, wood was almost the only fuel in use. Wood, dried dung, and crop residues still remain the main sources of heat for about one-third of the world's people.

One of the first mechanical devices used to convert energy to useful work was the waterwheel. The Egyptians first used waterpower about 2000 years ago, mainly for grinding grain. Later on, waterpower was used for sawmills, textile mills, and other small factories. Windmills were introduced into Western Europe during the Middle Ages, mainly for pumping water and grinding grain. More recently, wind power has been used to generate electricity.

Windmills and waterwheels are fairly simple devices for converting the kinetic energy of blowing wind and flowing water to mechanical energy. They were sufficient to power the early part of the Industrial Revolution. The development of the steam engine allowed factories to be located away from waterways. Since 1850, turbines turned by water, steam, and gas, the internal-combustion engine, and a variety of other energy-conversion devices have boosted the energy available for society's use by an estimated factor of 10,000.

The Industrial Revolution was fueled, in effect, by fossils—the buried remains of living organisms. Combustion of this material initiated modern industrial civilization. Today, more than 85% of the energy used to support our way of life comes from **fossil fuels**—coal, petroleum, and natural gas that formed during Earth's Carboniferous period around 300 million years ago. In the following sections, we consider the origin and chemical nature of these fuels that release the energy captured by ancient plants from rays of sunlight.

The energy to run an engine usually comes from the concentrated chemical energy inside molecules of oil or coal. In biochemistry, food molecules are the concentrated energy source. In either case, energy is spread out during the process. The spread-out energy in the product gases—CO_2 and H_2O, in each case—is less useful. A car won't run on exhaust gases, nor can organisms obtain energy for life processes from respiratory products.

▲ Waterwheels at Hama, Syria, are 2000 years old. Some are more than 20 m high. Several are still used to lift water into aqueducts.

Fuels are *reduced* forms of matter, and the burning process is an oxidation (Chapter 8). If an atom already has its maximum number of bonds to oxygen atoms (or to other electronegative atoms such as chlorine or bromine), the substance cannot serve as a fuel. Indeed, some such substances can be used to put out fires. Figure 15.5 shows some representative fuels and nonfuels.

▶ **Figure 15.5** (a) Some fuels. Fuels are reduced forms of matter that release relatively large quantities of heat when burned. (b) Some nonfuels. These compounds are oxidized forms of matter.

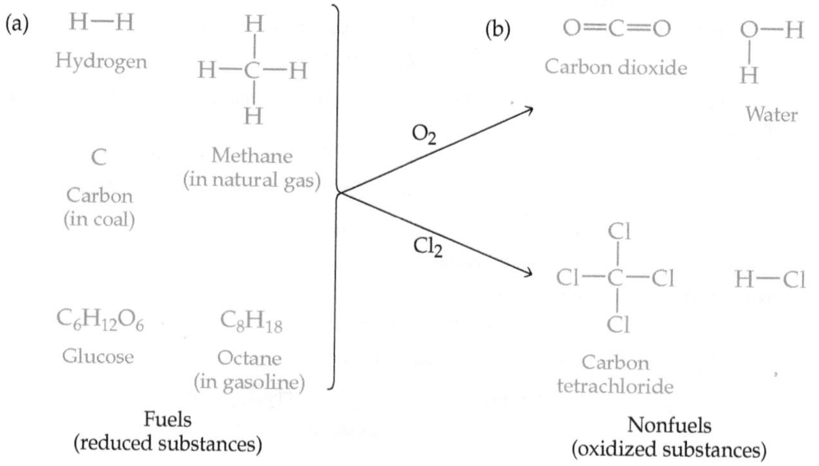

2. Do we really have an energy shortage? There is no shortage of energy itself, but not all energy is equally useful to us. The supply of materials like fossil fuels that provide convenient, useful energy is dwindling.

Energy *production* refers to conversion of some form of energy into a more useful form. For example, production of petroleum means pumping, transporting, and refining it. Energy *consumption* involves using it in a way that changes it to a less useful form. In either case, energy is neither created nor destroyed.

Reserves and Consumption Rates of Fossil Fuels

Earth has a limited supply of fossil fuels. Estimated U.S. and world reserves and annual U.S. and world consumption are given in Table 15.4. Estimates of reserves vary greatly, depending on the assumptions made, and the numbers in the table imply far greater certainty than there is in reality. Even the most optimistic estimates, however, lead to the conclusion that these nonrenewable energy resources are being depleted rapidly. Indeed, in just a century, we will have used up more than half the fossil fuels that were formed over the ages. In only a few hundred more years, we will have removed from Earth and burned virtually all the remaining recoverable fossil fuels. Of all that ever existed, about 90% will have been used in a period of 300 years.

Within the lifetime of today's 18-year-olds, natural gas and petroleum will likely become so scarce and so expensive that they won't be used much as fuels. At the current rate of production, U.S. reserves of petroleum and natural gas will be substantially depleted sometime during this century. Coal reserves should last perhaps 300 years. However, the rate of use of all fossil fuels is increasing, especially in developing nations.

Presumably, fossil fuels are still being formed in nature, a process that is perhaps most evident in peat bogs. The rate of formation is extremely slow, estimated to be only one fifty-thousandth of the rate at which fuels are being used.

Table 15.4	Estimated U.S. and World Reserves of Economically Recoverable Fuels and Annual Consumption of Fossil Fuels[a]			
	Reserves		**Consumption**	
Fuel	**United States**	**World**	**United States**	**World**
Coal	119,327	462,612	558	2,891
Petroleum	4,081	164,804	952	4,001
Natural gas	5,333	163,312	507	2,362
Total	128,741	790,728	2,017	9,254

Source: World Resources Institute, Washington, DC. The Web site (http://www.wri.org/) includes the assumptions made in making these estimates.

[a]Expressed in millions of metric tons of oil equivalents (Mtoe) for ready comparison of energy content. 1 metric ton oil equivalent (toe) = 7.8 barrels of oil = 1270 m^3 of natural gas = 2.3 metric ton (t) of coal.

Self-Assessment Questions

1. Coal, petroleum, and natural gas are called fossil fuels because they
   a. are burned to release energy
   b. are nonrenewable and will run out
   c. cause air pollution
   d. were formed over millennia from the remains of ancient plants and animals

2. Which of the following is *not* a fuel?
   a. C
   b. $CH_3CH_2CH_3$
   c. CH_3CH_2OH
   d. CO_2

3. All fuels are
   a. carbon compounds
   b. hydrocarbons
   c. oxidized forms of matter
   d. reduced forms of matter

Answers: 1, d; 2, d; 3, d

15.5 Coal: The Carbon Rock of Ages

Learning Objectives ❭ List advantages and disadvantages of coal as a fuel.

People probably have used small amounts of coal since prehistoric times. After the steam engine came into widespread use (by about 1850), the Industrial Revolution was powered largely by coal. By 1900, about 95% of the world's energy production came from the burning of coal. Today, coal supplies about 27% of worldwide energy production.

Coal is a complex combination of organic materials that burn and inorganic materials that produce ash. Its main element is carbon, but it also contains small percentages of other elements. The quality of coal is based on carbon content and those other elements. Complete combustion of carbon produces carbon dioxide.

▲ Coal is a fossil fuel. Giant ferns, reeds, and grasses that grew during the Carboniferous period 300 million years ago were buried and then, through the ages, were converted to the coal we burn today.

Carbon (from coal)   Oxygen (from air)

$$C(s) + O_2(g) \longrightarrow CO_2(g)$$

When combustion occurs in limited quantities of air, however, carbon monoxide and soot are formed.

$$2\,C(s) + O_2(g) \longrightarrow 2\,CO(g)$$

Soot is mostly unburned carbon.

Coal is ranked by carbon content, from low-grade peat and lignite to high-grade anthracite (Table 15.5). The energy obtained from coal is roughly proportional to

Table 15.5	**Approximate Composition (Percent by Mass) and Energy Content of Typical Grades of Coal (Dry Basis)**					
Grade of Coal	**Carbon**	**Hydrogen**	**Oxygen**	**Nitrogen**	**Sulfur**	**Energy Content (MJ/kg)**
Wood (for comparison)	50	6	43	1	0.05	—
Peat	60	6	33	2	0.26–0.48	14.7
Lignite (brown coal)	71	5	25	1	0.4	23
Bituminous (soft) coal	86–91	5	5–15	1	0.7–4.0	36
Anthracite (hard coal)	95	2–3	2–3	Trace	0.6–0.77	35.2

Source: Diessel, C. F. K. *Coal-Bearing Depositional Systems.* New York: Springer-Verlag, 1992.

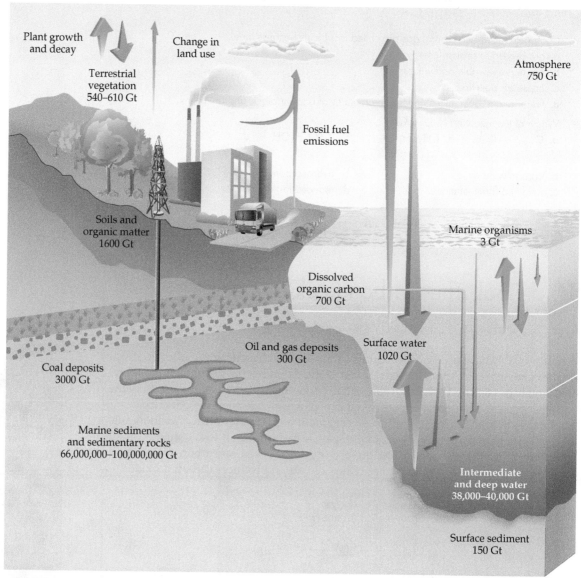

▲ **Figure 15.6** The carbon cycle. The numbers indicate the quantity of carbon, in gigatons (1Gt = 10⁹ t), in each location. The arrows indicate the general direction of travel of carbon during its cycle.

its carbon content. Soft (bituminous) coal is much more plentiful than hard coal (anthracite). Lignite and peat have become increasingly important as the supplies of higher grades of coal have been depleted.

Coal deposits that exist today are less than 600 million years old. For millions of years, Earth was much warmer than it is now, and plant life flourished. Most plants lived, died, and decayed—playing their normal role in the carbon cycle (Figure 15.6). But some plant material became buried under mud and water. There, in the absence of oxygen, it decayed only partially. The structural material of plants is largely cellulose [$(C_6H_{10}O_5)_n$]. Under increasing pressure, as the material was buried more deeply, the cellulose molecules broke down. Small molecules rich in hydrogen and oxygen escaped, leaving behind a material increasingly rich in carbon. Thus, peat is an immature coal, only partly converted, with plant stems and leaves clearly visible. Anthracite, on the other hand, has been almost completely carbonized.

Abundant but Inconvenient Fuel

Coal is by far the most plentiful fossil fuel. The United States has about a quarter of the world's reserves. Electric utilities in the United States burn 1.0 billion metric tons of coal each year, generating 3.78 trillion kWh of electricity (45% of the total).

Coal, a solid, is an inconvenient fuel to use and dangerous to obtain. Coal mining is one of the most dangerous occupations in the world, accounting for over

(a)   (b)

100,000 deaths in the United States in the twentieth century alone. Strip mining, although efficient, can devastate large areas. Coal is hauled in trains, barges, and trucks. We continue to pay great costs to extract coal from the ground and to transport it to the power plants and factories where it is used.

Source of Pollution

Unlike natural gas and liquid petroleum, solid coal contains minerals that are left as ash when the coal is burned. As Chapter 13 noted, some minerals enter the air as particulate matter, constituting a major pollution problem.

Much of our remaining coal reserves are high in sulfur. When it burns, the stack gases must be scrubbed, or choking sulfur dioxide pours into the atmosphere. The SO_2 reacts with oxygen and moisture in the air to form sulfuric acid, which damages metal structures, marble buildings and statues, and human lungs. And coal is currently the largest single source of airborne mercury emissions in the United States.

Some coal is cleaned before it is burned. A flotation method makes use of the different densities of coal and its major impurities. Coal has a density of about 1.3 g/cm³. Shale, a rock formed from hardened clay, has a density of about 2.5 g/cm³. Pyrite (FeS_2), the major source of sulfur in coal, has a density of about 5.0 g/cm³. A detergent solution of the proper density allows the coal to be floated off, leaving the heavier minerals behind. Coal can also be converted to more convenient gaseous and liquid fuels, again leaving the minerals behind. All these processes add to the cost of the coal.

Coal is more than just a fuel. When it is heated in the absence of air, volatile material is driven off, leaving behind a product—mostly carbon—called *coke*, which is used in the production of iron and steel. The more volatile material is condensed to liquid coal oil and a sticky mixture called *coal tar*, both of which are sources of organic chemicals for medical and industrial use.

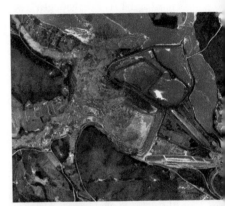

▲ **It DOES Matter!**
Once removed from the flue gases, fly ash may seem benign, but it is produced in enormous quantities that must be disposed of or stored. A coal-burning plant in Kingston, Tennessee, stored ash as a slurry (a mixture of fly ash and water) in ponds. In 2008, an ash dike ruptured, releasing 4 million m³ of coal fly-ash slurry, which covered 300 acres, damaging homes, washing out a road, rupturing a gas line and a water main, blocking a rail line, and felling trees.

The flotation method removes most inorganic sulfur compounds, such as pyrite, from coal. It does not remove sulfur atoms covalently bonded to the carbon atoms in the coal. This bound sulfur still contributes to pollution.

Self-Assessment Questions

1. Analysis of a solid fuel shows it to be 90% carbon. It is most likely
   a. anthracite coal
   b. bituminous coal
   c. peat
   d. wood

2. When coal is burned, the inorganic constituents end up as
   a. ash
   b. carbon monoxide
   c. flue gases
   d. organic matter

3. The most plentiful fossil fuel is
   a. coal
   b. natural gas
   c. petroleum
   d. propane

4. Which fossil fuel contributes the most to SO_x pollution?
   a. coal
   b. natural gas
   c. petroleum
   d. propane

5. On what physical property is the flotation method of coal cleaning based?
   a. density
   b. electrostatic precipitation
   c. melting point
   d. temperature

Answers: 1, b; 2, a; 3, a; 4, a; 5, a

15.6 Natural Gas and Petroleum

Both natural gas and petroleum consist of hydrocarbons formed by the anaerobic decomposition of remains of living microorganisms. These remains settled to the bottom of the sea millions of years ago. The organic matter was buried under layers of mud and converted over the ages by high temperature and pressure to gaseous and liquid hydrocarbons.

Natural Gas

Natural gas, composed principally of methane, is the cleanest of the fossil fuels. Minor components of this gaseous fossil fuel vary greatly. In North America, a pipeline natural gas supply might contain about 82% methane, 6% ethane, 2% propane, and smaller amounts of butanes and pentanes.

Natural gas burns with a relatively clean flame, and the products are mainly carbon dioxide and water.

$$CH_4(g) + 2 O_2(g) \longrightarrow CO_2(g) + 2 H_2O(g) + heat$$

The gas, as it comes from the ground, often contains nitrogen (N_2), sulfur compounds, and other substances as impurities. As in any combustion in air, some nitrogen oxides are formed. When natural gas is burned in insufficient air, carbon monoxide and soot can be major products.

$$2 CH_4(g) + 3 O_2(g) \longrightarrow 2 CO(g) + 4 H_2O(g)$$

$$CH_4(g) + O_2(g) \longrightarrow C(s) + 2 H_2O(g)$$

Natural gas is trapped in geological formations capped by impermeable rock. It is removed through wells drilled into the gas-bearing formations. About 90% of today's natural gas in the United States is obtained by hydraulic fracturing, or fracking, of shale formations 5000 feet below ground. Fracking involves forcing chemically treated water under high pressure into the layers of rock. The fractured rock releases the gas. Fracking produces millions of gallons of wastewater that is often contaminated with chemicals. The process of fracking can also contaminate groundwater.

Most natural gas is used as fuel, supplying about 23% of worldwide energy consumption, but it is also an important raw material. In North America, a portion of the two- to four-carbon alkanes is separated from the rest of the natural gas. Ethane and propane are *cracked*—decomposed by heating with a catalyst—to form ethylene and propylene. These alkenes are intermediates in the synthesis of plastics (Chapter 10) and many other useful commodities. Natural gas is also the raw material from which methanol and many other organic compounds are made. Like other fossil fuels, its supply is limited (refer to Table 15.4).

Petroleum: Liquid Hydrocarbons

With the development of the internal combustion engine, petroleum became increasingly important and by 1950 had replaced coal as the principal fuel. **Petroleum** is an extremely complex liquid mixture of organic compounds—as many as 17,000 were separated from a sample of Brazilian crude oil. Most are hydrocarbons: alkanes, cycloalkanes, and aromatic compounds. As with natural gas, complete combustion of these substances yields mainly carbon dioxide and water. A representative reaction is that of an octane.

$$2 C_8H_{18}(l) + 25 O_2(g) \longrightarrow 16 CO_2(g) + 18 H_2O(g)$$

Combustion of petroleum in air also produces nitrogen oxides. Incomplete burning yields carbon monoxide and soot. Petroleum usually contains small amounts of sulfur compounds that produce sulfur dioxide when burned.

▲ Composition of typical natural gas. Natural gas is mostly methane, with small amounts of other hydrocarbons, nitrogen, and a few other gases.

▲ Natural gas burns with a relatively clean flame.

Petroleum is thought to be formed mainly from the fats of ocean-dwelling, microscopic animals because it is nearly always found in rocks of oceanic origin. Fats are made up mainly of compounds containing carbon, hydrogen, and a little oxygen (for example, $C_{57}H_{110}O_6$). Removal of some oxygen and slight rearrangement of the carbon and hydrogen atoms in these fats form typical petroleum hydrocarbon molecules.

Fuel oil, used for heating homes and to produce electricity, can be burned efficiently and thus contributes only moderately to air pollution. Gasoline, however, is the major fraction of petroleum and is used to power automobiles. Because internal combustion engines are both numerous and rather inefficient, the combustion of gasoline contributes greatly to air pollution (Chapter 13). Petroleum-derived fuels are generally dirtier than natural gas because they contain more impurities. However, both types of fuel are major sources of CO_2 emissions that are causing global climate change.

Air pollution isn't the only problem: Burning up our petroleum reserves will leave us without a ready source of many familiar materials. Most industrial organic chemicals come from petroleum (others are derived from coal and natural gas). These chemicals yield plastics, synthetic fibers, solvents, and many other consumer products.

Worldwide, petroleum still appears to be quite abundant (see Table 15.4). However, U.S. petroleum reserves have been declining since 1972. Further tapping of offshore deposits and deeper drilling would produce only a few years' supply and would require a great deal more energy (and money) than drilling on land.

The developed countries of North America, Western Europe, and Japan depend heavily on oil imports from politically unstable developing nations, making the industrial nations economically and politically vulnerable.

U.S. dependence on imported oil leads to economic and political problems. Political events in the oil-rich Middle East have caused huge oil price increases several times. Continued military involvement in Iraq, disastrous hurricanes in the Gulf of Mexico, and increased demand in developing countries, especially China, caused crude oil prices to hit record highs in 2008, with only small price drops afterward.

Obtaining and Refining Petroleum

Crude oil is liquid, a convenient form for transportation. Petroleum is pumped easily through pipelines or hauled across the oceans in giant tankers. Pumping petroleum from the ground requires little energy. As domestic supplies diminish, however, we will have to expend an increasing fraction of the energy content of petroleum to transport it to where it is needed. Also, as petroleum is pumped out of the ground, the remaining oil becomes increasingly difficult to extract. The oil that is left behind is more scattered, and more energy is required to collect it.

As it comes from the ground, crude oil is of limited use. To make it better suited to our needs, we separate it into fractions by boiling it in a distillation column (Figure 15.7). Petroleum deposits nearly always have associated natural gas, part or all of which also goes through a separation process. The lighter hydrocarbon molecules come off at the top of the column, and the heavier ones at the bottom (Table 15.6).

Table 15.6	Typical Petroleum Fractions		
Fraction	**Typical Size Range of Hydrocarbons**	**Approximate Range of Boiling Points (°C)**	**Typical Uses**
Gas	CH_4 to C_4H_{10}	Less than 40	Fuel, starting materials for plastics
Gasoline	C_5H_{12} to $C_{12}H_{26}$	40–200	Fuel, solvents
Kerosene	$C_{12}H_{26}$ to $C_{16}H_{34}$	175–275	Diesel fuel, jet fuel, home heating, cracking to gasoline
Heating oil	$C_{15}H_{32}$ to $C_{18}H_{38}$	250–400	Industrial heating, cracking to gasoline
Lubricating oil	$C_{17}H_{36}$ and up	Above 300	Lubricants
Residue	$C_{20}H_{42}$ and up	Above 350 (some decomposition)	Paraffin, asphalt

Gasoline is usually the fraction of petroleum most in demand, and fractions that boil at higher temperatures are often converted to gasoline by cracking. This process, with $C_{14}H_{30}$ as an example, is illustrated in Figure 15.8. Cracking not only converts

▶ **Figure 15.7** The fractional distillation of petroleum. Crude oil is vaporized, and the column separates the components according to their boiling points. The lower-boiling constituents reach the top of the column, and the higher-boiling components come off lower in the column. A nonvolatile residue collects at the bottom.

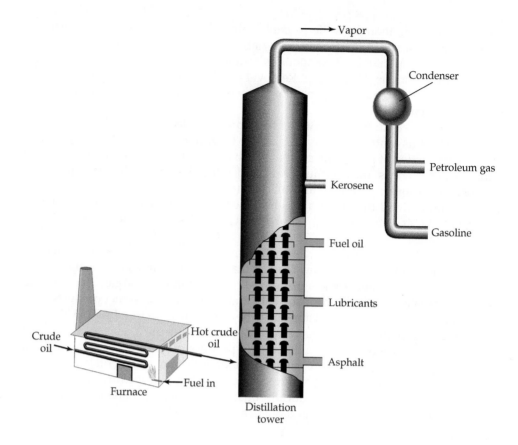

some of the large molecules to those in the gasoline range (C_5H_{12} through $C_{12}H_{26}$) but also produces a variety of useful by-products. The unsaturated hydrocarbons are starting materials for the manufacture of a host of petrochemicals.

▶ **Figure 15.8** Formulas of a few of the possible products formed when $C_{14}H_{30}$, a typical molecule in kerosene, is cracked. In practice, a wide variety of hydrocarbons (most of which have fewer than 15 carbon atoms), hydrogen gas, and char (mostly elemental carbon) are formed. Cyclic and branched-chain hydrocarbons are also produced.

$$CH_3CH_2CH_2CH_2CH_2CH_2CH_2CH_2CH_2CH_2CH_2CH_2CH_2CH_3 \xrightarrow[\text{catalyst}]{\text{heat}}$$

$$CH_3CH_2CH_2CH_2CH_2CH_2CH_2CH_2CH_2CH_2CH_2CH_3 \ + \ CH_2{=}CH_2$$
and
$$CH_3CH_2CH_2CH_2CH_2CH_2CH_2CH_2CH_2CH_2CH_3 \ + \ CH_3CH{=}CH_2$$
and
$$CH_3CH_2CH_2CH_2CH_2CH_2CH_2CH_3 \ + \ CH_3CH_2CH_2CH_2CH{=}CH_2$$
and so on

The cracking process illustrates the way chemists modify nature's materials to meet human needs and desires. Starting with petroleum or coal tar, chemists can create a dazzling array of substances with a wide variety of properties, including plastics, pesticides, herbicides, perfumes, preservatives, painkillers, antibiotics, stimulants, depressants, dyes, and detergents.

The ability to modify hydrocarbon molecules enables the petroleum industry to shift production to whatever fraction is desired. The industry can, on demand, increase the proportion of gasoline in summer, or of fuel oil in winter, from a given supply of petroleum. It can even make gasoline from coal. However, fossil fuels and other products from them are not sustainable. Scientists are seeking new sources of energy that do not depend on petroleum. Perhaps we can soon reduce this profligate waste of resources. Spaceship Earth has aboard it all the supplies it will have in the foreseeable future. We must use them wisely.

Gasoline

Gasoline, like the petroleum from which it is derived, is mainly a mixture of hydrocarbons. Commercial gasoline typically contains more than 150 different compounds, but up to 1000 have been identified in some blends. Among the hydrocarbons, a typical gasoline sample might have, by volume, 4–8% straight-chain alkanes, 25–40% branched-chain alkanes, 2–5% alkenes, 3–7% cycloalkanes, 1–4% cycloalkenes, and 20–50% aromatic hydrocarbons (0.5–2.5% benzene). Gasoline also contains a variety of additives, including antiknock agents, antioxidants, antirust agents, anti-icing agents, upper-cylinder lubricants, detergents, and dyes. Typical alkanes in gasoline range from C_5H_{12} to $C_{12}H_{26}$. There are also small amounts of some sulfur- and nitrogen-containing compounds.

The gasoline fraction of petroleum as it comes from a distillation column is called *straight-run gasoline*. It doesn't burn very well in modern high-compression automobile engines, but chemists are able to modify it to make it burn more smoothly.

The Octane Ratings of Gasolines

In an internal combustion engine, the gasoline–air mixture sometimes ignites before the spark plug "fires." This is called *knocking* and can damage the engine. Early on, scientists learned that some types of hydrocarbons, especially those with branched structures, burned more evenly and were less likely to cause knocking than others. An arbitrary performance standard, called the **octane rating**, was established in 1927. Isooctane was assigned an octane rating of 100. An unbranched-chain compound, heptane, was given an octane rating of 0. A gasoline rated 90 octane was one that performed the same as a mixture that was 90% isooctane and 10% heptane.

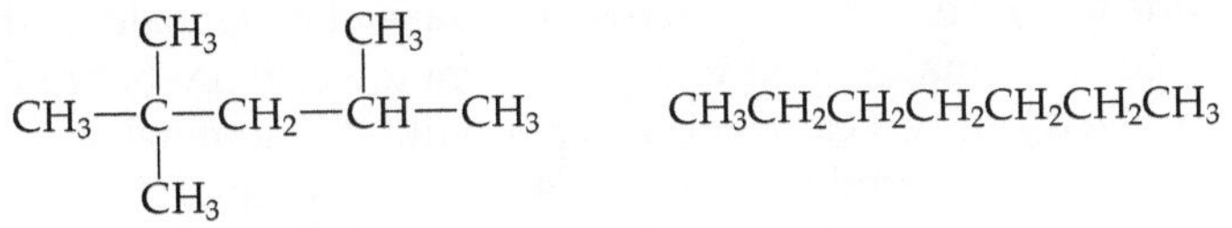

Isooctane
(Octane rating 100)

Heptane
(Octane rating 0)

During the 1930s, chemists discovered that the octane rating of gasoline could be improved by heating it in the presence of a catalyst such as sulfuric acid (H_2SO_4) or aluminum chloride ($AlCl_3$). This *isomerizes* some of the unbranched molecules to highly branched molecules. For example, heptane molecules can be isomerized so that they have branched structures.

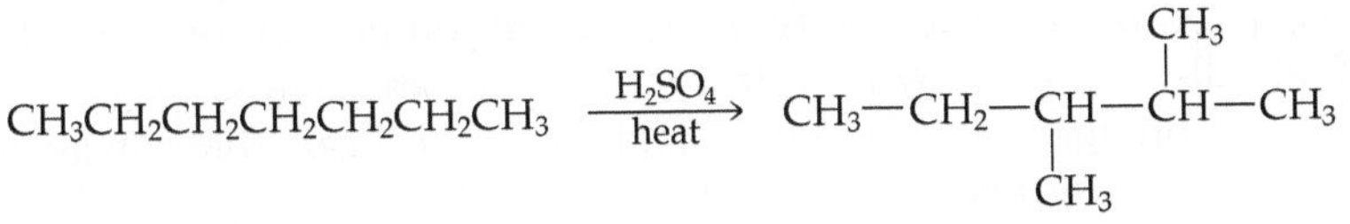

Unbranched, lower-octane fuel

Branched, higher-octane fuel

Chemists also can combine small hydrocarbon molecules (below the size range of gasoline) into larger ones more suitable for use as fuel. This process is called *alkylation*. In a typical alkylation reaction, shown below, isobutylene is reacted with propane.

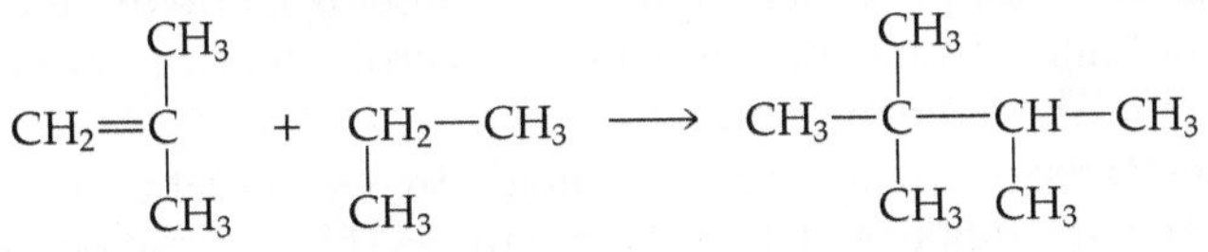

Light molecules,
unsuitable for automobile fuel

Heavier molecule,
more suitable for automobiles

The product molecules are in the right size range for gasoline, and the highly branched molecules are high in octane number.

▲ Fuel with the octane booster tetraethyllead, called "ethyl gasoline," was available at many gas stations before the additive was phased out, beginning in the 1970s.

Certain additives substantially improve the antiknock quality of gasoline. Tetraethyllead [$Pb(CH_2CH_3)_4$] was found to be especially effective. As little as 1 mL of tetraethyllead per liter of gasoline (1 part per 1000) increases the octane rating by 10 or more.

Lead fouls the catalytic converters used in modern automobiles. More important, lead is especially toxic to the brain. Even small amounts can lead to learning disabilities in children. In the United States, unleaded gasoline became available in 1974, and leaded gasoline has been phased out as automotive fuel.

Scientists have found other ways to get high octane ratings for unleaded fuels. For example, petroleum refineries use **catalytic reforming** to convert low-octane alkanes to high-octane aromatic compounds. Hexane (with an octane number of 25) is converted to benzene (octane number 106).

$$CH_3CH_2CH_2CH_2CH_2CH_3 \xrightarrow[\text{heat}]{\text{catalyst}} + 4\,H_2$$

Hexane
Octane 25

Benzene
Octane 106

Octane boosters that have replaced tetraethyllead include ethanol, methanol, *tert*-butyl alcohol, and methyl *tert*-butyl ether (MTBE). None of these is nearly as effective as tetraethyllead in boosting the octane rating. They must therefore be used in fairly large proportions. The EPA allows up to 15% ethanol in gasoline (E15 fuel) for cars built in 2001 or later.

Unlike gasoline, which is made up of hydrocarbons, the alcohols used as octane boosters all contain oxygen and therefore are sometimes called *oxygenates*. Not only do these additives improve the octane rating, but they also decrease the amount of carbon monoxide in auto exhaust gas. A disadvantage of oxygenates is that they are partially oxidized. That makes their energy content lower than that of pure hydrocarbon fuels, so the distance a car can travel per tankful is somewhat shorter.

MTBE, like ethers in general (Chapter 9), is rather unreactive chemically, but it is soluble in water to the extent of 4.8 g per 100 g of water. When gasoline spills or leaks from storage tanks, MTBE enters the groundwater, leading to widespread contamination. MTBE is listed as a hazardous substance under the federal Superfund Act and is considered a potential human carcinogen by the EPA. The exact threat to human health is far from clear, but use of MTBE in gasoline has been banned in many areas.

Alternative Fuels

An automobile engine can be made to run on nearly any liquid or gaseous fuel. There are cars on the road today powered by natural gas, by propane, by diesel fuel, by fuel cells, and even by used fast-food restaurant grease. There are electric cars that can be plugged into the power grid and hybrid cars that can switch from electricity to gasoline as needed.

Diesel fuel for automobiles overlaps the kerosene fraction of petroleum (refer to Table 15.6); it consists mainly of C_9 to C_{20} hydrocarbons with a boiling range of about 250–350 °C. Diesel fuel has a greater proportion of straight-chain alkanes than gasoline does. The standard for performance, called the *cetane number*, is based on hexadecane ($C_{16}H_{34}$), once known as cetane. A renewable fuel called *biodiesel* can be used in some unmodified diesel engines. Biodiesel is made by reacting ethanol with vegetable oils and animal fats. The triacylglycerol esters are converted to ethyl esters of the fatty acids in the oils and fats.

Brazil makes extensive use of ethanol, made by fermentation of sucrose from sugar cane. In the United States, flexible fuel vehicles (FFVs) are designed to run on E85 gasoline, a fuel that is 85% ethanol and 15% gasoline. Ethanol alone or blended with gasoline is not likely to be an answer to our energy problems. Most ethanol is made from corn, and widespread use would require conversion of huge tracts of farmland to corn production. And diversion of corn to ethanol production apparently leads to increased food prices.

Energy Return on Energy Invested

When evaluating an energy source, we need to consider the *energy return on energy invested* (EROEI) of exploiting the source. EROEIs are difficult to evaluate, and the results often have a high degree of uncertainty. However, these ratings can be quite important because if the EROEI of a source is 1 or less, it becomes an energy sink rather than a source.

In the early days of the petroleum industry, the EROEI for Texas crude oil may have been as much as 100:1; investing the equivalent of 1 barrel of oil could produce 100 barrels. The EROEI for oil from the Middle East is still about 10:1, and that of oil produced today in the United States is about 3:1. Oil from ever more remote places or ever deeper offshore wells will have ever lower EROEIs.

The EROEIs of alternative energy sources are often quite low. Canada has vast deposits of tar sands, but the EROEI is only about 1.5:1. Colorado has huge deposits of oil shale, but the EROEI is likely to be quite low.

The EROEI for ethanol is the subject of much debate, with proposed values ranging from a low of 0.78:1 to the highest estimate for ethanol from corn of 1.67:1. There are two reasons for the low EROEI for ethanol: Much energy is needed to distill or evaporate the ethanol after fermentation; and ethanol has a lower energy content than petroleum fuels.

The EROEI of wind energy in good locations is about 20:1, and that for silicon-based solar panels is about 12:1. Hydrogen has an EROEI of less than 1:1 because it can neither be extracted from the ground nor generated by a biosystem. Hydrogen can be generated by electricity or by heating steam to very high (2000 °C) temperatures. For now, those measures require more energy than the hydrogen produces when burned.

In addition to the EROEI, we have to consider the environmental consequences of exploiting an energy source. For example, getting oil from tar sands or oil shale is a messy process. Thus, our quest for plentiful energy will be costly and controversial.

Self-Assessment Questions

1. The main constituent in natural gas is
   a. CH_4 **b.** $CH_3CH_2CH_3$ **c.** C_6H_6 **d.** CH_3OH

2. Which of the fossil fuels is the cleanest and simplest in composition?
   a. coal
   c. petroleum
   b. it depends on the source
   d. natural gas

3. In the United States, oil production
   a. peaked in 1970
   c. peaked in 2010
   b. peaked in 1999
   d. will peak in 2030

Questions 4–7 refer to petroleum processing.

4. Cracking is used to
   a. convert heavier fractions to lighter ones
   b. improve the octane rating
   c. remove sulfur
   d. separate various fractions

5. An alkylation unit
   a. converts lighter fractions to heavier ones
   b. improves the asphalt yield
   c. removes sulfur
   d. separates various fractions

6. Isomerization is used to convert
   a. alcohols to ethers
   b. branched alkane molecules to straight-chain ones
   c. hexane to isooctane
   d. straight-chain molecules to branched ones

7. Catalytic reforming converts
   a. branched molecules to straight-chain ones
   b. branched molecules to aromatic ones
   c. straight-chain molecules to aromatic ones
   d. straight-chain molecules to branched ones

3. Why don't we use more alternative fuels like ethanol?
Use of alternative fuels is increasing, but the cost (EROEI) of those fuels is very high compared to that of fossil fuels. Also, the current infrastructure is set up to use fossil fuels, and it would be very costly to build new infrastructure (such as hydrogen filling stations or ethanol pumps and tanks).

8. The octane rating for gasoline is a measure of the fuel's
   a. concentration of octane (C_8H_{18})
   b. energy content in kilocalories
   c. power rating
   d. tendency to cause knocking

9. E15 fuel is
   a. 15% ethanol, 85% gasoline
   b. 85% ethanol, 15% gasoline
   c. 15% isooctane
   d. 15% ether

Answers: 1, a; 2, d; 3, a; 4, a; 5, a; 6, d; 7, c; 8, d; 9, a

15.7 Convenient Energy

Learning Objective ❯ Explain why gaseous and liquid fuels are more convenient to use than solid fuels.

The convenience of a fuel depends on its physical state: Gases and liquids are convenient, while solids are much less so. Perhaps the most convenient form of energy is electricity (Table 15.7). We can use electricity to provide light and hot water and to run motors of all sorts. We can use it to heat and cool our homes and workplaces. When looking at future energy sources, then, we look to a large degree at ways of generating electricity.

Table 15.7 Convenience of Fuels in Various Physical States

Physical State	Extraction	Transportation to Cities	Distribution within a City	In Use Convenience	In Use Cleanliness
Solids (coal, wood)	Shovels, borers, blasting	Trucks, trains, barges (slurry with water in pipe)	Trucks, buckets	Least	Dirtiest
Liquids (gasoline, fuel oil)	Pumps	Pipelines, tankers, barges, trucks	Trucks		
Gases (natural gas)	Pumps	Pipeline	Pipes		
Electricity[a] (electron flow)	—	Wires	Wires	Most	Cleanest

[a]Produced by burning any of the primary fuels and included for comparison.

Any fuel can be burned to boil water, and the steam produced can turn a turbine to generate electricity. Figure 15.9 shows a coal-fired steam power plant. At present, about 45% of U.S. electric energy comes from coal-burning plants (Figure 15.10). Such facilities are at best only about 40% efficient. Thus, about 60% of the energy of the fossil fuel is wasted as heat, though some power installations use this waste heat to warm buildings.

Coal Gasification and Liquefaction

Coal can be converted to gas or oil. When we run short of gas and petroleum, why not make them from coal? The technology has been around for years. Gasification and liquefaction do have some advantages: Gases and liquids are easy to transport, and the process of conversion leaves much of the sulfur and minerals behind, thus overcoming a serious disadvantage of coal as a fuel.

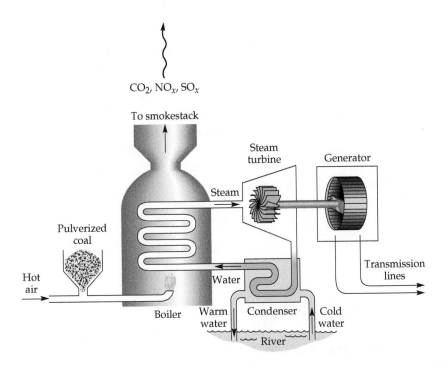

The basic process for converting coal to a synthetic gaseous fuel involves reduction of carbon by hydrogen. Passing steam over hot charcoal produces *synthesis gas*, a mixture of hydrogen and carbon monoxide.

$$C(s) + H_2O(g) \longrightarrow CO(g) + H_2$$

The hydrogen can be used to reduce the carbon in coal or other substances to form methane.

$$C(s) + 2 H_2(g) \longrightarrow CH_4(g)$$

Coal can also be converted to methanol by way of synthesis gas. Part of the CO in synthesis gas is reacted with water to form more H_2.

$$CO(g) + H_2O(g) \longrightarrow CO_2(g) + H_2(g)$$

The remaining CO is combined with H_2 to form methanol.

$$CO(g) + 2 H_2(g) \longrightarrow CH_3OH(l)$$

The methanol can be used directly as fuel or converted, in turn, to gasoline-like hydrocarbons that we represent as C_nH_m.

$$n\, CH_3OH(l) \longrightarrow C_nH_m(l) + x\, H_2O(l)$$

Each step requires an appropriate catalyst.

Both gasification and liquefaction of coal require a lot of energy: Up to one-third of the energy content of the coal is lost in the conversion. Liquid fuels from coal are high in unsaturated hydrocarbons and sulfur, nitrogen, and arsenic compounds, and their combustion products are high in particulate matter. Coal conversions also require large amounts of water, yet the large coal deposits that would be used are in arid regions. Furthermore, these processes are messy. Without stringent safeguards, conversion plants would seriously pollute both air and water.

Other processes that have been used to make liquid fuels from coal are the Bergius and Fischer–Tropsch methods. In the Bergius method, coal is reacted with hydrogen. In the Fischer–Tropsch method, coal is reacted with steam to make a mixture of carbon monoxide and hydrogen, which is then reacted over an iron catalyst to produce a mixture of hydrocarbons. Both processes were used in Germany during World War II. Since 1955, the Sasol company has used a variation of the Fischer–Tropsch method to provide a significant portion of liquid fuels for South Africa.

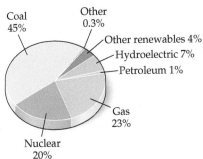

Industry total = 3800 billion kilowatt-hours

Coal 45%
Other 0.3%
Other renewables 4%
Hydroelectric 7%
Petroleum 1%
Gas 23%
Nuclear 20%

▲ **Figure 15.10** Percentages of electric power generation in the United States from various energy sources in 2009.

Self-Assessment Questions

1. About what percentage of the electricity produced in the United States comes from coal-burning plants?

   a. 25% **b.** 35% **c.** 50% **d.** 80%

2. Natural gas is transported mainly by

   a. ocean-going tanker **b.** pipelines
   c. railroad car **d.** truck

3. Coal gasification produces mainly

   a. coke **b.** H_2 **c.** CH_4 **d.** $CH_3CH_2CH_3$

4. The convenience of a fuel depends on its

   a. carbon content **b.** density
   c. odor **d.** physical state

Answers: 1, c; 2, b; 3, c; 4, d

15.8 Nuclear Energy

Learning Objectives ❭ List advantages and disadvantages of nuclear energy.
❭ Describe how a nuclear power plant generates electricity.

In Chapter 11, we explored nuclear reactions and noted that both nuclear fission and nuclear fusion can be used in bombs. So far, nuclear fusion reactions cannot be controlled for producing energy; they can be employed only in bombs. Nuclear fission reactions, however, can be controlled in a **nuclear reactor**. The energy released during fission can be used to generate steam, which can turn a turbine to generate electricity (Figure 15.11).

At the dawn of the nuclear age, some people envisioned nuclear power as likely to fulfill the biblical prophecy of a fiery end to our world. Others saw it as a source of unlimited energy. During the late 1940s, some claimed that electricity from nuclear power plants would become so cheap that it eventually would not have to be metered. Nuclear power has not yet brought either paradise or perdition, but it is highly controversial. Our great demand for energy indicates that the controversy will continue for years to come.

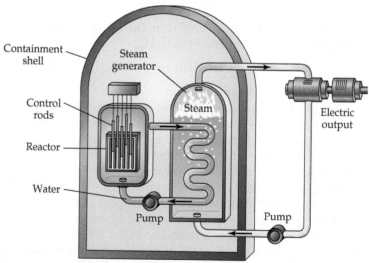

▲ **Figure 15.11** A diagram showing how a nuclear power plant generates electricity. Fission of uranium heats the water in the reactor, which generates steam that drives the turbines, producing electricity. Control rods absorb neutrons to slow the fission reaction as needed. Nuclear reactors are housed in containment buildings made of steel and reinforced concrete, designed to withstand nuclear accidents and prevent the release of radioactive substances into the environment.

Table 15.8 | Electricity Generation Using Nuclear Power Plants (Selected Countries)

Country	Total Electricity from Nuclear Power (%)	Number of Operating Nuclear Power Plants	Number of Nuclear Power Plants Under Construction
China	2	14	27
France	74	58	1
Germany	28	17	0
India	3	20	5
Japan	29	50	2
Russian Federation	17	32	11
Sweden	38	10	0
Ukraine	48	15	2
United States	20	104	1
Other countries	—	120	15
World total	14	440	64

Source: International Atomic Energy Agency, *PRIS Database.* Vienna: 2010.

At present, about 20% of U.S. electricity comes from nuclear power plants. The eastern seaboard and upper midwestern states, many of which have minimal fossil fuel reserves, are heavily dependent on nuclear power for electricity.

The United States could do as other nations do and rely more on nuclear power (Table 15.8), but the public is quite fearful of nuclear power plants. This apprehension was exacerbated in 2011 by the accident at Fukushima, Japan. The United States has 104 operating nuclear reactors, but only one new plant has been ordered since 1978. It takes about 10 years to build a nuclear power plant. There will have to be a dramatic change in public attitude if nuclear power is to play a big role in our energy future.

Nuclear Power Plants

There are several types of nuclear power plants, but we won't discuss the different designs. The one illustrated in Figure 15.11 is a pressurized water reactor. Earlier models were mainly boiling water reactors, in which the steam from the reactor was used to power the turbine directly.

Nuclear power plants use the same fission reactions employed in nuclear bombs, but nuclear power plants cannot blow up like bombs. The uranium used in power plants is enriched to only 3–4% uranium-235. A bomb requires about 90% uranium-235.

In a nuclear power plant, a *moderator* is used to slow down the neutrons produced by the fission reaction so that they can be absorbed by uranium-235 atoms. Ordinary water serves as the moderator in 75% of reactors worldwide, graphite is used in 20% of reactors, and heavy water (^2H_2O or D_2O) in 5% of reactors. The fission reaction is controlled by the insertion of boron steel or cadmium *control rods.* Boron and cadmium absorb neutrons readily, preventing them from participating in the chain reaction. These rods are installed when the reactor is built. Removing them partway starts the chain reaction; pushing them in all the way stops the reaction.

The Nuclear Advantage: Minimal Air Pollution

The main advantage of nuclear power plants over those that burn fossil fuels is in what they do not do. Unlike fossil-fuel-burning power plants, nuclear power plants produce no carbon dioxide to add to the greenhouse effect, and they add no sulfur oxides, nitrogen oxides, soot, or fly ash to the atmosphere. They contribute almost nothing to global warming, air pollution, or acid rain. They reduce our dependence on foreign oil and lower our trade deficit. If the 104 nuclear plants in the United States were replaced by coal-burning plants, airborne pollutants would increase by 18,000 tons per day!

Problems with Nuclear Power

Nuclear power plants have some disadvantages. Elaborate and expensive safety precautions must be taken to protect plant workers and the inhabitants of surrounding areas from radiation. The reactor must be heavily shielded and housed inside a containment building of metal and reinforced concrete. Because loss of coolant water can result in a meltdown of the reactor core, backup emergency cooling systems are required.

Despite what proponents call utmost precautions, some opponents of nuclear power still fear a runaway nuclear reaction in which a containment building is breached and massive amounts of radioactivity escape into the environment. The chance of such an accident is very small, but one did happen at Fukushima, Japan, when a tsunami caused by an earthquake hit the plant. Thousands of people were killed by the tsunami, and large areas were rendered uninhabitable by released radiation, perhaps for centuries. The benefit of nuclear power—abundant electric energy—is clear, but the small probability of a serious accident causes scientists and others to endlessly debate its desirability.

Another problem is that the fission products are highly radioactive and must be isolated from the environment for centuries. Again, scientists disagree about the feasibility of disposal of nuclear waste. Proponents of nuclear power say that such wastes can be safely stored in old salt mines or other geologic formations. Opponents fear that the wastes may rise from their "graves" and eventually contaminate the groundwater. It is impossible to do a million-year experiment in a few years to determine who is right. Federal funding for an underground repository at Yucca Mountain, Nevada, was terminated in 2011 after spending billions of dollars. This leaves the United States with no long-term storage site for high-level radioactive waste. These wastes are currently stored at 126 sites around the country.

Mining and processing of uranium ore produce wastes called *tailings*. Over 200 million tons of tailings now afflict ten western states. These tailings are mildly radioactive, giving off radon gas and gamma radiation. Dust from the mounds of tailings is dispersed to surrounding areas.

Any power plant has another problem, thermal pollution, that is unavoidable. As the energy from any material is converted to heat to generate electricity, some of the energy is released into the environment as waste heat. Nuclear power plants generate more thermal pollution than plants that burn fossil fuels, but this difference is perhaps not as important as the other problems we have mentioned.

Nuclear Accidents

In 1979, a loss-of-coolant accident at the Three Mile Island nuclear power plant near Harrisburg, Pennsylvania, released a tiny amount of radioactivity into the environment. Although no one was killed or seriously injured, the accident heightened public fear of nuclear power.

A 1986 accident at Chernobyl, Ukraine, was much more frightening. There, a reactor core meltdown killed several people outright. Others died from radiation sickness in the following weeks and months, and 135,000 people were evacuated. The Ukraine Radiological Institute estimates that the accident caused more than 2500 deaths overall. A large area will remain contaminated for decades. Radioactive fallout spread across much of Europe. The thyroid cancer rate among Ukrainians increased tenfold, and the overall risk of cancer rose because of exposure to radiation. At Three Mile Island, a containment building kept nearly all the radioactive material inside. The Chernobyl plant had no such protective structure.

The earthquake and tsunami at Fukushima, Japan in 2011 destroyed the external power supply, leading to partial core meltdowns in three reactors, with widespread release of radiation. The Fukushima accident is rated as the second worst in history,

Most of the nuclear waste currently awaiting disposal is from nuclear weapons production. High-level waste from nuclear power plant operation in the United States totals roughly 3000 tons per year. (Compare this to the coal ash produced in the U.S.: over 100 million tons per year!)

▲ Mildly radioactive tailings are a by-product of the processing of uranium ores.

after Chernobyl. Thousands were killed by the tsunami, but so far only a few by radiation.

There is considerable controversy over most aspects of nuclear power. Although scientists may be able to agree on the results of laboratory experiments, they don't always agree on what is best for society.

Breeder Reactors: Making More Fuel Than They Burn

The supply of the fissionable uranium-235 isotope is limited, as it makes up less than 1% of naturally occurring uranium. Separation of uranium-235 leaves behind large quantities of uranium-238, which is not fissionable. However, uranium-238 can be converted to fissionable plutonium-239 by bombardment with neutrons. Unstable uranium-239 is formed initially, but it rapidly decays to neptunium-239, which then decays to plutonium.

$$^{238}_{92}\text{U} + {}^{1}_{0}\text{n} \longrightarrow {}^{239}_{92}\text{U} \longrightarrow {}^{239}_{93}\text{Np} + {}^{0}_{-1}\text{e}$$

$$^{239}_{93}\text{Np} \longrightarrow {}^{239}_{94}\text{Pu} + {}^{0}_{-1}\text{e}$$

If a reactor is built with a core of fissionable plutonium surrounded by uranium-238, neutrons from the fission of plutonium convert the uranium-238 shield to more plutonium. In this way, the reactor, called a **breeder reactor**, produces more fuel than it consumes. There is enough uranium-238 to last a few centuries, so one of the disadvantages of nuclear plants could be overcome by the use of breeder reactors.

Breeder reactors have some problems of their own, however. Plutonium is fairly low melting (640 °C), and a plant is therefore limited to fairly cool, inefficient operation. Failure of the cooling system could cause the reactor's core to melt. Water is not adequate as a coolant, so molten sodium metal is used in the primary loop. These reactors are often called *liquid-metal fast breeder reactors*. If an accident occurred in such a breeder, the sodium could react violently with both the water and the air.

Plutonium is highly toxic and has a half-life of about 24,000 years. It emits alpha particles, making it especially dangerous if ingested. An estimated 1 µg in the lungs of a human is enough to induce lung cancer. Yet another problem is that plutonium is chemically different from uranium-238. That makes it much easier than uranium-235 to separate from uranium-238, for use in illicit nuclear weapons.

Another breeder reaction converts thorium-232 into fissionable uranium-233.

$$^{232}_{90}\text{Th} + {}^{1}_{0}\text{n} \longrightarrow {}^{233}_{90}\text{Th} \longrightarrow {}^{233}_{91}\text{Pa} + {}^{0}_{-1}\text{e}$$

$$^{233}_{91}\text{Pa} \longrightarrow {}^{233}_{92}\text{U} + {}^{0}_{-1}\text{e}$$

Uranium-233 is like plutonium in that it emits damaging alpha particles, but it is thought to be rather difficult to make bombs from reactor-grade uranium-233.

Only 11 breeder reactors with a production capacity of more than 100 MW have ever been built, none in the United States. And only one commercial breeder reactor is still operating (in Russia) in 2010, and it has never been fueled with plutonium.

Nuclear Fusion: The Sun in a Magnetic Bottle

Chapter 11 discussed the thermonuclear reactions that power the Sun and that occur in the explosion of hydrogen bombs. Control of these fusion reactions to produce electricity would give us nearly unlimited power. To date, fusion reactions have been useful only for making bombs, but research on the control of nuclear fusion is progressing (Figure 15.12).

Controlled fusion would have several advantages over nuclear fission as an energy source. The main fuel, deuterium (^2_1H), is plentiful and is obtained from *fractional electrolysis* (splitting apart by means of electricity) of water. (Only 1 hydrogen atom in 6500 is a deuterium atom, but we have oceans of water to work with.) The problem of radioactive wastes would be minimized. The end product, helium, is stable and biologically inert. Escape of tritium (^3_1H), which undergoes beta decay

▲ A tsunami in March 2011 caused a meltdown and release of radiation at this nuclear power plant in Fukushima, Japan. It is already classified as the second worst nuclear accident (after Chernobyl), and there are concerns about fish and other products in the vicinity being used for food or shipped to other countries.

A 20-year study of 70,000 nuclear shipyard workers found that they had 24% *lower* mortality than nonnuclear workers in the general population. Those with the highest chronic radiation exposure had the *lowest* mortality from all causes—including cancer. Could it be that small doses of radiation are beneficial?

Thorium-232 is especially attractive for use in breeder reactors because it is quite abundant. There is about as much thorium in the Earth's crust as there is lead.

▶ **Figure 15.12** A promising fusion reaction is the deuterium–tritium reaction. A hydrogen-2 (deuterium) nucleus fuses with a hydrogen-3 (tritium) nucleus to form a helium-4 nucleus. A neutron is released, along with a considerable quantity of energy.

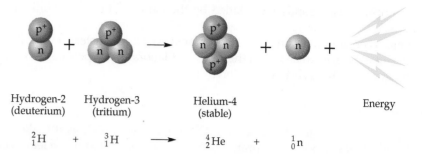

Hydrogen-2   Hydrogen-3   Helium-4   Energy
(deuterium)   (tritium)   (stable)

$$\ _{1}^{2}\text{H} \quad + \quad \ _{1}^{3}\text{H} \quad \longrightarrow \quad \ _{2}^{4}\text{He} \quad + \quad \ _{0}^{1}\text{n}$$

with a half-life of 12.3 years, might be a problem because this hydrogen isotope would be readily incorporated into organisms. Also, neutrons are emitted in most fusion reactions, and neutrons can convert stable isotopes into radioactive ones. Finally, we would still be concerned with thermal pollution—the unavoidable loss of part of the energy as heat.

Great technical difficulties have to be overcome before a controlled fusion reaction can be used to produce energy. A sustainable fusion reaction would require

- attainment of a critical ignition temperature between 100 million °C and 200 million °C,
- a confinement time of 1–2 s, and
- an ion density of between 2×10^{20} and 3×10^{20} ions per cubic meter.

In practice, the required conditions are measured by a combination of these three values.

No molecule could hold together at the fusion temperature. No material on Earth can withstand more than a few thousand degrees. Even atoms are unstable under these conditions. Atoms are stripped of their electrons, and the nuclei and free electrons form a mixture called a *plasma*. The plasma, made of charged particles (nuclei and electrons), can be contained by a strong magnetic field (Figure 15.13).

▶ **Figure 15.13** A giant, doughnut-shaped electromagnet called a *tokamak* is designed to confine plasma at the extremely high temperatures and pressures required for nuclear fusion.

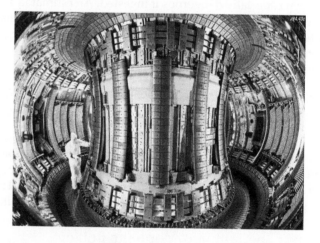

Nuclear fusion may well be our best hope for producing relatively clean, abundant energy in the future, but much work remains to be done. Once controlled fusion is achieved in a laboratory, it will still be decades before it becomes a practical source of energy.

Self-Assessment Questions

1. In a nuclear fission reactor,
   a. carbon-14 decays to nitrogen-14
   b. hydrogen nuclei fuse to form helium
   c. uranium-235 absorbs a neutron and splits into two smaller nuclei
   d. uranium-238 decays to plutonium-238

2. The control rods in a nuclear reactor
   a. absorb neutrons, allowing them to initiate fission
   b. absorb neutrons, preventing them from causing fission
   c. slow the neutrons down so the moderator can stop them
   d. speed the neutrons up so they will initiate fission

3. What percentage of the electricity used in the United States is produced by nuclear power plants?
   a. 5%   b. 10%   c. 20%   d. 50%

4. Nuclear reactors that produce more nuclear fuel than they consume
   a. are called breeder reactors   b. are called fusion reactors
   c. are called transuranic reactors   d. violate the law of conservation of energy

5. Approximately how many nuclear power plants are in operation in the United States?
   a. 50   b. 100   c. 200   d. 400

6. An advantage of nuclear power plants is that
   a. coal-burning plants have appalling safety records
   b. they produces no dangerous wastes
   c. they produces no greenhouse gases
   d. the reactor core cannot melt down

7. What is the missing product in the following nuclear reaction?

$$^2_1H + {}^3_1H \longrightarrow {}^1_0n + ?$$

   a. ^3_1H b. ^3_2He c. ^4_2He d. ^5_2He

8. Fission, not fusion, is used in nuclear power plants because fusion
   a. uses expensive transuranium elements as fuel
   b. produces less heat than fission
   c. produces waste products that are radioactive for centuries
   d. requires temperatures of millions of degrees, making the reaction difficult to contain

Answers: 1, c; 2, b; 3, c; 4, a; 5, b; 6, c; 7, c; 8, d

15.9 Renewable Energy Sources

Learning Objectives ❯ List important characteristics of renewable energy sources.
❯ List advantages and disadvantages of various kinds of renewable energy.

Burning fossil fuels leads to air pollution and to the depletion of vital resources. Using nuclear power also presents problems. Nuclear fuel is not unlimited, and the problem of waste disposal remains unsolved. We are turning to renewable energy sources, which account for about 8–11% of the energy production in the United States. This section discusses these sustainable energy sources.

Section 15.1 noted that most of the energy available on Earth comes from the Sun. With all that energy from our celestial power plant, why are we currently dependent on fossil fuels or nuclear power? The answer lies in the fact that solar energy is thinly spread out and difficult to capture directly.

Solar Heating

Solar energy can be used directly for heating. As it arrives on the surface of Earth, 30% of solar energy is simply reflected back into space. About half is converted to heat. We can increase the efficiency of this conversion rather easily. A black surface absorbs heat better than a light-colored one. To make a simple solar collector, we only have to cover a black surface with a glass plate. The glass is transparent to the incoming solar radiation, but it partially prevents the heat from escaping back into space. The hot surface is used to heat water or other liquids, and the hot liquids are usually stored in an insulated reservoir.

Water heated this way can be used directly for bathing, dish washing, and laundry, or it can be used to heat a building. Air is passed around the warm reservoir,

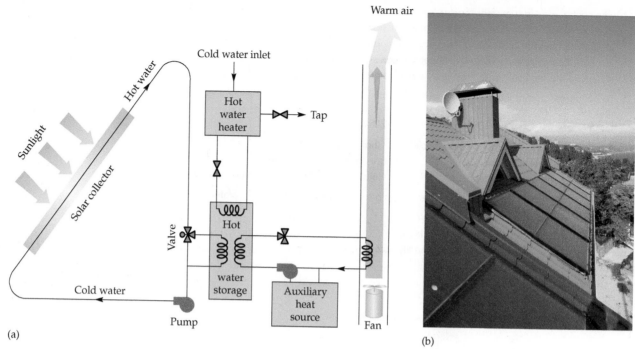

(a)

(b)

▲ **Figure 15.14** (a) Energy in sunlight is absorbed by solar collectors and used to heat water. The hot water can be used directly or circulated to partially heat a building. This diagram shows how a solar collector furnishes hot water and warm air for heating a building. (b) A variety of collectors can be used to absorb solar energy.

and the warmed air is then circulated through the building (Figure 15.14). Even in cold northern climates, solar collectors could meet about 50% of home heating requirements. These installations are expensive but can pay for themselves, through fuel savings, in a few years.

Solar Cells: Electricity from Sunlight

Sunlight also can be converted directly to electricity by devices called **photovoltaic cells**, or *solar cells*. These devices can be made from a variety of substances, but most are made from elemental silicon. In a crystal of pure silicon, each silicon atom has four valence electrons and is covalently bonded to four other silicon atoms (Figure 15.15). To make a solar cell, extremely pure silicon is "doped" with small amounts of specific impurities and formed into crystals.

▶ **Figure 15.15** Models of silicon crystals. Crystals doped with impurities such as arsenic and boron are more conductive than pure silicon and are used in solar cells.

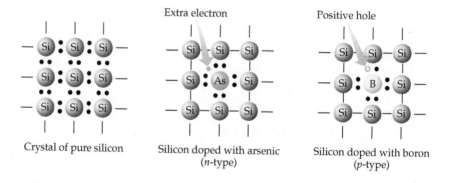

Crystal of pure silicon

Silicon doped with arsenic (*n*-type)

Silicon doped with boron (*p*-type)

One type of silicon crystal has about 1 ppm of arsenic added. Arsenic atoms have five valence electrons, four of which are used to form bonds to silicon atoms. The fifth electron is relatively free to move around. Because this material has extra electrons, and electrons are negatively charged, it is called an *n-type* (negative) *semiconductor*. Adding about 1 ppm of boron to silicon forms a different type of material. Boron has three valence electrons, producing a shortage of one electron and leaving a *positive hole* in the crystal. This boron-doped silicon is called a *p-type semiconductor*.

Joining the two types of crystals (*n*-type and *p*-type) forms a photovoltaic cell (Figure 15.16). Electrons flow from the *n*-type region, which has a high concentration of them, to the *p*-type region. However, the holes near the junction are quickly filled by nearby mobile electrons, and the flow ceases.

When sunlight hits the photovoltaic cell, an electric current is generated. The energetic photons knock electrons out of the Si—Si bonds, creating more mobile electrons and more positive holes. Because of the barrier at the junction between the two semiconductors, electrons cannot move through the interface. When an external circuit connects the two crystals, electrons flow from the *n*-type region around the circuit to the *p*-type region and that current can be used directly.

An array of solar cells, combined to form a solar battery, can produce about 100 W/m² of surface. That is, it takes 1 m² of cells to power one 100-W lightbulb. Solar batteries have been used for years to power artificial Earth satellites. They are now widely used to power small devices such as electronic calculators. They are also used to provide electricity for weather instruments in remote areas.

Current solar cells are not very efficient, converting about 12–18% of incident sunlight into electricity, though experimental systems using mirrors have achieved efficiencies of more than 40%. Much of the sunlight striking them is reflected back into space or converted to heat. The generation of enough energy to meet a significant portion of our demands would require covering vast areas of desert land with solar cells. It would require about 20 km² (or 5000 acres) of cloud-free desert land to produce as much energy as one nuclear power plant. However, research has led to more efficient solar cells, and their cost is decreasing.

Using solar energy requires storing the energy for use at night and on cloudy days. The technology is now widely available for using solar energy for space heating and for providing hot water. Several companies sell home-sized solar electric systems that can be connected to the normal supply line and can reduce electric bills to nearly zero. However, these systems are quite expensive. Solar power currently provides less than 1% of U.S. energy needs. Though use of solar energy is increasing, widespread use is still some years away.

Biomass: Photosynthesis for Fuel

Why bother with solar collectors and photovoltaic cells to capture energy from the Sun when green plants do it every day? Indeed, dry plant material, called **biomass** when used as a fuel, burns quite well. It could be used to fuel a power plant for the generation of electricity. Biomass burns cleanly. The emissions are almost entirely water vapor and the carbon dioxide the plants took from the air in the first place. "Energy plantations" could grow plants for use as fuel. Biomass is a renewable resource whose production is powered by the Sun.

Unfortunately, there are several disadvantages to this energy source, too. Most available land is needed for the production of food. Even where productive land is available, plants have to be planted, harvested, and transported to the power plant. Often, the land is far from where the energy is needed. However, some hybrid species of trees grow quickly and densely, reducing the needed growing area. The overall efficiency of biomass as an energy source is even less than that of solar cells—only about 3% at best. Nevertheless, there is considerable research activity focused on biomass, because nature "constructs" plants much more easily and more quickly than we can construct industrial plants.

Also, we don't have to burn plant material directly.

- Starches and sugars from plants can be fermented to form ethanol. Wood can be distilled in the absence of air to produce methanol. Both alcohols are liquids and thus convenient to transport, and both are excellent fuels that burn quite cleanly.
- Bacterial breakdown of plant material produces methane. Under proper conditions, this process can be controlled to produce a clean-burning fuel similar to natural gas.
- Oils and fats can be converted to a fuel called *biodiesel*. The triacylglycerols are converted into the methyl esters of the constituent fatty acids. A typical biodiesel molecule from palm oil is methyl palmitate, $CH_3(CH_2)_{14}COOCH_3$. Biodiesel from waste, algae, or nonfood plants can have a reasonably high EROEI and can be profitable.

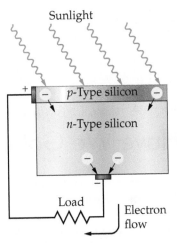

▲ **Figure 15.16** Schematic diagram of the operation of a solar cell. Electrons flow from the *n*-type region (lower layer) to the *p*-type region (upper layer) through the external circuit.

4. Is solar power or wind power the answer to the energy crisis? Both sources have made great progress but much work remains. Today's solar cells are far more expensive than fossil-fuel electricity and are too inefficient to provide a complete solution to our energy needs. Wind power is also expensive and has a high start-up cost. Neither source can directly power buses or cars.

Hemp, the fiber crop from which rope is made, is a good energy source. Its woody stalks are 77% cellulose, and hemp plants can produce 10 t of biomass per acre in just 4 months. The oil from hemp seeds can be used as diesel fuel. The problem is that hemp must be imported. It is illegal to raise hemp in the United States because the leaves and flowers of the female plant constitute the drug marijuana.

GREEN CHEMISTRY

Principles 1, 3, 4, 5, 6

Michael Heben, *University of Toledo*

Have We Got the Energy?

Energy permeates our existence. Energy is required anytime anything does "something." This is true whether we are considering a heart pumping blood in a body, an astronaut going to the Moon, a family driving to grandma's house, a plant fixing CO_2 to grow and produce food, an athlete playing sports, or a company making a chemical compound for industrial or pharmaceutical use.

Is there anything we do that does not require energy? No—and even thinking about the question can be exhausting—because thinking requires energy.

This chapter considers the sources of energy that are available to us. What we commonly consider to be energy sources, such as natural gas, coal, and oil, however, are not energy sources at all. Rather, these are fuels. They contain stored energy in carbon–carbon and carbon–hydrogen chemical bonds. These bonds react with oxygen during combustion, and the released heat can be used in homes or in industrial processes, to power an engine that does mechanical work, or to generate electricity.

The fossil fuels that we use today are the remains of ancient plant and animal matter. The energy source that produced the original organic matter via photosynthesis is our own star, the Sun (Section 15.1). Because the stored energy will be depleted in the not-too-distant future, it's good that we are working to use the energy from the Sun directly through technologies such as photovoltaic cells, wind power, and bioenergy. Consider this: If we covered an area comparable to a quarter of the area used for roads in the United States (around 9000 mi^2 or a little larger than the state of New Jersey) with 15% efficient solar panels, all of the country's electricity needs could be met.

Energy return on energy invested (EROEI) is a useful way to evaluate technology for fuel production (Section 15.6). The EROEI for fossil fuels has been dropping as easily tapped reserves have been depleted. Yet EROEI does not tell the whole story of a technology's impact because important aspects of its use are often ignored. A more complete analysis uses green chemistry principles and considers the impact of waste generation, toxic substances, renewable feedstocks, and overall energy efficiency. To generate energy efficiently, we need to minimize the inputs and maximize the energy output. Clearly, waste must be reduced, and other products are desired only if their formation and presence do not reduce or limit the primary goal—energy production.

An EROEI value measures only the energy inputs and outputs, and waste is not included. Combustion of oil, natural gas, and coal produces CO_2, which is the main contributor to the world's urgent climate-change problem. For technologies that have low EROEI values, CO_2 emissions are accelerated. For example, combustion of 100 units of a fuel obtained from a process with an EROEI of 2:1 would result in 43% more CO_2 emissions than combustion of 100 units of a fuel obtained from a process with an EROEI of 20:1.

An interesting case is the use of hydraulic fracturing (fracking) for production of natural gas (Section 15.6), in which high-pressure fluids are forced into fractures in rocks to remove the gas. Approximately 35,000 wells were fractured in 2010 in the United States, using about 100 billion gallons of water. Once considered an unconventional method, fracking now accounts for 50% of natural gas production in the United States. Hundreds of different chemicals, many of which are known carcinogens, are added to the fracture fluids. These and other species released by fracturing (including naturally occurring radioactive species) may reach aquifers or be diverted to municipal water-treatment facilities. Although EROEI values for fracking may not be terribly low, there are large amounts of waste that are not currently considered as part of the evaluation process. Also, besides the CO_2 emissions associated with combustion, considerable amounts of CH_4 leak into the atmosphere during natural gas production. Methane is 25 times more active as a greenhouse gas than CO_2.

The biggest hurdle to developing clean, renewable energy has to do with cost. If we do the accounting correctly and measure all inputs and outputs and impacts of a given process, the true costs to society will guide us in making good choices. New science and technology—and new mindsets—will be required. Perhaps you will want to help in this grand challenge.

▲ Biodiesel is another means of meeting our energy needs. It converts waste food oils and fats to fuel that can be used directly in many diesel-powered vehicles. However, it is not without its problems. Large quantities of corrosive sodium hydroxide or potassium hydroxide are used in this conversion.

All these conversions, however, result in the loss of a portion of the useful energy. The laws of thermodynamics tell us that we can get the most energy by burning the biomass directly rather than converting it to a more convenient liquid or gaseous fuel.

Biomass and biofuels currently provide about half of the renewable energy used in the United States, or about 5% of the country's overall energy needs. We could make greater use of these sources by converting appropriate materials to biodiesel, fermenting some agricultural wastes to ethanol, and fermenting human and animal wastes to produce methane. The technology for all these processes is available now and can be further improved.

Hydrogen: Light and Powerful

Natural gas is sent through pipes to wherever it is needed, and other fuel gases could be sent through the same pipes. One such gas is hydrogen.

When hydrogen burns, it produces water and gives off energy.

$$2 H_2(g) + O_2(g) \longrightarrow 2 H_2O(l) + 572 \text{ kJ}$$

Gram for gram, hydrogen yields more energy than any other chemical fuel. It is also a clean fuel, yielding only water as a chemical product. Although hydrogen is the most abundant element in the universe, elemental hydrogen (H_2) is almost nonexistent on Earth. There is a lot of hydrogen on Earth, but it is tied up in chemical compounds, mainly water, and releasing it requires more energy than the hydrogen produces when it is burned. Hydrogen can be made from seawater, so the supply is almost inexhaustible, but the production process is costly.

Fuel Cells

A **fuel cell** is a device in which fuel is oxidized in an electrochemical cell (Section 8.3) so as to produce electricity directly. Fuel cells differ from the usual electrochemical cell in two ways:

▪ The fuel and oxygen are fed into the cell continuously. As long as fuel is supplied, current is generated.
▪ The electrodes are made of an inert material such as platinum that does not react during the process.

Most of today's fuel cells use hydrogen and oxygen (Figure 15.17). At the platinum anode, H_2 is oxidized to yield hydrogen ions and electrons.

$$2 H_2(g) \longrightarrow 4 H^+ + 4 e^-$$

▲ These willow trees are grown specifically as fuel. The biomass is harvested by cutting the trees near ground level, which stimulates regrowth. Willow is especially suitable for biomass because of its rapid growth.

◀ **Figure 15.17** A hydrogen–oxygen fuel cell. The fuel cell continues to provide electricity as long as reactants are supplied.

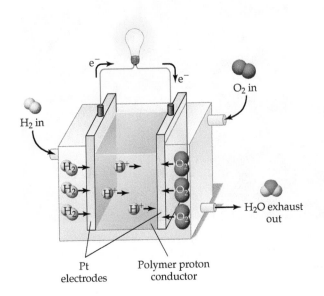

Hydrogen in Your Future (Car)

Hydrogen can be used as a fuel for cars, either directly or in fuel cells. Among the advantages of hydrogen as a fuel are the following:

▪ The exhaust is almost entirely water vapor, which cuts down on urban air pollution and the production of the greenhouse gas CO_2.

▪ It can be produced from renewable sources.

▪ It could reduce U.S. reliance on foreign oil and the associated economic and political costs.

There are, however, significant obstacles to making the transition to hydrogen, so the roads will not be filled with hydrogen cars anytime soon. Among the problems are the following:

▪ Hydrogen is not a *source* of energy; there are no hydrogen "mines" or "reservoirs."

▪ The hydrogen-powered cars now available are expensive novelties, costing $100,000 or more.

▪ There is no widespread distribution system of hydrogen fueling stations.

▪ Hydrogen is a low-density gas that liquefies at −253 °C (20 K). Use of the gas requires large, heavy tanks. Liquid hydrogen must be maintained at a temperature only a few degrees above absolute zero. Therefore, storage, transportation, and dispensing of the fuel is problematic.

Some progress has been made, mostly with fleets of vehicles that operate in a limited area. Fuel-cell technology is becoming more efficient and costs are coming down, but there is still the problem of producing hydrogen gas economically. Hydrogen has to be made using another energy source: fossil fuels, nuclear power, or—preferably—some renewable source such as solar energy or wind power. Some experimental cells make hydrogen on-board from methanol or natural gas by a high-temperature process called *reforming*.

$$CH_4(g) + 2\,H_2O(g) \longrightarrow CO_2(g) + 4\,H_2(g)$$

The drawback is that reforming emits carbon dioxide, negating one of the reasons for using fuel cells in the first place.

Even liquid H_2, with a density of 0.07 g/cm^3, requires a large fuel tank, and the tank must be well insulated. It may be possible to store hydrogen in other ways: Scientists have found that various metals can absorb up to a thousand times their own volume of hydrogen gas. Special forms of carbon, such as ultrathin carbon nanotubes, may also hold large quantities of the gas.

The cost of establishing pipelines and filling stations to handle hydrogen will be immense. It takes many years for revolutionary technologies to come to the marketplace. The increased emphasis on research into hydrogen fuel cells appears to be a step in the right direction.

▲ The BMW Hydrogen-7 is claimed to be the first production-ready hydrogen vehicle. It was designed to run on either hydrogen or gasoline. The hydrogen is stored as a liquid in a large vacuum-insulated tank. In 2007, 100 of these vehicles were leased to drivers.

The electrons produced at the anode travel through the external circuit and arrive at the cathode, where they combine with the hydrogen ions and oxygen molecules to form water.

$$4\,e^- + O_2(g) + 4\,H^+ \longrightarrow 2\,H_2O(g)$$

The overall reaction (below) is identical to direct combustion of hydrogen, but not all the chemical energy is converted to heat. About 40–55% of the chemical energy is converted directly to electricity, making fuel cells much more efficient than internal combustion engines.

$$2\,H_2(g) + O_2(g) \longrightarrow 2\,H_2O(l)$$

Fuel cells are often used on spacecraft to produce electricity, mainly because they have a weight advantage over storage batteries—an important consideration when launching a spaceship—and the water produced can be used for drinking. Because they have no moving parts, fuel cells are usually tough and reliable.

On Earth, research is under way to reduce costs and design long-lasting cells. Perhaps fuel cells will someday provide electricity to meet peak needs in large power plants. Unlike huge boilers and nuclear reactors, they can be started and stopped simply by turning the fuel on or off.

Some people are afraid of using hydrogen as fuel for home heating because of the possibility of explosion, but natural gas leaks can also lead to serious explosions. Hydrogen escapes more readily than natural gas or gasoline because of its smaller molecular size, but it also dissipates more readily, rather than forming a flammable low-lying vapor as gasoline sometimes does.

Other Renewable Energy Sources

Modern civilization requires tremendous amounts of energy and will require more and more in the coming years. We are depleting our reserves of fossil fuels, and many see significant disadvantages to nuclear power. Using the Sun's energy seems to be a good idea, but it would be difficult to meet all our needs with solar energy.

The Sun, by heating Earth, causes winds to blow and water to evaporate and rise into the air, later to fall as rain. The kinetic energy of blowing wind and flowing water can be used as sources of energy—as they have been for centuries.

Why not use wind power and waterpower to help solve the energy crisis? We do. Waterpower provides almost 7% of current electricity production in the United States, most of it in the mountainous west. In a modern hydroelectric plant, water is held behind huge dams. Some of it is released through penstocks against the blades of water turbines. The potential energy of the stored water is converted to the kinetic energy of flowing water. The moving water imparts mechanical energy to the turbine, which drives a generator that converts mechanical energy to electrical energy.

Hydroelectric plants are relatively clean, but most of the good dam sites in the United States are already in use. To obtain more hydroelectric energy, we would have to dam up scenic rivers and flood valuable cropland and recreational areas. Reservoirs silt up over the years, and sometimes dams break, causing catastrophic floods. Dams block the migration of fish upstream to spawning beds. Declining fish populations have led to closure of salmon fishing in waters off California and Oregon and removal of dams from a few rivers where salmon spawn.

Worldwide, hydroelectric plants provide about 20% of the electricity used, and more plants are being built in many developing countries. As a major example, China's huge Three Gorges project on the Yangtze River, completed in 2009, includes a 22,500-MW hydroelectric plant. It provides more than 10% of China's electricity. Unfortunately, the project displaced 1.3 million people and may cause significant environmental damage. Water quality in the Yangtze's tributaries is already deteriorating rapidly because the dammed river disperses pollutants less effectively and algae blooms flourish. The rising water caused extensive soil erosion, riverbank collapses, and landslides. Even renewable hydroelectric power has its problems.

5. Is hydrogen really a nonpolluting fuel? The only product from the combustion of hydrogen is water. However, an internal combustion engine runs at high temperatures and pressures. Under these conditions, some amount of nitrogen oxides, which are pollutants, forms. If hydrogen is used in a fuel cell instead of an internal combustion engine, pollution is negligible.

▲ Hoover Dam, on the Colorado River, was completed in 1936. It generates 4 billion kWh a year—enough to supply 1.3 million people.

We could use more wind power. The kinetic energy of moving air is readily converted to mechanical energy to pump water, grind grain, or turn turbines and generate electricity. Wind power currently supplies only about 2% of U.S. energy production, but it is the fastest-growing energy source, increasing at an annual rate of 20–30%.

▶ Wind turbines, such as these in an off-coast wind farm, supply about 20% of Denmark's electricity. By the end of 2010, windmills with a generating capacity of almost 200,000 MW were operating worldwide, producing about 2.5% of the world's electricity.

How does chemistry relate to waterpower and wind power? Chemists produce new materials, such as metal alloys, reinforced plastics, and lubricants, that are vital to the construction and operation of dams, windmills, and turbines. Chemists also monitor water quality above and below dams and participate in other activities vital to protection of the environment around generating facilities.

Wind is clean, free, and abundant. However, it does not blow constantly, and some means of energy storage or an alternative source of energy is needed. Not all regions have enough wind to make wind power feasible. Some environmentalists oppose wind power because the rotating blades kill thousands of birds each year, but so do domestic cats and collisions with television and microwave towers. The amount of land required for windmills might become a problem if wind power were used widely, but the land under windmills could be used for farming or grazing.

Geothermal Energy

The interior of Earth is heated by immense gravitational forces and by natural radioactivity. This heat comes to the surface in some areas through geysers and volcanoes. **Geothermal energy** has long been used in Iceland, New Zealand, Japan, and Italy. It has some potential in the United States—it is being used now in California (Figure 15.18)—but in the near future this potential could be realized only in areas where steam or hot water is at or near the surface. One drawback of geothermal energy is that the wastewater is quite salty, and its disposal could be a problem.

(a)

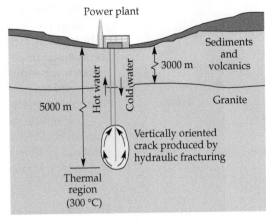

(b)

Oceans of Energy

The oceans that cover three-fourths of Earth's surface are an enormous reservoir of potential energy. The use of *ocean thermal energy* was first proposed in 1881 and was shown to be workable in the 1930s. The difference in temperature between the surface and the depths is 20 °C or more, enough to evaporate a liquid and use the vapor to drive a turbine. The liquid is then condensed by the cold from the ocean depths, and the cycle is repeated.

Other ways of using ocean energy have been tested. In some areas of the world, the daily rise and fall of the tide can be harnessed, in much the same way as the energy of a river is harnessed by a hydroelectric plant. At high tide, water fills a reservoir or bay. At low tide, the water escapes through a turbine to generate electricity. Even the energy of the waves crashing to shore can be used with the appropriate technology.

Energy: How Much Is Too Much?

Our energy future is quite uncertain. World petroleum production will peak soon—some claim this has already occurred. Developing nations will increasingly compete for fuels on the world market. Science and technology will have to be applied to provide an ever-growing supply of energy. The Energy Information Administration of the U.S. Department of Energy projected that world energy consumption will increase by 50% from 2007 to 2035, with much of the new demand from developing countries.

Each of the energy sources discussed in this chapter has advantages and disadvantages. How do we choose the best way to deal with energy problems? Wise choices require informed citizens who examine the process from beginning to end. We must realize what is involved in the construction of power plants, the production of fuels, and the ultimate use of energy in our homes and factories. We must recognize that energy is wasted (as heat) at every step in the process.

Will our profligate consumption of energy affect Earth's climate? Our activities have already modified the climate in and around metropolitan areas. The worldwide effects of our expanding energy consumption are harder to estimate.

What can we do as individuals? We can conserve. We can walk more and use cars less. We can reduce our wasteful use of electricity. We can buy more efficient appliances, and we can reduce our use of energy-intensive products (leaf blowers, lawn tractors, and larger automobiles).

Over the past three decades, we have made significant progress in energy conservation. Appliances are more energy efficient. New furnaces have efficiencies of 90–95%, as compared with the 60% efficiency of 20-year-old furnaces. New refrigerators and air conditioners use about 35% less energy than earlier models. Incandescent lamps are being replaced by compact fluorescent lamps, which are at least four times more energy efficient. Overall, U.S. industry has reduced its energy consumption per product by almost 30%.

Table 15.9 | Total Primary Energy Consumption Per Capita, 2007 (in GJ)

Canada	469
United States	356
Russia	222
Japan	184
European Union	172
South Africa	109
Mexico	71
China	54
India	17
World	76

We could significantly reduce energy consumption in the United States by greater use of public transportation. In Europe, where there is much wider use of public transit, per capita energy use is considerably less (Table 15.9), partly because the average price for gasoline is usually more than twice that in the United States. So far, few people used to the convenience of personal cars seem eager to start using buses and trains. As the price of gasoline in the United States continues to rise, perhaps public transportation will seem more attractive.

The simple facts are that our population on Spaceship Earth is increasing and our fuel resources are decreasing. People in developing countries want to raise their standard of living, and that will require more energy. We need to conserve energy and to look for new energy sources.

Self-Assessment Questions

1. Which of the following is an *n*-type semiconductor?
   a. arsenic doped with silicon
   b. arsenic doped with germanium
   c. silicon doped with arsenic
   d. silicon doped with boron

2. *p*-Type semiconductors feature crystal sites with
   a. photons
   b. positrons
   c. positive holes
   d. protons

3. Which of the following is a renewable energy source?
   a. biomass   b. hydrogen
   c. nuclear power   d. tar sands

4. Biodiesel *cannot* be made from
   a. corn starch   b. olive oil
   c. soybean oil   d. waste cooking fat

5. The major product from burning hydrogen gas as a fuel is
   a. CO_2 b. H_2 c. H_2O d. O_2

6. Which of the following fuels has the lowest EROEI?
   a. biodiesel   b. hydrogen
   c. natural gas   d. petroleum

7. Which of the following energy technologies does not use energy that originated in the Sun?
   a. biomass   b. hydroelectric   c. nuclear   d. wind

8. The fuel used by almost all current fuel cells is
   a. electricity   b. hydrogen   c. natural gas   d. propane

9. Fuel cells are
   a. dependent on fuels from other sources
   b. net sources of energy
   c. producers of new fuels
   d. renewable energy sources

10. The renewable energy source that provides the most electrical energy in the United States today is
    a. geothermal   b. hydroelectric   c. solar   d. wind

11. The energy that comes from the internal heat of the Earth is
    a. bioenergy
    b. geothermal energy
    c. hydroelectricity
    d. solar energy

Answers: 1, c; 2, c; 3, a; 4, a; 5, c; 6, b; 7, c; 8, b; 9, a; 10, b; 11, b

CRITICAL THINKING EXERCISES

Apply knowledge that you have gained in this chapter and one or more of the FLaReS principles (Chapter 1) to evaluate the following statements or claims.

15.1 A futurist and inventor predicts that advances in nanotechnology will result in solar energy powering the world in just 16 years.

15.2 In 1996, Indian inventor Ramar Pillai claimed to have discovered a secret herbal formula that converted water to a hydrocarbon fuel.

15.3 An inventor claims to have discovered a catalyst that speeds the conversion of linear alkanes, such as hexane, to branched-chain isomers.

15.4 While watching TV during the summer, you hear someone proclaim that a way to cool your kitchen is to keep the refrigerator door open.

15.5 A fuel cell in every house can give each household energy independence.

15.6 I know the claim that modern electric automobiles are zero-emission vehicles is true because I found it on Wikipedia.

15.7 A company claims that it can use a metal such as magnesium as a fuel for automobiles. A coil of the metal would be fed into a chamber where it would react with superheated steam to produce hydrogen gas, which would power a fuel cell that would run the car.

SUMMARY

Section 15.1—**Energy** is the ability to do work. The United States has about 5% of the world's population but uses about one-fifth of all the energy generated. Most of the energy used on Earth comes from the Sun. The SI unit of energy is the joule (J), and the unit of power is the watt (W), which is 1 joule per second. Energy can be classified as **potential energy** (energy of position) or **kinetic energy** (energy of motion). In the process called **photosynthesis**, solar energy is absorbed by plants and used to produce glucose, and oxygen is generated.

Section 15.2—Rates of reactions are affected by temperature, by concentrations of the reactants, and by the presence of catalysts. The study of energy changes that occur during chemical reactions and physical processes is called **thermochemistry**. We define a **system** as the part of the universe under consideration. The **surroundings** are everything else. A chemical reaction or a physical process may be either **exothermic** (giving off energy) or **endothermic** (requiring energy). Reactions involving burning of fuels are all exothermic.

Section 15.3—The **first law of thermodynamics (law of conservation of energy)** says that energy can be neither created nor destroyed. The **second law of thermodynamics** states that in a spontaneous process, energy is degraded from more useful forms to less useful forms. **Entropy** is a measure of the dispersal of energy among the possible states of a system. There is a tendency for a system to increase in entropy.

Section 15.4—Ancient societies used human and animal power to do work. The main fuel was wood. A **fuel** is a substance that will burn readily with the release of significant energy. The first mechanical devices for doing work were the waterwheel and the windmill. Energy from water, steam, gas, the internal combustion engine, and other sources fueled the Industrial Revolution. **Fossil fuels** are natural fuels derived from once-living plants and animals. They include coal, petroleum, and natural gas.

Section 15.5—**Coal** is a solid fuel that is also a source of chemicals. The main element in coal is carbon. The quality of coal is determined mostly by its carbon and energy content, with anthracite being highest in rank and peat lowest. Coal is the most plentiful fossil fuel but is inconvenient to use and produces more pollution than other fuels.

Section 15.6—**Natural gas** is mainly methane and burns relatively cleanly. It is important both as a fuel and a raw material for synthesis of plastics and other products. **Petroleum**, or crude oil, is a thick liquid mixture of organic compounds, mainly hydrocarbons. Petroleum products can be burned fairly cleanly, but inefficient combustion produces pollution. Petroleum is refined by separating it, by distillation, into different fractions. **Gasoline** is the fraction consisting of hydrocarbons from about C_5 to C_{12}. Branched-chain hydrocarbons such as isooctane burn more smoothly than straight-chain hydrocarbons. The **octane rating** of gasoline compares its antiknock performance to that of pure isooctane. To raise the octane rating of gasoline, refineries use isomerization (to increase branching), **catalytic reforming** (to convert straight-chain hydrocarbons to aromatic hydrocarbons), and alkylation (to convert small hydrocarbons to larger branched molecules). Octane boosters such as methanol, ethanol, MTBE, and *tert*-butyl alcohol are added as well. Tetraethyllead was used to improve octane rating for more than 50 years but has been discontinued.

Section 15.7—Electricity is the most convenient form of energy. About half of the electricity in the United States is generated from coal-burning steam power plants. Coal can be converted to more convenient gaseous or liquid fuels, but at an energy cost.

Section 15.8—Nuclear fission reactions can be controlled in a nuclear reactor, which uses a low concentration (3–5%) of uranium-235. The reactions are controlled with rods of cadmium or boron steel. The energy released generates steam that turns a turbine to generate electricity. Approximately 20% of the United States' electricity comes from nuclear fission reactors. A nuclear power plant cannot explode like a nuclear bomb, it produces minimal air pollution, and its wastes are collected rather than dispersed. But elaborate safety precautions are needed to prevent escape of radioactive material, the needed fuel is limited in availability, and ultimate disposal of radioactive waste is an ongoing problem. A breeder reactor converts other isotopes to useful nuclear fuel and can make more fuel than it consumes. Nuclear fusion cannot yet be controlled, as there are great technical difficulties. Temperatures in the millions of degrees are needed to generate a plasma consisting of free electrons and nuclei, for controlled fusion. But fusion has very important potential advantages over most other energy sources.

Section 15.9—Solar energy is diffuse and difficult to collect. Simple solar collectors can produce hot water for heating. Solar cells, or photovoltaic cells, produce electricity directly from sunlight, using n-type and p-type semiconductors. The cells are becoming less expensive and more efficient, and photovoltaic systems require storage systems or connection to the local electricity grid. Biomass such as wood can be burned directly or converted to liquid or gaseous fuels, but it requires much land area to produce and has a very low overall efficiency. Hydrogen is an energy storage and transport method rather than an energy source. It burns cleanly but requires more energy to make than it produces. One advantage of hydrogen is that it can be used in fuel cells, which consume fuel and oxygen continuously to generate electricity efficiently. Other renewable energy sources include wind power and hydroelectric power, which can be harnessed only in certain locations. Both sources have high initial costs. Heat energy from the interior of Earth is geothermal energy. It can be used only in areas where steam or hot water is near the surface. We can also make use of the temperature difference between the ocean's surface and deep waters, tidal energy, and the energy of the waves. Renewable energy sources produced more than 10% of the electricity generated in the U.S. in 2010. Each energy source has advantages, limitations, and consequences. We can all conserve energy by using more efficient appliances and simply by using less energy.

Green chemistry Applying green chemistry principles and accounting for all inputs, outputs, and impacts are important for assessing the true value of technologies for energy generation and use.

Learning Objectives

❯ Perform power and energy calculations.	Problems 17–22, 69–72
❯ Classify chemical reactions and physical processes as exothermic or endothermic.	Problems 67, 68
❯ List factors that affect the rates of chemical reactions.	Problems 15, 16, 72
❯ State the first and second laws of thermodynamics, and discuss their implications for energy production and use.	Problems 23–28
❯ List the common fossil fuels, and describe how modern society is based on their use.	Problems 29, 30, 37–41
❯ List advantages and disadvantages of coal as a fuel.	Problem 29
❯ List the characteristics of natural gas and petroleum.	Problems 37, 39, 42, 78
❯ List advantages and disadvantages of natural gas and petroleum as fuels.	Problems 31–34, 38
❯ Explain why gaseous and liquid fuels are more convenient to use than solid fuels.	Problems 29, 30, 38
❯ List advantages and disadvantages of nuclear energy.	Problems 45–52
❯ Describe how a nuclear power plant generates electricity.	Problems 45–48, 55
❯ List important characteristics of renewable energy sources.	Problems 58, 62
❯ List advantages and disadvantages of various kinds of renewable energy.	Problems 59–61, 64
❯ Explain how applying the green chemistry principles can help identify improved methods for energy generation.	Problems 79–81
❯ Identify waste products from some current energy-generation processes.	Problem 79

REVIEW QUESTIONS

1. What kind of reaction powers the Sun?

2. What was the main fuel used in the United States before 1800?

3. What was the main fuel used in the United States from about 1850 to 1950? What has been the main fuel since 1950?

4. List some advantages and disadvantages of hydrogen as a fuel for vehicles.

PROBLEMS

Fuels and Combustion

5. Which of the following can serve as a fuel?
   a. fructose ($C_6H_{12}O_6$)
   b. propane (C_3H_8)
   c. hydrogen peroxide (H_2O_2)

6. Which of the following can serve as a fuel?
   a. hexafluoroethane (C_2F_6)
   b. stearic acid ($C_{18}H_{36}O_2$)
   c. tridecane ($C_{13}H_{28}$)

7. For each substance in Problem 5 that can serve as a fuel, write a balanced equation for its complete combustion in oxygen gas (O_2).

8. For each substance in Problem 6 that can serve as a fuel, write a balanced equation for its complete combustion in oxygen gas (O_2).

9. Write the equation for the complete combustion of coal, assuming that the coal is simply carbon.

10. Write the equation for the incomplete combustion of coal to form carbon monoxide, assuming that the coal is simply carbon.

11. Write the equation for the complete combustion of methane.

12. Write the equation for the incomplete combustion of methane to form carbon monoxide and water vapor.

13. Water gas is a mixture of H_2 and CO. Can water gas serve as a fuel? Explain.

14. Water gas (see Problem 13) can be made by reacting red hot charcoal with steam. Write the equation for this reaction.

Energy and Chemical Reactions

15. How does temperature affect the rate of a chemical reaction?

16. Why does wood burn more rapidly in pure oxygen than in air?

17. Burning 1.00 mol of methane releases 803 kJ of energy. How much energy is released by burning 24.5 mol of methane?

$$CH_4(g) + 2\,O_2(g) \longrightarrow CO_2(g) + 2\,H_2O(g) + 803\ kJ$$

18. It takes 572 kJ of energy to decompose 2.00 mol of liquid water. How much energy does it take to decompose 55.5 mol of water?

$$2\,H_2O(l) + 572\ kJ \longrightarrow 2\,H_2(g) + O_2(g)$$

19. When burned, 1.00 g of gasoline yields 1060 cal. What is this quantity in kilojoules?

20. How much heat, in kilojoules, is released when 4.301 g $H_2(g)$ reacts with $O_2(g)$ to form steam $[H_2O(g)]$ according to the following equation?

$$2\,H_2(g) + O_2(g) \longrightarrow 2\,H_2O(g) + 483.6\ kJ$$

21. Refer to Problem 17, and determine how much energy, in kilojoules, must be supplied to convert 1.00 mol $CO_2(g)$ and 2.00 mol $H_2O(g)$ into $CH_4(g)$ and $O_2(g)$.

22. Refer to Problem 20, and determine how much energy, in kilojoules, must be supplied to convert 1 mol of water vapor into hydrogen gas and oxygen gas.

Energy and the Laws of Thermodynamics

23. State the first law of thermodynamics.

24. State the second law of thermodynamics in terms of energy flow and in terms of degradation of energy.

25. What is entropy? Does entropy increase or decrease when a fossil fuel is burned?

26. Energy is conserved. How can we ever run out of energy?

27. How does the statement "You can't get something for nothing" relate to the first law of thermodynamics?

28. How does the statement "You can't even break even" relate to the second law of thermodynamics?

Fossil Fuels

29. What are the advantages and disadvantages of coal as a fuel?

30. Why did the United States shift from coal to petroleum and natural gas when we have much larger reserves of coal than of the other two fuels?

Estimates in Problems 31–34 are from the U.S. Energy Information Administration.

31. The estimated proven world oil reserves in 2009 were 1342 billion barrels. The world annual rate of use was 31.1 billion barrels. How long will these reserves last if this rate of use continues? (The rate of use is actually likely to increase.)

32. The estimated proven U.S. oil reserves in 2009 were 21.3 billion barrels. **(a)** How long will these reserves last if there are no imports or exports and if the U.S. annual rate of use of 6.85 billion barrels continues? **(b)** Taking the mean projection for oil reserves in the Arctic National Wildlife Refuge—10.4 billion barrels—how long would exploiting that resource extend our reserves at the current U.S. annual rate of use?

33. The estimated world natural gas reserves in 2009 were 6254 trillion ft^3. The world annual rate of use was 103.8 trillion ft^3. How long will these reserves last if this rate of use continues?

34. The U.S. proven natural gas reserves in 2006 were 244 trillion ft^3. How long will these reserves last if there are no imports or exports and if the U.S. annual rate of use of 22.8 trillion ft^3 continues?

Natural Gas

35. Write a balanced equation for the combustion of ethane (C_2H_6, a component of natural gas) in oxygen gas to produce carbon dioxide and water vapor.

36. Write a balanced equation for the combustion of butane (C_4H_{10}, a minor component of natural gas) in oxygen gas to produce carbon dioxide and water vapor.

Petroleum

37. What is thought to be the origin of petroleum?

38. What are the advantages and disadvantages of petroleum as a source of fuels?

39. Use the term *molecular mass* to describe the difference between gasoline and kerosene.

40. How is crude petroleum modified to better meet our needs and wants? What are the advantages and disadvantages of tetraethyllead as an octane booster?

41. Consult Table 15.6, then suggest a reason why asphalt is so cheap that it is used to pave highways and driveways.

42. Which should have a higher octane rating: (a) octane ($CH_3CH_2CH_2CH_2CH_2CH_2CH_2CH_3$) or 2,3,3-trimethylpentane [$CH_3CH(CH_3)C(CH_3)_2CH_2CH_3$]? (b) benzene or hexane?

Nuclear Power

43. What proportion of U.S. electricity is generated by nuclear power plants?

44. What proportion of electricity in France is generated by nuclear power plants?

45. Can a nuclear power plant explode like a nuclear bomb? Explain.

46. Write nuclear equations showing how uranium-238 is converted to fissionable plutonium-239.

47. Can a nuclear bomb be made from reactor-grade uranium? Explain.

48. Can a nuclear bomb be made from reactor-grade plutonium?

49. How does a breeder reactor produce more fuel than it consumes? Does doing so violate the law of conservation of energy?

50. What are some of the disadvantages of breeder reactors?

51. List some possible advantages of a nuclear fusion reactor over a fission reactor. What is plasma?

52. List some possible problems with nuclear fusion reactors.

53. Write nuclear equations showing how thorium-232 is converted to fissionable uranium-233.

54. Write the nuclear equation that shows how deuterium and tritium fuse to form helium and a neutron.

55. The fission of 1 mol of uranium-235 can be represented by

$$^{235}_{92}U + ^{1}_{0}n \longrightarrow 2\,^{1}_{0}n + ^{139}_{54}Xe + ^{95}_{38}Sr + 1.8 \times 10^{10}\ kJ$$

See the equation in Problem 11 for the combustion of methane. How many moles of methane must be burned to generate the energy produced by fission of 1.00 mol (235 g) of uranium-235? What is the mass of this amount of methane, in metric tons (1 t = 1000 kg)?

56. Coal is mostly carbon. Burning 1 mol (12.0 g) of carbon to form carbon dioxide releases 393 kJ of energy. Refer to Problem 55, and determine how many moles of carbon must be burned to generate the energy produced by fission of 1.00 mol (235 g) of uranium-235. What is the mass of this amount of carbon, in metric tons?

Renewable Energy Sources

57. What is a photovoltaic cell?

58. What are some problems associated with the use of solar energy?

59. The average power demand of an American household with nonelectric cooking is 1.2 kW. Solar cells can produce about 100 W/m^2. What area of solar cells is needed to meet this demand? What are the limits of this source of energy?

60. Large wind turbines can produce 1.5 MW of electrical power. How many of the homes described in Problem 59 could be powered by one big wind turbine? What are the limits of this source of energy?

61. What is biomass?

62. List some advantages and disadvantages of the use of biomass as a source of energy.

63. List two ways in which fuel cells differ from electrochemical cells.

64. List the advantages, disadvantages, and limitations of each of the following as an energy source.
    a. wind power
    b. geothermal power
    c. biodiesel
    d. hydroelectric power

Synthetic and Converted Fuels

65. Write the chemical equations for the basic processes by which coal (carbon) is converted to (a) methane and (b) carbon monoxide and hydrogen.

66. Write the chemical equations for (a) the conversion of carbon monoxide and hydrogen to methanol and (b) the reaction that occurs in a hydrogen–oxygen fuel cell.

ADDITIONAL PROBLEMS

67. A cold pack works by the dissolving of ammonium nitrate in water. Cold packs are carried by athletic trainers when transporting ice is not possible. Is this process endothermic or exothermic? Explain.

68. A hot pack hand warmer contains iron powder, water, salt, activated carbon, and vermiculite. It is activated by exposing the contents to air. Hot packs are used by hunters and other outdoor sportsmen and workers in places where access to heaters or fires is not possible. Is this process endothermic or exothermic? Explain.

69. The average human expends about 2100 kcal of energy per day. (a) What is this output in watts? (b) How does one human power compare to one horsepower? (See Problem 70.)

70. For a day of sustained work, an average workhorse expends about—you guessed it—one horsepower (hp).

With the invention of the steam engine, inventors tried to standardize the unit to compare the output of steam engines to that of the horses the engines would replace. The modern value is about 1 hp = 745 W. A modern Formula One race car with a 2.4-L V8 engine can develop about 740 hp. What is its power output in kilowatts?

71. Both a banana and a hand grenade have about 170 kcal of energy. (a) What is the power output in watts of a banana if its energy is expended over 2.0 h by lying on a couch watching television? (b) What is the power output in watts of a hand grenade if its energy is expended in 0.0012 s? How do the banana and hand grenade compare in energy and in power?

72. Heats of combustion of several gaseous fuels, in kilojoules per mole, are given below. Which yields the most energy

(a) per kilogram and (b) per liter when the volume is measured under the same conditions of temperature and pressure?

Hydrogen (H_2), 286.6 kJ

Isobutane $[CH_3CH(CH_3)_2]$, 2868 kJ

Neopentane $[CH_3C(CH_3)_3]$, 3515 kJ

73. Name a natural process or processes by which carbon atoms are (a) removed from the atmosphere, (b) returned to the atmosphere, and (c) effectively withdrawn from the carbon cycle.

74. The United States leads the major developed countries in per capita emission of $CO_2(g)$ with a rate of 19.0 t per person per year (1 t = 1000 kg). What mass, in metric tons, of each of the following fuels would yield this quantity of CO_2?
   a. CH_4
   b. C_8H_{18}
   c. coal that is 94.1% C by mass

75. A large coal-burning power plant burns 2500 tons of coal per day. The coal contains 0.65% S by mass. Assume that all the sulfur is converted to SO_2. What mass of SO_2 is formed? If a thermal inversion traps all this SO_2 in a volume of air that is 45 km by 60 km by 0.40 km, will the level of SO_2 in the air exceed the primary national air quality standard of 365 $\mu g\ SO_2/m^3$ air?

76. The contribution of the combustion of various fuels to the buildup of CO_2 in the atmosphere can be assessed in different ways. One way relates the mass of CO_2 formed to the mass of fuel burned; another relates the mass of CO_2 to the quantity of heat evolved in the combustion. Which of the three fuels, C(graphite), $CH_4(g)$, or $C_4H_{10}(g)$, produces the smallest mass of CO_2 (a) per gram of fuel and (b) per kilojoule of heat evolved? The heat released per mole of each substance is C(graphite), 393.5 kJ; $CH_4(g)$, 803 kJ; and $C_4H_{10}(g)$, 2877 kJ.

77. Estimates of recoverable energy are notoriously uncertain, but some scientists think that a total of only

9.92 × 10^6 terawatt-hours (TWh) of recoverable energy is stored in the Earth (in the form of oil, coal, natural gas, and uranium). Worldwide use is about 1.32 × 10^5 TWh per year. (a) If demand for energy remains the same as today, approximately how many years will it be before all the energy stored in the Earth is gone? (b) Per capita consumption in the United States (population of about 313,000,000) is about four times that of the rest of the world (population of about 7.0 billion). If all the countries throughout the world consumed energy at the same per capita rate as the United States, approximately how many years would it be before all the energy stored in the Earth is used up? (c) Evaluate your answers to parts (a) and (b).

78. Which of the following could be done to make hydraulic fracturing a greener process?
   a. Increase the use of water as a fracking fluid
   b. Use more chemical additives in the fracking fluid
   c. Capture or sequester CO_2 generated in the production and use of natural gas
   d. Monitor the amount of methane that escapes into the environment

79. When using the green chemistry principles to evaluate energy-generation processes, which of the following are considered?
   a. Energy invested and energy generated
   b. Feedstock source
   c. Waste products
   d. All of the above

80. When using EROEI to evaluate energy-generation processes, which of the following are considered?
   a. Energy invested and energy generated
   b. Feedstock source
   c. Waste products
   d. All of the above

COLLABORATIVE GROUP PROJECTS

Prepare a PowerPoint, poster, or other presentation (as directed by your instructor) to share with your class.

1. Which would you rather have in your neighborhood, a nuclear or a coal-burning power plant? Why? Explain.

2. What characteristics should an ideal energy source have? Which of these characteristics do the different sources of energy discussed in this chapter have?

3. Social-cost pricing takes into account all the costs of a product or activity that are not part of market costs. For example, one of the social costs of gasoline-based transportation is air pollution. Select three sources of energy, and list the possible social costs that should be considered.

4. Compare the quantity of electricity used for two appliances that are alike except for different efficiencies. Extend this comparison to CO_2 emissions from the appliances, assuming that the electricity is generated by burning coal.

5. Compare qualitatively the efficiency of heating a home with natural gas versus heating it with electricity produced from burning natural gas at a power plant.

6. Describe how each of the following types of nuclear reactors might serve as a future source of energy. Discuss possible advantages and disadvantages of each.
   a. a liquid fluoride–thorium reactor (LFTR)
   b. a very high temperature helium-cooled reactor
   c. a supercritical–water-cooled reactor

7. Which of the following is the best fuel for heating your home? What problems with supply, use, and waste products are involved in each case?
   a. natural gas   b. electricity
   c. coal   d. fuel oil

8. There was an accident at nuclear power plants at Fukushima, Japan, following an earthquake and tsunami on March 11, 2011. Using your favorite search engine, find out what happened and compare this accident with the ones at Chernobyl and Three Mile Island. How could these accidents have been avoided? Do these incidents prove that nuclear power plants should be phased out? Why or why not?

9. Use Internet sources to find directions and construct (a) a simple solar heater or (b) a solar oven.

Glossary

absolute zero The lowest possible temperature, 0 K or −273.15 °C or −459.7 °F.

absorb Gather a substance on a surface in a condensed layer.

acid A substance that, when added to water, produces an excess of hydrogen ions; a proton donor.

acid–base indicator A substance that is one color in acid and another color in base.

acidic anhydride A substance, such as a nonmetal oxide, that reacts with water to form an acid.

acid rain Precipitation having a pH less than 5.6.

acquired immune deficiency syndrome (AIDS) A disease caused by a retrovirus (HIV) that weakens the immune system.

activated sludge method A technique for secondary sewage treatment in which the sewage is aerated and some sludge is recycled.

activation energy The minimum quantity of energy that must be available before a chemical reaction can take place.

active site The region on an enzyme or a catalyst where a reaction occurs.

addition polymerization A polymerization reaction in which all the atoms of the monomer molecules are included in the polymer.

addition reaction A reaction in which the single product contains all the atoms of two reactant molecules.

adipose tissue Connective tissue where fat is stored.

advanced treatment Sewage treatment designed to remove phosphates, nitrates, other soluble impurities, and metals and other contaminants; also called tertiary treatment.

aerobic exercise Physical activity in which muscle contractions occur in the presence of oxygen.

aerobic oxidation An oxidation process occurring in the presence of oxygen.

aerosol Particles of 1 μm diameter or less, dispersed in air.

aflatoxins Toxins produced by molds growing on stored peanuts and grains.

Agent Orange A combination of 2,4-D and 2,4,5-T used extensively in Vietnam to remove forest cover and destroy crops that maintained enemy armies.

agonist A molecule that fits and activates a specific receptor.

AIDS See **acquired immune deficiency syndrome**.

alchemy A mixture of chemistry and magic practiced in Europe during the Middle Ages (500 to 1500 C.E.).

alcohol (ROH) An organic compound composed of an alkyl group and a hydroxyl group.

aldehyde (RCHO) An organic compound with a carbonyl group that has a hydrogen atom attached to the carbonyl carbon.

aldose A monosaccharide with an aldehyde functional group.

aliphatic compound A nonaromatic substance. *See also* **aromatic compound**.

alkali metal A metal in group 1A in the customary U.S. arrangement of the periodic table or in group 1 of the IUPAC-recommended table.

alkaline earth metal An element in group 2A in the customary U.S. arrangement of the periodic table or in group 2 of the IUPAC-recommended table.

alkaloid A physiologically active nitrogen-containing organic compound that occurs naturally in a plant.

alkalosis A physiological condition in which the pH of the blood is too high.

alkane A hydrocarbon with only single bonds; a saturated hydrocarbon.

alkene A hydrocarbon containing one or more double bonds.

alkyl group (−R) The group of atoms that results when a hydrogen atom is removed from an alkane.

alkyne A hydrocarbon containing one or more triple bonds.

allergen A substance that triggers an allergic reaction.

allotropes Different forms of the same element in the same physical state.

alloy A mixture of two or more elements, at least one of which is a metal; an alloy has metallic properties.

alpha decay Emission of an alpha particle ($^4_2$He) by a radioactive nucleus.

alpha helix A secondary structure of a protein molecule in which the chains coil around one another in a spiral arrangement.

alpha (α) particle A cluster of two protons and two neutrons; a helium nucleus.

Ames test A laboratory test that screens for mutagens, which are usually also carcinogens.

amide group (−CON−) A functional group in which a carbon is joined to an oxygen atom by a double bond and to a nitrogen atom by a single bond.

amine A nitrogen compound derived from ammonia by replacing one or more hydrogen atoms with alkyl or aromatic group(s).

amino acid An organic compound that contains both an amino group and a carboxyl group; amino acids combine to produce proteins.

amino group (−NH₂) A functional group comprised of a nitrogen atom bonded to two hydrogen atoms.

amphetamines Stimulant drugs that are similar in structure to epinephrine and norepinephrine.

amphoteric surfactant A surfactant whose active part bears both a negative charge and a positive charge.

anabolic steroid A drug that aids in the building (anabolism) of body proteins and thus of muscle tissue.

anabolism The building up of molecules through metabolic processes.

anaerobic decay Decomposition in the absence of oxygen.

anaerobic exercise Physical activity that takes place without sufficient oxygen.

analgesic A substance that provides pain relief.

androgen A male sex hormone.

anesthetic A substance that causes loss of feeling or awareness.

anion A negatively charged ion.

anionic surfactant A surfactant whose active part (water-soluble head) bears a negative charge.

anode A positive electrode at which oxidation occurs.

antagonist A molecule that prevents the action of an agonist by blocking its receptor.

antibiotic A soluble substance, produced by a mold or bacterium, which inhibits growth of other microorganisms.

anticarcinogen A substance that inhibits the development of cancer.

anticholinergic A drug that acts on nerves using acetylcholine as a neurotransmitter.

anticoagulant A substance that inhibits the clotting of blood.

anticodon The sequence of three adjacent nucleotides in a tRNA molecule that is complementary to a codon on mRNA.

antihistamine A substance that relieves the symptoms caused by allergens: sneezing, itchy eyes, and runny nose.

anti-inflammatory A substance that inhibits inflammation.

antimetabolite A compound that inhibits the synthesis of DNA and thus slows the growth of cancer cells.

antioxidant A reducing agent that retards damaging oxidation reactions in living cells or reacts with free radicals to prevent rancidity in foods.

antiperspirant A formulation that retards perspiration by constricting the openings of sweat glands.

antipyretic A fever-reducing substance.

apoenzyme The pure protein part of an enzyme.

applied research An investigation aimed at creating a useful product or solving a particular problem.

aqueous solution A solution in which the solvent is water.

arithmetic growth A process in which a constant quantity is added during each period of time.

aromatic compound A compound that has a ring structure and properties like those of benzene.

asbestos A fibrous silicate mineral composed of chains of SIO_4 tetrahedra.

astringent A substance that constricts the openings of sweat glands, thus reducing the amount of perspiration that escapes.

atmosphere The thin blanket of air surrounding Earth.

atmosphere (atm) A unit of pressure equal to 760 mmHg.

atom The smallest characteristic particle of an element.

atomic mass unit (u) The unit of relative atomic masses, equal to $\frac{1}{12}$ the mass of a carbon-12 atom.

atomic number (Z) The number of protons in the nucleus of an atom.

atomic theory A model that explains the law of multiple proportions and the law of constant composition by stating that all elements are composed of atoms.

Avogadro's hypothesis Equal volumes of gases, regardless of their compositions, contain equal numbers of molecules when measured at a given temperature and pressure.

Avogadro's law At a fixed temperature and pressure, the volume of a gas is directly proportional to the amount (number of moles) of gas.

Avogadro's number The number of atoms (6.022×10^{23}) in exactly 12 g of pure carbon-12.

background radiation Constantly occurring radiation from cosmic rays and from natural radioactive isotopes in air, water, soil, and rocks.

base A substance that, when added to water, produces an excess of hydroxide ions; a proton acceptor.

base triplet The sequence of three bases on a tRNA molecule that determine which amino acid it can carry.

basic anhydride A substance, such as a metal oxide, that reacts with water to form a base.

basic research The search for knowledge for its own sake.

battery A series of two or more connected electrochemical cells.

becquerel (Bq) A measure of the rate of radioactive decay; 1 becquerel (Bq) = 1 disintegration/s.

beta decay Emission of a beta particle by a radioactive nucleus.

beta (β) particle An electron emitted by a radioactive nucleus.

beta pleated sheet A secondary protein structure in which arrays of chains form a zigzag sheet.

binary ionic compound A compound consisting of cations of a metal and anions of a nonmetal.

binding energy The energy that holds the nucleons together in an atom's nucleus.

biochemical oxygen demand (BOD) The quantity of oxygen required by microorganisms to remove organic matter from water.

biochemistry The study of the chemistry of living things and life processes.

biomass Dry plant material used as fuel.

bitumen A hydrocarbon mixture obtained from tar sands by heating.

bleach An oxidizing agent used to remove unwanted color from fabric or other material.

blood sugar Glucose, a simple sugar that is circulated in the bloodstream and used directly by cells for energy.

boiling point The temperature at which a substance changes state from a liquid to a gas throughout the bulk of the liquid.

bond See **chemical bond**.

bonding pair A pair of electrons shared by two atoms, forming a chemical bond.

Boyle's law For a given mass of gas at constant temperature, the volume varies inversely with the pressure.

breeder reactor A nuclear reactor that converts nonfissionable isotopes to nuclear fuel.

broad-spectrum antibiotic An antibiotic that is effective against a wide variety of microorganisms.

bronze An alloy of copper and tin.

buffer solution A mixture of a weak acid and its conjugate base or a weak base and its conjugate acid that maintains a nearly constant pH when a small amount of strong acid or strong base is added.

builder Any substance (often a complex phosphate) added to a surfactant to increase its detergency.

calorie (cal) The amount of heat required to raise the temperature of 1 g of water by 1 °C.

carbohydrate A compound consisting of carbon, hydrogen, and oxygen; a starch or sugar.

carbon-14 dating A radioisotopic technique for determining the age of artifacts, based on the half-life of carbon-14.

carbonyl group (C=O) A functional group consisting of a carbon atom joined to an oxygen atom by a double bond.

carboxyl group (—COOH) A carbon atom with a double bond to one oxygen atom and a single bond to a second oxygen atom, which in turn is bonded to a hydrogen atom; the functional group of carboxylic acids.

carboxylic acid (RCOOH) An organic compound that contains the carboxyl functional group.

carcinogen A substance or physical entity that causes the growth of tumors.

catabolism Any metabolic process in which complex compounds are broken down into simpler substances.

catalyst A substance that increases the rate of a chemical reaction without itself being used up.

catalytic converter A device that uses catalysts that oxidize carbon monoxide and hydrocarbons to carbon dioxide and reduce nitrogen oxides to nitrogen gas.

catalytic reforming A process that converts straight-chain alkanes to aromatic hydrocarbons.

cathode A negative electrode at which reduction occurs.

cathode ray A stream of high-speed electrons emitted from a cathode in an evacuated tube.

cation A positively charged ion.

cationic surfactant A surfactant whose active part (water-soluble head) bears a positive charge.

celluloid Cellulose nitrate, a synthetic material derived from natural cellulose by treating it with nitric acid.

cellulose A polymer comprised of glucose units joined by beta linkages.

Celsius scale A temperature scale on which water freezes at 0° and boils at 100°.

cement A complex mixture of calcium and aluminum silicates made from limestone and clay; mixed with water to make concrete.

ceramic A hard, solid product made by heating clay and other minerals to fuse them.

chain reaction A self-sustaining reaction in which one or more products of one event cause one or more new events.

charcoal filtration Filtration of water through charcoal to adsorb organic compounds.

Charles's law For a given mass of gas at constant pressure, the volume varies directly with the absolute temperature.

chelating Tying up metal ions by surrounding them.

chemical bond The force of attraction that holds atoms or ions together in compounds.

chemical change A change in chemical composition.

chemical equation A shorthand representation of a chemical change that uses symbols and formulas instead of words.

chemical property A characteristic of a substance that describes the way in which the substance reacts with another substance to change its composition.

chemical symbol An abbreviation, consisting of one or two letters, that stands for an element.

chemistry The study of matter and the changes it undergoes.

chemotherapy The use of chemicals to control or cure diseases.

chiral carbon A carbon atom that has four different groups attached to it.

coal A solid fossil fuel that is rich in carbon.

codon A sequence of three adjacent nucleotides in an mRNA molecule that specifies one amino acid.

coenzyme An organic molecule (often a vitamin) that combines with an apoenzyme to make a complete, functioning enzyme.

cofactor An ion or molecule that combines with an apoenzyme to make a complete, functioning enzyme.

cologne A diluted perfume.

combined gas law The single relationship that incorporates the simple gas laws.

compound A substance made up of two or more elements combined in a fixed ratio.

concentrated solution A solution that has a relatively large amount of solute per unit volume of solution.

concrete A building material made from cement, sand, gravel, and water.

condensation The reverse of vaporization; a change from the gaseous state to the liquid state.

condensation polymerization A polymerization reaction in which not all the atoms in the starting monomers are incorporated in the polymer because water (or other small) molecules are formed as by-products.

condensed structural formula A chemical formula for an organic compound that omits the bonds joining hydrogens to carbons.

conjugate acid–base pair Two molecules or ions that differ by one proton.

copolymer A polymer formed by the combination of two (or more) different monomers.

core electrons Electrons in any shell of an atom except the outermost shell.

corrosive waste A hazardous waste that requires a special container because it destroys conventional container materials.

cosmetics Substances defined in the 1938 U.S. Food, Drug, and Cosmetic Act as "articles intended to be rubbed, poured, sprinkled or sprayed on, introduced into, or otherwise applied to the human body or any part thereof, for cleaning, beautifying, promoting attractiveness or altering the appearance."

cosmic rays Extremely high-energy radiation from outer space.

covalent bond A bond formed when two atoms share one or more pairs of electrons.

cream An emulsion of tiny water droplets in oil.

critical mass The minimum amount of fissionable material required to achieve a self-sustaining chain reaction.

crystal A solid, regular array of ions.

cyclic hydrocarbon A ring-containing hydrocarbon.

daughter isotope An isotope formed by the radioactive decay of another isotope.

defoliant A substance that causes premature dropping of leaves by plants.

density The amount of mass per unit volume.

deodorant A product that contains perfume to mask body odor; some have a germicide to kill odor-causing bacteria.

deoxyribonucleic acid (DNA) The type of nucleic acid found primarily in the nuclei of cells; contains the sugar deoxyribose.

depilatory A hair remover.

deposition The direct formation of a solid from a gas without passing through the liquid state; the reverse of sublimation.

depressant drug A drug that slows both physical and mental activity.

detergent A cleansing agent, usually a synthetic surfactant.

deuterium An isotope of hydrogen with a proton and a neutron in the nucleus (mass of 2 u).

dextro isomer A "right-handed" isomer.

dietary mineral An inorganic substance required in the diet for proper health and well-being.

Dietary Reference Intakes (DRIs) A set of reference values for nutrients established by the U.S. Academy of Sciences for planning and assessing diets.

dilute solution A solution that has a relatively small amount of solute per unit volume of solution.

dioxins Highly toxic chlorinated cyclic compounds produced by burning wastes containing chlorinated compounds; once found as contaminants in the defoliant 2, 4, 5-T.

dipole A molecule that is polar.

dipole–dipole forces The attractive forces that exist among polar covalent molecules.

disaccharide A sugar that on hydrolysis yields two monosaccharide molecules per molecule of disaccharide.

dispersion forces The momentary, usually weak, attractive forces between molecules resulting from electron motions that create short-lived dipoles.

dissociative anesthetic A substance that causes gross personality disorders, including hallucinations similar to those in near-death experiences.

dissolved oxygen Oxygen dissolved in water; provides a measure of the water's ability to support fish and other aquatic life.

disulfide linkage A covalent linkage between cysteine units through two sulfur atoms.

diuretic A substance that increases the output of urine.

double bond The sharing of two pairs of electrons between two atoms.

doubling time The time it takes a population to double in size.

drug A substance that affects the functioning of living things; used to relieve pain, to treat illness, or to improve health or well-being.

drug abuse The use of a drug for its intoxicating effect.

drug misuse The use of a drug in a manner other than its intended use.

elastomer A polymeric material that returns to its original shape after being stretched.

electrochemical cell A device that produces electricity by means of a chemical reaction.

electrode A carbon rod or a metal strip inserted into an electrochemical cell, at which oxidation or reduction occurs.

electrolysis The process of using electricity to cause chemical change.

electrolyte A compound that conducts an electric current in water solution.

electron The subatomic particle that bears a unit of negative charge.

electron capture (EC) A type of radioactive decay in which a nucleus absorbs an electron from the first or second shell of the atom.

electron configuration The arrangement of an atom's electrons in its energy levels.

electron-dot symbol See **Lewis symbol**.

electronegativity The attraction of an atom in a molecule for a bonding pair of electrons.

electrostatic precipitator A device that removes particulate matter from smokestack gases by creating an electric charge on the particles, which are then removed by attraction to a surface of opposite charge.

element A substance composed of atoms that have the same number of protons.

emollient An oil or grease used as a skin softener.

emulsion A suspension of submicroscopic particles of fat or oil in water.

enantiomers Isomers that are not superimposable on their mirror image.

end note The fraction of a perfume that has the lowest volatility; composed of large molecules.

endorphins Naturally occurring peptides that bond to the same receptor sites as morphine.

endothermic Absorbing energy from the surroundings.

energy The ability to do work.

energy levels (shells) The specific, quantized values of energy that an electron can have in an atom.

enrichment (of food) Replacement of B vitamins and addition of iron to flour.

enrichment (of an isotope) The process by which the proportion of one isotope of an element is increased relative to those of the others.

entropy A measure of the dispersal of energy among the possible states of a system.

enzyme A biological catalyst.

essential amino acid An amino acid that is not produced in the body and must be included in the diet.

ester (RCOOR') A compound derived from a carboxylic acid and an alcohol; the —OH of the acid is replaced by an —OR group.

estrogen A female sex hormone.

ether (ROR') A molecule with two hydrocarbon groups attached to the same oxygen atom.

eutrophication The excessive growth of algae in a body of water, which causes some of the plants to die because of a lack of light; the water becomes choked with vegetation, depleted of oxygen, and useless as a fish habitat or for recreation.

excited state A state in which an atom has at least one electron that has moved from a lower to a higher energy level.

exothermic Releasing energy (usually heat) to the surroundings.

fast-twitch fibers The stronger, larger muscle fibers that are suited for short bursts of vigorous exercise.

fat An ester formed by the reaction of glycerol with three fatty-acid units; a triglyceride or triacylglycerol.

fat depots Storage places for fats in the body.

fatty acid A carboxylic acid that contains 4 to 20 or more carbon atoms in a chain.

first law of thermodynamics (law of conservation of energy) Energy cannot be created or destroyed, only transformed.

flammable waste A hazardous waste that burns readily on ignition, presenting a fire hazard.

FLaReS An acronym representing four rules used to test a claim: falsifiability, logic, replicability, and sufficiency.

flocculent A substance that causes particles to clump together and settle out.

food additive Any substance other than a basic foodstuff that is added to food to aid nutrition, enhance color or flavor, or provide texture.

formula A representation of a chemical substance in which the component chemical elements are represented by their symbols.

formula mass The sum of the masses of the atoms represented in the formula of a substance, expressed in atomic mass units (u).

fossil fuels Natural fuels derived from once-living plants and animals; especially coal, petroleum, and natural gas.

free radical A highly reactive chemical species that contains an unpaired electron.

freezing The reverse of melting; a change from the liquid to the solid state.

fuel A substance that burns readily with the release of significant energy.

fuel cell A device that produces electricity directly from continuously supplied fuel and oxygen.

functional group An atom or group of atoms that confers characteristic properties to a family of organic compounds.

fundamental particle An electron, proton, or neutron.

gamma decay Emission of a gamma ray ($^0_0\gamma$) by a radioactive nucleus.

gamma (γ) rays Radiation that is emitted by radioactive substances and has higher energy and is more penetrating than X-rays.

gas The state of matter in which the substance takes both the shape and volume of a container that it occupies.

gasoline The fraction of petroleum that consists of hydrocarbons, mainly alkanes, with five to twelve carbons and is used as automotive fuel.

gene The segment of a DNA molecule that contains the information necessary to produce a protein; the smallest unit of hereditary information.

general anesthetic A depressant that acts on the brain to produce unconsciousness and insensitivity to pain.

geometric growth A process in which the rate of growth itself increases during each period of time.

geothermal energy Energy derived from the heat of Earth's interior.

glass A noncrystalline solid material obtained by melting sand with soda, lime, and various other metal oxides.

glass transition temperature (T_g) The temperature above which a polymer is rubbery and tough and below which the polymer is brittle.

global warming An increase in Earth's average temperature.

globular protein A protein whose molecules are folded into compact spherical or ovoid shapes.

glycogen A polymer of glucose with alpha linkages and branched chains; stored in the liver and muscles.

GRAS list A list, established by the U.S. Congress in 1958, of food additives generally recognized as safe.

green chemistry An approach that uses materials and processes that are intended to prevent or reduce pollution at its source.

greenhouse effect The retention of the Sun's heat energy by Earth's atmosphere as a result of excess carbon dioxide and other gases in the atmosphere.

ground state The state of an atom in which all of its electrons are in the lowest possible energy levels.

group The elements in a column in the periodic table; a family of elements.

half-life The length of time required for one-half of the radioactive nuclei in a sample to decay.

hallucinogenic drug A drug that produces visions and sensations that are not part of reality.

halogen An element in group 7A in the customary U.S. arrangement of the periodic table or in group 17 of the IUPAC-recommended table.

hard water Water containing excessive concentrations of ions of calcium, magnesium, and/or iron.

hazardous waste A waste that, when improperly managed, can cause or contribute to death or illness or threaten human health or the environment.

heat Energy transfer that occurs as a result of a temperature difference.

heat of vaporization The amount of heat involved in the evaporation or condensation of a fixed amount of a substance.

heat stroke A failure of the body's heat regulatory system; unless the victim is treated promptly, the rapid rise in body temperature will cause brain damage or death.

herbicide A material used to kill weeds (plants classified as pests).

heterocyclic compound A cyclic compound in which one or more atoms in the ring is not carbon.

homogeneous Completely uniform; a property of a sample that has the same composition in all parts.

homologous series A series of compounds whose adjacent members differ by a fixed unit of structure.

hormone A chemical messenger secreted into the blood by an endocrine gland.

humectant A moistening agent added to food.

hydrocarbon An organic compound that contains only carbon and hydrogen.

hydrogen bomb A bomb based on the nuclear fusion of isotopes of hydrogen.

hydrogen bond A type of intermolecular force in which a hydrogen atom covalently bonded in one molecule is attracted to a nonmetal atom in a neighboring molecule; both the atom to which the hydrogen atom is bonded and the one to which it is attracted are small, highly electronegative atoms, usually N, O, or F.

hydrolysis The reaction of a substance with water; literally, a splitting by water.

hydrophilic Attracted to polar solvents such as water.

hydrophobic Not attracted to water; attracted to oil or grease.

hypoallergenic cosmetics Cosmetics claimed to cause fewer allergic reactions than regular products.

hypothesis A tentative explanation of observations that can be tested by experiment.

ideal gas law The volume of a gas is proportional to the amount of gas and its Kelvin temperature and inversely proportional to its pressure.

induced radioactivity Radioactivity caused by bombarding a stable isotope with elemental particles, forming a radioactive isotope.

industrial smog (sulfurous smog) Polluted air associated with industrial activities, characterized by sulfur oxides and particulate matter.

inorganic chemistry The study of the compounds of all elements other than carbon.

insecticide A substance that is used to kill insects.

iodine number The number of grams of iodine that reacts with 100 g of a fat or oil; an indication of the degree of unsaturation.

ion A charged atom or group of atoms.

ionic bond The chemical bond that results when electrons are transferred from a metal to a nonmetal; the electrostatic attraction between ions of opposite charge.

ionizing radiation Radiation that produces ions as it passes through matter.

isoelectronic Having the same electron configuration.

isomers Compounds that have the same molecular formula but different structures.

isotopes Atoms that have the same number of protons but different numbers of neutrons.

joule (J) The SI unit of energy (1 J = 0.239 cal).

juvenile hormone A hormone that controls the rate of development of young organisms; used to prevent insects from maturing.

kelvin (K) The SI unit of temperature; zero on the Kelvin scale is absolute zero.

keratin The tough, fibrous protein that comprises most of the outermost layer of the epidermis.

kerogen The complex material found in oil shale; has an approximate composition of $(C_6H_8O)_n$, where n is a large number.

ketone (RCOR') An organic compound with a carbonyl group between two carbon atoms.

ketose A monosaccharide with a ketone functional group.

kilocalorie (kcal) A unit of energy equal to 1000 cal; one food calorie.

kilogram (kg) The SI unit of mass, a quantity equal to about 2.2 lb.

kinetic energy The energy of motion.

kinetic–molecular theory An explanation of the behavior of gases based on the motion and energy of particles.

lanolin A natural wax obtained from sheep's wool.

law of combining volumes The volumes of gaseous reactants and products are in a small whole-number ratio when all measurements are made at the same temperature and pressure.

law of conservation of energy See *first law of thermodynamics*.

law of conservation of mass Matter is neither created nor destroyed during a chemical change.

law of definite proportions A compound always contains the same elements in exactly the same proportions by mass; also called the *law of constant composition*.

law of multiple proportions Elements may combine in different proportions to form more than one compound—for example, CO and CO_2.

LD$_{50}$ The dosage that is lethal to 50% of a population of test animals.

levo isomer A "left-handed" isomer.

Lewis formula A structural formula of a molecule or polyatomic ion that shows the arrangement of atoms, bonds, and lone pairs.

Lewis symbol A symbol consisting of the element's symbol surrounded by dots representing the atom's valence electrons; also referred to as an *electron-dot symbol*.

limiting reactant The reactant that is used up first in a reaction, after which the reaction ceases no matter how much remains of the other reactants.

line-angle formula A representation of a molecule in which the corners and ends of lines are understood to be carbon atoms and each carbon atom is understood to be attached to enough hydrogen atoms to give it four bonds.

line spectrum The pattern of colored lines emitted by an element.

lipid A substance from animal or plant cells that is soluble in solvents of low polarity and insoluble in water.

lipoprotein A protein combined with a lipid, such as a triglyceride or cholesterol.

liquid The state of matter in which the substance assumes the shape of its container, flows readily, and maintains a fairly constant volume.

liter (L) A unit of volume equal to a cubic decimeter.

local anesthetic A substance that renders part of the body insensitive to pain while leaving the patient conscious.

lone pair A pair of unshared electrons in the valence shell of an atom; also called a *nonbonding pair*.

lotion An emulsion of tiny oil droplets dispersed in water.

main group elements The elements in the A groups of the customary U.S. arrangement of the periodic table or in groups 1, 2, and 13–18 of the IUPAC-recommended table.

marijuana A hallucinogenic drug consisting of the leaves, flowers, seeds, and small stems of the *Cannabis* plant.

mass A measure of the quantity of matter.

mass–energy equation Einstein's equation $E = mc^2$, in which E is energy, m is mass, and c is the speed of light.

mass number (A) The sum of the numbers of protons and neutrons in the nucleus of an atom; also called the *nucleon number*.

matter The stuff of which all materials are made; anything that has mass and occupies space.

melanin A brownish-black pigment that determines the color of the skin and hair.

melting point The temperature at which a substance changes from the solid to the liquid state.

messenger RNA (mRNA) The type of RNA that contains the codons for a protein; travels from the nucleus of the cell to a ribosome.

metabolism The set of coordinated chemical reactions that keep the cells of an organism alive.

metalloid An element with properties intermediate between those of metals and those of nonmetals.

metals The elements that are to the left of the heavy, stepped line in the periodic table.

meter (m) The SI unit of length, slightly longer than a yard.

mica A mineral composed of SiO_4 tetrahedra arranged in a two-dimensional, sheetlike array.

micelle A tiny spherical oil droplet in which the hydrocarbon tails of soap molecules are embedded, with their hydrophilic heads lying along the outer surface.

micronutrient A substance needed by a plant or animal in only tiny amounts.

middle note The fraction of a perfume that is intermediate in volatility and is responsible for the lingering aroma after most top-note compounds have vaporized.

mineral (dietary) An inorganic substance required in the diet for good health.

mineral (geological) A naturally occurring inorganic solid with a definite composition.

mixture Matter with a variable composition.

moisturizer A substance that acts to retain moisture in the skin by forming a protective physical barrier.

molarity (M) The concentration of a solution in moles of solute per liter of solution.

molar mass The mass of one mole of a substance expressed in units of grams/mole.

molar volume The volume occupied by 1 mol of a substance (usually a gas) under specified conditions.

mole (mol) The amount of a substance that contains 6.022×10^{23} elementary units (atoms, molecules, or formula units) of the substance.

molecular mass The mass of a molecule of a substance; the sum of the atomic masses as indicated by the molecular formula, expressed in atomic mass units (u).

molecule An electrically neutral unit of two or more atoms joined by covalent bonds; the smallest fundamental unit of a molecular substance.

monomer A substance of relatively low molecular mass; monomer molecules are the building blocks of polymers.

monosaccharide A carbohydrate that cannot be hydrolyzed into simpler sugars.

mousse A foamy hair care product composed of resins and used to hold hair in place.

mutagen Any entity that causes changes in genes without destroying the genetic material.

narcotic A depressant, analgesic drug that induces narcosis (sleep).

natural gas A mixture of gases, mainly methane, found in underground deposits.

natural philosophy Philosophical speculation about nature.

neuron A nerve cell.

neurotransmitter A chemical that carries an impulse across a synapse from one nerve cell to the next.

neurotrophin A substance produced during exercise that promotes the growth of brain cells.

neutralization The combination of H^+ and OH^- to form water or the reaction of an acid and a base to produce a salt and water.

neutron A nuclear particle with a mass of approximately 1 u and no electric charge.

nitrogen cycle The various processes by which nitrogen is cycled among the atmosphere, soil, water, and living organisms.

nitrogen fixation A process that combines nitrogen with one or more other elements.

noble gases Generally unreactive elements that appear in group 8A of the customary U.S. arrangement of the periodic table or in group 18 of the IUPAC-recommended table.

nonbonding pair See **lone pair**.

nonionic surfactant A surfactant whose active part bears no ionic charge.

nonmetals The elements to the right of the heavy, stepped line in the periodic table.

nonpolar covalent bond A covalent bond in which there is equal sharing of the bonding pair of electrons.

nonsteroidal anti-inflammatory drug (NSAID) A type of anti-inflammatory drug that is milder than the more potent steroidal anti-inflammatory drugs such as cortisone and prednisone.

nuclear fission The splitting of an atomic nucleus into two smaller ones.

nuclear fusion The combination of two small atomic nuclei to produce one larger nucleus.

nuclear reactor A power plant that produces electricity using nuclear fission reactions.

nucleic acid A nucleotide polymer, DNA or RNA.

nucleon A proton or a neutron.

nucleon number See **mass number**.

nucleotide A combination of an amine base, a sugar unit, and a phosphate unit; the monomer unit of nucleic acids.

nucleus The tiny core of an atom, composed of protons and neutrons and containing all the positive charge and most of the mass of the atom.

octane rating The comparison of the antiknock quality of a gasoline to that of pure isooctane (with a rating of 100).

octet rule Atoms tend to have eight electrons in the outermost shell.

oil (food) A substance formed from glycerol and fatty acids, which is liquid at room temperature.

oil shale Fossil rock from which oil can be obtained at high cost.

optical brightener A compound that absorbs the invisible ultraviolet component of sunlight and reemits it as visible light at the blue end of the spectrum; added to detergents to make whites "whiter."

orbital A volume of space in an atom that is occupied by one or two electrons.

organic chemistry The study of the compounds of carbon.

organic farming Farming without using synthetic fertilizers or pesticides.

oxidation An increase in oxidation number; combination of an element or compound with oxygen; loss of hydrogen; loss of electrons.

oxidizing agent A substance that causes oxidation and is itself reduced.

oxygen cycle The various processes by which oxygen is cycled among the atmosphere, soil, water, and living organisms.

oxygen debt The demand for oxygen in muscle cells that builds up during anaerobic exercise.

ozone layer The layer of the stratosphere that contains ozone and shields living creatures on Earth from the Sun's ultraviolet radiation.

paint A surface coating that contains a pigment, a binder, and a solvent.

particulate matter (PM) An air pollutant composed of solid and liquid particles whose size is greater than that of a molecule.

peptide bond The amide linkage that joins amino acids in chains of peptides, polypeptides, and proteins.

percent by mass The concentration of a solution, expressed as (mass of solute $\div$ mass of solution) $\times$ 100%.

percent by volume The concentration of a solution, expressed as (volume of solute $\div$ volume of solution) $\times$ 100%.

perfume A fragrant mixture of plant extracts and other chemicals dissolved in alcohol.

period A horizontal row of the periodic table.

periodic table A systematic arrangement of the elements in columns and rows; elements in a given column have similar properties.

pesticide A substance that kills some kind of pest (weeds, insects, rodents, and so on).

petroleum A thick liquid mixture of (mostly) hydrocarbons occurring in various geologic deposits.

pH The negative logarithm of the hydronium ion concentration, which indicates the degree of acidity or basicity of a solution.

pharmacology The study of the response of living organisms to drugs.

phenol A compound with an OH group attached to a benzene ring.

pheromone A chemical secreted by an insect or other organism to mark a trail, send out an alarm, or attract a mate.

photochemical smog Smog created by the action of sunlight on hydrocarbons and nitrogen oxides, which come mainly from automobile exhaust.

photon A unit particle of energy.

photosynthesis The chemical process used by green plants to convert solar energy into chemical energy by reducing carbon dioxide and producing glucose.

photovoltaic cell A solar cell; a cell that uses semiconductors to convert sunlight directly to electric energy.

physical change A change in physical state or form.

physical property A quality of a substance that can be demonstrated without changing the composition of the substance.

phytoremediation A method of wastewater treatment that allows plants in a lagoon to remove metals and other contaminates.

placebo effect The phenomenon in which an inactive substance produces results in recipients for psychological reasons.

plasma A state of matter similar to a gas but composed of isolated electrons and nuclei rather than discrete whole atoms or molecules.

plasticizer A substance added to some plastics to make them more flexible and easier to work with.

poison A substance that causes injury, illness, or death of a living organism.

polar covalent bond A covalent bond in which the bonding pair of electrons is shared unequally by the two atoms, giving each atom a partial positive or negative charge.

polar molecule A molecule that has a separation between centers of positive and negative charge; a dipole.

pollutant A chemical that causes undesirable effects by being in the wrong place and/or in the wrong concentration.

polyamide A polymer that has monomer units joined by amide linkages.

polyatomic ion A charged particle consisting of two or more covalently bonded atoms.

polyester A polymer that has monomer units joined by ester linkages.

polymer A molecule with a large molecular mass that is formed of repeating smaller units (monomers).

polymerase chain reaction (PCR) A process that reproduces many copies of a DNA fragment.

polypeptide A polymer of amino acids, usually of lower molecular mass than a protein.

polysaccharide A carbohydrate, such as starch or cellulose, that consists of many monosaccharide units linked together.

polyunsaturated fat A fat containing fatty-acid units that have two or more carbon-to-carbon double bonds.

positron (β^+ or $_{+1}^{0}e$) A positively charged particle with the mass of an electron.

potential energy Energy due to position or composition.

preemergent herbicide A herbicide that is rapidly broken down in the soil and can therefore be used to kill weed plants before crop seedlings emerge.

primary plant nutrients Nitrogen, phosphorus, and potassium.

primary sewage treatment Treatment of wastewater in a holding pond to allow some of the sewage solids to settle out as sludge.

primary structure The amino-acid sequence in a protein.

product A substance produced by a chemical reaction; product formulas follow the arrow in a chemical equation.

progestin A steroid hormone that mimics the action of progesterone.

prostaglandin One of several hormone-like lipids that are derived from the fatty acid arachidonic acid; involved in increased blood pressure, the contractions of smooth muscle, and other physiological processes.

protein An amino acid polymer with a molecular weight exceeding about 10,000 u.

proton (H^+) The hydrogen ion in acid–base chemistry.

proton (nuclear) The unit of positive charge in the nucleus of an atom.

psychotropic drugs Drugs that affect the mind.

purine A heterocyclic amine base with two fused rings, found in nucleic acids.

pyrimidine A heterocyclic amine base with one ring, found in nucleic acids.

quantum A discrete unit of energy; one photon.

quartz A silicate composed of SiO_4 tetrahedra arranged in a three-dimensional array.

quaternary structure An arrangement of protein subunits in a particular pattern.

radiation therapy Use of radioisotopes to destroy cancer cells.

radioactive decay The disintegration of an unstable atomic nucleus with spontaneous emission of radiation.

radioactive fallout Radioactive debris produced by explosion of a nuclear bomb.

radioactivity The spontaneous emission of particles (for example, alpha or beta) or rays (gamma) from unstable atomic nuclei.

radioisotopes Atoms or ions with radioactive nuclei.

reactant A starting material in a chemical change; reactant formulas precede the arrow in a chemical equation.

reactive wastes Hazardous wastes that tend to react spontaneously or to react vigorously with air or water.

Recommended Daily Allowance (RDA) The recommended level of a nutrient necessary for a balanced diet.

reducing agent A substance that causes reduction and is itself oxidized.

reduction A decrease in oxidation number; a gain of electrons; a loss of oxygen; a gain of hydrogen.

replication Copying or duplication; the process by which DNA reproduces itself.

resin A polymeric organic material, usually a sticky solid or semisolid.

restorative drug A drug used to relieve the pain and reduce the inflammation resulting from overuse of muscles.

retrovirus An RNA virus that synthesizes DNA in a host cell.

reverse osmosis A method of pressure filtration through a semipermeable membrane; water flows from an area of high salt concentration to an area of low salt concentration.

ribonucleic acid (RNA) The form of nucleic acid found mainly in the cytoplasm but also present in all other parts of the cell; contains the sugar ribose.

risk–benefit analysis A technique for estimating a desirability quotient by dividing the benefits by the risks.

rule of 72 A mathematical formula that gives the doubling time for a population growing geometrically; 72 divided by the annual rate of growth expressed as a percentage equals the doubling time.

salt An ionic compound produced by the reaction of an acid with a base.

saponins Natural compounds in some plants that produce a soapy lather.

saturated fat A triglyceride composed of a large proportion of saturated fatty acids esterified with glycerol.

saturated hydrocarbon An alkane; a compound of carbon and hydrogen with only single bonds.

science An accumulation of knowledge about nature and the physical world.

scientific law A summary of experimental data; often expressed in the form of a mathematical equation.

scientific model A representation of an invisible process that uses tangible items or pictures.

sebum An oily secretion that protects the skin from moisture loss.

second law of thermodynamics The entropy of the universe increases in any spontaneous process.

secondary plant nutrients Magnesium, calcium, and sulfur.

secondary sewage treatment Passing effluent from primary sewage treatment through gravel and sand filters to aerate the water and remove suspended solids.

secondary structure The arrangement of a protein's polypeptide chains—for example, helix or pleated sheet.

sex attractant A pheromone released by an organism to attract a mate.

shell One of the specific, quantized energy levels that an electron can occupy in an atom.

significant figures Those measured digits that are known with certainty plus one uncertain digit.

silicone A polymer whose chains consists of alternating silicon and oxygen atoms.

single bond A pair of electrons shared between two atoms.

SI units (International System of Units) A measuring system that is used by scientists worldwide and has seven base quantities with their multiples and submultiples.

skin protection factor (SPF) The rating of a sunscreen's ability to absorb or block ultraviolet radiation.

slag A relatively low-melting product of the reaction of limestone with silicate impurities in iron ore.

slow-twitch fibers Muscle fibers suited for steady exercise of long duration.

smog The combination of smoke and fog; polluted air.

soap A salt (usually a sodium salt) of a long-chain carboxylic acid.

solar cell A device used for converting sunlight to electricity; a photoelectric cell.

solid A state of matter in which the substance has a definite shape and volume.

solute The substance that is dissolved in another substance (solvent) to form a solution; usually present in a smaller amount than the solvent.

solution A homogeneous mixture of two or more substances.

solvent The substance that dissolves another substance (solute) to form a solution; usually present in a larger amount than the solute.

specific heat The amount of heat required to raise the temperature of 1 g of a substance by 1 °C.

standard temperature and pressure (STP) Conditions of 0 °C and 1 atm pressure.

starch A polymer of glucose units joined by alpha linkages; a complex carbohydrate.

starvation The withholding of nutrition from the body, whether voluntary or involuntary.

steel An alloy of iron containing small amounts of carbon and usually another metal such as manganese, nickel, or chromium.

stereoisomers Isomers having the same formula but differing in the arrangement of atoms or groups of atoms in three-dimensional space.

steroid A molecule that has a four-ring skeletal structure, with one cyclopentane and three cyclohexane fused rings.

stimulant drug A drug that increases alertness, speeds up mental processes, and generally elevates the mood.

stoichiometric factor A factor that relates the numbers of moles of two substances through their coefficients in a chemical equation.

stoichiometry The quantitative relationship between reactants and products in a chemical reaction.

strong acid An acid that ionizes completely in water; a potent proton donor.

strong base A base that dissociates completely in water; a potent proton acceptor.

structural formula A chemical formula that shows how the atoms of a molecule are arranged, to which other atom(s) they are bonded, and the kinds of bonds.

sublevel See **subshell**.

sublimation Conversion of a solid directly to the gaseous state without going through the liquid state.

subshell A set of orbitals in an atom that are in the same shell and have the same energy; also called a *sublevel*.

substance A sample of matter that always has the same composition, no matter how it is made or where it is found.

substituent An atom or group of atoms substituted for a hydrogen atom on a hydrocarbon.

substrate The substance that attaches to the active site of an enzyme and is then acted upon.

sulfurous smog See **industrial smog**.

sunscreen A substance or mixture that blocks or absorbs ultraviolet (UV) radiation.

supercritical fluid An intermediate state having properties of both gases and liquids.

surface-active agent (surfactant) Any substance that stabilizes the suspension in water of a nonpolar substance such as oil.

surroundings Everything that is not part of the system being observed in a thermochemical study.

sustainable agriculture Farming practices that can produce food and fiber indefinitely, without causing irreparable damage to the ecosystem.

sustainable chemistry An approach designed to meet the needs of the present generation without compromising the needs of future generations.

synapse A tiny gap between nerve cells.

synergistic effect An effect greater than the sum of the effects expected from two or more phenomena.

system The part of the universe under consideration in a thermochemical study.

tar sands Sands that contain bitumen, a thick hydrocarbon material.

technology The practical application of knowledge by which humans modify the materials of nature to better satisfy their needs and wants.

temperature A measure of heat intensity, or how energetic the particles of a sample are.

temperature inversion A warm layer of air above a cool, stagnant lower layer.

teratogen A substance that causes birth defects when introduced into the body of a pregnant female.

tertiary structure The folding pattern of a protein.

tetracyclines Antibacterial drugs with four fused rings.

theory A detailed explanation of a phenomenon that is based on experimentation and may be revised if new data warrant.

thermochemistry The study of energy changes that occur during chemical reactions.

thermonuclear reactions Nuclear fusion reactions that require extremely high temperatures and pressures.

thermoplastic polymer A kind of polymer that can be heated and reshaped.

thermosetting polymer A kind of polymer that cannot be softened and remolded.

top note The fraction of a perfume that vaporizes most quickly, is composed of relatively small molecules, and is responsible for the odor when the perfume is first applied.

toxicology The branch of pharmacology that deals with the effects of poisons on the body, their identification and detection, and remedies for them.

toxic waste A waste that contains or releases poisonous substances in amounts large enough to threaten human health or the environment.

toxin A poisonous substance produced by a living organism.

tracers Radioisotopes used to trace the movement of substances or locate the sites of activity in physical, chemical, and biological systems.

transcription The process by which a segment of DNA transfers its information to a messenger RNA (mRNA) molecule during protein synthesis.

transfer RNA (tRNA) A small molecule that contains anticodon nucleotides; the RNA molecule that bonds to and carries an amino acid.

transition elements Metallic elements in the B groups of the customary U.S. arrangement of the periodic table or in groups 3–12 of the IUPAC-recommended table.

translation The process by which the information contained in the codon of an mRNA molecule is converted to a protein structure.

transmutation The conversion of one element into another.

triglyceride An ester of glycerol with three fatty-acid units; also called a triacylglycerol.

triple bond The sharing of three pairs of electrons between two atoms.

tritium A radioactive isotope of hydrogen with two neutrons and one proton in the nucleus (hydrogen-3).

unsaturated hydrocarbon An alkene, alkyne, or aromatic hydrocarbon; a hydrocarbon containing one or more double or triple bonds or aromatic rings.

valence electrons Electrons in the outermost shell of an atom.

valence shell electron pair repulsion theory (VSEPR theory) A theory of chemical bonding useful in determining the shapes of molecules; it states that valence shell electron pairs around a central atom locate themselves as far apart as possible.

vaporization The process by which a substance changes from the liquid to the gaseous (vapor) state.

variable A factor that changes during an experiment.

vitamin An organic compound that is required in the diet to protect against some diseases.

volatile organic compounds (VOCs) Compounds that cause pollution because they vaporize readily.

VSEPR theory See **valence shell electron pair repulsion theory**.

vulcanization The process of making naturally soft rubber harder by reacting it with sulfur.

wax An ester of a long-chain fatty acid with a long-chain alcohol.

weak acid An acid that ionizes only slightly in water; a poor proton donor.

weak base A base that ionizes only slightly in water; a poor proton acceptor.

weight A measure of the force of attraction between Earth (or another planet) and an object.

wet scrubber A pollution control device that uses water to remove pollutants from smokestack gases.

X-rays Radiation similar to visible light but of much higher energy and much more penetrating.

zwitterion A molecule that contains both a positive charge and a negative charge; a dipolar ion.

Brief Answers to Selected Problems

Answers are provided for *all in-chapter exercises*. Brief answers are given for *odd-numbered Review Questions*; more complete answers can be obtained by reviewing the text. Answers are provided for *all odd-numbered Problems and Additional Problems*.

NOTE: For numerical problems, your answer may differ slightly from ours because of rounding and the use of significant figures (see Appendix).

Chapter 1

1.1 **A. a.** DQ would probably be small.
   b. DQ would probably be large.
   B. a. DQ would be uncertain.
   b. DQ would probably be large.
1.2 **A. a.** 1.00 kg
   b. 179 lb
1.3 **A.** physical: a, c; chemical: b
   B. physical: b, d; chemical: a, c
1.4 **A.** elements: He, No, Os; compounds: CuO, NO, KF
   B. 8
1.5 **a.** 7.24 kg
   b. 4.29 μm
   c. 7.91 ms
   d. 2.29 cg
   e. 7.90 Mm
1.6 **a.** 7.45×10^{-9} m
   b. 5.25×10^{-6} s
   c. 1.415×10^{3} m
   d. 2.06×10^{-3} m
   e. 6.19×10^{3} m
1.7 **A.** 500 cm^2
   B. 1600 cm^3
1.8 **a.** 7.55×10^{2} mm
   b. 0.2056 L
   c. 2.06×10^{5} μg
   d. 73.8 mm
1.9 **A.** Ice
   B. Padauk floats, and ebony sinks. Both sink in ethyl alcohol.
1.10 **A.** 1.11 g/mL
   B. 11.8 g/cm^3
1.11 **A.** 316 g
   B. 47.7 kg
1.12 **A.** 14.8 cm^3
   B. No (1.33 L)
1.13 **A.** 351 K
   B. 77 K
1.14 **A.** 1799 kcal
   B. 34 kcal
1. Science is testable, reproducible, explanatory, predictive, and tentative. Testability best distinguishes science.
3. These problems usually involve too many variables to be treated by scientific methods.
5. Risk–benefit analysis compares benefits of an action with risks of that action.
7. A desirability quotient (DQ) is benefits divided by risks. A large DQ means that risks are minimal compared with benefits.
9. liter; milliliter
11. **(a)** applied; **(b)** applied; **(c)** basic.
13. Penicillin has saved thousands of lives, causing harm to a very few. The DQ for penicillin is large.
15. **(a)** high; **(b)** high, but lower than (a).

17. Food producers benefit through increased profits. The consumer assumes the greatest risk.
19. 100 g, 2 kg
21. Yes
23. 250 mL
25. 1.46×10^{9} km^3
27. Yes; the 26.3-mm i.d. tube is larger than 25.4 mm (1 inch).
29. physical property: a, c, d; chemical property: b.
31. physical change: a, c; chemical change: b
33. substance: a, c, d; mixture: b
35. homogeneous: a, b, c; heterogeneous: d
37. a substance
39. elements: a, b, d; compound: c
41. **a.** aluminum; **b.** calcium; **c.** chlorine; **d.** silver
43. f
45. **a.** 8.01 μg   **b.** 7.9 mL   **c.** 1.05 km
47. **a.** 0.0374 L   **b.** 1.55×10^{5} m   **c.** 198 mg
   d. 1.19×10^{4} cm^2 **e.** 0.078 ms
49. **a.** cm   **b.** kg   **c.** dL
51. 10.0 mm; 1830 mm
53. **a.** 1.17 g/mL   **b.** 1.26 g/mL
55. **a.** 120 g   **b.** 490 g
57. **a.** 344 mL   **b.** 495 cm^3
59.

61. Yes
63. 14.8 cm
65. −78 °C
67. 38.5 kcal
69. 52.6 min
71. b.
73. 5.7 y
75. 1, d; 2, e; 3, b; 4, a; 5, d
77. 600 g
79. Cabbage (lightest) < potatoes < sugar (heaviest)
81. 5.23 g/cm^3
83. 6.73×10^{-6} cm
85. 0.908 metric ton
87. **a.** 1.3 g/cm^3; **b.** 5.4 g/cm^3; **c.** 0.688 g/cm^3; Jupiter and Earth are more dense than water; Saturn is less dense and would float (in a large enough ocean!).
89. Green chemistry is an approach that uses materials and processes that are intended to prevent or reduce pollution at its source.
91. a

Chapter 2

2.1 **A.** 2.19 g nitrogen   **B.** 63.0 g nitrogen
2.2 3 atoms hydrogen/1 atom phosphorus
2.3 average Cl + I is 81.2; actual Br is 79.9.
1. **a.** atomic: matter is made of discrete particles; continuous: matter is infinitely divisible.
   b. Greek: four elements, no atoms; modern: each element has its own kind of atom.

3. discrete: a, c, e; continuous: b, d
5. An element is a substance that could not be broken down into simpler substances.
7. Different elements can combine in two or more different sets of proportions, each set corresponding to a different compound.
   a. 2:1   **b.** 3:1   **c.** 3:5
9. C has 15 oxygen atoms; the initial mixture has only 14.
11. **a.** conservation of mass: no atoms are created or destroyed.
    b. definite proportions: only whole atoms combine.
    c. multiple proportions; 1 C atom can combine with 1 O atom to make CO, or 1 C atom can combine with 2 O atoms to make CO_2.
13. Law of multiple proportions
15. No. In the open vessel, a gas has escaped and is not part of the weight after reaction.
17. No. The elements have only been mixed; they have not reacted chemically.
19. 6.60 g
21. The mass of titanium(IV) oxide formed cannot be greater than the masses of titanium and oxygen together.
23. (b)
25. **a.** 86.9 g hydrogen.   **b.** 688 g oxygen
27. 3.8 kg carbon
29. C:O ratio for carbon suboxide is 1.000:0.888. Ratio of 1.332:0.888 = 3:2; 2.664:0.888 = 3:1.
31. SnO_2
33. The S:F ratios are (T) 1.00:2.37 and (U) 1.00:3.56. 3.56:2.37 = 1.50:1 or 3:2.
35. **a.** Yes; Dalton assumed that atoms of different elements had different masses.
    b. No; Dalton assumed that atoms of one element differ (in mass) from atoms of any other element.
37. Contradict. Dalton regarded atoms as indivisible.
39. (d)
41. Yes; the ratio of carbon to hydrogen is the same for the different samples.
43. 0.4467 g nitrogen
45. Six fluorine atoms
47. Conservation of mass
49. 108.0 g of mercury oxide
51. 1.334:1.000 or 4:3
53. (1) Lead compounds, once used in paints, have been replaced with titanium dioxide, a much safer material. (2) Metal salts with lower toxicity now substitute for the lead stabilizers in plastics.

Chapter 3

3.1 **A.** 33 neutrons   **B.** 131; iodine-131
3.2 **A.** $^{90}_{37}X$ and $^{88}_{37}X$; $^{88}_{38}X$ and $^{93}_{38}X$ **B.** three
3.3 **A.** 32 electrons   **B.** 3
3.4 **a.** (Be) 2 2
    b. (Mg) 2 8 2; both have the same number of outer electrons.
3.5 **A. a.** $1s^22s^22p^5$
    b. $1s^22s^22p^63s^23p^5$ (Both have the valence configuration ns^2np^5.)
    B. a. $1s^22s^22p^63s^23p^63d^24s^2$
    b. $1s^22s^22p^63s^23p^63d^{10}4s^24p^1$
3.6 **A. a.** (Rb) $5s^1$
    b. (Se) $4s^24p^4$
    c. (Ge) $4s^24p^2$
    B. a. (Ga) $4s^24p^1$
    b. (In) $5s^25p^1$
1. **a.** Crookes invented the gas discharge tube.
   b. Goldstein discovered positive particles.
   c. Faraday developed electrolysis.
   d. Thomson determined mass-to-charge ratio of the electron.
3. Both are forms of radiation; gamma rays are more energetic.
5. A and B, no; A and C, no; A and D, yes; B and C, yes
7. A and B
9. Sc; scandium; 45.0 u
11. The atom in which the electron moves from the first to the third shell.
13. **a.** 3   **b.** 12   **c.** 17   **d.** 9   **e.** 13   **f.** 15

15. **a.** $^{42}_{20}Ca$, calcium-42
    b. $^{51}_{23}V$, vanadium-51
17. 4
19. **a.** 7   **b.** 13   **c.** 19
21. **a.** Excited state; one electron has been raised to the 2p subshell.
    b. Incorrect; a p subshell can only hold at most 6 electrons.
    c. Excited state; two electrons have been raised to the 2p subshell.
    d. Ground state; all six electrons are in the lowest possible subshell.
23. neon
25. Si has two 3p electrons; Ge has two 4p electrons; germanium is a much larger atom.
27. metal, a, b, and c; nonmetal, d
29. Ne and Kr
31. Four
33. **a.** 15   **b.** phosphorus   **c.** 15   **d.** 6   **e.** 0
35.

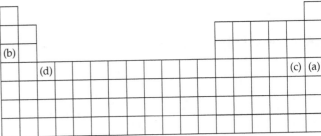

37. **a.** $1s^22s^22p^63s^23p^63d^64s^2$
    b. $1s^22s^22p^63s^23p^63d^{10}4s^24p^64d^{10}5s^25p^2$
    c. $1s^22s^22p^63s^23p^63d^{10}4s^24p^64d^{10}4f^{14}5s^25p^65d^{10}6s^26p^2$
39. The period 5 elements are in group 2A (only s electrons) and group 3B (d electrons). Therefore, the elements are strontium (Sr) and yttrium (Y).
41. b
43. d

Chapter 4

4.1 **a.** :Är: **b.** ·Ca· **c.** :F̈· **d.** :N̈· **e.** K· **f.** :S̈·
4.2 **A.** Li· + :F̈· ⟶ Li⁺ + :F̈:⁻
    B. Rb· + :Ï· ⟶ Rb⁺ + :Ï:⁻
4.3 2·Al· + 3:Ö· ⟶ 2 Al³⁺ + 3:Ö:²⁻
4.4 **A. a.** CaF_2 **b.** Li_2O
    B. $FeCl_2$ and $FeCl_3$
4.5 **a.** K_2O **b.** Ca_3N_2 **c.** CaS
4.6 **a.** calcium fluoride   **b.** copper(II) bromide
4.7 **a.** bromine trifluoride
    b. bromine pentafluoride
    c. dinitrogen monoxide
    d. dinitrogen pentoxide
4.8 **a.** PCl_3 **b.** Cl_2O_7
    c. NI_3 **d.** S_2Cl_2
4.9 **a.** :B̈r· + ·B̈r: ⟶ :B̈r:B̈r:
    b. H· + ·B̈r: ⟶ H:B̈r:
    c. :Ï· + ·C̈l: ⟶ :Ï:C̈l:
4.10 **A. a.** polar covalent **b.** ionic **c.** nonpolar covalent
     B. a. polar covalent **b.** polar covalent **c.** nonpolar covalent
4.11 **A. a.** $Ca(C_2H_3O_2)_2$ **b.** K_2O **c.** $Al_2(SO_4)_3$
     B. a. 3 **b.** 4
4.12 **A. a.** calcium carbonate   **b.** magnesium phosphate
     c. potassium chromate

B. a. ammonium sulfate
  b. potassium dihydrogen phosphate
  c. copper(II) dichromate

4.13 **A. a.** $:\!\ddot{F}\!-\!\ddot{O}\!-\!\ddot{F}\!:$ **b.** $H\!-\!\underset{\underset{H}{|}}{\overset{}{C}}\!-\!\ddot{\underset{..}{Cl}}\!:$

B. a. $\left[:\!\ddot{N}\!=\!N\!=\!\ddot{N}\!:\right]^{-}$ **b.** $:\!\ddot{O}\!=\!\underset{..}{N}\!-\!\ddot{\underset{..}{O}}\!-\!\ddot{F}\!:$

4.14 **A. a.** pyramidal **b.** triangular
  B. a. triangular **b.** bent (at both O)
1. Sodium metal is quite reactive; sodium ions (as in NaCl) are quite unreactive.
3. **a.** 1+ **b.** 2− **c.** 3− **d.** 2+
5. **a.** 1 **b.** 1 **c.** 2 **d.** 1
  e. 3 **f.** 3

7. **a.** $\cdot Ca \cdot$ **b.** $:\!\overset{\cdot}{\underset{..}{S}}\!:$ **c.** $\cdot \overset{\cdot}{Si}\cdot$

9. **a.** $Na^+\left[:\!\ddot{\underset{..}{I}}\!:\right]^-$ **b.** $2\,K^+\ \left[:\!\ddot{\underset{..}{S}}\!:^{2-}\right]$

  c. $Ca^{2+}\ 2\left[:\!\ddot{\underset{..}{Cl}}\!:^-\right]$ **d.** $Al^{3+}\ 3\left[:\!\ddot{\underset{..}{F}}\!:^-\right]$

11. **a.** Mg^{2+} **b.** sodium ion **c.** O^{2-}
  d. chloride ion **e.** Zn^{2+} **f.** copper(I) ion
13. **a.** chromium(II) ion **b.** chromium(III) ion
  c. chromium(VI) ion
15. **a.** V^{2+} **b.** Ti^{2+} **c.** Ti^{4+}
17. **a.** NaI **b.** potassium chloride
  c. Cu_2O **d.** magnesium fluoride
  e. $FeBr_2$ **f.** iron(III) bromide
19. Cr_2O_3, chromium(III) oxide, and CrO_3, chromium(VI) oxide
21. **a.** KOH **b.** magnesium carbonate
  c. $Fe(CN)_3$ **d.** FeC_2O_4
  e. copper(II) sulfate **f.** sodium dichromate

23. $H\cdot + \cdot\ddot{\underset{..}{F}}\!: \longrightarrow H\!:\!\ddot{\underset{..}{F}}\!:$

25. $\cdot\overset{\cdot}{\underset{\cdot}{P}}\cdot + 3\,H\cdot \longrightarrow H\!:\!\underset{\underset{H}{\cdot\cdot}}{\overset{}{P}}\!:\!H$

27. $\cdot\overset{\cdot}{\underset{\cdot}{C}}\cdot + 4\,:\!\ddot{\underset{..}{Cl}}\cdot \longrightarrow :\!\ddot{\underset{..}{Cl}}\!:\!\underset{\underset{:\ddot{Cl}:}{:\ddot{Cl}:}}{\overset{}{C}}\!:\!\ddot{\underset{..}{Cl}}\!:$

29. **a.** N_2O_4 **b.** $BrCl_3$
  c. oxygen difluoride **d.** NI_3
  e. carbon tetrabromide **f.** dinitrogen tetrasulfide

31. **a.** $H\!-\!\underset{\underset{H}{|}}{\overset{\overset{H}{|}}{Si}}\!-\!H$ **b.** $:\!\underset{\underset{:\ddot{F}:}{|}}{\overset{\overset{:\ddot{F}:}{|}}{N}}\!-\!\underset{\underset{:\ddot{F}:}{|}}{\overset{\overset{:\ddot{F}:}{|}}{N}}\!:$

  c. $H\!-\!\underset{\underset{H}{|}}{\overset{\overset{H}{|}}{C}}\!-\!\underset{\underset{H}{|}}{\overset{}{N}}\!:$ **d.** $H\!-\!\underset{}{\overset{\overset{:O:}{||}}{C}}\!-\!H$

  e. $:\!\underset{\underset{H}{|}}{\overset{}{N}}\!-\!\ddot{\underset{..}{O}}\!:$ **f.** $H\!-\!\ddot{\underset{..}{O}}\!-\!\underset{\underset{:\ddot{O}\!-\!H}{|}}{\overset{}{P}}\!-\!\ddot{\underset{..}{O}}\!-\!H$

33. **a.** $\left[:\!\ddot{\underset{..}{Cl}}\!-\!\ddot{\underset{..}{O}}\!:\right]^-$ **b.** $\left[H\!-\!\ddot{\underset{..}{O}}\!-\!\underset{\underset{:\ddot{O}:}{|}}{\overset{\overset{:\ddot{O}:}{||}}{P}}\!-\!\ddot{\underset{..}{O}}\!:\right]^{2-}$

  c. $\left[:\!\ddot{\underset{..}{O}}\!-\!\underset{\underset{:\ddot{O}:}{|}}{\overset{}{Br}}\!-\!\ddot{\underset{..}{O}}\!:\right]^-$

35. **a.** polar **b.** polar **c.** polar
37. **a.** $\overset{\longrightarrow}{H\!-\!O}$ **b.** $\overset{\longrightarrow}{N\!-\!F}$ **c.** $\overset{\longleftarrow}{Cl\!-\!B}$
39. **a.** $\overset{\delta+}{Si}\ —\ \overset{\delta-}{O}$
  b. is not polar
  c. $\overset{\delta-}{F}\ —\ \overset{\delta+}{N}$
41. **a.** ionic **b.** nonpolar covalent
  c. ionic **d.** nonpolar covalent
43. **a.** tetrahedral **b.** bent
  c. pyramidal **d.** tetrahedral
  e. bent **f.** triangular
45. Nonpolar; the two polar Be—F bonds cancel.
47. **a.** nonpolar bonds; 109.5°; nonpolar molecule
  b. nonpolar bonds; 109.5°; nonpolar molecule
  c. nonpolar bonds; 109.5°; nonpolar molecule
  d. polar bonds; 109.5°; nonpolar molecule
  e. polar bonds; 109.5°; polar molecule
  f. polar bonds; 120°; polar molecule
49. a, c

51. **a.** $\underset{\underset{:\ddot{Br}:}{|}}{\overset{\overset{:\ddot{Br}:}{|}}{Al}}\!-\!\ddot{\underset{..}{Br}}\!:$ **b.** $H\!-\!Be\!-\!H$ **c.** $H\!-\!\underset{\underset{H}{|}}{\overset{}{B}}\!-\!H$

53. Neon has an octet of valence electrons (a full outer shell).
55. AlP; Mg_3P_2
57. Polar covalent
59. No; a potassium salt, to avoid having the mouth catch fire!
61. **a.** $Ca^{2+}: 1s^2 2s^2 2p^6 3s^2 3p^6$
  b. $Rb^+: 1s^2 2s^2 2p^6 3s^2 3p^6 3d^{10} 4s^2 4p^6$
  c. $S^{2-}: 1s^2 2s^2 2p^6 3s^2 3p^6$
  d. $I^-: 1s^2 2s^2 2p^6 3s^2 3p^6 3d^{10} 4s^2 4p^6 4d^{10} 5s^2 5p^6$
  e. $N^{3-}: 1s^2 2s^2 2p^6$
  f. $Se^{2-}: 1s^2 2s^2 2p^6 3s^2 3p^6 3d^{10} 4s^2 4p^6$
63. The halogens have seven valence electrons. Forming single bonds by sharing a bond with one other atom gives them an octet of electrons.
65. $Al_2(WO_4)_3$
67. $Q_3(ZX_4)_2$
69. Molecular recognition
71. Medicinal chemists design new drug molecules to resemble biological molecules that bind to enzymes which recognize the molecules by shapes and partial charges.

Chapter 5

5.1 **A.** $3\,H_2 + N_2 \longrightarrow 2\,NH_3$
  B. $2\,Fe_2O_3 + 3\,C \longrightarrow 3\,CO_2 + 4\,Fe$
5.2 **A.** 1.48 L CO_2
  B. propane; 8 L
5.3 **A. a.** 65.0 u **b.** 98.0 u
  c. 147.0 u **d.** 234.1 u
5.4 **a.** 13.8% N **b.** 41.1% N
5.5 **A. a.** 2.04 g Si **b.** 1000 g H_2O
  c. 17.0 g $Ca(H_2PO_4)_2$
  B. a. 0.0664 mol Fe **b.** 2.84 mol C_4H_{10}
  c. 0.000674 mol $Mg(NO_3)_2$

5.6 *Molecular:* 2 molecules H₂S react with 3 molecules O₂ to form 2 molecules SO₂ and 2 molecules H₂O
Molar: 2 mol H₂S react with 3 mol O₂ to form 2 mol SO₂ and 2 mol H₂O
Mass: 68.2 g H₂S react with 96.0 g O₂ to form 128.1 g SO₂ and 36.0 g H₂O
5.7 **A. a.** 1.59 mol CO₂   **b.** 0.168 mol CO₂
   B. propane; 15 mol
5.8 **A.** 0.763 g O₂
   B. a. 2130 g CO₂   **b.** 2350 g CO₂
5.9 **A.** 0.00870 M
   B. 0.968 M
5.10 **A. a.** 9.00 M   **b.** 1.26 M
   B. 0.274 M
5.11 **a.** 673 g KOH   **b.** 5.61 g KOH
5.12 **A.** 29.7 mL
   B. 6.30 × 10⁻⁴ g HNO₃
5.13 **A.** 90.7% ethanol
   B. 34.8% toluene
5.14 **A.** 2.81% H₂O₂
   B. 51.3% NaOH
5.15 **A.** Dissolve 5.62 g glucose in enough water to make 125 g solution.
   B. Dissolve 15.6 g NaCl in enough water to make 1750 g solution.
1. **a.** The smallest repeating unit of a substance
   b. The sum of the atomic masses of a chemical compound
   c. The amount of a substance that contains 6.022 × 10²³ formula units of the substance
   d. The number of atoms (6.022 × 10²³) in exactly 12 g of pure carbon-12
   e. The formula mass of a substance expressed in grams; mass of one mole
   f. The volume occupied by 1 mol of a gas under specified conditions
3. Avogadro's hypothesis states that equal volumes of all gases contain the same number of molecules at fixed temperature and pressure. It explains why volumes of gaseous reactants and products combine in small whole-number ratios.
5. **a.** A homogeneous mixture of two or more substances
   b. The substance that dissolves another substance (solute) to form a solution
   c. The substance that is dissolved in another substance (solvent) to form a solution
   d. A solution in which the solvent is water.
7. **a.** 12   **b.** 3   **c.** 6
9. 6 N; 3 P; 27 H; 12 O
11. **a.** Two molecules of H₂O₂ decompose to give two molecules of H₂O and one molecule of O₂.
   b. 2 mol H₂O₂ decompose to give 2 mol H₂O and 1 mol O₂.
   c. 68 g H₂O₂ decompose to give 36 g H₂O and 32 g O₂.
13. **a.** 2 Mg + O₂ → MgO
   b. C₃H₈ + 5 O₂ → 3 CO₂ + 4 H₂O
   c. 3 H₂ + Ta₂O₅ → 2 Ta + 3 H₂O
15. **a.** N₂ + O₂ → 2 NO
   b. 2 O₃ → 3 O₂
   c. UO₂ + 4 HF → UF₄ + 2 H₂O
17.
Hydrogen gas (two volumes) + Oxygen gas (one volume) → Steam (two volumes)
19. **a.** 124 L   **b.** 3.05 mL
21. 6:1 or 6 times
23. **a.** 6.02 × 10²³ S₈ molecules   **b.** 4.82 × 10²⁴ S atoms
25. c
27. **a.** 169.9 g   **b.** 127.2 g   **c.** 447.2 g   **d.** 104.1 g
29. **a.** 1770 g BaSO₄   **b.** 6.35 g CuCl₂   **c.** 85.6 g C₁₂H₂₂O₁₁

31. **a.** 0.0195 mol Sb₂S₃   **b.** 0.133 mol MoO₃
   c. 3.56 mol AlPO₄
33. **a.** 16.5%   **b.** 26.2%
35. **a.** 32.5 mol CO₂   **b.** 20.3 mol O₂
37. **a.** 2480 g NH₃   **b.** 193 g H₂
39. **a.** 2.34 M HCl   **b.** 0.138 M Li₂CO₃
41. **a.** 70.0 g NaOH   **b.** 17.0 g C₆H₁₂O₆
43. **a.** 0.416 L   **b.** 0.900 L
45. **a.** 9.28% water by vol   **b.** 10.5% methanol by vol
47. Add 277 g NaCl to 3098 g water.
49. Add 40.0 mL acetic acid to enough water to make 2.00 L of solution.
51. Charge is not balanced in the equation Al(s) + 2 H⁺(aq) → Al³⁺(aq) + H₂(g).
53. **a.** Hg(NO₃)₂(s) ⟶ Hg(l) + 2 NO₂(g) + O₂(g)
   b. Na₂CO₃(aq) + 2 HCl(aq) ⟶ H₂O(l) + CO₂(g) + 2 NaCl(aq)
55. **a.** yes   **b.** 0.50 mol C₂H₂
57. 2.65 × 10⁹ g CaO
59. 0.418 mol H₂O₂
61. **a.** 90.7% ethanol   **b.** 0.800% acetone
63. **a.** 2.38 × 10⁻²² g U   **b.** 602 atoms!
65. 0.00825 L (8.25 mL)
67. There are about 2000 times as many molecules in a cup of water as there are cups of water in Earth's oceans. The statement is valid.
69. 53,000 kg
71. 55.5 mol H₂O
73. **a.** (1) C₆H₁₂O₆ → 2 C₂H₅OH + 2 CO₂; (2) C₂H₄ + H₂O → C₂H₅OH
   b. (1) 51.1%; (2) 100%
   c. (1) CO₂ is a byproduct ("waste"); (2) no byproduct
   d. (1) sustainable; (2) not sustainable
   e. reaction (1) does produce a byproduct, but is sustainable and does not consume valuable, non-renewable petroleum.
75. **a.** 67.1%   **b.** 30.6 g CO₂   **c.** 83.0%

Chapter 6

6.1 400 mm Hg
6.2 **A.** 1800 mL   **B.** 503 mm Hg
6.3 **A. a.** 2.98 L   **b.** 234 L
   B. −167 °C
6.4 **A.** 5.86 g/L
   B. 1.29 g/L; only 0.22 times that of Xe
6.5 921 mL
6.6 **A. a.** 0.0526 atm   **b.** 9.99 L
   B. 112 L
1. Both solids and liquids are difficult to compress because the particles are close together. Liquids flow because their particles are free to move; solids have fixed shapes because their particles have fixed positions.
3. Dispersion forces in helium; dipole-dipole interactions in HCl; hydrogen bonding in water; ionic bonds in NaCl
5. Volume is inversely proportional to pressure, directly proportional to absolute temperature.
7. b, d
9. HBr
11. No. Hexane is nonpolar; it has no dipole to attract the K⁺ and NO₃⁻ ions of KNO₃.
13. **a.** 1740 mL   **b.** 3790 mm Hg
15. **a.** 9730 L   **b.** 1620 min (27 h)
17. 6.93 L
19. 819 K (546 °C)
21. **a.** 22.4 L   **b.** 39.2 L   **c.** 5.04 L
23. 9.91 g/L
25. **a.** 47.5 g/mol   **b.** 66.5 g/mol
27. **a.** decrease   **b.** decrease   **c.** increase
29. **a.** temperature decreases   **b.** pressure decreases
31. **a.** 0.172 L   **b.** 1.04 atm
33. 0.0208 mol Kr
35. 3.00 g He

37. b, c, and d

39. d; one mole of each occupies the same volume; PF_3 has the largest molar mass.

41. 0.394 L

43. **a.** All three flasks contain the same number of atoms.
b. flask Z
c. flask X
d. All three flasks still have the same number of moles.

45. 1.25 atm

47. C_4H_{10}

49. e

51. Perchloroethylene and methylene chloride

Chapter 7

7.1 A. a. $HBr(aq) \xrightarrow{H_2O} H^+(aq) + Br^-(aq)$
b. $Ca(OH)_2(s) \xrightarrow{H_2O} Ca^{2+}(aq) + 2\,OH^-(aq)$
B. $CH_3COOH(aq) \xrightarrow{H_2O} H^+(aq) + CH_3COO^-(aq)$

7.2 A. $HBr(aq) + H_2O \longrightarrow H_3O^+(aq) + Br^-(aq)$
B. $HBr(aq) + CH_3OH \longrightarrow CH_3OH_2^+(aq) + Br^-(aq)$

7.3 A. H_2SeO_3 **B.** HNO_3

7.4 A. $Sr(OH)_2$ **B.** KOH

7.5 A. $NaOH(aq) + HC_2H_3O_2(aq) \longrightarrow NaC_2H_3O_2(aq) + H_2O$
B. $2\,HCl(aq) + Mg(OH)_2(aq) \longrightarrow MgCl_2(aq) + 2\,H_2O$

7.6 A. pH = 11 **B.** pH = 3

7.7 A. 1.0×10^{-2} M (0.010 M) **B.** 1.0×10^{-3} M (0.0010 M)

7.8 (c)

7.9 Beaker III: HNO_3; Beaker II: KOH

1. a. Arrhenius: forms H^+ in water; Brønsted–Lowry: proton donor
b. Arrhenius: forms OH^- in water; Brønsted–Lowry: proton acceptor
c. Ionic compound from acid-base neutralization

3. An acid turns litmus red, tastes sour, dissolves active metals, and neutralizes bases. A base turns litmus blue, tastes bitter, feels slippery, and neutralizes acids.

5. A strong base in water ionizes to a much greater extent than does a weak base.

7. Acidic anhydrides react with water to form acids. Basic anhydrides react with water to form bases.

9. $Mg(OH)_2$ is insoluble in water, so that few $OH^-(aq)$ ions form.

11. A condition in which the blood is too alkaline

13. $HClO_4(aq) \xrightarrow{H_2O} H^+(aq) + ClO_4^-(aq)$

15. $RbOH(s) \xrightarrow{H_2O} Rb^+(aq) + OH^-(aq)$

17. base: a, b, c; acid: none

19. $HCl(g) + H_2O \longrightarrow H_3O^+(aq) + Cl^-(aq)$; hydrochloric acid

21. $NH_3(aq) + H_2O \longrightarrow NH_4^+(aq) + OH^-(aq)$

23. a. hydrochloric acid **b.** $Sr(OH)_2$
c. potassium hydroxide **d.** H_3BO_3

25. a. phosphoric acid (an acid)
b. cesium hydroxide (a base)
c. carbonic acid (an acid)

27. a. HNO_2 **b.** H_3PO_3

29. a. H_2SO_4 (an acid) **b.** $Mg(OH)_2$ (a base)

31. strong acid

33. weak base

35. a. strong base **b.** strong acid
c. weak acid **d.** salt

37. highest: a; lowest, b

39. a. $HNO_2(aq) \xrightarrow{H_2O} H^+(aq) + NO_2^-(aq)$
b. $Ba(OH)_2(s) \xrightarrow{H_2O} Ba^{2+}(aq) + 2\,OH^-(aq)$
c. $HBr(aq) \xrightarrow{H_2O} H^+(aq) + Br^-(aq)$

41. a. $HClO(aq) + H_2O \rightleftharpoons H_3O^+(aq) + ClO^-(aq)$
b. $HNO_2(aq) + H_2O \rightleftharpoons H_3O^+(aq) + NO_2^-(aq)$
c. $H_2S(aq) + H_2O \rightleftharpoons H_3O^+(aq) + HS^-(aq)$

43. a. $KOH(aq) + HCl(aq) \longrightarrow KCl(aq) + H_2O$
b. $LiOH(aq) + HNO_3(aq) \longrightarrow LiNO_3(aq) + H_2O$

45. $H_2SO_3(aq) + Mg(OH)_2(aq) \longrightarrow MgSO_3(aq) + 2\,H_2O$

47. acidic: a, c; basic: d; neutral: b

49. pH = 5

51. 1.0×10^{-3} M H^+

53. 10 and 11

55. a. acid: HNO_3; base: NH_3
b. NO_3^-
c. NH_4^+

57. $3\,HCl(aq) + Al(OH)_3(s) \longrightarrow AlCl_3(aq) + 3\,H_2O$
$2\,HCl(aq) + Mg(OH)_2(s) \longrightarrow MgCl_2(aq) + 2\,H_2O$

59. No. Covalent OH-containing compounds do not produce OH^- ions in water.

61. a. weak base **b.** strong base

63. a. 3 **b.** 2

65. $HPO_4^{2-}(aq) + H_2O \longrightarrow H_3O^+(aq) + PO_4^{3-}(aq)$
$HPO_4^{2-}(aq) + H_2O \longrightarrow OH^-(aq) + H_2PO_4^-(aq)$

67. $Al_2(CO_3)_3(s) + 6\,HCl(aq) \longrightarrow 2\,AlCl_3(aq) + 3\,CO_2(g) + 3\,H_2O(l)$

69. $HS^-(aq) + H_2O \longrightarrow H_2S(g) + OH^-(aq)$

71. Decrease

73. $HC_{16}H_{31}O_2(s) + KOH(aq) \longrightarrow KC_{16}H_{31}O_2 + H_2O(l)$; a soap

Chapter 8

8.1 oxidation: a, b, d; reduction: c

8.2 reduction: a; oxidation: b

8.3 reduction: a; oxidation: b, c, d

8.4 a. oxidizing agent: O_2; reducing agent: Se
b. oxidizing agent: CH_3CN; reducing agent: H_2
c. oxidizing agent: V_2O_5; reducing agent: H_2
d. oxidizing agent: Br_2; reducing agent: K

8.5 oxidation: $Al \longrightarrow Al^{3+} + 3\,e^-$; reduction: $Br_2 + 2\,e^- \longrightarrow 2\,Br^-$

8.6 A. Half-reactions: $Fe \longrightarrow Fe^{3+} + 3\,e^-$; $Mg^{2+} + 2\,e^- \longrightarrow Mg$
Overall: $2\,Fe + 3\,Mg^{2+} \longrightarrow 2\,Fe^{3+} + 3\,Mg$
B. Half-reactions:
$Pb \longrightarrow Pb^{2+} + 2\,e^-$; $Ag(NH_3)_2^+ + e^- \longrightarrow Ag + 2\,NH_3$
Overall: $Pb + 2\,Ag(NH_3)_2^+ \longrightarrow Pb^{2+} + 2\,Ag + 4\,NH_3$

8.7 A. $2\,Zn + O_2 \longrightarrow 2\,ZnO$
B. $Se + O_2 \longrightarrow SeO_2$

8.8 A. $2\,PbS + 3\,O_2 \longrightarrow 2\,PbO + 2\,SO_2$
B. $C_2H_5OH + 3\,O_2 \longrightarrow 2\,CO_2 + 3\,H_2O$

1. Oxidation: oxidation number increases; reduction: oxidation number decreases

3. To allow ions to flow from one compartment to the other and thus keep the solutions electrically neutral

5. Zinc; it is the anode; oxidized to Zn^{2+}

7. $PbSO_4$ is converted to Pb and PbO_2.

9. Iron is oxidized to iron(III) hydroxide; salt water acts as an electrolyte.

11. Silver is oxidized by hydrogen sulfide to (black) silver sulfide; use aluminum to reduce the silver sulfide back to metallic silver.

13. a. oxidized (Fe loses e^-)
b. oxidized (H_2O loses H)
c. oxidized (Sr loses e^-)
d. reduced (P_4 gains e^-)
e. oxidized (CH_4O loses H)

15. a. $Ca \longrightarrow Ca^{2+} + 2\,e^-$
b. $Al \longrightarrow Al^{3+} + 3\,e^-$
c. $Cu \longrightarrow Cu^+ + e^-$; $Cu \longrightarrow Cu^{2+} + 2\,e^-$

17. a. oxidizing agent: Fe_2O_3; reducing agent: C
b. oxidizing agent: O_2; reducing agent: P_4
c. oxidizing agent: H_2O; reducing agent: C
d. oxidizing agent: H_2SO_4; reducing agent: Zn

19. Cu

21. oxidizing agent: MnO_2; reducing agent: Zn

23. a. oxidation: $Fe \longrightarrow Fe^{2+} + 2\,e^-$; reduction:
$2\,H^+ + 2\,e^- \longrightarrow H_2$
b. oxidation: $Al \longrightarrow Al^{3+} + 3\,e^-$ reduction:
$Cr^{2+} + 2\,e^- \longrightarrow Cr$

25. a. oxidation: $2\,H_2O_2 \longrightarrow 2\,O_2 + 4\,H^+ + 4\,e^-$ reduction:
$Fe^{3+} + e^- \longrightarrow Fe^{2+}$
overall: $2\,H_2O_2 + 4\,Fe^{3+} \longrightarrow 2\,O_2 + 4\,Fe^{2+} + 4\,H^+$

b. oxidation: $C_2H_6O \longrightarrow C_2H_4O + 2\,H^+ + 2\,e^-$
reduction: $WO_3 + 6\,H^+ + 6\,e^- \longrightarrow W + 3\,H_2O$
overall: $3\,C_2H_6O + WO_3 \longrightarrow 3\,C_2H_4O + W + 3\,H_2O$

27. a. SO_2 is oxidized; HNO_3 is the oxidizing agent
    b. HI is oxidized, CrO_3 is the oxidizing agent

29. Reduced; ethylene gains hydrogen.

31. Ta_2O_5 is reduced; the reducing agent is Na.

33. Zr was oxidized; water was the oxidizing agent.

35. Nitrite ion is reduced; ascorbic acid is the reducing agent.

37. a. SO_2 **b.** $CO_2 + H_2O$ **c.** $CO_2 + H_2O$

39. Indoxyl is oxidized; O_2 is the oxidizing agent.

41. $2\,Al(s) + 3\,Cu^{2+}(aq) \longrightarrow 2\,Al^{3+}(aq) + 3\,Cu(s)$

43. $H_2S + Pb^{2+} \longrightarrow PbS + 2\,H^+$
    $S^{2-} + 4\,H_2O_2 \longrightarrow SO_4^{2-} + 4\,H_2O$

45. $160\ \text{L}\ O_2$

47. a. V^{2+} is oxidized; it loses an electron when forming V^{3+}.
    b. neither; there are two O atoms per N atom in both NO_2 and N_2O_4.
    c. CO is reduced; C gains H.

49. $H_2 + Cl_2 \longrightarrow 2\,HCl$; Cl_2 is the oxidizing agent.

51. $2\,Al(s) + 6\,H_2O(l) \longrightarrow 2\,Al(OH)_3 + 3\,H_2$; H_2O is the oxidizing agent and Al is the reducing agent.

53. a. $NAD^+ + H^+ + 2\,e^- \longrightarrow NADH$; $CH_3CH_2OH \longrightarrow$
    $CH_3CHO + 2\,H^+ + 2\,e^-$
    b. $NADH \longrightarrow NAD^+ + H^+ + 2\,e^-$; $CH_3COCOOH + 2\,H^+ +$
    $2\,e^- \longrightarrow CH_3CHOHCOOH$
    Overall: $NADH + CH_3COCOOH + H^+ \longrightarrow NAD^+ +$
    $CH_3CHOHCOOH$

55. a. industrial   **b.** specialty
    c. specialty   **d.** industrial

57. Organic parts may undergo oxidation, inactivating the catalyst.

Chapter 9

9.1 a. molecular: C_6H_{14}; complete structural:

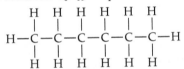

    condensed structural: $CH_3CH_2CH_2CH_2CH_2CH_3$

    b. molecular: C_8H_{18}; complete structural:

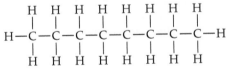

    condensed structural: $CH_3CH_2CH_2CH_2CH_2CH_2CH_2CH_3$

9.2 A.

CH₂ / CH₂ CH₂ / CH₂—CH₂ (cyclopentane)

    B. C_nH_{2n}

9.3 a. C_6H_{12} **b.** C_7H_{12}

9.4 a. $CHCl_3$ **b.** CCl_4

9.5 a. $CH_3CH_2CH_2CH_2OH$
    b.

H—C—C—C—C—H with O—H

9.6 a. alcohol   **b.** ether
    c. ether   **d.** phenol
    e. ether

9.7 A. $CH_3OCH_2CH_2CH_3$ **B.** $CH_3CH_2OC(CH_3)_3$

9.8 a. ketone   **b.** aldehyde   **c.** aldehyde

9.9 a. $CH_3CH_2CH_2COOH$
    b. CH_3CHO
    c. $CH_3CH_2COCH_2CH_3$
    d. $CH_3CH_2COCH_2CH_2CH_2CH_3$
    e. $CH_3CH_2CH_2CH_2CH_2CHO$
    f. $CH_3CH_2CH_2CH_2CH_2COOH$

9.10 a. $CH_3CH_2CH_2CH_2NH_2$
    b. $CH_3CH_2NHCH_2CH_3$
    c. $CH_3NHCH_2CH_2CH_3$
    d. $(CH_3)_2CHNHCH_3$

9.11 a. amine (NH)   **b.** amide (CONH)
    c. amine (N)   **d.** both (NH and $CONH_2$)

9.12 heterocyclic compounds: (a) and (d)

1. Carbon atoms can bond strongly to each other; can bond strongly to other elements; can form chains, rings, and other kinds of structures.

3. Isomers have the same molecular formula but different structural formulas.

5. A set of six delocalized electrons

7. 1–4 C, gases; 5–16 C, liquids; >18 C, solids

9. a. ethanol   **b.** 2-propanol   **c.** methanol

11. Historical use: anesthetic; modern use: solvent

13. a. alcohol   **b.** ketone   **c.** ester
    d. ether   **e.** carboxylic acid   **f.** aldehyde

15. organic: a, b; inorganic: c, d

17. a. 6   **b.** 10   **c.** 5   **d.** 5

19. a. C_9H_{20} **b.** $C_{13}H_{28}$

21. a. butane   **b.** ethylene (ethene)   **c.** acetylene (ethyne)

23. a. C_5H_{12}; $CH_3CH_2CH_2CH_3$
    b. C_9H_{20}; $CH_3CH_2CH_2CH_2CH_2CH_2CH_2CH_3$

25. a. methyl   **b.** *sec*-butyl

27. a. methanol   **b.** propyl alcohol (1-propanol)
    c. CH_3CH_2OH
    d. $CH_3CH_2CH_2CH_2CH_2CH_2CH_2OH$

29.

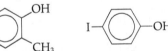

31. a. $CH_3CH_2CH_2OCH_2CH_2CH_3$
    b. $CH_3CH_2CH_2CH_2OCH_2CH_3$

33. a.

$CH_3-\overset{\overset{\displaystyle O}{\|}}{C}-CH_3$ **b.** HCHO

    c. butyraldehyde (butanal)
    d. butyl ethyl ketone (3-heptanone)

35. a. acetic acid (ethanoic acid)
    b. pentanoic acid
    c. HCOOH
    d. $CH_3CH_2CH_2CH_2CH_2CH_2CH_2COOH$

37. a. $CH_3COOCH_2CH_3$
    b. $CH_3CH_2CH_2COOCH_3$
    c. ethyl propionate (ethyl propanoate)

39. a. CH_3NH_2 **b.** $CH_3CH_2NHCH_3$
    c. propylamine   **d.** ethylmethylamine

41. same: a, b; isomers, c

43. a. homologs   **b.** none of these

45. a. unsaturated; alkene   **b.** saturated; alkane

47. a. ester   **b.** aldehyde   **c.** amine
    d. ether   **e.** ketone   **f.** carboxylic acid

49. a. heterocyclic, amine   **b.** not heterocyclic, amine

51. $C_{18}H_{27}NO_3$; ether, phenol, amide

53. a. $CH_3CH_2C \equiv CCH_3 + 2\,H_2 \xrightarrow{\text{Ni}} CH_3CH_2CH_2CH_2CH_3$
    b. $CH_3CH = C(CH_3)CH_2CH_2CH_2CH_3 + H_2 \xrightarrow{\text{Ni}}$
    $CH_3CH_2CH(CH_3)CH_2CH_2CH_2CH_3$

55. a. $CH_3CH_2CH_2CH_2OH$ **b.** $CH_3CH_2CH(OH)CH_2CH_3$
    c. $(CH_3)_2CHCH(OH)CH_3$ **d.** $C_6H_5CH_2OH$

57. isomerism

59. Equation is balanced as is. 731 g

61. a. dispersion and (weak) dipole-dipole

b. hydrogen bonds. The stronger hydrogen bonds cause ethanol to remain a liquid at room temperature.

63.
  a. HO—⟨benzene ring⟩—OH   b. O=⟨cyclohexadiene ring⟩=O

65. a. 0.000655 g/mL
  b. 0.001250 g/mL
  c. 0.001830 g/mL
  d. 0.002410 g/mL. Grams per liter would be more appropriate.

67. b

69. Solvent is renewable and less toxic, and less solvent is used.

71. Less energy is used; molecules absorb energy directly so less energy is lost to the surroundings.

Chapter 10

10.1 —$CH_2CH(C \equiv N)$—

10.2 A. $+CH_2CH(COCH_3)CH_2CH(COCH_3)CH_2CH(COCH_3)$⌐
  ⌐$CH_2CH(COCH_3)$+

  B. $+CH_2CH(OCOCH_3)CH_2CH(OCOCH_3)$⌐
  ⌐$CH_2CH(OCOCH_3)CH_2CH(OCOCH_3)$+

10.3 a. $+OCH_2COOCH_2COOCH_2CO$+
  b. $+OCH_2(C=O)+_n$

1. PVC has a Cl atom on alternate C atoms.

3. Polymerization in which all the monomer atoms are incorporated in the polymer; a double bond

5. styrene

7. The first synthetic polymer; phenol and formaldehyde

9. Synthetic fibers; they are cheaper and have a wider range of properties.

11. For many applications, plastics must be separated by type, melted, and formed into new objects.

13. LDPE has highly branched molecules—a loosely packed, amorphous structure that makes it soft and flexible compared with HDPE.

15. a. $CH_2=CH_2$ b. $CH_2=CH—C\equiv N$

17. a. $+CH_2CHClCH_2CHClCH_2CHClCH_2CHCl$+
  b. $+CH_2CF_2CH_2CF_2CH_2CF_2CH_2CF_2$+

19. a. $+CH_2CH(CH_2CH_2CH_3)CH_2CH(CH_2CH_2CH_3)$⌐
  ⌐$CH_2CH(CH_2CH_2CH_3)$+
  b. $+CH_2CH(CN)(COOCH_3)CH_2CH(CN)(COOCH_3)$⌐
  ⌐$CH_2CH(CN)(COOCH_3)CH_2CH(CN)(COOCH_3)$+

21. $CH_2=CH—CH=CH_2$

23. When stretched, rubber's coiled molecules are straightened. When released, the molecules coil again.

25. SBR is made by copolymerization of styrene and butadiene.

27. $+CO(CH_2)_6CONH(CH_2)_8NHCO(CH_2)_6CONH(CH_2)_8NH$+

29. $+OCH_2COOCH_2COOCH_2COOCH_2CO$+

31. The long chains can entangle with one another; intermolecular forces are greatly multiplied in large molecules; large polymer molecules move more slowly than do small molecules.

33. The temperature at which the properties of the polymer change from hard, stiff, and brittle to rubbery and tough; rubbery materials such as automobile tires should have a low T_g; glass substitutes, a high T_g.

35. Monomer: a; repeating unit: b; polymer: c. addition polymerization

37. $CH_2=CHCl$ and $CH_2=CCl_2$

39.

$$n \quad CH_2=C \overset{\displaystyle C\equiv N}{\underset{\displaystyle O=COC_8H_{17}}{|}} \longrightarrow \left[CH_2-C \overset{\displaystyle C\equiv N}{\underset{\displaystyle O=COC_8H_{17}}{|}} \right]_n$$

41. ~$CH_2C(CH_3)_2CH_2C(CH_3)_2CH_2C(CH_3)_2CH_2C(CH_3)_2$~

43. $CH_3CH(OH)CH_2COOH$

45. There are only two C atoms in a backbone segment of polypropylene; the CH_3 is a pendant group.

47. Elastomer; the golf ball

49. A simple diester, dibutylterephthalate, rather than a polymer

51.

$$\left[O—Si—O—Si—O—Si—O—Si \right]$$

with each Si bearing CH_2CH_3 (top) and $CH(CH_3)_2$ (bottom)

53. a. $+CH_2CH_2OCH_2CH_2OCH_2CH_2OCH_2CH_2O$+
  b. $+CH_2CH_2SCH_2CH_2SCH_2CH_2SCH_2CH_2S$+

55. b

57. c

Chapter 11

11.1 a. $^{235}_{92}U \longrightarrow ^{4}_{2}He + ^{231}_{90}Th$ b. $^{210}_{82}Pb \longrightarrow ^{0}_{-1}e + ^{210}_{83}Bi$
  c. $^{18}_{9}F \longrightarrow ^{0}_{+1}e + ^{18}_{8}O$ d. $^{13}_{8}O + ^{0}_{-1}e \longrightarrow ^{13}_{7}N$

11.2 A. 6.25%   B. 500 Bq; 4 Bq

11.3 a. yes (3 Bq left)   b. no (4.0×10^{10} Bq remain)

11.4 a. 11,460 y;   b. 49 y

11.5 a. A neutron ($^{1}_{0}n$)   b. Thorium-232 ($^{232}_{90}Th$)

11.6 Silicon-30 ($^{30}_{14}Si$)

11.7 Higher; the gas can be absorbed by inhalation and decay in the body.

1. (i), (b); (ii), (a); (iii), (c)

3 $^{1}_{1}H$, $^{2}_{1}H$, $^{3}_{1}H$

5. a. $^{60}_{27}Co$ b. $^{127}_{53}I$ c. $^{22}_{11}Na$ d. $^{42}_{20}Ca$

7. Isotopes: b, c

9. 155

11. a. A, down 4; Z, down 2   b. no change in either
  c. A, down 1; Z, down 1

13. a. alpha   b. gamma

15. more massive; energy dissipated over a short distance

17. Fission is the splitting of large atoms. Fusion is the joining of small atoms. Both liberate energy because, in each case, the nuclei formed have greater nuclear stability than the reacting nuclei (Fig. 11.10).

19. a. $^{250}_{98}Cf \longrightarrow ^{4}_{2}He + ^{246}_{96}Cm$
  b. $^{210}_{83}Bi \longrightarrow ^{210}_{84}Po + ^{0}_{-1}e$
  c. $^{117}_{53}I \longrightarrow ^{117}_{52}Te + ^{0}_{+1}e$

21. a. $^{179}_{79}Au \longrightarrow ^{175}_{77}Ir + ^{4}_{2}He$
  b. $^{12}_{6}C + ^{2}_{1}H \longrightarrow ^{13}_{6}C + ^{1}_{1}H$
  c. $^{154}_{62}Sm + ^{1}_{0}n \longrightarrow 2 ^{1}_{0}n + ^{153}_{62}Sm$

23. beta particle; $^{99}_{42}Mo \longrightarrow ^{99m}_{43}Tc + ^{0}_{-1}e$

25. $^{24}_{12}Mg + ^{1}_{0}n \longrightarrow ^{1}_{1}H + ^{24}_{11}Na$; sodium-24

27. $^{215}_{85}At \longrightarrow ^{4}_{2}He + ^{211}_{83}Bi$; astatine-215

29. $^{210}_{87}Fr$

31. 156 h (6.5 d)

33. b

35. 26 s

37. 2 counts/min

39. 5730 y

41. 5730 y; 11,460 y

43. a. $^{121}_{51}Sb + ^{4}_{2}He \longrightarrow ^{124}_{53}I + ^{1}_{0}n$ b. $^{124}_{53}I \longrightarrow ^{124}_{52}Te + ^{0}_{+1}e$

45. $^{247}_{97}Bk + ^{48}_{20}Ca \longrightarrow ^{293}_{117}117 + 2 ^{1}_{0}n$; $^{247}_{97}Bk + ^{48}_{20}Ca \longrightarrow ^{294}_{117}117 + ^{1}_{0}n$

47. $^{223}_{88}Ra \longrightarrow ^{219}_{86}Rn + ^{4}_{2}He$; $^{223}_{88}Ra \longrightarrow ^{209}_{82}Pb + ^{14}_{6}C$

49. 853 cm³; 131 cm³; smaller than a baseball (~200 cm³)

51. a. 1900 y   b. 14,400 y

53. the neutron, $^{1}_{0}n$

55. a. 2.2×10^{13} cal; 2.2×10^{10} kcal
  b. 2.0×10^{8} bowls

57. 7.5×10^{17} atoms

59. false

61. The presence of two amides increases the ability to bind to metal ions without losing the benefits of using this type of molecule.

Chapter 12

1. One substance enhances the effect of another; asbestos fibers and cigarette smoke

3. Mining operations, particulate matter from crushing, high energy consumption

5. Copper and tin are easier to obtain from ores than is iron.
7. Most aluminum is found in aluminum-containing clays and is too widely scattered to be mined.
9. The problem is keeping the metal in a usable form and not dispersed through the environment.
11. Lithosphere: solid portion of Earth; hydrosphere: watery portion; atmosphere: gaseous mass surrounding Earth
13. Al, Fe, Ca; differences in atomic mass
15. $PbS(s) + 2 HCl(aq) \longrightarrow PbCl_2(aq) + H_2S(g)$
17. SiO_2; the SiO_4 tetrahedra are arranged in a three-dimensional array.
19. The SiO_4 tetrahedra are arranged in flat two-dimensional arrays.
21. Sand (silicon dioxide), soda (sodium carbonate), and limestone (calcium carbonate)
23. Other metal oxides are substituted for silica, soda, or lime.
25. Limestone and clay
27. Iron ore or scrap iron (source of iron), limestone (removes impurities), and coke or coal (reducing agent)
29. Reduction; $Fe_2O_3 + 3 CO \longrightarrow 2 Fe + 3 CO_2$.
31. The limestone reacts with impurities to form slag.
33. Iron drawn off a blast furnace; phosphorus, silicon, and excess carbon
35. $V_2O_5 + 5 Ca \longrightarrow 2 V + 5 CaO$;
    a. V_2O_5 b. Ca   c. Ca   d. V_2O_5
37. $Al_2O_3 + 3 C + 3 Cl_2 \longrightarrow 2 AlCl_3 + 3 CO$;
    a. Cl_2 b. C   c. C   d. Cl_2
39. 102 g Nd
41. 133 million kg Al_2O_3; 279 million kg bauxite
43. 20.4 m
45. 1.7×10^7 kg ore per day
47. 282,000 cubic feet, 28 feet deep
49. a. $Fe_2O_3 + 3 H_2 \longrightarrow 2 Fe + 3 H_2O$
    b. $Fe_2O_3 + 3 CO \longrightarrow 2 Fe + 3 H_2O$
51. 69.0% (paper, cardboard, yard wastes, plastics, and wood)
53. a. 3.4×10^9 kg   b. 7.7 km   c. 5.7×10^{10} km
55. a. 46%
    b. less than either route to Fe from magnetite (49% and 70%)
57. Saves material (Al) and saves energy

Chapter 13

13.1 **A.** 3790 g H_2O **B.** 4940 kg CO_2
1. Refrigerant; molding of plastic foams
3. Solid mineral matter left behind after burning coal is bottom ash. Fly ash goes out the smokestack.
5. Gases that trap heat in the atmosphere; CO_2, CH_4, H_2O
7. A combination of smoke and fog; polluted air
9. Conversion of N_2 to a form usable by plants; increases the food supply
11. Thermosphere
13. a. $4 Fe(s) + 3 O_2(g) \longrightarrow 2 Fe_2O_3(s)$
    b. $4 Cr(s) + 3 O_2(g) \longrightarrow 2 Cr_2O_3(s)$
15. Cold, damp, still
17. $S + O_2 \longrightarrow SO_2$
19. $SO_2 + 2 H_2S \longrightarrow 3 S + 2 H_2O$
21. The lime reacts with SO_2 to form an easily collected solid.
    $CaCO_3(s) \xrightarrow{\text{heat}} CaO(s) + CO_2(g)$;
    $CaO(s) + SO_2(g) \longrightarrow CaSO_3(s)$.
23. High temperatures; $N_2 + O_2 \longrightarrow 2 NO$
25. Peroxyacetylnitrate; hydrocarbons, oxygen, and nitrogen dioxide; makes breathing difficult and causes the eyes to smart and itch
27. a, c
29. NO
31. By hindering O_2 transport and thus adding to the workload of the heart
33. Allotropes
35. Global warming
37. HNO_3; H_2SO_4
39. $2 Fe(s) + 6 HNO_3(aq) \longrightarrow 3 H_2(g) + 2 Fe(NO_3)_3(aq)$
41. Carbon monoxide from poorly ventilated heaters indoors; from automobiles outdoors

43. The crawl space allows gaseous radon to dissipate through vents; the concrete slab traps it inside.
45. A gas; it can escape from rocks and enter houses, and is readily inhaled.
47. The warming of Earth caused by gases absorbing infrared radiation
49. Some waste heat is formed in every process (second law of thermodynamics).
51. 6900 µg (6.9 mg)
53. Water vapor will form clouds and might even lead to cooling by reflecting sunlight back to space.
55. There would be about two air molecules from the Buddha's breath in a breath you take today.
57. $3 NO_2 + H_2O \longrightarrow 2 HNO_3 + NO$; $2 NO + O_2 \longrightarrow 2 NO_2$
59. a
61. 54 million metric tons

Chapter 14

14.1 **A. a.** 0.1 ppb   **b.** 100 ppt
    B. 1×10^{-9} M
1. The crude oil would not dissolve; it would float.
3. Microorganisms that cause disease
5. VOCs from fueling and dry cleaning, nitrates from farms and lawns, illegal dumping, many other sources
7. Chlorinated hydrocarbons are unreactive and do not break down readily.
9. Water expands when it freezes because it forms a rigid hydrogen-bonded structure with relatively large holes. The ice floats, protecting the deeper water from freezing.
11. 3.0×10^4 cal
13. Vaporization of water (sweat) cools our bodies.
15. Water evaporates from the skin, removing heat.
17. Dust, dissolved atmospheric gases such as carbon dioxide and oxygen, nitric acid from lightning storms; various pollutants
19. 51 mg/L
21. Acid rain and mine runoff
23. The limestone that neutralizes the acid leaves calcium ions in the water.
25. It mobilizes toxic (to fish) Al^{3+} ions from clays.
27. About 1 ppm
29. Yes. Ultraviolet light kills microorganisms.
31. Sewage is collected in a pond; it removes solids that are allowed to settle.
33. Organic molecules and inorganic ions such as nitrates and phosphates
35. tertiary: a; secondary: c; primary: b
37. $2 HNO_3(aq) + CaCO_3(s) \longrightarrow$
    $Ca^{2+}(aq) + 2 NO_3^-(aq) + CO_2(g) + H_2O(l)$
39. a. 11 ppb   b. 140 ppm
41. No, the levels (0.009 mg Cu/L, 8 mg NO_3^-/L) are below the standards.
43. a. $CHCl_3$ b. NaCl, phosphate ion, sand   c. sand
45. Boiling water; to boil water the molecules must be separated to relatively large distances.
47. Cl_2 is reduced; it is the oxidizing agent. SO_2 is the reducing agent.
49. A positron ($_{+1}^{0}e$)
51. a. 9120 kcal   b. 687 g   c. 33.9 ft^3 d. 38 cents
53. c
55. a
57. Microporous: pores less than 2 nm in diameter; mesoporous: between 2 nm and 50 nm; macroporous; larger than 50 nm

Chapter 15

15.1 **A.** 39,000 J   **B.** 6.1 ¢
15.2 **A.** 183 kJ   **B.** 2700 kJ
15.3 **A.** 2210 kJ   **B.** 1.43 kcal
1. Nuclear fusion
3. Coal; petroleum

5. a, b
7. a. $C_6H_{12}O_6(s) + 6 O_2(g) \longrightarrow 6 CO_2(g) + 6 H_2O(l)$
   b. $C_3H_8(g) + 5 O_2(g) \longrightarrow 3 CO_2(g) + 4 H_2O(l)$
9. $C(s) + O_2(g) \longrightarrow CO_2(g)$
11. $CH_4(g) + 2 O_2(g) \longrightarrow CO_2(g) + 2 H_2O(l)$
13. Yes. Both H_2 and CO are readily oxidized (will burn), forming water and CO_2, respectively.
15. A reaction goes faster at a higher temperature.
17. 19,700 kJ
19. 4.44 kJ
21. 803 kJ
23. Energy is conserved.
25. A measure of the degree of distribution of energy in a system; increased
27. It is not possible to create energy.
29. Coal is plentiful and a good fuel, but burning it leads to significant air pollution from particulates, SO_x, and CO.
31. 43.2 y
33. 60.3 y
35. $2 C_2H_6 + 7 O_2 \longrightarrow 4 CO_2(g) + 6 H_2O(l)$
37. Ancient marine animals
39. Molecules in kerosene have higher molecular masses than do molecules in gasoline.
41. Asphalt is a residue left from petroleum distillation.
43. 19.3%
45. No; the uranium is enriched to only about 3% uranium-235; to explode, it would have to be enriched to about 90%.
47. No; reactor grade uranium is enriched to only about 3% uranium-235; to make a bomb, it would have to be enriched to about 90%.
49. By converting nonfissionable uranium-238 to fissile plutonium-239. No, the plutonium-239 is simply an easier-to-use source of energy than uranium-238.
51. Little radioactivity produced; plentiful fuel (deuterium). Plasma is a hot, gaseous mixture of positive and negative ions.
53. $^{232}_{90}Th + ^{1}_{0}n \longrightarrow ^{233}_{90}Th$
    $^{233}_{90}Th \longrightarrow ^{0}_{-1}e + ^{233}_{91}Pa$
    $^{233}_{91}Pa \longrightarrow ^{0}_{-1}e + ^{233}_{92}U$
55. 2.24×10^7 mol CH_4; 360 t CH_4
57. An electronic device that produces electricity directly from light
59. 12 m^2; it works only when the sun shines; energy storage is needed for nighttime and very cloudy days.
61. Plant material used directly as fuel
63. Oxidizing and reducing agents are fed into a fuel cell continuously; the cell does not go "dead" as long as reactants are supplied.
65. $C(s) + 2 H_2(g) \longrightarrow CH_4(g)$;
    $C(s) + H_2O(g) \longrightarrow CO(g) + H_2(g)$
67. Endothermic; the reaction absorbs heat, cooling the treated area.
69. 100 watts; 1 hp = 7.45 human power
71. a. 99 W   b. 5.9×10^8 W
    c. They provide the same energy. The grenade provides more power so you wouldn't want to eat a hand grenade.
73. a. Removal by photosynthesis
    b. Animal respiration
    c. Converted to insoluble carbonates.
75. 29 metric tons SO_2; no, there would be 260 µg SO_2/m^3.
77. a. 75 y   b. 19 y
    c. Rate of energy use will likely grow instead of remain the same, and so reserves might not last the 75 y calculated in part (a). Worldwide use is unlikely to reach the U.S. level anytime soon, if ever, and so the estimate in (b) is not at all realistic.
79. d

Chapter 16

16.1 Mannose differs from glucose in configuration about C-2 only.
16.2 A. a. H-P-V-A   b. histidylprolylvalylalanine
     B. a. Thr-Gly-Ala-Ala-Leu   b. T-G-A-A-L

16.3 A. 3   B. 24
16.4 A. Sugar: ribose; base: uracil; RNA
     B. Neither; thymine occurs only in DNA, ribose only in RNA.
1. Photosynthesis converts solar energy to carbohydrates, which provide energy to plants and to organisms that eat plants.
3. In every cell; muscles, skin, hair, nails
5. Polyamides
7. If the molar mass of a polypeptide exceeds about 10,000 g, it is called a protein.
9. Hydrogen bonds
11. DNA is a double helix; RNA is a single helix with some loops.
13. A process that produces millions of copies of a specific DNA sequence
15. Step 1: isolation and amplification
    Step 2: gene is spliced into a plasmid
    Step 3: plasmid is inserted into a host cell
    Step 4: plasmid replicates, making copies of itself
17. A carbohydrate that cannot be further hydrolyzed; glucose, fructose, and galactose
19. Glycogen is animal starch. Amylose is a plant starch with glucose units joined in a continuous chain. Amylopectin is a plant starch with branched chains of glucose units.
21. c, d
23. Sucrose and lactose
25. a. glucose   b. glucose
27. Ketone and alcohol (hydroxyl)
29. Aldehyde and alcohol (hydroxyl); in configuration about C-4
31. Structurally, oils have more C-to-C double bonds than fats have. At room temperature, fats are solids, and oils are liquid.
33. saturated: a, d; unsaturated: b, c
35. a. 18   b. 16
    c. 18
37. Liquid oil (right); it is unsaturated.
39. An amino group and a carboxyl group; a zwitterion is a molecule that carries both a positive and a negative charge.
41. lysine and leucine
43. a.

$$H_3N^+-CH-C\begin{matrix}O\\\\O^-\end{matrix} \qquad CH_3$$

b.

$$H_3N^+-CH-C\begin{matrix}O\\\\O^-\end{matrix} \qquad CH_2SH$$

45. a. $H_3N^+ CH_2CO-NH\ C\ HCOO^-$
                    CH_3

    b. $H_3N^+ CH_2CO-NH\ C\ HCOO^-$
                    CH_3 CH_2OH

47. Aspartylphenylalanine
49. Hydrogen bonds, ionic bonds, disulfide linkages, and dispersion forces
51. DNA: a; RNA: b, c
53. Ribose; uracil
55. a. guanine   b. thymine
    c. cytosine   d. adenine
57. Each strand of the parent DNA double helix remains associated with the newly synthesized DNA strand.
59. a. DNA and mRNA   b. mRNA and tRNA
61. 3'-TACTCGCTGAAACGCCCTAAT-5'
63. 5'-AGGCTA-3'
65. a. 3'-AAC-5'   b. 3'-CUU-5'   c. 3'-AGG-5'
67. a. glutamine   b. phenylalanine   c. glycine
69. a. primary   b. secondary
71. a. pyrimidine   b. pyrimidine
73. a. purine   b. RNA
75. a. ~Thr-Ser-Met-Ala~
    b. ~Thr-Ser-Ala-Ala~
77. 3'-AUG-5' (The sequences must be antiparallel.)
79. Water
81. d

Chapter 17

17.1 **A.** About 64% **B.** About 34%

17.2 **A.** Fatty acid I

    B. Fatty acid I, because fatty acid III is a cis fatty acid and not a trans fatty acid

1. Energy source
3. All vitamins are organic; all minerals are inorganic.
5. Fat soluble; an excess is stored and accumulated; excess water-soluble vitamins are excreted.
7. Substances other than basic foodstuffs that are put into food for various reasons related to production, processing, packaging, or storage
9. Monosodium glutamate, a flavor enhancer
11. α-Tocopherol (vitamin E)
13. The methyl ester of the dipeptide aspartylphenylalanine
15. Add nutritional value, enhance flavor or color, retard spoilage, provide texture, sanitize (and others)
17. **a.** glucose **b.** sucrose
    c. fructose
19. Hydrolysis
21. Hydrolysis; fatty acids, glycerol, mono- and diglycerides
23. Most animal fats are solids; most vegetable oils are liquids; animal fats generally have fewer C-to-C double bonds than vegetable oils.
25. An adequate protein provides all the essential amino acids in sufficient quantities; meat, eggs, milk.
27. Corn: lysine and tryptophan; beans: methionine
29. Yes; it has grains and beans.
31. **a.** iodine **b.** hemoglobin (oxygen transport)
    c. calcium
    d. nucleic acids, ATP (obtaining, storing, and using energy from foods), bones, teeth
33. Water soluble: pantothenic acid, biotin; fat soluble: phylloquinone
35. Ascorbic acid, vitamin C; calciferol, vitamin D; cyanocobalamin, vitamin B_{12}; retinol, vitamin A; tocopherol, vitamin E
37. **a.** niacin (vitamin B_3)
    b. thiamine (vitamin B_1)
    c. pernicious anemia
39. Water soluble: b, c, d; fat soluble: a, e
41. **a.** improve nutrition **b.** SO_2
    c. inhibit spoilage
43. **a.** antioxidant **b.** color
    c. artificial sweetener
45. d
47. Reducing agents, usually free-radical scavengers added to foods to prevent fats and oils from becoming rancid; vitamin E; BHT, and BHA
49. About 53% from carbohydrates; 23% from fat; 27% from protein
51. About 81 kcal; about 56% from fat
53. About 11 g saturated fat
55. c, e
57. About 45%
59. About 23%
61. **a.** about 60% **b.** about 40%
63. Riboflavin and cyanocobalamin; they are water soluble and not easily stored.
65. Double bonds in unsaturated fats are more reactive than single bonds in saturated fats; unsaturated fats and oils would have spoiled more readily than saturated fats.
67. The thick polymeric starch is broken down to smaller, more soluble molecules by enzymes in saliva.
69. **a.** 3 **b.** 2 **c.** 4 **d.** 1
71. Less toxic; easily removed.

Chapter 18

1. A drug that kills or slows the growth of bacteria; originally limited to formulations derived from living organisms
3. Cortisol: a hormone released in the body during stressed or agitated states; prednisone: a semisynthetic hormone similar to cortisone
5. Mediators of hormone action; prostaglandins act near where they are produced; hormones act throughout the body.

7. Ketamine, PCP
9. A drug that produces stupor and relief of pain
11. Brain amines are made from dietary amino acids; for example, high-carbohydrate diets produce high serotonin levels in the brain.
13. No; they help control some symptoms.
15. Acetylsalicylic acid
17. Acetaminophen does not promote bleeding.
19. Amide, phenol
21. Both are analgesics and addictive; heroin is more potent and more addictive.
23. **a.** Acupuncture needles may stimulate nerves that trigger release of endorphins, peptides that block pain signals.
    b. The wounds cause the body to secrete pain-killing endorphins.

25.

27. They are effective against a wide variety of bacteria.
29. No; vaccination
31. Antimetabolites and alkylating agents
33. A female sex hormone; a male sex hormone
35. An ethynyl group, $H-C\equiv C-$
37. One that changes the way we perceive things
39. a
41. a, b, c
43. **a.** 2.55 g **b.** 1.7 (about 2)
45.

47. Fat soluble; 17 C atoms with only 1 O atom, 1 N atom
49.

51. Timber rattlesnake; its lower LD_{50} means that less of its toxin is required in a fatal dose.
53. Nicotine, because it takes a smaller amount to kill the rat—2500 mg procaine; 50 mg nicotine.
55.

57.

59. Ester; hydrolysis
61. 6-mercaptopurine; antimetabolite
63. **a.** Removing the polar —OH group would make the compound less soluble in water.
    b. Removing the polar —OH group would make the compound more soluble in fat.
65. **a.** The long hydrocarbon chain would make the drug much less soluble in water.
    b. The ionic and polar groups of the sodium succinate derivative would make the drug more soluble in water.
67. c

69. Use of lipolase allows the wrong enantiomer to be recycled and used instead of being discarded. Also, small, amino acid catalysts are being used as replacements for larger expensive enzymes.

Chapter 19

19.1 **A.** 3.6 lb **B.** 7.4 lb
19.2 **A.** 35 mi **B.** 2700 kcal
19.3 **A.** 23.5 **B.** 174 lb
1. Meat and other animal products
3. Deplete glycogen stores and dehydrate yourself; no, it would be mostly water loss.
5. Better understanding of muscle physiology; drugs; improved equipment
7. Skinfold calipers (inaccurate and measure water retention as well as fat); displacement of water (cannot get all of the air out of the lungs)
9. Often deficient in B vitamins, iron, and other nutrients; slows metabolism, making future dieting more difficult and weight gain easier
11. Most do not.
13. Avoid pernicious anemia
15. Arthritis; B_6 is a cofactor for more than 100 enzymes.
17. Promotes absorption of calcium and phosphorus. The upper limit is 2000 IU; more than that can be toxic.
19. Promotes production of urine; ADH acts to retain urine.
21. No. Thirst is often a delayed response.
23. Depletion of glycogen and water loss
25. 2.0 h
27. 92 g
29. 20 km
31. **a.** Leptin protects against weight loss.
    b. Ghrelin is an appetite stimulant.
33. 19.6
35. About 600
37. No
39. **a.** anaerobic **b.** aerobic
41. Store needed oxygen
43. ATP can be generated rapidly and hydrolyzed rapidly.
45. No; the best way to build muscles is by exercise.
47. Anti-inflammatory; fluid retention, hypertension, ulcers, disturbance of sex hormone balance
49. The body releases endorphins that have much the same effect as some narcotics.
51. The athlete might perform better briefly, but fatigue follows quickly.
53. Heart disease; stroke; lung cancer; emphysema; pneumonia; cancers of the pancreas, bladder, breast, kidney, and cervix
55. 2400 kcal
57. 1.06 g/mL; lean
59. **a.** 26.7% **b.** 3.61% **c.** Person B **d.** 1.077 g/cm³
61. **a.** 27 **b.** 144
63. **a.** 20 mL O_2 **b.** 1200 mL O_2
65. 2 lb lighter
67. c

Chapter 20

20.1 **A.** $2 NH_3 + H_3PO_4 \longrightarrow (NH_4)_2HPO_4$
    B. $ZnO + H_2SO_4 \longrightarrow ZnSO_4 + H_2O$
20.2 980 mg
20.3 **A.** In 270 y; by 2281
    B. In 92 y; by 2103
1. CO_2 and H_2O
3. Kills weed plants before crop seedlings emerge
5. Population would increase faster than the food supply unless the birthrate were controlled; poverty and war would serve as restrictions.
7. C, H, O
9. Lightning, bacteria, the Haber process

11. Ammonia without water; as fertilizer
13. Phosphate rock is treated with phosphoric acid to make calcium dihydrogen phosphate; plays a role in the energy transfer processes of photosynthesis.
15. DDT is effective against many insects, but it remains toxic long after initial use.
17. They are fat soluble and become concentrated in fats moving up the food chain.
19. Mostly to bait traps and monitor infestations to determine when best to use a pesticide
21. Male insects are sterilized by radiation, chemicals, or cross-breeding, and then released for nonproductive breeding. Expensive and time consuming.
23. 35 g DDT
25. Addition of a constant amount each growth period; adding $10 to a savings account each week
27. 20 months; arithmetically
29. 53.6 y; changes in birthrate or death rate (war, famine, …)
31. $6 CO_2 + 6 H_2O \longrightarrow C_6H_{12}O_6 + 6 O_2$
33. (1), b; (2), b; (3), d; (4), a; (5), c
35. **a.** N, P **b.** $2 NH_3 + H_3PO_4 \longrightarrow (NH_4)_2HPO_4$
37. **a.** alkene, alcohol **b.** ester, alkene, ether (epoxide)
    c. ether, alkene, ester
39. $10,737,418.24
41. $K_2CO_3 + CO_2 + H_2O \longrightarrow 2 KHCO_3$
    $2 KCl + 2 H_2O \longrightarrow 2 KOH + H_2 + Cl_2$
    $2 KOH + CO_2 \longrightarrow K_2CO_3 + H_2O$
    not organic
43. 16.7 y; changes in birthrate or death rate (war, famine, …)
45. a and b
47. d

Chapter 21

21.1 **a.** nonionic **b.** anionic
    c. anionic **d.** cationic
1. An excellent cleanser in soft water, relatively nontoxic, derived from renewable sources, biodegradable; doesn't work well in hard water or acidic water
3. 1, a; 2, f; 3, b; 4, c; 5, d; 6, e
5. Loosens baked-on grease and burned-on food, excellent glass cleaner; vapors are irritating, toxic; don't mix with chlorine bleaches
7. Mildly abrasive and absorbs odors
9. It is softer and produces a finer lather.
11. Abrasives
13. Sodium palmitate and glycerol
15. $3 CH_3(CH_2)_{10}COO^-Na^+ + HOCH_2CHOHCH_2OH$ (glycerol)
17. Precipitates hard water ions; makes the water more alkaline
19. $PO_4^{3-} + H_2O \longrightarrow HPO_4^{2-} + OH^-$
    $CO_3^{2-} + H_2O \longrightarrow HCO_3^- + OH^-$
21. A substance added to a surfactant to increase its detergency
23. By binding Ca^{2+} and Mg^{2+} in soluble complexes
25. A surfactant molecule that carries both a positive and a negative charge
27. Cationic surfactants have germicidal action.
29. All three
31. II
33. Hexadecyltrimethylammonium chloride
35. They slowly release chlorine in water.
37. To remove paint, varnish, adhesives, waxes, etc.
39. Flammability, toxic fumes
41. A skin softener
43. OMC is insoluble in water and does not wash off as easily as PABA from sweat or while swimming.
45. Lipstick is harder, contains more wax, and is usually colored with pigments.
47. Bacteria
49. Enamel is converted from hydroxyapatite to fluorapatite, a harder substance.

51. A complex mixture of compounds used as a fragrance; cologne is diluted perfume.
53. Makes the face feel cool
55. Temporary dyes are water soluble and can be washed out; permanent dyes last until the hair is cut off or falls out.
57. A reducing agent; redox reaction
59. Oxidation
61. II
63. I
65. $CH_3(CH_2)_{14}COOCH(CH_3)_2$
67. 11.6 g SnF_2
69. Cationic (quaternary ammonium compounds)
71. No. Brighteners convert energy in the form of ultraviolet light into visible light, but no energy is destroyed.
73. **a.** $CH_3(CH_2)_{24}COOH$ **b.** $CH_3(CH_2)_{28}CH_2OH$
75. c
77. **a.** 3   **b.** 1   **c.** 4   **d.** 2

Chapter 22

1. In a sense; enormous amounts of sugar can be harmful; large amounts for a diabetic.
3. The route of administration determines the speed of the poison's action, the rate at which it is detoxified, etc.
5. Mercury: occupational exposure; eating contaminated fish, etc. Lead: leaded paint chips; soldered pipes (water) and cans (food).
7. Sunlight, radon, safrole, PAHs
9. b, d
11. Hydrolysis of amides; catalyst
13. A substance that blocks the transport of oxygen in the bloodstream; CO, nitrate ions
15. By blocking the oxidation of glucose inside the cell
17. a, d
19. By tying up sulfhydryl groups, thus deactivating enzymes
21. By chelating Pb^{2+} ions, thus enhancing their excretion
23. Sarin, tabun, soman
25. Poisons that block cholinesterase
27. By oxidizing ethanol to acetaldehyde, then to acetic acid, and finally to carbon dioxide and water
29. No. Some are oxidized to more toxic substances.
31. Cotinine is less toxic and is more water soluble (more readily excreted) than nicotine.

33. 7.94 g
35. Genes that regulate cell growth; they sustain the abnormal growth characteristic of cancer.
37. Incomplete burning of almost any organic material
39. Humans are not exposed to comparable doses; human metabolism is different from test-animal metabolism.
41. A mutagen causes mutations; a teratogen causes birth defects.
43. A waste that burns readily on ignition, presenting a fire hazard; hexane, gasoline
45. 5.3×10^{10} molecules
47. **a.** $C_{10}H_{16}O$ **b.** 4800 mg
    c. 5 mg
49. **a.** 99.48%; % smokers in control group: 95.50%
    b. 0.9948:1 for cancer cases; 0.9550:1 for controls
    c. 0.96:1
51. Some substances are harmless or even necessary at low levels; toxic at high levels.
53. **a.** No   **b.** Yes
55. The body converts inert benzene to a carcinogenic epoxide.
57. **a.** 38.8 mL vodka   **b.** 15.4 mg/mL
59. b
61. Saving millions of dollars, improved consumer safety, and reducing the load of poisons in the environment.

Appendix

A.1 **a.** 0.0163 g   **b.** 1.53 lb
     c. 370 mL
A.2 **a.** 0.0903 m   **b.** 0.2224 km
     c. 150 fl oz
A.3 **a.** 24.4 m/s   **b.** 1.34 km/h
     c. 0.136 oz/qt
A.4 **a.** No   **b.** No
A.5 0.12 m^3
A.6 56.8 g
A.7 **a.** 100.5 m   **b.** 6.3 L
     c. 1800 m^2 (1.80×10^3 m^2)   **d.** 2.33 g/mL
A.8 **a.** 185 °F   **b.** 10.0 °F
     c. 179 °C   **d.** −29.3 °C
A.9 80,000 cal; 80.0 kcal; 334 kJ

Credits

Chapter 1 Page 1 (TL): Arne Naevra. Page 1 (TR): Tomukas/Shutterstock. Page 1 (B): Armin Rose/Shutterstock. Page 2 (T): Jupiter Images/Creatas. Page 2 (B): Stephen Denness/Shutterstock. Page 3 (T): Getty Images/Photos.com/Jupiterimages. Page 3 (B): Hieronymus Brunschwig. Page 4 (T): Library of Congress. Page 4 (B): HANDOUT/MCT/Newscom. Page 6: James Steidl/Shutterstock. Page 8: iofoto/Shutterstock. Page 11: Everett Collection/Alamy. Page 12: AP photo/Karen Tam. Page 13: NASA. Page 14 (R): Pearson Education/Tom Bochsler. Page 14 (L): Charles D. Winters/Photo Researchers, Inc. Page 18 (L to R): US Mint; jmatzick/Shutterstock; Theasis/iStockphoto; bryngelzon/iStockphoto. Page 20: Richard Megna/Fundamental Photographs. Page 26: Pearson Education/Eric Schrader. Page 30 (L): niderlander/Shutterstock. Page 30 (R): Dhoxax/Shutterstock. Page 31: Dmitrijs Bindemanis/Shutterstock. Page 36: Terry McCreary. Page 37: Buquet Christophe/Shutterstock. Page 38: David Anderson/iStockphoto. Page 39 (T): Yana Petruseva/Shutterstock. Page 39 (B): David A. Aguilar/Harvard-Smithsonian Center for Astrophysics. Chapter 2 Page 41 (TL): Viennaphoto/allOver photography/Alamy. Page 41 (TR): Stockbyte/Getty Images, Inc. Page 41 (B): Wilson Ho. Page 42 (T): Haydn Hansell/Alamy. Page 42 (b): konradlew/iStockphoto. Page 42 (inset): Susumu Nishinaga/Photo Researchers, Inc. Page 44: Jacques-Louis David. Page 45 (T, L to R): Morozova Tatyana/Shutterstock; Katharina Wittfeld/Shutterstock; Richard Megna/Fundamental Photographs. Page 45 (B): C. Marvin Lang. Page 47: PRISMA/Visual & Written/The Image Works. Page 48: Mat Meadows/Peter Arnold/Alamy. Page 51: Library of Congress. Page 53: Drs. Ali Yazdani & Daniel J. Hornbaker/Photo Researchers, Inc. Page 54 (T, L to R): Harry Taylor/Dorling Kindersley; Mark Wragg/iStockphoto; Sieto/iStockphoto; Tammy Peluso/iStockphoto. Page 54 (B, L to R): Harry Taylor/Dorling Kindersley; Michael Shake/Shutterstock; Joe Potato Photo/iStockphoto; Lya Cattel/iStockphoto. Page 55: © Libby Welch/Alamy. Page 59 (both): Richard Megna/Fundamental Photographs. Chapter 3 Page 61 (TL): Gary718/Dreamstime. Page 61 (B): Angelo Cavalli/SuperStock. Page 62: Getty Images/Photos.com/Jupiter Images. Page 63: Richard Megna/Fundamental Photographs. Page 65: Otto Glasser/Images from the History of Medicine/National Library of Medicine. Page 66: Photos 12/Alamy. Page 67: STR/AFP/Getty Images/Newscom. Page 73 (T): Shutterstock. Page 73 (BA): Richard Megna/Fundamental Photographs. Page 74 (TL): David Parker/Science Photo Library/Photo Researchers, Inc. Page 74 (TR): Wabash Instrument Corp./Fundamental Photographs. Page 74 (ML): Gary J. Shulfer/C. Marvin Lang. Page 82 (both): Richard Megna/Fundamental Photographs. Page 83 (T): Yuriko Nakao/REUTERS. Page 83 (B): Dorling Kindersley/Colin Keates. Chapter 4 Page 89 (TL): Phase4Photography/Shutterstock. Page 89 (TR): moodboard/Alamy. Page 89 (B): Fotocrisis/Shutterstock. Page 91: Lawrence Berkeley National Laboratory/Photo Researchers, Inc. Page 93 (A): Richard Megna/Fundamental Photographs. Page 94 (T): Charles D. Winters/Photo Researchers, Inc. Page 94 (B): Richard Megna/Fundamental Photographs. Page 96: Alexander Dvorak/Shutterstock. Page 99: Pearson Education/Eric Schrader. Page 112: Pearson Education/Eric Schrader. Chapter 5 Page 125 (TL): STR/AFP/Getty Images/Newscom. Page 125 (TR): andibyte/Shutterstock. Page 129: Summit Oxygen International Ltd. Page 130: Gary J. Shulfer/C. Marvin Lang. Page 135: Richard Megna/Fundamental Photographs. Page 136: GENT SHKULLAKU/AFP/Getty Images/Newscom. Page 141: Lynnea Kleinschmidt. Page 143: Pearson Education/Eric Schrader. Page 144 (T): Pearson Education/Eric Schrader. Page 144 (B): Pearson Education/Nathan Eldridge. Chapter 6 Page 152 (TR): Josh Resnick/Shutterstock. Page 152 (TL): Shutterstock. Page 152 (B): Juliya_strekoza/Shutterstock. Page 153 (L): GTS Production/Shutterstock. Page 153 (R): Eric Skiff, used under a Creative Commons License. http://creativecommons.org/licenses/by-sa/2.0/deed.en. Page 154: Nikita Tiunov/Shutterstock. Page 156 (TL): Ariel Bravy/Shutterstock. Page 156 (ML): Richard Megna/Fundamental Photographs. Page 156 (MR): Richard Megna/Fundamental Photographs. Page 160 (L): Tony Freeman/PhotoEdit Inc. Page 160 (M): George Mattei/Photo Researchers, Inc. Page 160 (R): Liv Friis-Larsen/Shutterstock. Page 166 (both): Richard Megna/Fundamental Photographs. Page 167: Oleksiy Mark/Shutterstock. Chapter 7 Page 175 (TL): Image Source/Alamy. Page 175 (TR): schankz/Shutterstock. Page 175 (B): Valentyn Volkov/Shutterstock. Page 176 (BA): Lajos Repasi/iStockphoto. Page 176 (T): Pearson Education/Eric Schrader. Page 177 (TL): Pearson Education/Eric Schrader. Page 177 (TR): Tyler Boyes/Shutterstock. Page 177 (MR): Denise Kappa/Shutterstock. Page 177 (BR): Richard Megna/Fundamental Photographs. Page 178: Science and Society/SuperStock. Page 182: a11/ZUMA Press/Newscom. Page 184: Everett Collection. Page 187 (A): Richard Megna/Fundamental Photographs. Page 189: Richard Megna/Fundamental Photographs. Page 193: Pearson Education/Creative Digital Vision. Page 194: Pearson Education/Eric Schrader. Page 195 (T): Michael Page Gadomski/Photo Researchers, Inc. Page 195 (B): Tom McNemar/Shutterstock. Chapter 8 Page 201 (TL): Evoken68/Dreamstime. Page 201 (TR): eyecraveeyecrave/iStockphoto. Page 201 (B): Ben Willmore/Digital Mastery.

Page 202 (both): Paul Silverman/Fundamental Photographs. Page 208 (both): Peticolas/Megna-Fundamental Photographs. Page 210 (both): Spencer Grant/PhotoEdit. Page 211: Marianne de Jong/Shutterstock. Page 212: Rkasprzak/Dreamstime. Page 214: Rich Chartier/Walter Drake Company. Page 216 (T): Kzenon/Shutterstock. Page 216 (B): NASA/Jim Grossmann. Page 217: Richard Megna/Fundamental Photographs. Page 218: Pearson Education/Eric Schrader. Page 219: Paul Reid/Shutterstock. Page 221: Pearson Education/Eric Schrader. Page 222 (L): SuperStock/SuperStock. Page 222 (R): Karl R. Martin/Shutterstock. Page 223: vovan/Shutterstock. Page 227 (T): Sherri R. Camp/Shutterstock. Page 227 (B): Jacob Kearns/Shutterstock. Chapter 9 Page 229 (TL): The Scoville Food Institute. Page 229 (TR): Paul Paladin/Shutterstock. Page 229 (B): Abel Tumik/Shutterstock. Page 231: VladimirB/Shutterstock. Page 233: naphtalina/iStockphoto. Page 236: Richard Megna/Fundamental Photographs. Page 237: Bon Appetit/Alamy. Page 238: Clive Freeman/The Royal Institution/SPL/Photo Researchers, Inc. Page 241: Pearson Education/Eric Schrader. Page 245: Pearson Education/Eric Schrader. Page 246: Pearson Education/Eric Schrader. Page 247: Southern Illinois University/Photo Researchers, Inc. Page 252: Pearson Education/Eric Schrader. Chapter 10 Page 266 (TL): Konkolas/Shutterstock. Page 266 (TR): BALDUCCI/SINTESI/SIPA/Newscom. Page 266 (B): BALDUCCI/SINTESI/SIPA/Newscom. Page 267: Shutterstock. Page 269: Richard Megna/Fundamental Photographs. Page 271 (T): AP Photo/Joe Appel. Page 271 (B): Richard Megna/Fundamental Photographs. Page 273 (ML): Shutterstock. Page 273 (M): James Edward Bates/Biloxi Sun-Herald/MCT/Newscom. Page 273 (MR): Inara Prusakova/Shutterstock. Page 273 (BR): Shutterstock. Page 274 (T): Shutterstock. Page 274 (B): Zoonar/richterfoto/age footstock. Page 276: Geoff Tompkinson/Photo Researchers, Inc. Page 278 (T): Shutterstock. Page 278 (B): Shutterstock. Page 282 (T): Pearson Education/Eric Schrader. Page 282 (B): Mar Photographics/Alamy. Page 283 (T): Shutterstock. Page 283 (B): REUTERS/Toshiyuki Aizawa. Page 285: Amoco Fabrics & Fibers Co. Page 286: Ambient Images Inc./Alamy. Page 287: Xinhua/Photoshot/Newscom. Chapter 11 Page 295 (TL): Scott Camazine/Alamy. Page 295 (TR): Steven Needell, MD/Custom Medical Stock Photo. Page 295 (B): SergeyIT/Shutterstock. Page 298: Nora D. Volkow, MD/National Institute of Health. Page 308: Bain News Service/Library of Congress. Page 309 (T): William Paul Quick. Page 309 (B): Richard Megna/Fundamental Photographs. Page 310: Simon Fraser/SPL/Photo Researchers, Inc. Page 311 (A): Bristol Myers Squibb Medical Imaging MA. Page 312 (L): Olivier Voisin/Photo Researchers, Inc. Page 312 (R): Wellcome Dept. of Cognitive Neurology/Science Photo Library/Photo Researchers, Inc. Page 315: SuperStock/agefotostock. Page 316 (T): Pictorial Press Ltd/Alamy. Page 316 (B): Robert R. Davis, AIP Emilio Segre Visual Archives, Physics Today Collection. Page 320: Lawrence Berkeley National Lab. Page 321: US Air Force. Page 322: JIJI PRESS/AFP/Getty Images/Newscom. Page 323 U.S. Department of Energy. Page 324: GeoEye Inc. Chapter 12 Page 331 (TL): holgs/iStockphoto. Page 331 (R): cardiae/Shutterstock. Page 331 (B): Monkey Business Images/Shutterstock. Page 333: Galyna Andrushko/Shutterstock. Page 334 (L): Dr. Richard Busch/American Geological Institute, AGI. Earth Science World Image Bank. Page 334 (R): AIRMAN MELODY A. WEISS/US Air Force. Page 335 (T): Chip Clark. Page 335 (B): From *Asbestos and Other Fibrous Materials: Mineralogy, Crystal Chemistry, and Health Effects* by H. Catherine W. Skinner, Malcolm Ross, and Clifford Frondel. New York: Oxford University Press, 1988. Page 336 (L): Lee Prince/Shutterstock. Page 336 (R): Lebazele/iStockphoto. Page 337 (T): nikkytok/Shutterstock. Page 337 (B): Bruce C. Murray/Shutterstock. Page 338: polat/iStockphoto. Page 342 (T): Arturo Limon/Shutterstock. Page 342 (M): ITAR-TASS/Alexander Kolbasov/Newscom. Page 342 (B): Charles D. Winters/Photo Researchers, Inc. Page 345: Mike Morley/iStockphoto. Page 348: Photolibrary, Inc. Chapter 13 Page 350 (R): Yellowj/Shutterstock. Page 350 (L): frescomovie/Shutterstock. Page 351: Mario Babiera/Alamy. Page 355: NASA. Page 356: EcoSphere Associates, Inc. 2006. Page 357 (T): Tim Graham/Alamy. Page 357 (B): Sergei Butorin/Shutterstock. Page 358 (T): AP Photo. Page 358 (B): Dr. Gerald L. Fisher/Science Photo Library/Photo Researchers, Inc. Page 359: Tennessee Valley Authority. Page 362: Jens Peermann/Shutterstock. Page 366: Richard Megna/Fundamental Photographs. Page 369: ITAR-TASS/Alexei Filippov/Newscom. Page 370: bluebird13/iStockphoto. Page 371: Susan Solomon. Page 372: NASA. Page 376: Johnathan Patz/Center for Sustainability and the Global Environment (SAGE). Chapter 14 Page 385 (TL): Jonutis/Shutterstock. Page 385 (TR): McIek/Shutterstock. Page 385 (B): ifong/Shutterstock. Page 386: NASA. Page 387: NASA. Page 388: age fotostock/SuperStock. Page 389: Ieva Geneviciene/Shutterstock. Page 391: U.S. Environmental Protection Agency Headquarters/H.D.A. Linquist, U.S. EPA. Page 392 (T): ZUMA Press/Newscom. Page 392 (M): Peter Arnold, Inc./Alamy. Page 392 (B): monap/iStockphoto. Page 393: Robert Brook/Alamy. Page 396: Pearson Education/Eric Schrader. Page 397: AP Photo/EyePress. Page 398 (T): U.S. Geological Survey, Denver. Page 398 (B): Mike Segar/Reuters.

Index